MATHEMATICS OF FINANCE

Combined edition including
COMMERCIAL ALGEBRA

CLIFFORD BELL
University of California
Los Angeles

L. J. ADAMS
Santa Monica City College

HENRY HOLT AND COMPANY · New York

Copyright, 1949, by Henry Holt and Company, Inc.
Printed in the United States of America

Preface

This book is a one-volume edition of the authors' textbooks, *Commercial Algebra* and *Mathematics of Finance*. It is designed primarily for use in a three-hour, one-year course for students majoring in commerce and business administration.

The scope of the material can be judged from the table of contents.

There are certain features that are common to Part I and Part II. Some of them are:

1. The problems are numerous, carefully graded in order of difficulty, and pointed toward common business practice and applications.

2. There is a miscellaneous exercise at the end of each chapter that can be used for review purposes.

3. There are many illustrative examples, solved in detail and with explanations, to aid the student in studying.

4. Definitions are stated carefully, and attention is called to important terms by the use of boldface print.

5. The appendix includes the new CSO mortality table, the values of the commutation symbols based on a $2\frac{1}{2}\%$ interest rate, a six-place table of logarithms with proportional parts, and an adequate set of tables of the mathematics of finance functions.

Some of the salient features of Part I that warrant special mention are:

1. The thorough and comprehensive presentation of algebraic techniques and processes;

2. The chapters on percentage and simple interest, with their emphasis on commercial applications;

3. The detailed treatment of logarithms and interpolation;

4. The application of the principles of probability to the mortality table;

5. The introduction to statistics.

With regard to Part II we should like to call special attention to the following items:

1. The emphasis placed on the equation of value and the line diagram in analyzing problems;
2. The adequate supply of drill problems, placed at the beginning of nearly every exercise;
3. The practical nature of the stated problems;
4. The unusually complete treatment of bonds;
5. The simplification of the matter of general case annuities, by converting the interest rate to the conversion period corresponding to the payment interval;
6. The lucid description of the manner in which the commutation symbols are used in the analysis of life annuities and life insurance.

In comparing this combined edition with the separate volumes, notice that the articles and pages of Part II of this book have been renumbered. This was done to avoid the duplication of the two chapters on *Simple Interest and Discount* and *Permutations and Combinations; Probability*. That is, this volume is not merely a tandem combination of the separate volumes, but is rather a distinct and integrated entity in itself.

In writing this textbook, we have at all times attempted to keep in mind the needs and desires of the teacher and student, and it is our sincere hope that we have succeeded in producing a book that will be useful to both.

We wish to acknowledge the encouragement and helpful suggestions given by many of the members of the Departments of Mathematics at Santa Monica City College and the University of California.

University of California, Los Angeles   C. B.
Santa Monica City College   L. J. A.
March 3, 1949

Contents

1 FUNDAMENTALS OF ALGEBRA **1**

1. Algebraic language 2. The four fundamental operations of algebra 3. Addition and subtraction 4. Multiplication 5. Division 6. Factoring 7. Substitution in formulas 8. Symbols of grouping

2 EQUATIONS OF THE FIRST DEGREE . . . **15**

9. Equations 10. Equations of the first degree 11. Stated problems 12. Systems of equations of the first degree 13. Elimination by addition or subtraction 14. Elimination by substitution 15. Solution of stated problems, using two unknowns 16. Three equations in three unknowns

3 FRACTIONS **35**

17. Fractions 18. Operations with fractions 19. Reduction to lowest terms 20. Addition and subtraction of fractions 21. Multiplication and division of fractions 22. Substitution in formulas 23. Complex fractions 24. Equations involving fractions 25. Changing the subject of a formula 26. Ratio and proportion

4 PERCENTAGE: COMMERCIAL TRANSACTIONS **51**

27. Per cent 28. Percentage, base, and rate 29. Buying and selling merchandise 30. Cash discount 31. Trade discount

5 EXPONENTS AND RADICALS **65**

32. Positive integral exponents 33. Fractional exponents 34. Zero exponent 35. Negative exponents 36. Rational and irrational numbers 37. Radicals 38. Radicals in the simplest form 39. Operations with radicals 40. Multiplication and division of radicals 41. Special types of equations

6 LOGARITHMS **81**

42. Definition of common logarithm 43. Significant digits 44. Properties of logarithms 45. Characteristic 46. Logarithm of a given number; interpolation

v

47. Proportional parts: logarithm of a given number 48. Number which corresponds to a given logarithm; interpolation 49. Number corresponding to a given logarithm, by use of a table of proportional parts 50. Multiplication and division, using logarithms 51. Use of logarithms in powers and roots 52. Exponential equations; another type of equation 53. Other bases for logarithms 54. Calculation of logarithms

7 SIMPLE INTEREST AND DISCOUNT 105

55. Simple interest 56. Methods of counting time 57. Ordinary and exact interest 58. Sixty-day, 6% method for ordinary simple interest. Simple interest table 59. Present value and simple discount 60. Present value of a debt that bears interest 61. Bank discount 62. Promissory notes 63. Drafts and trade acceptances 64. Comparision of discount at a discount rate and discount at a simple interest rate 65. Comparison of interest rate and discount rate 66. Partial payments 67. Equation of value 68. Equation of time 69. Installment buying

8 QUADRATIC EQUATIONS 141

70. Typical form 71. Special or incomplete quadratics 72. Imaginary numbers 73. Incomplete quadratics, with b = 0 74. Solution by factoring 75. Solution by completing the square 76. Solution by quadratic formula 77. Summary: solution of quadratic equations 78. Theorems concerning the roots of quadratic equations 79. Problems leading to quadratic equations

9 GRAPHICAL REPRESENTATION 163

80. Functions 81. Rectangular coordinate system 82. Linear function 83. Quadratic function 84. Logarithmic and exponential functions 85. Other functions 86. Graphical solution of a system of linear equations 87. Fitting curves to data: straight lines 88. Fitting curves to data: parabolas

10 PROGRESSIONS; BINOMIAL THEOREM . . 193

89. Arithmetical progressions 90. Relations among the elements 91. Arithmetical means 92. Geometrical progressions 93. Relations among the elements 94. Geometrical means 95. Infinite geometrical progressions 96. Binomial theorem; positive integral index 97. General term of the binomial formula 98. Computations by the binomial formula 99. Binomial theorem; negative and fractional indices

CONTENTS

11 PERMUTATIONS AND COMBINATIONS; PROBABILITY **210**

100. A fundamental principle   101. Permutations   102. Permutations of things not all different   103. Combinations   104. Binomial coefficients   105. A priori probability   106. Independent events, mutually exclusive events, and dependent events   107. Empirical probability   108. Mortality table   109. Mathematical expectation   110. Expectation of life

12 STATISTICS **228**

111. Preliminary remarks   112. Arithmetic mean   113. Median, mode, and geometric mean   114. A comparison   115. Aids to computation   116. Frequency distributions; histograms   117. Frequency curves   118. Standard deviation

13 COMPOUND INTEREST AND COMPOUND DISCOUNT **247**

119. Preliminary concepts and definitions   120. The compound amount formula   121. Nominal and effective rates of interest   122. Interest for a fractional part of a period   123. Compound amount at changing rates   124. The time and rate problems   125. Present value. Compound discount   126. Equation of value and equated time

14 INTRODUCTION TO ANNUITIES **269**

127. Preliminary concepts and definitions   128. Evaluation of ordinary annuities   129. Determination of the rent of an annuity   130. Determination of the time   131. Determination of the interest rate

15 OTHER TYPES OF ANNUITIES CERTAIN, PERPETUITIES AND CAPITALIZED COST . . . **288**

132. Annuities due   133. Deferred annuities   134. General case annuities   135. Increasing and decreasing annuities   136. Perpetuities   137. Capitalized cost

16 RETIREMENT OF DEBTS BY INSTALLMENT PAYMENTS **316**

138. Methods and definitions   139. The amortization method of retiring a debt using equal payments at equal intervals of time   140. Amortization of a bonded debt

and other methods of amortization   141. The sinking fund method of retiring a debt   142. Amortizing debts by fixed payment—unknown time methods

17 DEPRECIATION VALUATION OF INCOME PROPERTY 336

143. Definitions   144. The straight line method   145. The constant per cent method   146. The sinking fund method   147. Unit cost method of evaluating a machine   148. Evaluation of exhaustible income properties

18 BONDS AND REINVESTMENTS 356

149. Introduction and definitions   150. Purchase price of a bond to yield a given investment rate   151. Premium and discount   152. Amortization of premium and accumulation of discount   153. Bonds bought between interest payment dates   154. Yield rate of interest of a bond bought at a given price   155. Callable bonds   156. Other types of bonds   157. The reinvestment problem

19 LIFE ANNUITIES 391

158. Introduction and definitions   159. Present value of a pure endowment   160. Immediate whole life annuities   161. Deferred whole life annuities   162. Temporary life annuities   163. Other types of life annuities   164. Life annuities with payments m times a year   165. Summary of important formulas

20 LIFE INSURANCE 414

166. Introduction and definitions   167. Whole life policy   168. Deferred life policy   169. Term policy   170. Endowment policy   171. Combination policies   172. Premiums payable m times a year   173. Summary of formulas for simple insurance policies

21 POLICY RESERVES 437

174. The reserve fund. Definitions   175. Numerical computation of the reserve   176. Fackler's formula   177. Retrospective and prospective methods of computing the reserve   178. Surrender value of a policy

TABLES 452

ANSWERS TO ODD-NUMBERED PROBLEMS . . . 539

INDEX 561

1

Fundamentals of Algebra

1. Algebraic language

Algebra differs from arithmetic in many ways. One of the essential characteristics of algebra is the use of letters to stand for numbers. In the formula for the circumference of a circle,

$$C = \pi d,$$

the letter C stands for the number of units of length in the circumference of a circle, π stands for the number 3.1416 (approximately), and d stands for the number of units of length in the diameter of the circle. In a certain sense, algebra is a type of shorthand, because the letters and symbols of algebra can be used to express relations very briefly and concisely. It is necessary to learn how to transform English sentences into algebraic symbolism, and vice versa.

EXERCISE 1

1. One pencil costs c cents. Express the cost of 8 pencils.
2. The wholesale price of one dozen fountain pens is x dollars. Express the wholesale price of one fountain pen.
3. One orange sells for x cents and one apple sells for y cents. Express the total selling price of 3 oranges and 5 apples.
4. A certain man earns d dollars per month and another man earns $20 more per month. Express the monthly earnings of the second man.
5. One type of notebook sells for x cents each and another type sells for 5 cents less. Express the selling price of the second type of notebook.
6. Write an expression for the number of days in n years.
7. Write an expression for the number of weeks in n years.
8. The area of a rectangle is given by the formula $A = bh$. Write the equivalent of this formula in a complete sentence.
9. The area of a triangle is given by the formula $A = \frac{1}{2}bh$. Write the equivalent of this formula in a complete sentence.

10. A druggist has 30 gallons of alcohol in a container and adds x gallons of alcohol. How many gallons of alcohol are in the container?

11. A man makes two investments totaling $5000. If x represents the number of dollars in one of the investments, write an expression representing the number of dollars in the other investment.

12. The percentage, p, equals the base, b, multiplied by the rate, r. Express this as a formula.

2. The four fundamental operations of algebra

The four fundamental operations of algebra are addition, subtraction, multiplication, and division. These are also the four fundamental operations of arithmetic. In arithmetic these operations are used in connection with the numbers of arithmetic, which are positive integers (whole numbers) and fractions. One of the essential differences between algebra and arithmetic is the introduction of negative numbers in algebra. In arithmetic the expression $3 - 5$ has no meaning, since 5 is larger than 3. In algebra $3 - 5 = -2$. The number -2 is a negative number. The number system of arithmetic is enlarged, in algebra, to include negative numbers. The justification for introducing negative numbers in algebra lies in the fact that they turn out to be very useful. If the temperature is 3° Fahrenheit, and the temperature then drops 5°, the subsequent temperature is 2° below zero, or $-2°$ Fahrenheit.

For convenience in stating the rules for operating with signed numbers, the concept of "the absolute value" of a number is useful. The **absolute value** of a signed number is its value without regard to sign. The absolute value of $+6$ is 6, and the absolute value -6 is 6.

When no sign is given, plus is understood. That is, 6 means $+6$.

The rules for operating with signed numbers are given below.

ADDITION. *To add two numbers with like signs, add their absolute values and prefix their common sign.*

Examples.
$$\begin{array}{r} +5 \\ +3 \\ \hline +8 \end{array} \qquad \begin{array}{r} -5 \\ -3 \\ \hline -8 \end{array}$$

To add two numbers with unlike signs, subtract the smaller absolute value from the larger, and prefix the sign of the number with the larger absolute value.

Examples.
$$\begin{array}{r} +6 \\ -2 \\ \hline +4 \end{array} \qquad \begin{array}{r} -6 \\ +2 \\ \hline -4 \end{array} \qquad \begin{array}{r} +6 \\ -10 \\ \hline -4 \end{array} \qquad \begin{array}{r} -6 \\ +10 \\ \hline +4 \end{array}$$

THE FOUR FUNDAMENTAL OPERATIONS OF ALGEBRA

SUBTRACTION. *Change the sign of the subtrahend (or the quantity to be subtracted), and proceed as in addition.*

Examples.

$$\begin{array}{r} +5 \\ +3 \\ \hline +2 \end{array} \qquad \begin{array}{r} +5 \\ -3 \\ \hline +8 \end{array} \qquad \begin{array}{r} -5 \\ +3 \\ \hline -8 \end{array} \qquad \begin{array}{r} -5 \\ -3 \\ \hline -2 \end{array}$$

MULTIPLICATION. *To multiply two numbers with like signs, multiply their absolute values and prefix a plus sign.*

Examples.

$$\begin{array}{r} +5 \\ +3 \\ \hline +15 \end{array} \qquad \begin{array}{r} -5 \\ -3 \\ \hline +15 \end{array}$$

To multiply two numbers with unlike signs, multiply their absolute values and prefix a minus sign.

Examples.

$$\begin{array}{r} +5 \\ -3 \\ \hline -15 \end{array} \qquad \begin{array}{r} -5 \\ +3 \\ \hline -15 \end{array}$$

DIVISION. *To divide one signed number by another, perform the division with their absolute values, and apply the same rule for the sign of the quotient as is used in multiplication.*

Examples. $\dfrac{+8}{+2} = +4; \quad \dfrac{-8}{-2} = +4; \quad \dfrac{-8}{+2} = -4; \quad \dfrac{+8}{-2} = -4.$

EXERCISE 2

Add:

1. $\begin{array}{r} +9 \\ -3 \end{array}$ 2. $\begin{array}{r} +5 \\ +2 \end{array}$ 3. $\begin{array}{r} -8 \\ 2 \end{array}$ 4. $\begin{array}{r} -6 \\ -2 \end{array}$ 5. $\begin{array}{r} -3 \\ 2 \end{array}$

6. $\begin{array}{r} -7 \\ 3 \end{array}$ 7. $\begin{array}{r} -2 \\ -9 \end{array}$ 8. $\begin{array}{r} +8 \\ -3 \end{array}$ 9. $\begin{array}{r} -2 \\ -2 \end{array}$ 10. $\begin{array}{r} -3 \\ -6 \end{array}$

Subtract:

11. $\begin{array}{r} -3 \\ -5 \end{array}$ 12. $\begin{array}{r} -2 \\ -6 \end{array}$ 13. $\begin{array}{r} -4 \\ 6 \end{array}$ 14. $\begin{array}{r} 7 \\ -3 \end{array}$ 15. $\begin{array}{r} 2 \\ 6 \end{array}$

16. $\begin{array}{r} -3 \\ 2 \end{array}$ 17. $\begin{array}{r} +6 \\ -6 \end{array}$ 18. $\begin{array}{r} 7 \\ 7 \end{array}$ 19. $\begin{array}{r} 8 \\ -3 \end{array}$ 20. $\begin{array}{r} -9 \\ 3 \end{array}$

Multiply:

21. $\begin{array}{r} -6 \\ 2 \end{array}$ 22. $\begin{array}{r} -3 \\ -4 \end{array}$ 23. $\begin{array}{r} -5 \\ +8 \end{array}$ 24. $\begin{array}{r} 3 \\ -2 \end{array}$ 25. $\begin{array}{r} 3 \\ 6 \end{array}$

26. $\begin{array}{r} -4 \\ -2 \end{array}$ 27. $\begin{array}{r} -8 \\ 6 \end{array}$ 28. $\begin{array}{r} 6 \\ -8 \end{array}$ 29. $\begin{array}{r} +3 \\ +4 \end{array}$ 30. $\begin{array}{r} -2 \\ +2 \end{array}$

Divide:

31. $\dfrac{+8}{+4}$ 32. $\dfrac{-8}{-4}$ 33. $\dfrac{10}{-2}$ 34. $\dfrac{-12}{6}$ 35. $\dfrac{-14}{-2}$

36. $\dfrac{6}{-2}$ 37. $\dfrac{-8}{2}$ 38. $\dfrac{-26}{13}$ 39. $\dfrac{12}{2}$ 40. $\dfrac{-6}{3}$

3. Addition and subtraction

Expressions such as $-5x^3$ and $7x^2y$ are used in algebra. In $-5x^3$, -5 is the **numerical coefficient** of x^3, x is a **literal number,** and x^3 means x times x times x. In x^3, the 3 is the **exponent** of the literal number x. In $7x^2y$, x^2y means the result of multiplying x^2 by y. The 7 is the numerical coefficient of x^2y, and $7x^2$ can be considered the coefficient of y, while $7y$ can be considered the coefficient of x^2.

When no numerical coefficient is given, the coefficient 1 is understood. Thus, x means $1x$. When no exponent is given, the exponent 1 is understood. Thus x means x^1.

The sum of two or more numbers is the same in whatever order they are added. Thus,

$$a + b = b + a.$$

The sum of three or more numbers is the same in whatever manner the numbers are grouped. Thus,

$$a + b + c = (a + b) + c = a + (b + c),$$

where the parentheses are used to indicate grouping.

Example 1. Add $7a - 3x$, $-5a + 2x$, $3a - 5x$.
Solution.
$$\begin{array}{r} 7a - 3x \\ -5a + 2x \\ 3a - 5x \\ \hline 5a - 6x \end{array}$$

Example 2. Subtract the second expression from the first: $3a - 2b + 5c$, $a - 8b + 6c$.
Solution.
$$\begin{array}{r} 3a - 2b + 5c \\ a - 8b + 6c \\ \hline 2a + 6b - c \end{array}$$

EXERCISE 3

Add:

1. $6x, -3x, 4x, -2x$
2. $3a, -2a, -5a, 6a$
3. $5x - 2y, 6x - 5y$
4. $8m - 3n, -6m + 2n, -3m + 4n$
5. $x^2 + y^2, 3x^2 + 2y^2$
6. $-3x^2 + 6y^2, 4x^2 - 3y^2, 5x^2 - 2y^2$
7. $8a^2b - 3a^2b^3, -3a^2b + 8a^2b^3, -6a^2b + 2a^2b^3$

8. $6a - 2b + 3c$, $-4a + b - 3c$, $a - 4b + 7c$
9. $5m - 3n + 2p$, $-2m + 4p$, $6n - 5p$
10. $a^2 - 3b^2 + 4c^2$, $-3a^2 + 2b^2 - c^2$, $5a^2 - 6b^2 + 2c^2$

Subtract the second expression from the first:
11. $8x$, $-3x$
12. $-5a$, $2a$
13. $6a - 5b$, $-3a + 2b$
14. $7m - 2n$, $-3m + 8n$
15. $a + 5b - 2c$, $-3a + b - 4c$
16. $x^2 - 5y^2 + 6z^2$, $-3x^2 + 4y^2 - 2z^2$
17. $6x^3 - 5x^2 + 8x - 2$, $-3x^3 + 7x^2 - 9x + 8$
18. $6x^2y - 8xy^2$, $3x^2y + 9xy^2$
19. $x^2 - 8x + 2$, $x^2 - 9x + 6$
20. $m^2 - 6m + 3$, $2m^2 - 9m + 3$

Add the first two expressions, and from their sum subtract the third expression:
21. $9x$, $-3x$, $4x$
22. $3a$, $4a$, $-6a$
23. $a + 2b$, $a + 3b$, $a - 4b$
24. $3a - b$, $a - 5b$, $2a + 7b$
25. $x^2 + y^2$, $x^2 - y^2$, $3x^2 - y^2$
26. $3a^2 - b^2$, $a^2 + b^2$, $4a^2 - 2b^2$
27. $a + b - c$, $3a - b + c$, $a - 2b + 6c$
28. $a + 8b - 3c$, $a + 9b - 2c$, $5a - b + c$
29. $x^2 - 3xy + y^2$, $4x^2 - 6xy - y^2$, $x^2 - 2xy + 3y^2$
30. $5x^2 + 2xy - y^2$, $6x^2 - 8xy + 3y^2$, $x^2 - 4xy + 5y^2$
31. $a - 3b + 2c - 4d$, $a - 3c + d$, $3a - b + 2d$
32. $x - 4y + 6z - 2w$, $6x - z + w$, $z - 3w$
33. $3ab - 4ac + 2bc$, $ac + 8bc$, $3ab - 4bc$
34. $6x^3 - 5x^2 + 8x - 3$, $x^3 - 6x + 4$, $6x^2 - 9x$
35. $a^3 - 3a^2b + 3ab^2 - 2b^3$, $4a^2b - b^3$, $6ab^2 - 8b^3$
36. $5a^2 - 3ab + 6b^2$, $a^2 - ab$, $3ab - 8b^2$
37. $4m^2 - 5m - 3$, $5m + 6$, $-3m^2 - 8$
38. $4pq - 6pr + 8qr$, $-9pq + 6pr$, $9pq - 5qr$
39. $6s^3 - 3s^2 + 7$, $-8s^3 + 6s - 3$, $5s^2 - 6s + 2$
40. $6x^4 - 7x^2 + 3x$, $5x^3 - 7x + 2$, $x^2 + x + 8$

4. Multiplication

If two or more numbers are multiplied to form a product, the numbers are the **factors** of the product. Thus in ab, a and b are the factors of the product ab.

The factors of a product may be multiplied in any order. Thus,
$$ab = ba.$$

The factors of a product may be grouped in any manner. Thus,
$$abc = (ab)c = a(bc).$$

Example 1.
$$(10ab)(3ab) = (10 \cdot a \cdot b)(3 \cdot a \cdot b),$$
$$= (10 \cdot 3)(a \cdot a)(b \cdot b),$$
$$= 30a^2b^2.$$

An expression consisting of a number with an exponent is called a **power** of the number. Thus a^2 is a power of a. The number to which the exponent applies is called the **base** of the power. Thus, a is the base of a^2.

The exponent of the product of two powers of a number is the sum of the exponents of the powers taken singly. The student will recall that

$$x^2 = x \cdot x,$$
$$x^3 = x \cdot x \cdot x,$$
$$x^4 = x \cdot x \cdot x \cdot x, \text{ and so on.}$$

Example 2. $\quad a^3 \cdot a^4 = (a \cdot a \cdot a)(a \cdot a \cdot a \cdot a),$
$\qquad\qquad\qquad = a^7.$

Example 3. $\quad 5^2 \cdot 5^4 = (5 \cdot 5)(5 \cdot 5 \cdot 5 \cdot 5),$
$\qquad\qquad\qquad = 5^6.$

If an expression is composed of several parts, the parts being connected by $+$ or $-$ signs, then each part, together with the sign preceding it, is called a **term**. Thus, in the expression $3a - 2b + 6c$, the terms are $3a$, $-2b$, and $6c$.

An algebraic expression consisting of one term only is called a **monomial**. Thus $4x$, $6x^2y$, and $-5x^3$ are monomials.

An algebraic expression of two terms is called a **binomial**, and an algebraic expression of three terms is called a **trinomial**. Thus $6x - 3y$ is a binomial and $x^2 - 5x + 3$ is a trinomial.

An algebraic expression of more than one term is called a **multinomial**. For example:

$$\frac{6x^3}{y} + \frac{3x^2}{z^2} - 3x \quad \text{and} \quad 5x^3 - 6x^2 + 8x - 4$$

are multinomials.

A multinomial of the form

$$ax^n + bx^{n-1} + cx^{n-2} + \cdots + k,$$

where $a, b, c, \cdots, k$ are numbers and n is a positive integer, is called a **polynomial** in x. Thus $5x^3 - 6x^2 + 8x - 4$ is a polynomial in x.

The multiplication of two monomials is illustrated in Example 1 of this article, and in the following example.

Example 4.

$$(-5x^2y^3)(6xy^2) = (-5 \cdot x \cdot x \cdot y \cdot y \cdot y)(6 \cdot x \cdot y \cdot y),$$
$$= -30x^3y^5.$$

Notice that the numerical coefficient of the literal part of the product is equal to the product of the numerical coefficients of the literal parts of the monomials, and that the exponent of each letter in the

DIVISION

product is equal to the sum of the exponents of that letter in the two given monomials.

To multiply a multinomial by a monomial, use the law

$$a(b + c + d + \cdots) = ab + ac + ad + \cdots$$

Example 5. $5x^2y(x + y + z) = 5x^3y + 5x^2y^2 + 5x^2yz.$

The multiplication of two multinomials can be illustrated by an example.

Example 6. Multiply $3a^2 - 2ab + 4b^2$ by $a^2 - 6ab + 2b^2$.

Solution.
$$\begin{array}{r} 3a^2 - 2ab + 4b^2 \\ a^2 - 6ab + 2b^2 \\ \hline 3a^4 - 2a^3b + 4a^2b^2 \\ - 18a^3b + 12a^2b^2 - 24ab^3 \\ 6a^2b^2 - 4ab^3 + 8b^4 \\ \hline 3a^4 - 20a^3b + 22a^2b^2 - 28ab^3 + 8b^4 \end{array}$$

EXERCISE 4

Multiply:

1. $x^2 \cdot x^3 \cdot x^4$ 2. $a^3 \cdot a \cdot a^5$ 3. $2^3 \cdot 2^4$ 4. $3^2 \cdot 3^5$ 5. $ab \cdot a^2b$
6. $r^2s \cdot rs^2$ 7. $6ab \cdot 2a^2b^3$ 8. $-5xy^3 \cdot 6x^2y^4$ 9. $(1+i)^{100} \; (1+i)^{25}$
10. $(1+i)^{50} \cdot (1+i)^{30}$ 11. $x(x + y - z)$ 12. $m^2(m + n)$
13. $ab(a - 2b + 3c)$ 14. $x^2y^3(x^2 - y^2 + z^2)$ 15. $a(b + cd)$
16. $m^2(m - n)$ 17. $(x + 2)(x + 3)$ 18. $(a + 3)(a + 5)$
19. $(x - 4)(x - 5)$ 20. $(a - 1)(a - 2)$ 21. $(x - 3)(x + 2)$
22. $(a - 4)(a + 4)$ 23. $(3x - 2y)(3x + 2y)$ 24. $(x - 5y)(3x + 2y)$
25. $(a + b)(a^2 - ab + b^2)$ 26. $(r - s)(r^2 + rs + s^2)$
27. $(1 - x)(1 + x^2 + x^3)$ 28. $(x^2 - y^2 + z^2)(3x^2 - 4y^2 - 2z^2)$
29. $(a^3 - a^2b + ab^2 - b^3)(a^2 - ab + b^2)$
30. $(1 - x)(1 - x)(1 - x)$ 31. $(1 - a)(1 - b)$
32. $(1 - a)(1 - b)(1 - c)$ 33. $(5x^3 - 6x^2 + 8x - 2)(x - 4)$
34. $(x^3 - 9x^2 - 2x + 6)(x^2 - 3x + 6)$
35. $(2a^3 - 3a^2 + 2a - 1)(a^3 - a^2 + a - 1)$
36. $(a + b)(a - b)(a + b)$ 37. $(1 - x + x^2)^2$
38. $(a - ab + b)^2$ 39. $(a^2 - 2ab + b^2)^2$ 40. $(a - b)^3$

5. Division

In multiplication, exponents are added. Thus,

$$x^2 \cdot x^3 = x^5.$$

In division, exponents are subtracted. Thus,

$$x^6 \div x^2 = x^4.$$

FUNDAMENTALS OF ALGEBRA

In dividing a monomial by another monomial, the numerical coefficient of the literal part of the quotient is the quotient of the numerical coefficients of the literal parts of the monomials, and the exponent of any letter in the quotient is equal to the exponent of that letter in the dividend minus its exponent in the divisor. Thus:

Example 1. $\quad \dfrac{-8x^3y^5}{2xy^4} = -4x^2y.$

To divide a multinomial by a monomial, divide each term separately:

Example 2. $\quad \dfrac{9a^2b^2 - 18ab^4 + 6ab^3}{3ab^2} = 3a - 6b^2 + 2b.$

To divide a multinomial by another multinomial, proceed as in the following example:

Example 3. $\quad$ Divide $x^2 - 8x + 12$ by $x - 2$.

$$\begin{array}{r|l} x^2 - 8x + 12 & x - 2 \\ \underline{x^2 - 2x} & x - 6, \text{ quotient} \\ -6x + 12 & \\ \underline{-6x + 12} & \end{array}$$

Division by zero is excluded from the operations of algebra. The role of zero in the operations of algebra is shown in the following examples:

$$a + 0 = a$$
$$a - 0 = a$$
$$a \cdot 0 = 0$$

$\dfrac{a}{0}$ is not permissible.

EXERCISE 5

Divide:

1. x^6 by x^2
2. a^8 by a^3
3. $6a^2b^3$ by $2ab$
4. $-13a^5b^8$ by $-3a^2b^3$
5. 2^8 by 2^2
6. 4^5 by 4^2
7. $a^3b^4 - a^2b^5 + ab^6$ by ab^2
8. $24x^2y^2 + 18x^3y^3 - 12x^4y^4$ by $6x^2y$
9. $x^2 - 9x + 20$ by $x - 4$
10. $x^2 + 6x + 8$ by $x + 2$
11. $x^2 - y^2$ by $x - y$
12. $49m^2 - 16n^2$ by $7m - 4n$
13. $a^3 + 3a^2b + 3ab^2 + b^3$ by $a + b$
14. $m^3 - 3m^2n + 3mn^2 - n^3$ by $m - n$
15. $a^3 - b^3$ by $a - b$
16. $a^3 + b^3$ by $a + b$
17. $a^3 + 3a^2b + 3ab^2 + b^3$ by $a^2 + 2ab + b^2$
18. $x^4 - y^4$ by $x - y$
19. $x^6 - y^6$ by $x - y$
20. $x^5 - y^5$ by $x - y$
21. $1 - 2x + x^2$ by $1 - x$
22. $1 - 3x + 3x^2 - x^3$ by $1 - x$
23. $1 + 3x + 3x^2 + x^3$ by $1 + x$
24. $1 - 4x + 6x^2 - 4x^3 + x^4$ by $1 - 2x + x^2$
25. $a^4 + 4a^3b + 6a^2b^2 + 4ab^3 + b^4$ by $a^2 + 2ab + b^2$

6. Factoring

By actual multiplication, the following type products can be obtained:

1. $a(x+y) = ax + ay$
2. $(a+b)(a-b) = a^2 - b^2$
3. $(a+b)^2 = a^2 + 2ab + b^2$
4. $(x+a)(x+b) = x^2 + (a+b)x + ab$
5. $(a+b)(a^2 - ab + b^2) = a^3 + b^3$
6. $(a-b)(a^2 + ab + b^2) = a^3 - b^3$
7. $(a+b)(x+y) = ax + ay + bx + by$

The student should be able to obtain such products mentally. The right-hand sides of these examples are the products, and the left-hand sides are the factors. Thus, the factors of $a^2 - b^2$ are $(a-b)$, $(a+b)$.

EXERCISE 6

Multiply mentally:

1. $x(a-b)$ 2. $P(1+i)$ 3. $(a+3)(a-3)$ 4. $(x-2)(x+2)$
5. $(2x+y)(2x-y)$ 6. $(3m-4n)(3m+4n)$ 7. $(x+y)^2$ 8. $(x-y)^2$
9. $(2x+3y)^2$ 10. $(3r-4s)^2$ 11. $(x+2)(x+3)$ 12. $(a+5)(a+8)$
13. $(r-4)(r-5)$ 14. $(m-2)(m-3)$ 15. $(x+8)(x-1)$
16. $(x-3)(x+4)$ 17. $(2x+3)(4x-5)$ 18. $(2a-3b)(4a+7b)$
19. $(6m-3n)(4m-n)$ 20. $(x+y)(x^2 - xy + y^2)$
21. $(x-y)(x^2 + xy + y^2)$ 22. $(a+3)(a^2 - 3a + 9)$
23. $(x-2)(x^2 + 2x + 4)$ 24. $(x-y)(m+n)$
25. $(3a-2b)(4c-5d)$

Factor:

26. $xy + xz$ 27. $P + Pi$ 28. $P^2 + P^2 i$ 29. $r^2 - x^2$ 30. $s^2 - t^2$
31. $9x^2 - 16y^2$ 32. $25m^2 - 4n^2$ 33. $16x^2 - 9$ 34. $x^2 + 2xy + y^2$
35. $m^2 - 2mn + n^2$ 36. $9x^2 + 12xy + 4y^2$ 37. $4a^2 - 12ab + 9b^2$
38. $x^2 - 6xy + 9y^2$ 39. $9m^2 + 6mn + n^2$ 40. $x^2 + 10x + 24$
41. $m^2 + 8m + 7$ 42. $x^2 + 9x + 18$ 43. $x^2 + x - 12$
44. $x^2 - 7x - 18$ 45. $a^2 - 7a + 12$ 46. $m^2 - 4m + 3$
47. $x^2 + x - 90$ 48. $8x^2 + 2x - 15$ 49. $x^3 - m^3$ 50. $n^3 + m^3$
51. $27x^3 + 64y^3$ 52. $a^3 + 8b^3$ 53. $x^3 - 125y^3$
54. $cx + cy + dx + dy$ 55. $ax + ay - bx - by$

By factoring, show that:

56. $P(1+i) + P(1+i)i = P(1+i)^2$
57. $P(1+i)^2 + P(1+i)^2 i = P(1+i)^3$
58. $L(1-r_1)(1-r_2) - L(1-r_1)(1-r_2)r_3 = L(1-r_1)(1-r_2)(1-r_3)$
59. $S(1-r) - S(1-r)t - S(1-t-p) = S[p - r(1-t)]$

60. $x(1+a) + x(1+a)a = x(1+a)^2$
61. $y(1+x)^2 + y(1+x)^2 x = y(1+x)^3$
62. $y(1-x) - y(1-x)z = y(1-x)(1-z)$

7. Substitution in formulas

In the applications of algebra, it is often necessary to substitute given numbers for letters occurring in formulas and expressions. Practice in substitution helps the student to understand the meanings of the symbols and operations of algebra. Substitution of numerical values for letters can be used as a partial check on operations involving algebraic expressions.

Example 1. If $x = 2$, $y = 3$, and $z = 4$ find the value of $2x^2 - y^2 + 3z$.

Solution.
$$\begin{aligned}2x^2 - y^2 + 3z &= 2(2^2) - (3^2) + (3 \cdot 4), \\ &= 2(4) - 9 + 12, \\ &= 8 - 9 + 12, \\ &= 11.\end{aligned}$$

Example 2. In the formula $S = P(1 + ni)$ find S if $P = 50$, $n = 6$, $i = 0.04$.

Solution.
$$\begin{aligned}S &= P(1 + ni), \\ &= 50[1 + 6(0.04)], \\ &= 50(1 + 0.24), \\ &= 50(1.24), \\ &= 62.0.\end{aligned}$$

Example 3. Multiply $x^2 - x + 1$ by $x + 1$. Check by using $x = 2$.

Solution.

$$\begin{array}{ll} x^2 - x + 1 & = 2^2 - 2 + 1 = 3 \\ x + 1 & = 2 + 1 \qquad = 3 \\ \hline x^3 - x^2 + x & \\ \quad\; x^2 - x + 1 & \\ \hline x^3 \qquad\qquad + 1 & = 2^3 + 1 = 9 \\ \quad (3)(3) = 9. & \end{array}$$

Notice that this is only a *partial* check; it shows that the result is correct for $x = 2$, and no more. In making partial checks of this kind, be careful not to use values of the literal numbers that make one of the expressions equal to zero.

In some formulas, letters with subscripts are used. For example, in the formula
$$F = P(1 - r_1)(1 - r_2)$$
the r_1 is r with subscript 1, and may be read "r sub one", and r_2 is r with subscript 2, and may be read "r sub two." In this case r_1 and r_2 refer to two rates.

The formula might have been written
$$F = P(1 - a)(1 - b),$$

SUBSTITUTION IN FORMULAS

where a and b refer to the two rates, but the use of r_1 and r_2 to denote the rates is preferable, because it emphasizes the fact that both quantities are rates, and the subscripts distinguish between the two rates.

In the formula
$$F = P(1 - r_1)(1 - r_2)(1 - r_3),$$
the letters r_1, r_2, and r_3 refer to three rates.

In general, the size of the subscript has no meaning whatever in connection with the size of the quantity. That is, r_3 is not necessarily larger than r_2.

The use of the subscript notation is very convenient and is common in both pure and applied mathematics.

EXERCISE 7

If $a = 2$, $b = -3$, and $c = 4$, find the value of:

1. $a + 3b - 4c$
2. $3a - b + c$
3. $a^2 + b^2$
4. $(a - b)^2$
5. $a^3 - 4b^2 + c^2$
6. $a^3 - c^3$
7. $5a^3b - 4ab^2 + 3b^2c^2$
8. $b^2 - 3c^2$
9. $ab + bc - ac$
10. $a^4 - 3bc + 2c^3$

Substitute the value of the letters given, and calculate the value of the unknown letter in the following formulas:

11. $S = P(1 + ni)$ $P = 100$, $n = 3$, $i = 0.05$
12. $S = P + Pni$ $P = 25$, $n = 2$, $i = 0.03$
13. $I = Pni$ $P = 200$, $n = 5$, $i = 0.02$
14. $D = Snd$ $S = 1000$, $n = 0.1$, $d = 0.06$
15. $F = (1 - r_1)(1 - r_2)$ $r_1 = 0.20$, $r_2 = 0.30$
16. $N = LF$ $L = 120$, $F = 0.06$
17. $S = P(1 + i)^n$ $P = 50$, $i = 0.04$, $n = 3$
18. $r = (1 + i)^m - 1$ $i = 0.03$, $m = 3$
19. $d = rt$ $r = 40$, $t = 3$
20. $A = \frac{1}{2}bh$ $b = 10$, $h = 8$
21. $A = \pi r^2$ $\pi = 3.14$, $r = 6$ (give answer correct to nearest integer)
22. $C = 2\pi r$ $\pi = 3.1416$, $r = 20$ (give answer correct to two decimal places)
23. $V = \pi r^2 h$ $\pi = 3.1416$, $r = 6$, $h = 10$ (give answer correct to one decimal place)
24. $P = 2l + 2w$ $l = 15$, $w = 12$
25. $V = \frac{1}{3}\pi r^2 h$ $\pi = 3.14$, $r = 4$, $h = 2$ (give answer correct to one decimal place)

Perform the indicated multiplications, and check by letting $x = 2$, $y = 3$, $z = 4$:

26. $2x - 5y + 3z$ by $x - y + z$
27. $x^2 - y^2 + z^2$ by $x + y - z$
28. $x^2 + xy + y^2$ by $x - y$
29. $y^2 - yz + z^2$ by $y + z$
30. $(x + y)^2$ by $x - y$

Perform the indicated divisions, and check by letting $a = 2, b = 3$:

31. $a^3 + 3a^2b + 3ab^2 + b^3$ by $a + b$ **32.** $a^3 + b^3$ by $a + b$
33. $a^4 - b^4$ by $a - b$ **34.** $a^4 + 4a^3b + 6a^2b^2 + 4ab^3 + b^4$ by $a + b$
35. $a^4 - 4a^3b + 6a^2b^2 - 4ab^3 + b^4$ by $a - b$

8. Symbols of grouping

Parentheses, ( ), have been used for grouping terms. Other symbols used for grouping terms are brackets, [ ], braces, { }, and the vinculum, ———.

Illustrations. $(a + 3b) + 3(a - 4b)$
$(x - 3y) - r\,[(3a - b) - (a - b)]$
$3x - \{(3x - 5) - [2(x - 4) - (2x - 3)]\}$
$2x - (\overline{3x - 2} + 4\overline{x - 5})$

If a plus sign precedes the parentheses, the parentheses may be removed, and the signs of the terms included within the parentheses are unchanged. Thus:

Example 1. Simplify $(x + 2) + (x - 5)$.

Solution. $(x + 2) + (x - 5) = x + 2 + x - 5 = 2x - 3$.

If a minus sign precedes the parentheses, the parentheses may be removed if the sign of each term included within the parentheses is changed. Thus:

Example 2. Simplify $(2x - 5) - (x - 8)$.

Solution. $(2x - 5) - (x - 8) = 2x - 5 - x + 8 = x + 3$.

If several parentheses or other signs of grouping are involved together, one within the other, they may be removed by removing the innermost ones in turn. Thus:

Example 3. Simplify $3a - \{2(a - 3) - 5(a - 4)\}$.

Solution. $3a - \{2(a - 3) - 5(a - 4)\} = 3a - \{2a - 6 - 5a + 20\},$
$= 3a - 2a + 6 + 5a - 20,$
$= 6a - 14.$

EXERCISE 8

Simplify by removing signs of grouping and combining like terms:

1. $(x - 3) - (2x + 3) - (3x - 4)$
2. $(2x - 8) + (x - 6) - (-3x + 2)$
3. $3(a - 4) - 2(a + 5) + 5(a - 3)$
4. $2(b - 2) + 3(b + 5) - 3(2b - 6)$
5. $3a - 5(b - 6) + 2(2a - 5) - 6(3b - 2)$
6. $8(2a - 3b) - 2(6a + 2b) - 4(-3a + 4b)$

SYMBOLS OF GROUPING

7. $6x - [(3x - 5) - 8 - (2x - 7)]$
8. $2x - 3y - [(3x - 2y) - 4(5x - 6y)]$
9. $3m - 2n - 6[(4m - 3n) + 2(3m + 8n)]$
10. $2r - \{4r - [(3r - 2) - 4(r - 7)] - (3r - 2)\}$
11. $3r - 2s - \{(3r - 4s) - 5[(2r - 7s) - 2(r - s)]\}$

Substitute the values of the letters given, and calculate the value of the unknown quantity:

12. $S = P(1 + i)^n$ $P = 50,\ i = 0.04,\ n = 2$
13. $S_n = R\left[\dfrac{(1 + i)^n - 1}{i}\right]$ $i = 0.03,\ R = 100,\ n = 2$
14. $r = (1 + i)^m - 1$ $i = 0.04,\ m = 3$
15. $S = P(1 + ni)$ $i = 0.05,\ n = 3,\ P = 200$
16. $I = P[(1 + i) - 1]$ $i = 0.06,\ P = 300$
17. $I = P[(1 + i)^2 - 1]$ $i = 0.05,\ P = 400$
18. $I = P[(1 + i)^3 - 1]$ $i = 0.02,\ P = 500$
19. $y = 1 + ni + \dfrac{n(n - 1)}{2} i^2$ $n = 2,\ i = 0.02$
20. $S = P\left[1 + \dfrac{j}{m}\right]^{mn}$ $P = 1000,\ j = 0.06,\ m = 2,\ n = 2$
21. $F = P(1 - r_1)(1 - r_2)(1 - r_3)$ $P = 50,\ r_1 = 0.05,\ r_2 = 0.06,\ r_3 = 0.04$
22. $S = \dfrac{n}{2}[2a + (n - 1)d]$ $n = 30,\ a = 3,\ d = 2$

MISCELLANEOUS EXERCISE

Add:

1. $3x - 4y + 6z$
     $-8x + 2y - 3z$
     $9x + 7y - z$
     $x - 8y + 5z$

2. $5x^2 - 8x + 3$
     $-2x^2 + 7x - 4$
     $x^2 + x - 3$
     $6x^2 - 5x + 9$

Subtract:

3. $6x^3 - 5x^2 + 8x - 3$
     $9x^3 - 2x^2 - 7x + 3$

4. $3m^2 - 6mn + 8n^2$
     $-5m^2 + 6mn - n^2$

Multiply:

5. $x^2 - 6x + 8$
     $x - 3$

6. $x^3 - 5x^2 + 6x - 2$
     $5x^2 - 4x + 7$

Divide:

7. $24x^2 - 62x + 14$ by $3x - 7$ 8. $x^4 - 1$ by $x - 1$

If $a = -2,\ b = -3,\ c = 4$, find the value of:

9. $a - b + 2c$
10. $-5a + 2b - 3c$
11. $a^2 - b^2 + c^2$
12. $a^2 - ab + bc - ac + b^2$
13. $5a^2 - 3b^2 - c^2$

Factor:

14. $P + Pni$ **15.** $P(1 - x) + P(1 - x)y$ **16.** $9m^2 - 16n^2$
17. $3r^2 + 17r - 56$ **18.** $8a^3 - 27n^3$ **19.** $P - Pa$

Substitute the values of the letters given, and calculate the value of the unknown quantity:

20. $p = br$ $b = 200, r = 0.25$

21. $b = \dfrac{p}{r}$ $p = 50, r = 0.20$

22. $r = \dfrac{p}{b}$ $p = 75, b = 600$

23. $y = (1 + x)^2$ $x = 0.03$
24. $y = (1 + x)^3$ $x = 0.04$
25. $D = b^2 - 4ac$ $a = 5, b = -3, c = -2$
26. $l = ar^{n-1}$ $a = 2, r = 2, n = 3$
27. $l = a + (n - 1)d$ $a = 3, n = 5, d = 2$
28. $S = P(1 + ni)$ $P = 400, n = 4, i = 0.02$
29. $I = Pni$ $P = 20, n = 5, i = 0.03$
30. $y = x(1 - nd)$ $x = 300, n = 4, d = 0.06$
31. $A = P(1 - r_1)(1 - r_2)$ $P = 50, r_1 = 0.02, r_2 = 0.08$
32. $S = P(1 + i)^n$ $P = 2000, i = 0.03, n = 2$

33. $S = P\left(1 + \dfrac{j}{m}\right)^{mn}$ $P = 1000, j = 0.08, m = 2, n = 2$

34. $i = \left(1 + \dfrac{j}{m}\right)^m - 1$ $j = 0.06, m = 2$

35. $y = 1 + ni + n\left(\dfrac{n-1}{2}\right)i^2$ $n = 2, i = 0.04$

36. $S = \dfrac{n}{2}[2a + (n - 1)d]$ $n = 8, a = 3, d = 5$

Simplify by removing parentheses and brackets, and collecting terms:

37. $3a - [(2a - 5b) - (3a - 5b) - (a - b)]$
38. $5a - 2b - [(a - 6b) - 2(a - b) - 5(a + b)]$
39. $2b - [3a - (6a - b) + 3(a - 5b) - (2a + 3b)]$

Find the exact value of:

40. $100(1.05)$ **41.** $100(1.05)^2$ **42.** $200(1.05) + 200(1.05)^2$
43. $50(1.03)^3$ **44.** $50(1.03) + 50(1.03)^2 + 50(1.03)^3$

Multiply:

45. $2 \cdot 2^2 \cdot 2^3 \cdot 2^4 = 2?$ **46.** $3x^2y^3z \cdot 5xy^3z^2$
47. $(1 + x)^{25} \cdot (1 + x)^{100} = (1 + x)?$ **48.** $8abc^2 \cdot 2a^2bc$
49. $(1.04)^{15} \cdot (1.04)^{100} = (1.04)?$

Divide, and prove by multiplication:

50. $1 - x^4$ by $1 - x$ **51.** $1 + x^5$ by $1 + x$

2

Equations of the First Degree

9. Equations

An **equation** is a symbolic expression of the statement that two quantities are equal. For example,

$$x + 2 = 8$$

is an equation, expressing the fact that $x + 2$ equals 8. The two quantities are called the members of the equation. In the above example, $x + 2$ is commonly referred to as the left member of the equation, and 8 is referred to as the right member of the equation.

There are two kinds of equations, namely, conditional equations and identical equations. A **conditional equation** is true only for certain values of the unknown quantities involved. Thus, $x + 2 = 8$ is a conditional equation, because it is true only for $x = 6$. An **identical equation** is true for all values of the unknown quantities for which the quantities are defined. For example,

$$(x + 2)(x - 2) = x^2 - 4$$

is an identical equation because it is true for all values of x.

Conditional equations are often simply called equations, and identical equations are often called identities.

An equation (conditional equation) may be thought of as asking a question. Thus, $x + 2 = 8$ asks the question, "For what values of x does $x + 2$ equal 8?"

An identity (identical equation) may be thought of as a declarative sentence. Thus, $(x + 2)(x - 2) = x^2 - 4$ states the fact that the expression $(x + 2)(x - 2)$ is equal to the expression $x^2 - 4$, for all values of x.

To "solve" an equation is to find values of the unknown that make the left member equal to the right member. The values found are roots of the equation and are said to satisfy the equation. Thus, $x = 6$ is the single root of the equation $x + 2 = 8$, and the value

$x = 6$ satisfies the equation. Some equations have only one root, while others have more than one root.

Two equations that have the same roots are said to be **equivalent equations**. The equations

$$x + 4 = 9 \quad \text{and} \quad 2x + 8 = 18$$

are equivalent equations, since they both have the same root, $x = 5$.

In order to solve an equation it is permissible to:

1. *Add the same number to both members.*
2. *Subtract the same number from both members.*
3. *Multiply both members by the same number, with the exception of the number zero.*
4. *Divide both members by the same number, with the exception of the number zero.*

These operations are all permissible because they lead to equivalent equations.

10. Equations of the first degree

An equation of the form

$$ax + b = 0,$$

with $a \neq 0$, is called an **equation of the first degree** in the unknown x. Such equations can be solved by making use of the permissible operations listed in Article 9.

Example 1. Solve the following equation for x:

$$x + 3 = 7.$$

Solution. Subtracting 3 from both members,

$$x = 4.$$

Example 2. Solve the following equation for x:

$$x - 3 = 7.$$

Solution. Adding 3 to both members,

$$x = 10.$$

Example 3. Solve the following equation for x:

$$x + 3 = 7.$$

Solution. $\quad\quad\quad x = 7 - 3 = 4.$

The process in the second line of Example 3 is known as **transposition**. The number 3 is transposed from one member to the other. When a number is transposed, its sign is changed. This operation is equivalent

EQUATIONS OF THE FIRST DEGREE

to adding (or subtracting) the same number to both members of the equation.

Example 4. Solve the following equation for x:
$$x - 3 = 7.$$
Solution. Transposing, $\quad x = 7 + 3,$
$$= 10.$$

Example 5. Solve the following equation for x:
$$3x = 21.$$
Solution. Dividing both members by 3,
$$x = 7.$$

Example 6. Solve the following equation for x:
$$\tfrac{1}{2}x = 10.$$
Solution. Multiplying both members by 2,
$$x = 20.$$

In this last example, the same result would be obtained if both members were divided by $\tfrac{1}{2}$.

Example 7. Solve the following equation for x:
$$12x + 3 = 3x + 48.$$
Solution. Transposing the terms involving x to the left member and the terms not involving x to the right member, we have:
$$12x - 3x = 48 - 3.$$
Collecting terms, $\quad 9x = 45.$
Dividing both members by 9, $\quad x = 5.$

In the solution of equations it is advisable to check the answer obtained, by substitution in the original equation. Thus in Example 7, if 5 is substituted for x, we have
$$12 \cdot 5 + 3 = 3 \cdot 5 + 48,$$
$$63 = 63.$$
Hence $x = 5$ is a root of the given equation.

EXERCISE 1

Solve the following equations for x, and check by substitution:

1. $x + 4 = 7$ 2. $x + 3 = 8$ 3. $x - 2 = 9$ 4. $x - 8 = 2$
5. $3x = 15$ 6. $4x = 48$ 7. $\tfrac{1}{2}x = 12$ 8. $\tfrac{1}{3}x = 15$
9. $2x + 3 = 7$ 10. $2x - 8 = 12$ 11. $3x = x + 6$ 12. $5x = 2x + 18$

13. $6x - 2 = 10x - 18$ 14. $5x + 2 = 7x - 1$ 15. $x + 8 = 5x + 16$
16. $x - 3x + 6 = 14 - x + 8$ 17. $3(x - 2) = 2x + 2$
18. $x = 5(x - 10)$ 19. $3x + 7(x - 5) = 6(2x - 1) - 8$
20. $8(x - 3) = 500 - x$ 21. $5x - (2x - 50) = x + 7$
22. $2x + b = 7b$ 23. $5(a - x) = 7a$
24. $(x + 5)(x + 2) = (x - 6)(x + 1)$
25. $500(1.05) + 200(1.03) + 800(1.02) = 1.03x + x$
26. $200(1.06) + 100(1.04) + 600(1.03) = 1.04x + x$
27. $800(1.05) + 400(1.04) + 700(1.03) = 1.04x + x$

Substitute the values given and solve for the unknown quantity:
28. $l = a + (n - 1)d$, $l = 14, n = 7, d = 2$
29. $l = a + (n - 1)d$, $l = 17, a = 3, n = 8$
30. $l = a + (n - 1)d$, $l = 30, a = 5, d = 5$
31. $y = 2x + 8$, $y = 12$
32. $y = 6x - 4$, $y = 14$
33. $y = -8x + 2$, $y = 18$
34. $2x + 3y = 6$, $y = 1$
35. $5x - 8y = 60$, $x = 4$
36. $2S = a + l$, $a = 10, l = 50$
37. $2S = a + l$, $S = 30, a = 2$
38. $2S = a + l$, $S = 100, l = 20$

11. Stated problems

One of the chief uses of algebra lies in the solution of stated problems. Before studying the following examples, the student should review Article 1 and the exercises following it.

Example 1. The sum of two numbers is 34. One of the numbers is two more than the other number. What are the numbers?

Solution.   Let $x =$ the smaller number,
                and $x + 2 =$ the larger number.
Then $x + (x + 2) = 34$,
                 $2x + 2 = 34$,
                 $2x = 32$,
                 $x = 16$, the smaller number,
             $x + 2 = 18$, the larger number.
Check: $16 + 18 = 34$.

The above example illustrates the general principles used in solving stated problems:

1. *Let x equal one of the unknown quantities.*
2. *Express other unknown quantities as algebraic expressions involving* x.

STATED PROBLEMS

3. *Form an equation by expressing algebraically a statement showing the relation between the given quantities and the unknown quantities.*

4. *Solve the equation for x.*

A careful reading of the problem is essential. Problems like this example can be solved by arithmetical "reasoning" or "trial and error," without resorting to algebra. The use of algebraic symbolism and the algebraic method of solving equations reduces the solution of such problems to an orderly, logical process. The "trial and error" is entirely eliminated, and the arithmetical "reasoning" is largely replaced by algebraic reasoning.

The first step is to set up the equation. Several readings of the problem may be necessary before this can be done. Once the equation has been established, the solution is comparatively simple, depending only upon the more or less mechanical routines for solving equations as outlined in Article 9.

Example 2. A druggist has 50 gallons of alcohol 80% pure. He wishes to add water until it is 70% pure. How much water must he add?

Solution.

Let x = number of gallons of water to be added.
Then $x + 50$ = number of gallons of final mixture.
Hence $0.70(x + 50) = 0.80(50)$,
or $0.70x + 35 = 40$,
$0.70x = 5$,
$x = 7\frac{1}{7}$, number of gallons of water to be added.

Check: $0.70(7\frac{1}{7} + 50) = 0.80(50)$,
$40 = 40$.

In this problem and its solution, notice that:

1. The unknown quantity is "the number of gallons of water to be added," and the first step in solving the problem is to let the symbol x represent this unknown quantity.

2. The number of gallons of pure alcohol is not changed. This gives the clue to setting up the equation.

3. The total mixture is at first 50 gallons, and is later $x + 50$ gallons, after the water is added.

4. The equation represents the fact that the number of gallons of pure alcohol before adding the water, which is $0.80(50)$ gallons, is equal to the number of gallons of pure alcohol after adding the water, which is $0.70(x + 50)$.

Example 3. A man made two investments, totaling $5000. On one investment he gained 6% and on the other investment he lost 4%. His net gain was $100. What was the amount of each investment?

Solution.

Let x = number of dollars in the first investment.

and $5000 - x$ = number of dollars in the other investment.

Then, $0.06x - 0.04(5000 - x) = 100,$
$0.06x - 200 + 0.04x = 100,$
$0.10x = 300.$
$x = 3000,$ number of dollars in the first investment.
$5000 - x = 2000,$ number of dollars in other investment.

Check: $0.06(3000) - 0.04(2000) = 100,$
$180 - 80 = 100,$
$100 = 100.$

In this problem and its solution, notice that:

1. One of the unknown quantities is "the number of dollars in the first investment" and the symbol x is used to represent this quantity.

2. The other unknown quantity is "the number of dollars in the second investment" and this quantity is expressed in the form $5000 - x$.

3. The net gain is $100. This statement furnishes the clue to the equation to be used.

4. The equation represents the statement that the gain on the 6% investment minus the loss on the other investment is equal to the net gain.

Example 4. A can do a piece of work in 10 days. B can do the same work in 6 days. Working together how long will it take A and B to complete the work?

Solution. Since A can do all the work in 10 days, he can complete $\frac{1}{10}$ of the work in 1 day. Likewise, B can do $\frac{1}{6}$ of the work in one day.

Let x = number of days it will take A and B, working together, to complete the work. Then $\frac{1}{x}$ = part of work completed by A and B, working together, in one day.

It follows that, $\frac{1}{10} + \frac{1}{6} = \frac{1}{x}.$

Multiplying both members of the equation by $60x$, we have
$6x + 10x = 60,$
$16x = 60,$
$x = 3\frac{3}{4},$ the number of days it takes A and B, working together, to complete the work.

Check:
$$\frac{1}{10} + \frac{1}{6} = \frac{1}{3\frac{3}{4}},$$
$$\frac{4}{15} = \frac{4}{15}.$$

Example 5. It takes a man 2 hours to row a boat upstream a distance of 8 miles. It takes him only 1 hour 20 minutes to return. What is the rate of the current?

Solution. Let x = rate of current,
$\frac{8}{2} = 4$, rate of rowing upstream,
$4 + x$ = rate in still water,
$4 + x + x = 4 + 2x$, rate downstream.

Hence, since distance = rate × time, we have
$$8 = (4 + 2x)(1\tfrac{1}{3}),$$
$$24 = 16 + 8x,$$
$$x = 1, \text{ rate of current in miles per hour.}$$

Check:
$$8 = (4 + 2)(1\tfrac{1}{3}),$$
$$8 = 8.$$

EXERCISE 2

1. The sum of two numbers is 73. One of the numbers is 31 more than the other number. What are the numbers?

2. The sum of two numbers is 69. The smaller number is 11 less than the larger number. What are the numbers?

3. Two boys together have $6.98. One of the boys has $2.28 more than the other boy. How much money does each boy have?

4. Two men invest a total of $12,165 in a certain business. One of the men invests $4,431 more than the other man. How much does each man invest?

5. A man traveled 795 miles in two days. On the second day he traveled 77 miles more than on the first day. How many miles did he travel each day?

6. A pharmacist has 10 gallons of alcohol 75% pure. He wishes to add water to reduce the percentage of alcohol to 60%. How much water must he add?

7. A druggist has 188 gallons of a 5% solution of acid. How much acid must he add to make a 6% solution?

8. A man bought two lots for a total of $8000. He sold the lots, making a profit of 8% on one lot and suffering a loss of 2% on the other lot. His net gain was $200. How much did each lot cost, and how much did he receive for each lot?

9. A man bought two pieces of income property for a total of $85,000. He sold them later, making a profit of 12% on one and 3% on the other. His total gain was $6150. Find the cost of each of the two pieces of property and the selling price of each.

10. How many pounds of coffee worth 30 cents per pound must be mixed with what number of pounds of coffee worth 40 cents per pound to make a mixture of 60 pounds of coffee worth 36 cents per pound?

11. How many pounds of tea worth 30 cents per pound must be mixed with 10 pounds of tea worth 24 cents per pound to yield a mixture worth 26 cents per pound? How many pounds of the mixture will there be?

12. At a Little Theater production the charge was $1.50 for each reserved seat ticket and 75 cents for each general admission ticket. A total of 400 tickets were sold for a total price of $435. How many reserved seat tickets and how many general admission tickets were sold?

13. Ten coins, consisting of dimes and quarters, amount to $1.45. How many dimes and how many quarters are there?

14. A man invests $1436 at a certain rate of interest, and he invests $785 at twice that rate of interest. His total annual income from the two investments is $90.18. Find the rates.

15. A boy has 12 coins, consisting of nickels, dimes, and quarters. The number of quarters is 2 more than the number of nickels. The total value of all of the coins is $1.80. How many nickels, dimes, and quarters does he have?

16. A man bought 150 shares of a certain stock for $20 per share. He sold part of them for twice the original cost per share, and the remainder for one half of the original cost per share. His total profit was $300. How many did he sell at each price?

17. A farmer sold 33 bushels of oats and 42 bushels of wheat for a total of $46.41. The selling price of the oats was 48 cents per bushel less than the selling price of the wheat. What was the selling price per bushel of the wheat? of the oats?

18. The sum of two numbers is 42, and the difference of the same two numbers is 16. Find the numbers.

19. A man takes 3 hours to row upstream a certain distance and 1 hour to row back. If the current is flowing at the rate of 2 miles per hour, how far upstream did he row and what is his rate of rowing in still water?

20. A motor boat takes 2 hours to travel upstream a distance of 30 miles and only $1\frac{1}{2}$ hours to return. Find the rate of the current.

21. Mr. Jones can paint a house in 20 days. Mr. Reynolds can paint the same house in 25 days. How long would it take the men to paint the house if they work together?

22. A tank can be filled through one pipe in 4 hours, while a drain pipe can empty it in 5 hours. Starting with an empty tank how long will it take for the tank to be filled with both pipes open?

23. Two towns, A and B, are joined by a straight road 120 miles long. An automobile starts from A traveling at a uniform rate of 35 miles per hour and at the same time another automobile starts from B traveling towards A at a uniform rate of 45 miles per hour. When will the automobiles meet?

24. Hobsonville has a population of 50,000 people and grows at the rate of 1000 people per year. Ritton has a population of 20,000 and is growing at

the rate of 2000 people per year. How many years will it take Ritton to equal Hobsonville in population?

12. Systems of equations of the first degree

A pair of equations of the first degree in two unknowns is called a **system of equations** of the first degree in two unknowns. Thus,
$$2x + 3y = 14,$$
$$3x - 4y = 4$$
is a system of equations of the first degree in x and y. To solve such a system of equations is to find values of x and y that satisfy both equations. In the above example the solution is the pair of values $x = 4, y = 2$, because
$$2(4) + 3(2) = 14,$$
and $$3(4) - 4(2) = 4.$$

Sometimes no solution exists. In this case the system of equations is called **incompatible** or **inconsistent**. An example of an inconsistent system is
$$2x + 3y = 14,$$
$$2x + 3y = 18.$$
There is no pair of values of x and y that will satisfy both of these equations simultaneously.

Sometimes an unlimited number of solutions exists. In this case the system is called **equivalent** or **dependent**. An example of a dependent system is
$$2x + 3y = 14,$$
$$4x + 6y = 28.$$
An unlimited number of pairs of values of x and y exist that satisfy both of these equations. Some of these pairs of values are $x = 1$ and $y = 4$, $x = 4$ and $y = 2$, $x = 0$ and $y = 4\frac{2}{3}$.

Two equations of the first degree in two unknowns can be solved by eliminating one of the unknowns, thus reducing the system to one equation of the first degree in one unknown. The method of solving such an equation in one unknown has been described in Article 9. After the value of one unknown has been found, the value of the other unknown can be calculated by substituting in one of the original pair of equations.

The elimination of one of the unknowns can be accomplished by the method of addition or subtraction, or by substitution.

13. Elimination by addition or subtraction

Consider the system of equations
$$2x + 3y = 14,$$
$$4x - 2y = 4.$$

If both members of the first equation be multiplied by 2 and if the resulting equation be subtracted from the second given equation, the result is

$$4x - 2y = 4,$$
$$4x + 6y = 28.$$

Subtracting, $\quad\quad\quad\quad -8y = -24.$

The unknown x has been eliminated and the system of two equations in two unknowns has been reduced to one equation in one unknown. Dividing both members by -8 gives $y = 3$. Substituting 3 for y in either one of the original equations gives $x = 2.5$.

Generally speaking, the method consists of multiplying the members of the two given equations by numbers that make the coefficients of one of the unknowns numerically equal. Then, by addition or subtraction of the members of the resulting equations, this unknown can be eliminated.

Example 1. Solve for x and y:
$$x + y = 8,$$
$$x - y = 4.$$

Solution. Adding corresponding members of the equations,
$$2x = 12.$$
Dividing by 2, $\quad\quad\quad\quad x = 6.$

Substituting 6 for x in the first given equation,
$$6 + y = 8.$$

Transposing and collecting terms,
$$y = 2.$$
Check: $\quad\quad\quad\quad 6 + 2 = 8,$
$$6 - 2 = 4.$$

Example 2. Solve for x and y:
$$3x + 2y = 31,$$
$$2x - y = 2.$$

Solution. Multiplying the members of the second equation by 2,
$$4x - 2y = 4.$$

Adding this equation to the first equation of the given system,
$$3x + 2y = 31,$$
$$4x - 2y = 4.$$

ELIMINATION BY ADDITION OR SUBTRACTION

Adding corresponding members of the two equations,
$$7x = 35.$$
Dividing by 7, $\qquad x = 5.$

Substituting 5 for x in the first equation of the given system,
$$3(5) + 2y = 31.$$
Solving for y,
$$15 + 2y = 31,$$
$$2y = 16,$$
$$y = 8.$$
Check:
$$3(5) + 2(8) = 31,$$
$$2(5) - 8 = 2.$$

Example 3. Solve for x and y:
$$4x - 3y = 15,$$
$$3x + 5y = 33.$$

Solution. Multiplying the members of the first equation by 5, and the members of the second equation by 3,
$$20x - 15y = 75,$$
$$9x + 15y = 99.$$

Adding the corresponding members of these two equations,
$$29x = 174.$$
Dividing by 29, $\qquad x = 6.$

Substituting 6 for x in the first equation of the given system,
$$4(6) - 3y = 15.$$
Solving for y,
$$24 - 3y = 15,$$
$$-3y = -9,$$
$$y = 3.$$
Check:
$$4(6) - 3(3) = 15,$$
$$3(6) + 5(3) = 33.$$

Example 4. Solve for x and y:
$$x + y = 18,$$
$$x - y = 2.$$

Solution. Adding the corresponding members of the equations,
$$2x = 20.$$
Dividing by 2, $\qquad x = 10.$

Subtracting the corresponding members of the equations,
$$2y = 16.$$
Dividing by 2, $\qquad y = 8.$

Notice that Examples 1, 2, and 3 can be solved by the method used in Example 4. That is, both unknowns can be determined by addition or subtraction.

Example 5. Solve for x and y:

$$\frac{1}{x} + \frac{4}{y} = 9,$$
$$\frac{3}{x} + \frac{2}{y} = 12.$$

Solution. Let $\frac{1}{x} = u$, and let $\frac{1}{y} = v$. Then

$$u + 4v = 9,$$
$$3u + 2v = 12.$$

Multiplying the members of the second equation by -2,

$$-6u - 4v = -24.$$

Adding the members of the first equation to the corresponding members of this equation,

$$-5u = -15,$$

or,

$$u = 3.$$

Since $u = \frac{1}{x}$ then $3 = \frac{1}{x}$ and $x = \frac{1}{3}$.

Multiplying the members of $u + 4v = 9$ by -3,

$$-3u - 12v = -27,$$

Adding the members of this equation to the corresponding members of $3u + 2v = 12$,

$$-10v = -15,$$
$$v = \frac{15}{10} = \frac{3}{2}.$$

Since $v = \frac{1}{y}$, then $\frac{3}{2} = \frac{1}{y}$, and $y = \frac{2}{3}$.

Check:

$$\frac{1}{\frac{1}{3}} + \frac{4}{\frac{2}{3}} = 9,$$
$$3 + 6 = 9,$$
$$9 = 9.$$

$$\frac{3}{\frac{1}{3}} + \frac{2}{\frac{2}{3}} = 12,$$
$$9 + 3 = 12,$$
$$12 = 12.$$

EXERCISE 3

Solve for x and y, and check:

1. $x + y = 5,$
$x - y = -1$

2. $x + y = 1,$
$x - y = -7$

3. $2x - y = 6,$
$3x + y = 19$

ELIMINATION BY SUBSTITUTION

4. $x + 3y = 14,$
   $x + 2y = 12$

5. $x + y = 8,$
   $x + y = 2$

6. $x + 4y = 35,$
   $x - y = 0$

7. $x - 2y = 9,$
   $3x - y = 7$

8. $x + 3y = 30,$
   $4x - y = 42$

9. $3x + y = 84,$
   $x - 2y = -14$

10. $4x + 5y = 42,$
    $7x + 3y = 39$

11. $6x - 5y = -33,$
    $9x + 2y = 36$

12. $x + 2y = 16,$
    $3x + 6y = 48$

13. $4x + y = 24,$
    $5x + 9y = 154$

14. $x + y = 100,$
    $0.45x + 0.25y = 40$

15. $x + y = 60,$
    $0.05x + 0.02y = 2.40$

16. $x + y = 45,$
    $0.5x + 0.3y = 18$

17. $x + y = 5000,$
    $0.06x + 0.05y = 280$

18. $x + y = 5000,$
    $0.01x - 0.01y = 2$

19. $1.8x + 4.6y = 2.28,$
    $7.2x + 2.4y = 4.32$

20. $1.6x + 3.2y = 2.56,$
    $4.2x - 2.7y = 1.17$

21. $ax + by = c,$
    $dx + ey = f$

22. $a_1x + a_2y = a_3,$
    $b_1x + b_2y = b_3$

23. $\dfrac{3}{x} + \dfrac{4}{y} = 23,$
    $\dfrac{8}{x} - \dfrac{5}{y} = 30$

24. $\dfrac{4}{x} + \dfrac{6}{y} = 3,$
    $\dfrac{12}{x} + \dfrac{42}{y} = 13$

25. $\dfrac{5}{x} + \dfrac{12}{y} = 38,$
    $\dfrac{20}{x} + \dfrac{1}{y} = 5$

26. $\dfrac{1}{x} - \dfrac{2}{y} = -1,$
    $\dfrac{3}{x} + \dfrac{4}{y} = 32$

14. Elimination by substitution

In a system of two equations of the first degree in two unknowns, one of the unknowns may be eliminated by substitution. The method of elimination by substitution consists of solving one of the given equations for one of the unknowns in terms of the other unknown, and then substituting the expression obtained in the other given equation.

Consider the system of equations

$$2x + 3y = 14,$$
$$4x - 2y = 4.$$

In the first equation, solve for x in terms of y:

$$2x = 14 - 3y,$$
$$x = \frac{14 - 3y}{2}.$$

Substitute this expression for x in the second given equation,
$$4\left(\frac{14-3y}{2}\right) - 2y = 4.$$

This is an equation in y alone. The system of two equations has been reduced to one equation in one unknown. Solve this equation for y, and obtain the value of x by substitution in either of the two given equations.

Example 1. Solve for x and y:
$$7x + y = 20,$$
$$3x + 2y = 18.$$

Solution. Solving the first equation for y in terms of x,
$$y = 20 - 7x.$$

Substituting $20 - 7x$ for y in the second given equation,
$$3x + 2(20 - 7x) = 18.$$

Solving this equation for x,
$$3x + 40 - 14x = 18,$$
$$-11x = -22,$$
$$x = 2.$$

Substituting 2 for x in the first given equation,
$$7(2) + y = 20,$$
$$14 + y = 20,$$
$$y = 6.$$

Check:
$$7(2) + 6 = 20,$$
$$3(2) + 2(6) = 18.$$

Example 2. Solve for x and y:
$$3x + 4y = 39,$$
$$5x - 6y = -11.$$

Solution. Solving for x in terms of y in the first equation,
$$3x = 39 = 4y,$$
$$x = \frac{39 - 4y}{3}.$$

Substituting $\frac{39 - 4y}{3}$ for x in the second given equation,
$$5\left(\frac{39-4y}{3}\right) - 6y = -11.$$

Multiplying both members of this equation by 3,
$$5(39 - 4y) - 18y = -33.$$

Solving for y,
$$195 - 20y - 18y = -33,$$
$$-38y = -228,$$
$$y = 6.$$

Substituting 6 for y in the first given equation,
$$3x + 4(6) = 39.$$

Solving for x,
$$3x + 24 = 39,$$
$$3x = 15,$$
$$x = 5.$$

Check:
$$3(5) + 4(6) = 39,$$
$$5(5) - 6(6) = -11.$$

EXERCISE 4

Solve for x and y, using the method of elimination by substitution:

1. $x + y = 9,$
   $x - y = 3$
2. $2x - y = 5,$
   $x + 3y = 13$
3. $3x - 2y = 5,$
   $2x + 3y = -4$
4. $5x + 2y = -2,$
   $-2x + 3y = 16$
5. $8x - 5y = -1,$
   $6x + 3y = 33$
6. $x + y = 10,$
   $0.02x + 0.05y = 0.38$
7. $x - y = 5,$
   $0.5x - 0.3y = 4.3$
8. $6x + 4y = 0,$
   $2x - 8y = -7$
9. $30x - 45y = 29,$
   $75x + 60y = 38$
10. $2x + 6y = 3,$
    $4x + 3y = 3$

15. Solution of stated problems, using two unknowns

In the stated problems of Article 11 the letter x was used to represent one of the unknowns in the problem, and an expression involving x was used to represent the other unknown.

An alternative method is to use x to represent one unknown and to use y to represent the other unknown. From the stated problem it is then possible to form two equations involving two unknowns. This system can be solved by the methods described in Article 14.

Example 1. The sum of two numbers is 39. If four times the first number be added to three times the second number, the result is 133. What are the numbers?

Solution.   Let x = first number,
and y = second number.

Then
$$x + y = 39,$$
$$4x + 3y = 133.$$

Solving this system of equations by the method of elimination by subtraction, the results are $x = 16$ and $y = 23$.

Check:
$$16 + 23 = 39,$$
$$4(16) + 3(23) = 133.$$

Example 2. A man makes two investments totaling $1080. From one investment he receives a return of 6%, and from the other investment he receives a return of 3%. His total income on the two investments is $39.30. How much did he invest at each rate?

Solution. Let $x =$ number of dollars invested at 6%, and $y =$ number of dollars invested at 3%.

Then
$$x + y = 1080,$$
$$0.06x + 0.03y = 39.30.$$

Solving, $x = \$230$ and $y = \$850$.

Check:
$$230 + 850 = 1080,$$
$$0.06(230) + 0.03(850) = 39.30.$$

EXERCISE 5

1. The sum of two numbers is 387. One of the numbers is 83 more than the other number. What are the numbers?

2. A man makes two investments totaling $830. On one of the investments he receives a return of 4% per year, and on the other he receives 2% per year. The total annual income on the two investments is $30. Find the amount of each investment.

3. A dairy wishes to sell milk containing 4% butterfat. Milk containing 3% butterfat is mixed with cream containing 25% butterfat. How much of each is needed to make 500 pounds of 4% milk?

4. Three handkerchiefs and 4 neckties sell for $6.35, while 2 handkerchiefs and 5 neckties sell for $7.50. What is the selling price of one handkerchief? of one necktie?

5. A man rows at the rate of 5 miles per hour in still water. If it takes him $1\frac{1}{4}$ hours to row downstream a certain distance and 5 hours to row back, what is the rate of the current and how far did the man row downstream?

6. A house and lot together cost $16,674. The cost of building the house was $9,774 more than the cost of the lot. How much did the lot cost?

7. Working together, a man and his son can do a piece of garden work in 5 hours. On a certain day they work together for 3 hours, at the end of which time the son quits and the father completes the work alone in $4\frac{1}{2}$ more hours. How long would it take each to do the work alone?

8. A storekeeper has a number of sports coats that cost him $12.50 each and a number of slacks that cost him $11.90 per pair. If he sells the coats for $15.60 each and the slacks for $13.50 per pair, his profit is $69.20. If he sells the coats for $16 each and the slacks for $13 per pair, his profit is $64. How many coats and how many pairs of slacks has he?

9. A student's grade in geometry was 8 less than his grade in algebra. The average of his grades in algebra and geometry was 86. What were his grades?

10. A haberdasher has two brands of suits. He has 10 suits of one brand and 20 suits of the other brand. If he marks them so as to gain $\frac{1}{10}$ of the selling price on the first brand, and $\frac{2}{10}$ of the selling price on the second brand, his total profit on the 30 suits is $265. If he marks them so as to gain $\frac{2}{10}$ of the selling price on the first brand and $\frac{1}{10}$ of the selling price on the second brand, his total profit on the 30 suits is $200. Find the selling price of each brand.

11. In the equation $y = mx + b$, it is given that $y = 7$ when $x = 4$; also, it is given that $y = 13$ when $x = 6$. Substituting these two pairs of values of x and y in the given equation yields two equations involving m and b. Solve these two equations for m and b.

12. In the equation $l = a + (n - 1)d$, it is given that $l = 6$ when $n = 2$; also, it is given that $l = 18$ when $n = 6$. Substituting these two pairs of values of l and n in the given equation yields two equations involving a and d. Solve these equations for a and d.

13. A farmer sells 43 bushels of oats and 28 bushels of wheat for a total of $39.30; he sells 23 bushels of oats and 17 bushels of wheat for a total of $22.68. What was the selling price per bushel of the wheat? of the oats?

14. A man bought 3 rolls of high-quality wallpaper and 2 rolls of less expensive wallpaper for a total of $5.54. Later, he bought 4 rolls of the better wallpaper and 5 rolls of the other wallpaper for a total of $8.67. What was the cost of each kind per roll?

15. A collection of 32 coins consists of nickels and dimes. If the collection amounts to $2.35, find the number of nickels and the number of dimes in the collection.

16. A road 140 miles in length joins the towns A and B. One car leaves A at the same time that a second car leaves B. If they travel towards each other they meet in two hours. If the slower car travels on the road extended in the direction from A through B and the faster car travels in the same direction, the cars meet in 14 hours. What is the average speed of each?

16. Three equations in three unknowns

To solve a system of three equations of the first degree in three unknowns, eliminate one letter from a pair of the given system of equations, and then eliminate the same letter from another pair of the given system. This procedure yields a system of two equations in two unknowns. Solve this system by the method of elimination by addition or subtraction, as explained in Article 13. Having obtained the values of two of the unknowns, substitute these values in one of the equations of the original system and thus find the value of the third unknown.

Sometimes the addition or subtraction of a pair of equations of the given system results in the elimination of two unknowns at the same time. In this case it is possible to find the value of one of the unknowns immediately. Find the value of this unknown and substitute it in another pair of the original system. This yields a system of two equations in two unknowns. Solve this system for the values of these two unknowns.

Example 1. Solve for x, y, and z:

$$x + 2y - 3z = -4, \qquad (1)$$
$$x - 3y + 7z = 21, \qquad (2)$$
$$x + 3y + 4z = 27. \qquad (3)$$

Solution. Subtracting (2) from (1),

$$5y - 10z = -25. \qquad (4)$$

Subtracting (3) from (2),

$$-6y + 3z = -6. \qquad (5)$$

Solving (4) and (5),

$$y = 3, \; z = 4.$$

Substituting 3 for y and 4 for z in (1),

$$x + 6 - 12 = -4,$$
$$x = 2.$$

These results may be checked by substitution in (2) and (3).

Example 2. Solve for a, b, and c:

$$a + b + 4c = 4, \qquad (1)$$
$$a + b - 3c = 11, \qquad (2)$$
$$3a - 2b + c = -2. \qquad (3)$$

Solution. Subtracting (2) from (1),

$$7c = -7, \qquad (4)$$
$$c = -1. \qquad (5)$$

Substituting -1 for c in (2) and (3), and simplifying,

$$a + b = 8, \qquad (6)$$
$$3a - 2b = -1. \qquad (7)$$

Solving (6) and (7),

$$a = 3, \; b = 5.$$

EXERCISE 6

Solve for x, y and z:

1. $x + y + z = 11,$
   $x + 3y + 2z = 24,$
   $3x - 4y + 5z = 15$

2. $x + 8y - 3z = 1,$
   $2x - 8y + 4z = 14,$
   $7x + 16y - 2z = 41$

3. $3x - 2y + 4z = -28,$
   $4x + 3y - 2z = 9,$
   $2x - 5y + 3z = -31$

4. $x + y - 3z = -10,$
   $x + y + 6z = 8,$
   $3x - 2y + z = -15$

THREE EQUATIONS IN THREE UNKNOWNS

5. $3x + 2y + 2z = 31$,
$x + 2y + 2z = 21$,
$2x - 5y + 7z = -6$

6. $2x + 3y + 5z = 3$,
$4x - 6y + 15z = 0$,
$6x - 3y - 5z = -7$

7. $x + y = 27$,
$y + z = 14$,
$x + z = 3$

8. $2x = z$,
$x + y + z = 41$,
$x - 2y = -40$

9. $\dfrac{1}{x} + \dfrac{1}{y} + \dfrac{1}{z} = 14$,
$\dfrac{1}{x} - \dfrac{1}{y} + \dfrac{2}{z} = 7$,
$\dfrac{3}{x} - \dfrac{1}{y} - \dfrac{4}{z} = 1$

10. $\dfrac{2}{x} + \dfrac{3}{y} - \dfrac{4}{z} = 7$,
$\dfrac{6}{x} - \dfrac{4}{y} - \dfrac{2}{z} = -11$,
$\dfrac{4}{x} - \dfrac{1}{y} + \dfrac{1}{z} = 4$

11. $7x - 8y + 2z = 15$,
$14x + 8y - 4z = 3$,
$7x + 8y + 8z = 48$

12. $8x - 20y + 19z = -79$,
$7x - 11y - 13z = 66$,
$3x - 5y - 9z = 46$

13. $x + 2y + 2 = 0$,
$3x - y - z = 10$,
$x + y + 3z - 16 = 0$

14. $x + y = z$,
$2z - y = x + 8$,
$y = 3z - 4x + 2$

MISCELLANEOUS EXERCISE

Solve for x and check:

1. $5x - 2 = 3(x - 2)$
2. $3(x + 5) = -4 - 2(x - 17)$
3. $4x - 5 = 2(x - 3)$
4. $2x + 5(x - 1) = 3(x + 2)$
5. $(x + 3)(x - 4) = (x + 2)(x + 5)$

Substitute the values given and solve for the unknown quantity:

6. $y = 2x - 3$, $x = 5$
7. $y = 5x + 3$, $y = -7$
8. $3x + 2y - 6 = 0$, $y = -7$
9. $4x - 3y + 1 = 0$, $x = 2$
10. $2x + 3y + 7 = 0$, $x = 3$

11. The perimeter of a rectangle is 85. A side is 15 more than its adjacent side. Find the lengths of the adjacent sides.

12. The perimeter of a rectangle is 55. A side is 4 times its adjacent side. Find the lengths of the adjacent sides.

13. The perimeter of an isosceles triangle is 27. The base is 3 more than one of the equal sides. Find the sides of the triangle.

14. A ship leaves a port, traveling at the rate of 30 miles per hour. Eight hours later an airplane, traveling at the rate of 200 miles per hour, leaves the same port for the same destination. How long will it take the airplane to overtake the ship?

Solve for the unknowns and check:

15. $3x - 2y = 0$,
$5x + 3y = 19$

16. $7x + 11y = -17$,
$2x + 5y = -3$

17. $2x - 5y = 3$,
$3x - 7y = 3$

18. $4x + 3y = 4,$
    $-2x + 9y = 5$

19. $5x + 6y = -1,$
    $10x + 3y = 1$

20. $7x - 14y = 8,$
    $14x + 7y = 6$

21. $\dfrac{2}{x} + \dfrac{3}{y} = 18,$
    $\dfrac{-3}{x} + \dfrac{1}{y} = -5$

22. $\dfrac{4}{x} - \dfrac{3}{y} = 21,$
    $\dfrac{6}{x} - \dfrac{4}{y} = 29$

23. $2x - y + 3z = 3,$
    $3x - 2y + 2z = -3,$
    $x + 3y - 8z = 0$

24. $x + 2y + 3z = -2,$
    $4x + y - 2z = -8,$
    $2x - 2y + z = -11$

25. $\dfrac{1}{x} - \dfrac{1}{y} + \dfrac{1}{z} = 10,$
    $\dfrac{2}{x} + \dfrac{3}{y} + \dfrac{4}{z} = 15,$
    $\dfrac{3}{x} - \dfrac{2}{y} + \dfrac{3}{z} = 27$

Use two unknowns in solving the following problems:

26. A man rows downstream a distance of 9 miles in one hour. If it takes him 3 hours to return, find the rate of the current and the man's rate of rowing in still water.

27. A grocer wishes to mix two grades of coffee to make 75 pounds of mixture to sell for 40 cents per pound. If the two grades sell for 35 cents per pound and 50 cents per pound, respectively, how many pounds of each must he use?

28. A jobber bills one store for 4 dozen shirts and 2 dozen pairs of shoes and he bills another store for 3 dozen shirts and 3 dozen pairs of shoes. If the bill for the first store was $396, and the bill for the second store was $480.60, what was the price of 1 shirt? of 1 pair of shoes?

29. A farmer wants to buy a herd of 40 cows in which there are $\frac{3}{5}$ as many Guernseys as there are Holsteins. How many of each kind of cow should he buy?

30. A man bought a certain number of shares of General Copper at $60 per share, and a certain number of shares of Southern Electric at $50 per share. If he had sold the General Copper for $65 per share and the Southern Electric for $45 per share, he would have gained $10 altogether. However, he sold General Copper at $63 per share and the Southern Electric at $46 per share, and thereby lost $22. How many shares of each stock had he bought?

31. A city department needs 30 workmen, some of whom will be paid $7.30 each per day and the balance $9 each per day. If the department has $227.50 per day available for wages, how many of each type of workman can be hired?

32. If 2 be added to both the numerator and the denominator of a given fraction, the new fraction equals $\frac{3}{4}$. If 4 be subtracted from both numerator and denominator, the new fraction is $\frac{1}{2}$. Find the fraction.

3

Fractions

17. Fractions

A **fraction** is the indicated quotient of two expressions. Thus, $\dfrac{a}{b}$ means a divided by b, and $\dfrac{2}{3}$ means 2 divided by 3.

18. Operations with fractions

The following rules are useful in operations involving fractions.

I. *The value of a fraction is not changed if the numerator and denominator are multiplied or divided by the same number.* Thus,

$$\frac{a}{b} = \frac{ak}{bk},$$

and

$$\frac{a}{b} = \frac{\frac{a}{k}}{\frac{b}{k}}.$$

II. *Changing the sign of either the numerator or denominator of a fraction is equivalent to changing the sign of the fraction.* Thus,

$$\frac{-a}{b} = -\frac{a}{b} = \frac{a}{-b}.$$

III. *Adding or subtracting two like fractions (fractions having a common denominator) gives a fraction whose numerator is the sum or difference, respectively, of the numerators, and whose denominator is the common denominator.* That is,

$$\frac{a}{c} + \frac{b}{c} = \frac{a+b}{c},$$

and

$$\frac{a}{c} - \frac{b}{c} = \frac{a-b}{c}.$$

IV. *The sum of two fractions is*

$$\frac{a}{b} + \frac{c}{d} = \frac{ad+bc}{bd},$$

and the difference of two fractions is

$$\frac{a}{b} - \frac{c}{d} = \frac{ad-bc}{bd}.$$

V. *The product of two fractions is given by*

$$\frac{a}{b} \cdot \frac{c}{d} = \frac{ac}{bd}.$$

The numerator of the product is equal to the product of the numerators, and the denominator of the product is equal to the product of the denominators.

VI. *To divide one fraction by another, invert the divisor and then multiply.* Thus,

$$\frac{a}{b} \div \frac{c}{d} = \frac{a}{b} \cdot \frac{d}{c} = \frac{ad}{bc}.$$

The **reciprocal** of a number is 1 divided by the number. The reciprocal of a is $\frac{1}{a}$; the reciprocal of 2 is $\frac{1}{2}$; the reciprocal of $\frac{2}{3}$ is

$$\frac{1}{\frac{2}{3}} = 1 \cdot \frac{3}{2} = \frac{3}{2}.$$

Therefore, to divide by a fraction multiply by its reciprocal.

19. Reduction to lowest terms

To reduce a fraction to its lowest terms, separate the numerator and denominator into their prime factors, and then divide both numerator and denominator by common factors, if they occur. This is an application of Rule I.

Example 1. Reduce to lowest terms: $\frac{27}{45}$.

Solution. $\qquad \frac{27}{45} = \frac{\cancel{9} \cdot 3}{\cancel{9} \cdot 5} = \frac{3}{5}.$

Example 2. Reduce to lowest terms: $\frac{x^2 - 5x + 6}{x^2 - 6x + 8}$.

Solution. $\qquad \frac{x^2 - 5x + 6}{x^2 - 6x + 8} = \frac{\cancel{(x-2)}(x-3)}{\cancel{(x-2)}(x-4)} = \frac{x-3}{x-4}.$

ADDITION AND SUBTRACTION OF FRACTIONS

EXERCISE 1

Reduce to lowest terms:

1. $\dfrac{12}{27}$ 2. $\dfrac{26}{39}$ 3. $\dfrac{6x}{7x}$ 4. $\dfrac{5a}{15a}$

5. $\dfrac{a^2b^3}{ab}$ 6. $\dfrac{a^7b^5}{a^9b^2}$ 7. $\dfrac{a^2 + ab}{a^2 - ab}$ 8. $\dfrac{x^2 - 2xy}{x^2 + 2xy}$

9. $\dfrac{x^2}{x^2 + 3xy}$ 10. $\dfrac{x}{x - xy}$ 11. $\dfrac{x^2 + xy}{x^2 - y^2}$

12. $\dfrac{a^2 - b^2}{a^2 - ab}$ 13. $\dfrac{m}{m - m^2}$ 14. $\dfrac{x - x^2}{x}$

15. $\dfrac{x^2 - 5x + 6}{x^2 - 10x + 16}$ 16. $\dfrac{a^2 - 2ab + b^2}{a^2 - b^2}$

17. $\dfrac{a^3 - b^3}{a - b}$ 18. $\dfrac{x + y}{x^3 + y^3}$

20. Addition and subtraction of fractions

To add and subtract fractions, use Rules III and IV in Article 18.

Example 1. Add: $\dfrac{2}{3} + \dfrac{5}{3}$.

Solution.
$$\dfrac{2}{3} + \dfrac{5}{3} = \dfrac{2 + 5}{3} = \dfrac{7}{3}.$$

Example 2. Add: $\dfrac{3}{5} + \dfrac{7}{8}$.

Solution.
$$\dfrac{3}{5} + \dfrac{7}{8} = \dfrac{(3)(8) + (5)(7)}{40} = \dfrac{59}{40}.$$

Example 3. Add: $\dfrac{3}{4} + \dfrac{5}{6}$.

Solution. $\dfrac{3}{4} + \dfrac{5}{6} = \dfrac{(3)(3)}{(4)(3)} + \dfrac{(5)(2)}{(6)(2)} = \dfrac{9}{12} + \dfrac{10}{12} = \dfrac{9 + 10}{12} = \dfrac{19}{12}.$

Notice the application of Rule I in the first step of the solution of this example.

Example 4. Subtract: $\dfrac{3x + 1}{4} - \dfrac{2x - 6}{5}$.

Solution.
$$\dfrac{3x + 1}{4} - \dfrac{2x - 6}{5} = \dfrac{5(3x + 1) - 4(2x - 6)}{20},$$
$$= \dfrac{15x + 5 - 8x + 24}{20},$$
$$= \dfrac{7x + 29}{20}.$$

Example 5. Add: $\dfrac{3x+2}{x+1} + \dfrac{x^2+1}{x^2-1}$.

Solution. $\dfrac{3x+2}{x+1} + \dfrac{x^2+1}{x^2-1} = \dfrac{(3x+2)(x-1)+(x^2+1)}{(x+1)(x-1)},$

$= \dfrac{3x^2 - x - 2 + x^2 + 1}{x^2 - 1} = \dfrac{4x^2 - x - 1}{x^2 - 1}.$

In Example 5, notice that the **least common denominator (L.C.D.)** is used. Instead of using $(x+1)(x^2-1)$ as the common denominator, use x^2-1, since both of the given denominators are factors of x^2-1; that is, x^2-1 is the least common denominator.

EXERCISE 2

Perform the following additions and subtractions:

1. $\dfrac{x}{2} + \dfrac{3x}{2}$
2. $\dfrac{a}{b} + \dfrac{c}{b} - \dfrac{d}{b}$
3. $\dfrac{2a}{c} - \dfrac{3a}{c} + \dfrac{8a}{c}$
4. $\dfrac{x}{3} + \dfrac{x}{4}$
5. $\dfrac{a}{6} - \dfrac{3a}{7}$
6. $\dfrac{5x}{3} + \dfrac{8x}{5} - \dfrac{3x}{2}$
7. $\dfrac{x}{2} - \dfrac{1}{2} + \dfrac{x+2}{2}$
8. $\dfrac{x-1}{3} - \dfrac{2x-1}{4} + \dfrac{x-4}{5}$
9. $\dfrac{2x-y}{3} + \dfrac{8x-3y}{7}$
10. $\dfrac{3x-1}{5} - \dfrac{6x-8}{3}$
11. $\dfrac{2m-n}{7} - \dfrac{3m+6n}{5}$
12. $\dfrac{1}{a} + \dfrac{1}{b}$
13. $\dfrac{1}{5} - \dfrac{2}{3} + \dfrac{6}{7}$
14. $\dfrac{1}{a} - \dfrac{1}{b} + \dfrac{1}{c}$
15. $\dfrac{1}{x-2} + \dfrac{3}{x-1}$
16. $\dfrac{2}{x-5} - \dfrac{4}{x+6}$
17. $\dfrac{3}{a-b} + \dfrac{4}{a-b}$
18. $\dfrac{7}{a-b} - \dfrac{8}{a+b}$
19. $\dfrac{x}{y-1} - \dfrac{x}{y+1}$
20. $\dfrac{a+x}{a-x} - \dfrac{a-x}{a+x}$
21. $\dfrac{x^2+xy}{x^2-1} + \dfrac{3x^2-xy}{x-1} - \dfrac{4x^2+3xy}{x+1}$
22. $\dfrac{5x-1}{a-b} + \dfrac{6x-2}{a-b} - \dfrac{x}{a^2-b^2}$
23. $\dfrac{3}{x-2} + \dfrac{4}{x+3} - \dfrac{8}{x^2+x-6}$
24. $\dfrac{2}{x^2-5x+6} + \dfrac{3}{x^2-6x+8}$
25. $\dfrac{3}{a^2-6a+5} - \dfrac{2}{a^2-8a+15}$
26. $\dfrac{P_b}{1-nd} - P_b$

21. Multiplication and division of fractions

To multiply and divide fractions, use Rules V and VI in Article 18.

Example 1. Perform the following multiplication and simplify:
$$\frac{3ab}{7xy} \cdot \frac{21xz}{a^2c}.$$

Solution.
$$\frac{3ab}{7xy} \cdot \frac{21xz}{a^2c} = \frac{9bz}{acy}.$$

Example 2. Perform the indicated multiplication and simplify:
$$\frac{x^2-9}{a^2-b^2} \cdot \frac{a^3-b^3}{x^2-8x+15}.$$

Solution.
$$\frac{x^2-9}{a^2-b^2} \cdot \frac{a^3-b^3}{x^2-8x+15} = \frac{(x+3)(x-3)}{(a-b)(a+b)} \cdot \frac{(a-b)(a^2+ab+b^2)}{(x-3)(x-5)},$$
$$= \frac{(x+3)(a^2+ab+b^2)}{(a+b)(x-5)}.$$

Example 3. Perform the indicated division and simplify:
$$\frac{x^2-6x+8}{x^2-5x+4} \div \frac{x^2-7x+10}{x^2-16}.$$

Solution.
$$\frac{x^2-6x+8}{x^2-5x+4} \div \frac{x^2-7x+10}{x^2-16} = \frac{(x-4)(x-2)}{(x-4)(x-1)} \cdot \frac{(x+4)(x-4)}{(x-5)(x-2)},$$
$$= \frac{(x-4)(x+4)}{(x-1)(x-5)}.$$

EXERCISE 3

Perform the following multiplications and divisions and simplify:

1. $\dfrac{a}{c} \cdot \dfrac{m}{n}$

2. $a \cdot \dfrac{b}{a}$

3. $\dfrac{6x}{13y} \cdot \dfrac{26y^2}{x^3}$

4. $\dfrac{7}{16} \cdot \dfrac{32}{7} \cdot \dfrac{9}{4}$

5. $\dfrac{8x}{3y} \div \dfrac{3x}{7y}$

6. $\dfrac{3}{a-1} \cdot \dfrac{2a-2}{3a-4}$

7. $\dfrac{a}{a^2-b^2} \div \dfrac{c}{a-b}$

8. $3\tfrac{1}{5} \cdot \tfrac{5}{7} \cdot \tfrac{9}{32}$

9. $3\tfrac{2}{3} \div 5$

10. $6x \div \tfrac{3}{5}$

11. $\left(\dfrac{x}{y} - \dfrac{y}{x}\right) \div \dfrac{x-y}{xy}$

12. $\dfrac{x^2-4}{x^3-8} \cdot \dfrac{x^2-2x}{x^2-7x+10}$

13. $\dfrac{c^2-d^2}{c^2-cd} \cdot \dfrac{c}{c+d}$

14. $\dfrac{a^2-9a+14}{a^2-5a+6} \div \dfrac{a^2-10a+21}{a^2-7a+12}$

15. $\left(\dfrac{a}{b} + \dfrac{b}{a}\right)\left(\dfrac{ab}{a+b}\right)$

16. $\dfrac{x}{x-y} \cdot \dfrac{y-x}{y}$

17. $3x \div \left(6 - \dfrac{4}{x}\right)$

18. $\dfrac{P_b d}{1 - nd} \div P_b$

22. Substitution in formulas

In order to be able to substitute numbers for letters in formulas and thus to find the value of one letter in the formula, it is often necessary to perform operations involving fractions.

Example 1. If $n = 3$, $i = 0.04$, and $S = 50$, find the value of P in the formula
$$P = \dfrac{S}{1 + ni}.$$

Solution.
$$P = \dfrac{S}{1 + ni}$$
$$P = \dfrac{50}{1 + (3)(0.04)} = \dfrac{50}{1.12} = 44.64,$$
rounding off the answer to two decimal places.

Example 2. If $a = 3$, $r = 2$, and $l = 48$, find the value of S in the formula
$$S = \dfrac{a - rl}{1 - r}.$$

Solution.
$$S = \dfrac{a - rl}{1 - r}.$$
$$S = \dfrac{3 - (2)(48)}{1 - 2} = \dfrac{3 - 96}{-1} = 93.$$

EXERCISE 4

Calculate the value of the unknown letter for the given values of the letters indicated:

1. $n = \dfrac{I}{Pi}$ $\qquad I = 0.15, P = 20, i = 0.03$

2. $P = \dfrac{S}{1 + ni}$ $\qquad S = 1000, n = 10, i = 0.05$

3. $S = \dfrac{a}{1 - r}$ $\qquad a = 2, r = 0.5$

4. $i = \dfrac{d}{1 - d}$ $\qquad d = 0.04$

5. $i = \dfrac{d}{1 - nd}$ $\qquad d = 0.08, n = 0.25$ (Round off to three decimal places.)

6. $d = \dfrac{i}{1 + ni}$ $\qquad i = 0.05, n = 0.5$

7. $i = \dfrac{I}{Pn}$ $\qquad I = 2.5, P = 200, n = 0.25$

8. $n = \dfrac{P_1 n_1 + P_2 n_2}{P_1 + P_2}$ $\qquad P_1 = 1200, n_1 = 30, P_2 = 800, n_2 = 45$

9. $F = \dfrac{S}{(1+i)^n}$ $\qquad S = 100, i = 0.03, n = 2$ (Round off to two decimal places.)

10. $S_n = R \cdot \dfrac{(1+i)^n - 1}{i}$ $\qquad R = 200, i = 0.04, n = 2$

23. Complex fractions

A **complex fraction** is one that contains a fraction in its numerator, its denominator, or both. Thus,

$$\dfrac{\dfrac{a}{b}}{\dfrac{c}{}}, \quad \dfrac{a}{\dfrac{b}{c}}, \quad \dfrac{\dfrac{a}{b}}{\dfrac{c}{d}}, \quad \dfrac{\dfrac{a}{b} + \dfrac{c}{d}}{\dfrac{e}{f} + \dfrac{g}{h}}$$

are examples of complex fractions.

Complex fractions are simplified by the rules for division of fractions.

Example 1. Simplify the complex fraction: $\dfrac{\dfrac{a}{b}}{c}$.

Solution. $\qquad \dfrac{\dfrac{a}{b}}{c} = a \cdot \dfrac{c}{b} = \dfrac{ac}{b}.$

Example 2. Simplify the complex fraction: $\dfrac{\dfrac{a}{b}}{c}$.

Solution. $\qquad \dfrac{\dfrac{a}{b}}{c} = \dfrac{a}{b} \cdot \dfrac{1}{c} = \dfrac{a}{bc}.$

Example 3. Simplify the complex fraction: $\dfrac{\dfrac{a}{b}}{\dfrac{c}{d}}$.

Solution. $\qquad \dfrac{\dfrac{a}{b}}{\dfrac{c}{d}} = \dfrac{a}{b} \cdot \dfrac{d}{c} = \dfrac{ad}{bc}.$

Example 4. Simplify the complex fraction: $\dfrac{\dfrac{a}{b} + \dfrac{c}{d}}{\dfrac{e}{f}}$.

Solution.
$$\frac{\frac{a}{b}+\frac{c}{d}}{\frac{e}{f}} = \frac{\frac{ad+bc}{bd}}{\frac{e}{f}}$$
$$= \frac{ad+bc}{bd} \cdot \frac{f}{e} = \frac{f(ad+bc)}{bde}.$$

An alternative procedure for simplifying complex fractions is to multiply both numerator and denominator by the least common denominator of the fractions which are in the numerator and denominator of the complex fraction. This operation is permissible by Rule I of Article 18.

Example 5. Simplify: $\frac{\frac{2}{3}-\frac{1}{4}}{\frac{1}{2}-\frac{5}{12}}$.

Solution. The least common denominator of the numerator and denominator of this complex fraction is 12. Multiplying the numerator and denominator of the complex fraction by 12,

$$\frac{\frac{2}{3}-\frac{1}{4}}{\frac{1}{2}-\frac{5}{12}} = \frac{12(\frac{2}{3}-\frac{1}{4})}{12(\frac{1}{2}-\frac{5}{12})} = \frac{8-3}{6-5} = 5.$$

EXERCISE 5

Simplify the following complex fractions:

1. $\dfrac{6}{\frac{2}{3}}$ 2. $\dfrac{\frac{3}{5}}{10}$ 3. $\dfrac{\frac{1}{2}}{\frac{3}{4}}$

4. $\dfrac{\frac{x}{y}}{z}$ 5. $\dfrac{x}{\frac{y}{z}}$ 6. $\dfrac{\frac{r}{s}}{\frac{m}{n}}$

7. $\dfrac{\frac{1}{2}+\frac{1}{4}}{\frac{3}{4}}$ 8. $\dfrac{\frac{1}{2}}{\frac{3}{5}+\frac{2}{3}}$ 9. $\dfrac{\frac{3}{4}+\frac{1}{2}}{\frac{1}{5}-\frac{2}{3}}$

10. $\dfrac{\frac{a}{b}+\frac{b}{a}}{\frac{c}{d}}$ 11. $\dfrac{\frac{x}{y}}{\frac{x}{y}-\frac{y}{x}}$ 12. $\dfrac{\frac{a}{b}+\frac{x}{y}}{\frac{a}{b}-\frac{x}{y}}$

13. $\dfrac{a-\frac{1}{x}}{x-\frac{1}{a}}$ 14. $\dfrac{\frac{1}{m}+m}{\frac{1}{m}-n}$ 15. $\dfrac{\frac{a}{b}+c}{\frac{b}{a}-c}$

16. $\dfrac{\frac{3}{x}}{\frac{4}{x}-\frac{2}{x}}$ 17. $\dfrac{\frac{5}{x}-\frac{1}{x}}{\frac{3}{x}}$ 18. $\dfrac{\frac{a}{a-b}-a}{a+\frac{a}{a-b}}$

EQUATIONS INVOLVING FRACTIONS

19. $\dfrac{\dfrac{Pnd}{1-nd}}{n}$ 20. $\dfrac{\dfrac{Pd}{1-nd}}{P}$ 21. $\dfrac{\dfrac{a}{a-x} - \dfrac{b}{b-x}}{\dfrac{b}{a-x} - \dfrac{a}{b-x}}$

22. $\dfrac{a}{b+\dfrac{c}{d}}$ 23. $\dfrac{u-\dfrac{b}{c}}{d-\dfrac{e}{f}}$ 24. $\dfrac{\dfrac{1}{x^2} - \dfrac{1}{y^2}}{\dfrac{1}{x} - \dfrac{1}{y}}$

24. Equations involving fractions

In order to solve an equation involving fractions it is usually convenient to multiply both members of the equation by the least common denominator (L.C.D.) of the denominators. This clears the equation of fractions.

Example 1. Solve for x and check:

$$\frac{x+2}{3} = \frac{5x-2}{12}$$

Solution. Multiplying each member by 12,

$$4x + 8 = 5x - 2.$$

Solving for x,

$$x = 10.$$

Check:

$$\frac{10+2}{3} = \frac{50-2}{12},$$

$$4 = 4.$$

Example 2. Solve for x and check:

$$\frac{2x+1}{3} = \frac{x-8}{3} - \frac{x-4}{6}.$$

Solution. Multiplying each member by 6,

$$2(2x+1) = 2(x-8) - (x-4).$$

Simplifying,

$$4x + 2 = 2x - 16 - x + 4.$$

Solving for x,

$$3x = -14,$$
$$x = -\tfrac{14}{3}.$$

Check:

$$\frac{\tfrac{-28}{3} + 1}{3} = \frac{\tfrac{-14}{3} - 8}{3} - \frac{\tfrac{-14}{3} - 4}{6}.$$

Multiplying numerator and denominator of each fraction involved by 3 we have,

$$\frac{-28+3}{9} = \frac{-14-24}{9} - \frac{-14-12}{18},$$

$$\frac{-25}{9} = \frac{-38}{9} + \frac{13}{9},$$

$$\frac{-25}{9} = \frac{-25}{9}.$$

EXERCISE 6

Solve for x and check:

1. $\dfrac{x}{2} = \dfrac{x+3}{3}$
2. $\dfrac{x}{5} = \dfrac{x-10}{3}$
3. $\dfrac{2x-3}{13} = \dfrac{3x+2}{26}$
4. $\dfrac{x}{12} = \dfrac{35}{60}$
5. $\dfrac{x}{6} = \dfrac{47}{85}$
6. $\dfrac{x-4}{8} = \dfrac{3x-50}{5}$
7. $\dfrac{3x-40}{5} + \dfrac{x-20}{5} = \dfrac{x}{5} + 9$
8. $\dfrac{x}{9} - \dfrac{x}{4} = \dfrac{1-x}{7}$
9. $5x + \dfrac{x}{3} = \dfrac{x}{6} + 62$
10. $\dfrac{5x+6}{2} - \dfrac{x-2}{3} = \dfrac{x+10}{6} + 18$

25. Changing the subject of a formula

In the formula

$$P = \frac{S}{1+ni}$$

P is called the **subject** of the formula. A formula can be thought of as a declarative sentence, and in this illustration P is the subject of the sentence.

To change the subject of a formula means to solve the formula for some letter other than the letter that appears as the subject in its given form.

In order to change the subject of a formula it is often necessary to perform operations involving fractions.

Example 1. Solve for i:

$$P = \frac{S}{1+ni}.$$

Solution. Clearing of fractions by multiplying both members by $(1+ni)$:

$$P(1+ni) = S.$$

Simplifying, $\qquad P + Pni = S.$

Solving for i, $\qquad Pni = S - P,$

$$i = \frac{S-P}{Pn}.$$

CHANGING THE SUBJECT OF A FORMULA

Example 2. Solve for p:

$$\frac{1}{f} = \frac{1}{p} + \frac{1}{q}.$$

Solution. Multiplying both members of the equation by fpq,

$$pq = fq + fp.$$

Solving for p,

$$pq - fp = fq,$$
$$p(q - f) = fq,$$
$$p = \frac{fq}{q - f}.$$

EXERCISE 7

Solve for the letter indicated:

1. $I = Pni$; P

2. $n = \dfrac{I}{Pi}$; i

3. $P = \dfrac{S}{1 + ni}$; n

4. $S = \dfrac{P}{1 - nd}$; d

5. $d = \dfrac{i}{1 + ni}$; i

6. $S = \dfrac{n}{2}(a + l)$; l

7. $S = \dfrac{a}{1 - r}$; r

8. $S = \dfrac{a - rl}{1 - r}$; r

9. $i = \dfrac{d}{1 - d}$; d

10. $l = a + (n - 1)d$; d

11. $l = a + (n - 1)d$; n

12. $S = \dfrac{n}{2}[2a + (n - 1)d]$; d

13. $I = \dfrac{Pti}{360}$; i

14. $\dfrac{1}{a} - \dfrac{1}{s} = i$; a

15. $F = (1 - r_1)(1 - r_2)$; r_1

16. $y = \dfrac{x}{x + a}$; x

17. $I(1 - C) = P$; C

18. $S = \dfrac{C}{1 - m}$; m

19. $I = \dfrac{100rp}{1 - r}$; r

20. $r = \dfrac{2mC}{b(n + 1)}$; n

21. $r_2 = \dfrac{r - r_1}{1 - r_1}$; r_1

22. $P = \dfrac{r_1 s_1 + r_2 s_2}{1 - (r_1 + r_2)}$; r_1

23. $P = K + \dfrac{g'}{j}(C - K)$; K

24. $r = \dfrac{d}{1 - dt}$; d

Substitute the numbers given, and solve for the letter indicated:

25. $I = Pni$ $i = 0.06$, $P = 150$, $I = 27$; n

26. $I = Pni$ $I = 20$, $P = 100$, $n = 3$; i

27. $P = \dfrac{S}{1 + ni}$ $\qquad$ $P = 200$, $S = 240$, $i = 0.04$; n

28. $P = \dfrac{S}{1 + ni}$ $\qquad$ $P = 400$, $S = 496$, $n = 8$; i

29. $d = \dfrac{i}{1 + ni}$ $\qquad$ $d = 0.0525$, $n = 7$; i

30. $S = \dfrac{a}{2}(a + l)$ $\qquad$ $S = 45$, $a = 3$, $n = 5$; l

31. $S = \dfrac{a}{1 - r}$ $\qquad$ $S = 2$, $a = 1$; r

32. $S = \dfrac{a - rl}{1 - r}$ $\qquad$ $S = 170$, $a = 2$, $l = 128$; r

33. $i = \dfrac{d}{1 - d}$ $\qquad$ $i = 0.0204$; d (round off to 5 decimal places)

34. $l = a + (n - 1)d$ $\qquad$ $l = 27$, $a = 7$, $d = 5$; n

35. $S = \dfrac{n}{2}[2a + (n - 1)d]$ $\qquad$ $S = 126$, $a = 6$, $n = 7$; d

36. $I = \dfrac{Pti}{360}$ $\qquad$ $I = 0.60$, $t = 120$, $P = 60$; i

37. $F = (1 - r_1)(1 - r_2)$ $\qquad$ $F = 0.9408$, $r_2 = 0.04$; r_1

38. $S = \dfrac{C}{1 - m}$ $\qquad$ $S = 158$, $C = 150$; m

26. Ratio and proportion

The **ratio** of a number x to a number y is the quotient $\dfrac{x}{y}$. Thus, the ratio of 3 to 2 is $\dfrac{3}{2}$. The ratio $\dfrac{x}{y}$ is sometimes written $x:y$.

From this definition of a ratio, it follows that a ratio is a fraction, and any fraction expresses a ratio.

When two quantities have a common unit of measure, it is often convenient to refer to the ratio of the two quantities. Thus, the ratio of 9 feet to 7 feet is $\dfrac{9}{7}$. Notice that a ratio is a pure number, and does not involve the unit of measure. The ratio of $5 to $3 is $\dfrac{5}{3}$.

A **proportion** is an equation that expresses the equality of two ratios. Thus,

$$\frac{x}{y} = \frac{w}{z}$$

is a proportion, and states that the ratio $\dfrac{x}{y}$ is equal to the ratio $\dfrac{w}{z}$.

RATIO AND PROPORTION

The proportion $\frac{x}{y} = \frac{w}{z}$ is sometimes written $x:y = w:z$. In either case, the proportion is read "x is to y as w is to z."

In the proportion $x/y = w/z$, the numbers x and z are called the **extremes** of the proportions, and y and w are called the **means** of the proportion.

Notice that a proportion is an equation involving fractions, so the methods and principles developed in this chapter apply to problems involving proportions.

Example 1. Express the ratio of 3 to 12 in fractional form.

Solution. The ratio of 3 to 12 is $\frac{3}{12}$, which can be reduced to $\frac{1}{4}$.

Example 2. Find the value of x in the proportion $\frac{x}{5} = \frac{7}{2}$.

Solution.
$$\frac{x}{5} = \frac{7}{2}.$$

Multiplying both members of the equation by 10,
$$2x = 35.$$

Dividing by 2,
$$x = 17.5.$$

If $\frac{x}{m} = \frac{m}{z}$, then m is said to be the **mean proportional** between x and z. Thus, in $\frac{2}{4} = \frac{4}{8}$, 4 is the mean proportional between 2 and 8.

In $\frac{x}{y} = \frac{w}{z}$, z is called the **fourth proportional** to x, y, and w.

In $\frac{x}{y} = \frac{y}{z}$, where the means are equal, z is called the **third proportional** to x and y. Thus, in $\frac{5}{2} = \frac{2}{0.8}$, 0.8 is the third proportional to 5 and 2.

Proportions have certain properties, some of which we state here:

1. If $\frac{x}{y} = \frac{w}{z}$, then $xz = yw$.

2. If $\frac{x}{y} = \frac{w}{z}$, then $\frac{x}{w} = \frac{y}{z}$.

3. If $\frac{x}{y} = \frac{w}{z}$, then $\frac{y}{x} = \frac{z}{w}$.

4. If $\frac{x}{y} = \frac{w}{z}$, then $\frac{x+y}{y} = \frac{w+z}{z}$.

5. If $\dfrac{x}{y} = \dfrac{w}{z}$, then $\dfrac{x-y}{y} = \dfrac{w-z}{z}$.

6. If $\dfrac{x}{y} = \dfrac{w}{z}$, then $\dfrac{x+y}{x-y} = \dfrac{w+z}{w-z}$.

EXERCISE 8

Express the following ratios as fractions and simplify:

1. The ratio of 18 to 6
2. The ratio of 3 to 36
3. 85:17
4. 16:48
5. The ratio of $180 to $360
6. The ratio of $1.25 to $3.75
7. The ratio of 8 feet to 3 feet
8. The ratio of 8 inches to 3 yards
9. 25:150
10. 90:45

Find the value of x in the following proportions:

11. $\dfrac{x}{4} = \dfrac{16}{2}$
12. $\dfrac{x}{6} = \dfrac{15}{2}$
13. $\dfrac{x}{9} = \dfrac{4}{3}$
14. $\dfrac{9}{x} = \dfrac{45}{10}$
15. $\dfrac{25}{x} = \dfrac{5}{4}$
16. $x:28 = 2:7$
17. $x:30 = 9:5$
18. $18:x = 9:5$
19. $\dfrac{6}{7} = \dfrac{x}{21}$
20. $\dfrac{5}{9} = \dfrac{15}{x}$
21. $\dfrac{x}{3} = \dfrac{4}{9}$
22. $\dfrac{2}{x} = \dfrac{5}{6}$
23. $\dfrac{x}{130} = \dfrac{5}{7}$
24. $\dfrac{x}{3} = \dfrac{9}{23}$
25. $\dfrac{5}{x} = \dfrac{2}{19}$

26. Separate the number 57 into two parts in the ratio 2:1.

27. Separate the number 130 into two parts in the ratio 7:3.

28. On a certain map the distance between two cities 300 miles apart is $3\frac{1}{2}$ inches. On the same map the distance between two other cities is 0.07 inch. How far apart are these two cities?

29. If a man 6 feet tall casts a shadow of 5 feet, how tall is a tree that casts a 45-foot shadow at the same time?

30. If the scale of a map is $\frac{3}{4}$ inch to 100 miles, how many miles are equivalent to a distance of 3.25 inches on the map?

31. If the selling price of a man's belt is $3.50, and if the profit is $0.50, what is the ratio of the profit to the selling price?

32. In an algebra class there are 15 boys and 20 girls. What is the ratio of the number of boys to the number of girls?

33. Is 5 the mean proportional between 2 and 12.5?

34. Is 7 the mean proportional between 2 and 24?

35. Find the third proportional to 2 and 3.

36. If $\dfrac{a}{b} = \dfrac{c}{d}$, prove that $\dfrac{a}{c} = \dfrac{b}{d}$.

37. If $\dfrac{a}{b} = \dfrac{c}{d}$, prove that $\dfrac{a+b}{b} = \dfrac{c+d}{d}$.

RATIO AND PROPORTION

38. The total sales in a grocery store amounted to $324 on a certain day. The sales in the canned goods department of the store on the same day amounted to $216. What was the ratio of the sales of canned goods to total sales?

39. In March, 1946, the sales in the men's clothing department of a department store amounted to $2,800, while total sales for the store was $400,000. In April, 1946, total sales for the store was $450,000. What should the sales in the men's clothing department be, in order to maintain the same ratio to total sales?

40. If the cost of building a home was estimated at $9 per square foot in 1945, and it cost $9450 to build a certain home, what would it cost to build the same home if the cost increased to $10 per square foot?

41. If the ratio of cost of labor to cost of materials on a construction job is 3 to 5, how much did the materials cost if the cost of labor was $8400?

42. If the rate of a fire insurance policy on household furniture and personal property is $0.65 per $100, what is the premium due on a $2500 policy?

43. If a baseball player made 25 hits in 75 times at bat, how many hits would he make in 120 times at bat, if he maintained the same average?

44. A manager of a clothing store ordered merchandise that cost $48,000 in June, 1946. Of that amount, $2,000 was for shoes. In June, 1947, his total order was $54,000. What should be the shoe order, if the same ratio is to be maintained?

45. The assets of a bankrupt firm are $12,000 and its liabilities are $16,000. How much can it afford to pay on a debt of $200?

MISCELLANEOUS EXERCISE

Reduce to lowest terms:

1. $\dfrac{1 - i^2}{1 - i}$ **2.** $\dfrac{1 - i}{1 - i^3}$ **3.** $\dfrac{x - 1}{(x - 1) + (x - 1)^2}$

Add algebraically:

4. $\dfrac{1}{x} + \dfrac{1}{y} - \dfrac{3}{y}$ **5.** $\dfrac{1}{1 - i} + \dfrac{1}{1 - i^2}$

6. $\dfrac{x + 2}{x - 3} - \dfrac{x - 2}{x + 4} + \dfrac{3x - 2}{x - 3}$ **7.** $\dfrac{m}{m - n} + \dfrac{n}{m + n} - \dfrac{m^2}{m^2 - n^2}$

Multiply:

8. $\dfrac{1}{x} \cdot \dfrac{y}{1 - x} \cdot \dfrac{1 - x^2}{xy}$ **9.** $\dfrac{2}{3} \cdot \dfrac{7}{15} \cdot \dfrac{30}{11} \cdot \dfrac{3}{14}$

10. $(1 - \tfrac{1}{3})(1 - \tfrac{1}{10})$ **11.** $\dfrac{r^2 - 3rs + 2s^2}{r^2 - rs} \cdot \dfrac{r^2 + rs}{r^2 - rs - 2s^2}$

12. $200 \cdot \tfrac{40}{360} \cdot \tfrac{3}{100}$

FRACTIONS

Divide:

13. $\dfrac{y}{1-x} \div \dfrac{x}{1-x^2}$ 14. $\dfrac{2}{3} \div \dfrac{5}{6}$

15. $\left(\dfrac{1}{a} - \dfrac{1}{b}\right) \div \left(\dfrac{1}{a} + \dfrac{1}{b}\right)$ 16. $\dfrac{x^3 - 8}{x+2} \div \dfrac{x-2}{x^2 + 4x + 4}$

Find the values of the following expressions, rounding off your answers to 2 decimal places:

17. $\dfrac{100}{1 + \frac{9}{12}(0.08)}$ 18. $\dfrac{2020.50}{1 + \frac{2}{12}(0.06)}$

19. $(1 - \tfrac{1}{4})(1 - \tfrac{1}{5})(1 - \tfrac{3}{20})$ 20. $\dfrac{50}{350 \cdot \frac{50}{360}}$

21. $\dfrac{100}{500 \cdot \frac{60}{360}}$ 22. $\dfrac{0.06}{1 - \tfrac{1}{4}(0.08)}$ 23. $\dfrac{721.16}{1 - \frac{0.04}{12}}$

24. Show that:
$$\dfrac{1 - (1+i)^n}{1 - (1+i)} = \dfrac{(1+i)^n - 1}{i}$$

25. Show that:
$$\dfrac{i}{1 - \dfrac{1}{(1+i)^3}} - \dfrac{i}{(1+i)^3 - 1} = i$$

Simplify:

26. $\dfrac{1}{x + \dfrac{1}{x + \dfrac{1}{x}}}$ 27. $\dfrac{\dfrac{x-1}{x+1} - \dfrac{x+1}{x-1}}{\dfrac{x+1}{x-1} - \dfrac{x-1}{x+1}}$ 28. $\dfrac{3 - \tfrac{1}{2}}{4 + \tfrac{1}{3}} \cdot \dfrac{4 - \tfrac{1}{3}}{3 + \tfrac{1}{2}}$

Solve for x:

29. $\dfrac{x+1}{2} = 9 - \dfrac{x}{2\frac{1}{4}}$ 30. $\dfrac{x-2}{4} + \dfrac{3x-5}{8} = 3\tfrac{7}{8}$

Solve for the letter indicated:

31. $S = \dfrac{n}{2}(a + l); a$ 32. $S = \dfrac{n}{2}[2a + (n-1)d]; a$

33. $S = \dfrac{P}{1 - nd}; n$ 34. $y = a + \dfrac{b}{x}; x$ 35. $x = k + \dfrac{g}{i}(c - k); k$

36. The sum of two numbers is 120, and the ratio of the first number to the second number is 2:3. Find the numbers.

37. If $\dfrac{a+b}{b} = \dfrac{c+d}{d}$, prove that $\dfrac{a}{b} = \dfrac{c}{d}$.

38. Find the mean proportional between 3 and 12.

39. If the profit on a sale of $72 was $18, what was the ratio of the profit to the amount of the sale?

40. If the school tax rate is $2.05 per $100 of assessed valuation, what is the school tax on a residence assessed at $6200?

4

Percentage: Commercial Transactions

27. Per cent

The term **per cent** is derived from the Latin "per centum," which means "by the hundred," or simply "hundredths." The symbol for per cent is %. Thus 6%, which means "six hundredths," may be written as $\frac{6}{100}$ or 0.06.

Example 1. Express 0.23 as a per cent.
Solution. $\quad\quad\quad\quad 0.23 = \frac{23}{100} = 23\%.$

Example 2. Express the fraction $\frac{1}{4}$ as a per cent.
Solution. $\quad\quad\quad\quad \frac{1}{4} = \frac{25}{100} = 25\%.$

Example 3. Express as a common fraction: $2\frac{1}{2}\%$.
Solution. $\quad\quad 2\frac{1}{2}\% = \frac{2.5}{100} = \frac{25}{1000} = \frac{1}{40}.$

EXERCISE 1

Express the following decimal fractions as per cents:

1. 0.24
2. 0.02
3. 0.12
4. 0.035
5. 0.065
6. 0.075
7. 0.0225
8. 0.0375
9. 0.015
10. 0.0125
11. 0.01125
12. 0.067
13. 0.00125
14. 0.005
15. 0.00625
16. 0.01375

Express the following fractions as per cents:

17. $\frac{1}{2}$
18. $\frac{3}{4}$
19. $\frac{1}{8}$
20. $\frac{3}{8}$
21. $\frac{5}{8}$
22. $\frac{7}{8}$
23. $\frac{1}{3}$
24. $\frac{2}{3}$
25. $\frac{5}{12}$
26. $\frac{7}{12}$
27. $\frac{1}{24}$
28. $\frac{5}{24}$
29. $\frac{7}{24}$
30. $\frac{9}{24}$

Express the following per cents as common fractions and then as decimal fractions:

31. 3%
32. 8%
33. $6\frac{1}{2}\%$
34. $3\frac{1}{2}\%$
35. $1\frac{1}{4}\%$
36. $1\frac{3}{4}\%$
37. $1\frac{1}{8}\%$
38. $1\frac{1}{2}\%$
39. $\frac{3}{4}\%$
40. $1\frac{5}{8}\%$
41. $\frac{5}{8}\%$
42. $2\frac{1}{4}\%$
43. $2\frac{3}{4}\%$
44. $\frac{5}{12}\%$
45. $\frac{7}{12}\%$
46. $1\frac{3}{8}\%$

28. Percentage, base, and rate

In the example
$$0.06 \times 150 = 9,$$
0.06 is the rate, 150 is the base, and 9 is the percentage. The number of which a per cent is taken is the **base,** the per cent of the base to be taken is the **rate,** and the result obtained by multiplying the base by the rate is the **percentage.**

There are three types of problems involving the base, rate, and percentage. They may be classified as follows:

1. Percentage = base × rate.

2. Rate = $\dfrac{\text{percentage}}{\text{base}}$.

3. Base = $\dfrac{\text{percentage}}{\text{rate}}$.

In these formulas the rate is expressed in the decimal form.

Example 1. Find the number that is 4% of 200.

Solution. In this example, 4% is the rate, 200 is the base, and it is required to find the percentage.

Let x = the number.
Then $x = (0.04)(200) = 8$.

Example 2. What per cent of 125 is 25?

Solution. In this example, 125 is the base, 25 is the percentage, and it is required to find the rate.

Let x = the rate,
Then $x = \frac{25}{125} = \frac{1}{5} = 0.20$, which in per cent form is 20%.

Example 3. If 5% of a certain number is 20, what is the number?

Solution. In this example, 5% is the rate, 20 is the percentage, and it is required to find the base.

Let x = the number.
Then $0.05x = 20$.

Dividing both members by 0.05,
$$x = 400.$$

Example 4. A dealer buys a car for $1200 and sells it for $1500. What per cent of the cost is the profit? What per cent of the selling price is the profit?

Solution. Since the profit is the selling price less the cost,
$$\text{Profit} = \$1500 - \$1200 = \$300.$$
$$\text{Per cent profit on cost} = \tfrac{300}{1200} = \tfrac{1}{4} = 25\%.$$
$$\text{Per cent profit on the selling price} = \tfrac{300}{1500} = \tfrac{1}{5} = 20\%.$$

PERCENTAGE, BASE, AND RATE

Example 5. The Acme Furniture Co. makes a profit of 10% on the cost of a certain type of chair. If the profit per chair is $5, what is the cost of the chair?

Solution. Let x = number of dollars in the cost of the chair.

Then $0.10x = 5$,

and $x = \dfrac{5}{0.10} = 50.$

The cost of the chair is $50.

Example 6. A bicycle cost a dealer $30. At what price should he sell it in order to make a profit of 20% on the sales price?

Solution. Let x = number of dollars in sales price.

Selling price − cost = profit.
$$x - 30 = 0.20x,$$
$$x - 0.20x = 30,$$
$$0.80x = 30,$$
$$x = \dfrac{30}{0.80} = 37.50.$$

Sales price = $37.50.

Check: $(0.20)(\$37.50) = \$7.50$ = profit.
$\$37.50 - \$30 = \$7.50$

EXERCISE 2

Find the number that is:

1. 6% of 300
2. $2\frac{1}{2}$% of 35
3. 8% of 1500
4. 25% of 400
5. $33\frac{1}{3}$% of 600
6. 1.5% of 34
7. $3\frac{1}{4}$% of 320
8. 16% of 2000
9. $1\frac{5}{8}$% of 1600
10. 160% of 28

Find the number, if

11. 5% of the number is 20
12. 10% of the number is 13
13. 6% of the number is 1200
14. 2% of the number is 6.5
15. $3\frac{1}{2}$% of the number is 26
16. 75% of the number is 52
17. 80% of the number is 1.25
18. 120% of the number is 36
19. 150% of the number is 25.75
20. 125% of the number is 13.62

What per cent of the first number is the second number?

21. 25; 5
22. 30; 6
23. 150; 15
24. 225; 15
25. 16; 2
26. 32.5; 1.5
27. 81; 9
28. 32; 48
29. 15.62; 1.3277
30. 12; 48

31. Mr. Smith's taxes on his real estate amounted to $180 for 1946. Find the valuation of his real estate if the tax rate was $1\frac{3}{4}$%.

32. George Johnson buys a lot for $2000 and sells it for $2200. His gain is what per cent of the cost price?

33. A shoe store buys a certain type of shoe for $8.00 per pair and sells them for $9.00 per pair. The gain is what per cent of the selling price?

PERCENTAGE: COMMERCIAL TRANSACTIONS

34. James Brown's salary for 1945 was $3000. He received a $12\frac{1}{2}\%$ increase in salary for 1946. What was his salary for 1946?

35. The Triangle Real Estate Co. sells a piece of property for $35,000, thereby gaining 15% of the amount the property cost. What was the cost of the property?

36. The Perfection Radio Shop makes a profit of 16% on a radio that they manufacture, basing the profit on the selling price. What does it cost to manufacture the radio, if the unit profit is $8?

37. Mrs. A. B. Chalmers sells a lot at a profit of 18%. She figures her profit on the selling price. What did the lot cost her, if her profit amounted to $800?

38. A retail store receives a consignment of shirts that cost $18.00 per dozen. If they sell the shirts at $2.50 each, what is the per cent profit on each shirt, if the profit is calculated as a per cent of the cost price? What is the per cent profit if the profit is calculated as a per cent of the selling price?

39. A watchmaker repairs a watch for $12, which is 24% of the value of the watch. What is the value of the watch?

40. The Center Street Grocery Store makes a profit of $1\frac{1}{2}$ cents per can on peaches that cost 30 cents per can. What per cent of the cost is the profit?

41. The price of a certain refrigerator was increased 6%, and it now sells for $215. What was the original price?

42. The price of a certain bicycle was lowered 5%, and it now sells for $55. What was the original price?

43. A house and lot together cost $12,000. If the house cost $7730 more than the lot, what did the lot cost? What per cent of the cost of the house was the cost of the lot?

44. An 8-ounce bottle of 3% hydrogen peroxide contains how many ounces of pure hydrogen peroxide?

45. A druggist has 50 gallons of a 40% solution of alcohol. How many gallons of pure alcohol are there in the solution?

46. If a sales tax of 2% nets a certain city $50,000, what are the total sales of taxable items?

47. The overhead expenses of the Union Drug Store amount to 5% of the gross sales. If the overhead expenses for 1946 were $15,000, what were the gross sales for 1946?

48. The sales tax in a certain state is $2\frac{1}{2}\%$. To find the sales tax on an article, point off one decimal place to the left in the sales price of the article, and divide the result by 4. Explain why this rule gives the correct answer.

49. On a certain bottle of perfume, the sales price is $12.00. If the sales tax is 3%, and if there is a luxury tax of 20%, find the actual sales price, including the two taxes.

50. If a certain type of suit sells for $37.50, and if this sales price includes a profit of 25% on the sales price, find the cost of the suit to the clothing store.

51. The Knoxville Clothing Co. buys a quantity of dresses for $20 each. How much must they sell for in order to realize a profit of 20% on the sales price?

BUYING AND SELLING MERCHANDISE

52. A haberdasher buys some ties for $0.85 each. How much must he sell them for in order to make a profit of 25% on the sales price?

53. Is it possible to make a profit of 100% on the sales price?

54. George Jones and James Merton form a business partnership. Merton's share of the profits is to exceed that of Jones by 10%. If the total profits are $42,000, how much should each receive as his share?

55. A real estate agent receives a commission of 5%. If he earned $450 in the month of September, how much property did he sell?

29. Buying and selling merchandise

In the buying and selling of merchandise, practices and terms used may vary considerably. However, the following list of terms and their definitions are commonly accepted and used by present-day business:

The **net cost** is the cost before certain expenses such as buying expenses are added.

The **gross cost** is the net cost plus these expenses.

The **net selling price** is the price at which the merchandise is actually sold.

Gross profit (or **margin**) is the difference between net selling price and gross cost.

Net profit is gross profit less certain expenses, such as rent, publicity, administration, selling, and delivery.

In order to obtain a better understanding of these terms, let

$N.C.$ = net cost,
E_1 = expenses added to net cost to compute gross cost,
$G.C.$ = gross cost,
$N.S.P.$ = net selling price,
$G.P.$ = margin = gross profit,
$N.P.$ = net profit,
E_2 = expenses subtracted from margin to obtain net profit.

Then the following relations hold:

$$N.C. + E_1 = G.C.$$
$$G.P. = N.S.P. - G.C.$$
$$N.P. = G.P. - E_2.$$

From these relations can be obtained other relations, such as

$$N.P. = N.S.P. - E_2 - N.C. - E_1,$$
or, $$N.S.P. = N.C. + N.P. + E_1 + E_2.$$

To illustrate these concepts, consider the following table showing the computation of margin and net profit for a retail store:

Net Sales	$1,000,000
Net Cost of Merchandise	$600,000
Expenses (E_1)	$10,000
Gross Cost of Merchandise	$610,000
Margin	$390,000
Expenses (E_2)	$300,000
Net Profit	$90,000

The student should use these figures to substitute in the relations given above, to fix in mind the various relationships existing among these basic concepts.

Another technical term that occurs in retailing merchandise is mark-up. **Mark-up** is the difference between the cost and the retail price of merchandise. For example, if a suit of clothes costs $40 and sells for $60, the mark-up is $60 - $40 = $20. The mark-up per cent is usually expressed as a per cent of sales price. In the case of the suit of clothes mentioned above, the mark-up per cent is $\frac{20}{60} \times 100\% = 33\frac{1}{3}\%$. Let

C = cost,
M = mark-up (in dollars),
R = retail sales price,
$M.P.$ = mark-up per cent (in hundredths).

Then
$$C + M = R$$
$$R - M = C$$
$$R - C = M$$
$$\frac{M}{R} = M.P.$$
$$M = (M.P.)(R)$$
$$R = C + (M.P.)(R)$$
$$C = R - (M.P.)(R)$$
$$C = R(1 - M.P.)$$
$$R = \frac{C}{1 - M.P.}.$$

The quantity $1 - M.P.$ is called the **complement** of the mark-up per cent. For example, if the mark-up per cent is 30%, then the complement of the mark-up per cent is $1 - 0.30 = 0.70$, or 70%.

Notice particularly that the retail sales price is equal to the cost divided by the complement of the mark-up per cent, and the cost

BUYING AND SELLING MERCHANDISE

price is equal to the retail price multiplied by the complement of the mark-up per cent.

Example 1. A certain type of overcoat cost the Allen Haberdashery $50. If their mark-up per cent on overcoats is 20%, what is the selling price of each overcoat?

Solution. Mark-up per cent = 20%.
Complement of mark-up per cent = 1 − 0.20 = 0.80 = 80%.
Retail sales price = $\dfrac{\$50}{0.80}$ = $62.50.

Example 2. The retail sales price of a certain hat is $10. If the mark-up per cent on this type of hat is 25%, what is the cost of the hat to the retailer?

Solution. Mark-up per cent = 25%.
Complement of mark-up per cent = 1 − 0.25 = 0.75 = 75%.
Cost to retailer = ($10)(0.75) = $7.50.

EXERCISE 3

1. The United Furniture Co. prepared the following data for the year 1947 for the purpose of computing net profit:

Net Sales	$2,000,000
Net Cost of Merchandise	$1,200,000
Expenses (E_1)	$20,000
Gross Cost of Merchandise	$1,220,000
Margin	$780,000
Expenses (E_2)	$500,000
Net Profit	$280,000

Find the per cent of net sales for each of the above items.

2. For the year 1946, the United Furniture Co. showed net sales of $1,500,000; net cost of $900,000; expenses ($E_1$) of $15,000 to be added to net cost. Find the margin, and find the per cent of net sales represented by the margin.

3. A hat cost $4 and sells for $6. What is the mark-up? the mark-up per cent?

4. A consignment of paint cost $800 and sells for $950. What is the mark-up? the mark-up per cent (to the nearest per cent)?

5. One dozen fishing rods cost $150. The mark-up is $30. What is the total retail sales price? What is the mark-up per cent?

6. The retail sales price of a certain camera is $80. The mark-up is $20. What is the cost? What is the mark-up per cent?

7. One gross of handkerchiefs cost $14. What should be the sales price of each handkerchief to secure a 20% mark-up?

8. Two dozen dresses cost $480. What should be the sales price of each dress to secure a 30% mark-up?

9. Prove the following rules:

(a) to secure a 20% mark-up, divide the cost by 8; and move the decimal point one place to the right.

(b) to secure a 25% mark-up, divide by 7.5 and move the decimal point one place to the right.

10. If the retail price of an item is $16 and the mark-up per cent is 30%, what is the cost price?

11. If the mark-up is 20% and the retail price is $25, what is the cost price?

12. An article cost $8 and sells for $10. What is the mark-up per cent? What per cent of cost is the mark-up?

30. Cash discount

A **cash discount** is a deduction from the amount of a bill, offered as a reward for prompt payment of the bill. The notation 5/10, $n/30$ on an invoice means that a 5% cash discount is allowed if the bill is paid on or before the tenth day after the date of the bill, but the total amount of the bill is due and payable if payment is deferred to a time after the tenth day but not later than the thirtieth day. After the thirtieth day, interest is charged.

Example 1. An invoice has 5/10, $n/30$ noted on it, and the date of the invoice is April 8. The amount of the invoice is $520. What amount is payable if payment is made on April 16? on May 2?

Solution. $0.05 \times \$520 = \$26.00$.

$520 - \$26 = \$494$, amount payable on April 16.

$520 =$ amount payable on May 12.

Notice that April 16 is less than 10 days after April 8, and May 2 is more than 10 days but less than 30 days after April 8.

The notation "Terms: Cash 10, 5/10, 2/30, $n/60$" on a bill means that a 10% discount is allowed for immediate payment, a 5% discount is allowed for payment within 10 days, a 2% discount is allowed for payment after the tenth day but not later than the thirtieth day, and no discount is allowed if payment is made after the thirtieth day but not later than the sixtieth day.

Example 2. An invoice of $1500 has on it the notation "Cash 10, 5/10, 1/30, $n/60$." The date of the invoice is July 2. What amount is payable if payment is made on (a) July 2 (b) July 6 (c) July 15 (d) August 8?

Solution. (a) Payment on July 2 indicates immediate payment.

$0.10 \times \$1500 = \$150$, discount.

$1500 - \$150 = \$1350$, amount payable on July 2.

TRADE DISCOUNT

Solution. (b) Payment on July 6 indicates payment within 10 days.

$0.05 \times \$1500 = \$75$, discount.

$\$1500 - \$75 = \$1425$, amount payable on July 6.

Solution. (c) Payment on July 15 indicates payment after 10 days but within 30 days.

$0.01 \times \$1500 = \$15$, discount.

$\$1500 - \$15 = \$1485$, amount payable on July 15.

Solution. (d) Payment on August 8 indicates payment after 30 days but within 60 days.

$\$1500 =$ amount payable on August 8.

EXERCISE 4

1. An invoice for $316 has the terms 5/15, n/30. If the invoice is dated May 23, find the amount payable on June 2.

2. A filling station proprietor buys accessories with an invoice total of $1350. The terms are 3/10, n/30, and the invoice is dated November 7. The proprietor pays the bill on November 15. How much should he pay?

3. The Reliable Hardware Co. receives an invoice of $1200 dated December 3, with terms cash 5, 2/15, n/30. How much would the company save by paying the bill December 3 instead of December 10?

4. The Perfection Radio Shop receives an invoice amounting to $1475 for radio sets purchased from a manufacturer. The invoice is dated January 10 and carries the terms cash 5, 2/10, n/15. How much would the shop lose by paying the bill on January 22 instead of on January 10?

5. R. C. Jones buys machine tools from the Apex Tool Co. The invoice is dated February 15 and he pays the bill on February 28. If the amount of the invoice is $75.85 and the terms are 2/10, n/30, what amount should he pay?

6. An invoice of $135.75 carries the terms cash 5, 2/10, 1/30, n/60. How much would be saved by paying cash instead of waiting until 12 days after the date of the invoice?

7. The Reliable Hardware Company receives a shipment of 2 dozen saws listed at $1.45 each. A cash discount of 5% is allowed. If the company pays cash, how much should they pay for the entire shipment?

8. The Acme Furniture Co. pays cash for a shipment of furniture. If the amount they pay is $1330, and if the discount rate was 5%, what was the original total amount of the invoice?

31. Trade discount

Manufacturers and wholesalers usually publish a catalogue describing the articles they offer for sale to their clients. The price of an article as listed in the catalogue is called the **list price** of the article.

Subsequent to the publication of the catalogue, the manufacturer may offer deductions from the list price to some (or all) of his clients. Such a deduction is called a **trade discount.** Trade discounts are usually expressed as a per cent of the list price, in which case the per cent is called a **trade discount rate.** Some of the reasons for offering trade discounts are as follows:

1. To compensate for fluctuations in market price,
2. To reward steady customers and customers who place large orders for merchandise,
3. To attract new customers,
4. To meet the competition of other manufacturers.

In fact, any deduction from the list price is called a trade discount, with the exception of a deduction for prompt payment of the bill, which has been defined in Article 30 as a cash discount.

Example 1. The list price of a certain radio is $15. The trade discount rate offered on a certain date is 20%. Find the net price.

Solution. $15 = list price.
                (0.20)($15) = $3, amount of discount.
                $15 − $3 = $12, net price.

A series of two or more successive trade discounts is often offered. In this case each successive discount is computed on the remainder left after the previous discount has been deducted.

Example 2. The list price of a certain refrigerator is $250. Trade discounts of 25%, 10%, and 5% are allowed. Compute the net price.

Solution.
$250 = list price.
(0.25)($250) = $62.50, amount of first discount.
$250 − $62.50 = $187.50, price after first discount.
(0.10)($187.50) = $18.75, amount of second discount.
$187.50 − $18.75 = $168.75, price after second discount.
(0.05)($168.75) = $8.44, amount of third discount.
$168.75 − $8.44 = $160.31, net price after deduction of all discounts.

Notice particularly that the application of successive discounts as in Example 2 *is not* equivalent to a single discount of the sum of 25%, 10%, and 5%.

If L represents the list price, and if r represents a single trade discount rate, then the amount remaining after deducting the trade discount is given by

$$L - Lr = L(1 - r).$$

TRADE DISCOUNT

If there are two successive trade discounts, and if the rates are represented by r_1 and r_2, the amount remaining after the first discount is given by

$$L - Lr_1 = L(1 - r_1)$$

and the amount remaining after the second discount is

$$L(1 - r_1) - L(1 - r_1)r_2 = L(1 - r_1)(1 - r_2).$$

This procedure can be repeated. If there are three successive discounts, the rates being represented by r_1, r_2, and r_3, the amount remaining after applying the three successive discounts is

$$L(1 - r_1)(1 - r_2)(1 - r_3),$$

and so on for any given number of trade discounts.

Example 3. Solve Example 2 by using the preceding formula.

Solution. $L = \$250$, $r_1 = 0.025$, $r_2 = 0.10$, $r_3 = 0.05$.

$$\$250(1 - 0.25)(1 - 0.10)(1 - 0.05) = \$250(0.75)(0.90)(0.95),$$
$$= \$250(0.64125),$$
$$= \$160.31, \text{ net price after deduction of all discounts.}$$

Example 4. Find the single discount rate that is equivalent to trade discount rates of 25%, 20%, and 10%.

Solution.

$$(1 - 0.25)(1 - 0.20)(1 - 0.10) = (0.75)(0.80)(0.90),$$
$$= 0.54,$$
$$1 - 0.54 = 0.46, \text{ equivalent single discount rate.}$$

In general, if there are n successive discount rates designated by $r_1, r_2, \ldots, r_n$ then

$$\text{Net price} = L(1 - r_1)(1 - r_2) \cdots (1 - r_n),$$

and the single discount rate equivalent to n successive discount rates is given by

$$\text{Single discount rate} = 1 - [(1 - r_1)(1 - r_2) \cdots (1 - r_n)].$$

If a retailer or jobber purchases several lots of merchandise, all subject to the same set of discount rates, it may be convenient to calculate a single factor to use in multiplying the list prices of the various articles in order to obtain the net prices. The single factor is given by the value of

$$(1 - r_1)(1 - r_2) \cdots (1 - r_n).$$

Example 5. A retailer receives a shipment of several quantities of articles, all subject to trade discount rates of 25%, 20%, and 5%. Find a single factor with which to multiply the list prices in order to obtain the net prices.

Solution.   Factor = $(1 - 0.25)(1 - 0.20)(1 - 0.05)$,
= $(0.75)(0.80)(0.95)$,
= 0.57.

Each list price can be multiplied by 0.57 in order to obtain the corresponding net price.

EXERCISE 5

1. The Zenith refrigerator is listed at $250. The manufacturer allows the Reliable Hardware Co. trade discounts of 10% and 5%. Find the net price.
2. The list price of a table model radio is $22.50. Trade discounts of 12% and 5% are allowed. Find the net price.
3. The list price of a certain electric fixture is $5.25. If the trade discounts allowed are 10% and 5%, find the net price of two dozen fixtures.
4. Find the single discount rate that is equivalent to successive trade discount rates of 20%, 15%, and 10%.
5. A rug merchant is offered trade discount rates of 25%, 15%, and 5% by a certain importer, and he is offered trade discount rates of 20%, 20%, and 10% by another importer. Other things being equal, which offer should he choose?
6. An aluminum drip coffeepot is listed in the manufacturer's catalogue at $1.29. If trade discounts of 15% and 10% are offered, what is the net price of 3 dozen coffeepots?
7. The Perfection Radio Shop received a consignment of several types of radio sets. For each type, the trade discount rates allowed are 20% and 5%. By what factor would the list price of each type be multiplied in order to give the net price?
8. The Reliable Hardware Co. receives a shipment of several different items. If the trade discount rates are 20%, 10%, and 5%, what single factor may they use to multiply the list price, in order to obtain the net price?
9. A couch is to be sold for $144 by its manufacturers. What should its list price be, in order to allow trade discounts of 20% and 10%?
10. A dress manufacturer desires to determine the list price of a certain type of dress, necessary to allow discounts of 20% and 5%, the price to the retail trade being set at $14.35. What is the list price?
11. The Knoxville Clothing Store features a certain brand of women's dresses that list for $8.00. The store is allowed trade discounts of 10% and 5% by the wholesaler. All expenses, including buying expenses and selling expenses, amount to $1.70 per garment. How much should the selling price be in order to guarantee a net profit of 20% on the selling price?
12. The Perfection Radio Shop receives a consignment of twelve Bell radios. The radios list at $24. The shop is allowed trade discounts of 5% and 2%. Buying expenses and selling expenses total $0.96 per radio. If the radio is sold for $28.75, what is the per cent of profit, as figured on the selling price? Round off your answer to the nearest per cent.

TRADE DISCOUNT

13. The Union Drug Co. has a large stock of a certain brand of shaving lotion that sells for $1.50 per bottle. This sales price includes a profit of 30% of the sales price. If the lotion is sold for $1.25, what is the per cent of profit, as figured on this lower sales price? If the cost price to the drug store includes a trade discount of 10%, what is the list price of the lotion as quoted by the wholesaler?

14. Which is the larger discount rate: a single trade discount rate of 30% or two successive trade discount rates of 20% and 10%?

15. Which yields the larger single discount rate: successive trade discount rates of 30% and 10%, or successive trade discount rates of 20% and 20%?

16. If the net price of an automobile tire is $24, and if the trade discount rates were 10% and 5%, what was the list price of the tire?

17. A manufacturer of electric ranges finds that the cost of manufacturing each range is $300. If he allows trade discount rates of 20% and 10%, how much should he list the range in order to make a profit of 20% on his net selling price?

18. A retailer receives several lots of merchandise, all subject to trade discount rates of 20% and 10%. Calculate the single factor by which each list price can be multiplied in order to find the net price.

19. A jobber receives lots of hammers at $0.95 each, saws at $1.30 each, and planers at $2.40. These list prices are all subject to trade discount rates of 20%, 10%, and 5%. Find a factor to replace these discount rates, and use the factor to find the net prices.

20. In Problem 19, suppose that the jobber wishes to sell these articles to a retailer at a profit of 10% on the sales price to the retailer. Find a single factor by which he can multiply the manufacturer's list price in order to obtain the price he will charge the retailer.

MISCELLANEOUS EXERCISE

1. Solve for r_2 the formula $N = L(1 - r_1)(1 - r_2)$.

2. If 5% of the student body of a college are seniors and if there are 142 seniors, how many students are there in the entire student body?

3. A jeweler paid $48 for a watch and he wishes to sell it so that he may gain 20% of the selling price. For how much should he sell the watch?

4. An antique dealer has been quoting a sales price of $100 on a clock. This sales price included a profit of 25% on the sales price. For how much should he sell the clock in order to gain 20% of the new sales price?

5. What single discount rate is equivalent to the series of discount rates: 20%, 15%, 10%, 5%?

6. The gross sales of the Knoxville Clothing Co. are $20,000 for the month of July. If 20% of the gross sales are made in the shoe department, and if 30% of the sales in the shoe department are for infants' shoes, what are the total sales of infants' shoes?

7. Mr. and Mrs. R. L. Smith made a 300-mile trip in their car. They averaged 15 miles to the gallon of gasoline. Gasoline cost $0.20 per gallon.

Total expenses of the trip were $20. What per cent of the total expenses was the cost of the gasoline?

8. An invoice carries the notation "cash 5, 2/10." The amount of the invoice is $130.50. What amount is due if the bill is paid in 3 days?

9. An invoice notes trade discount rates of 15% and 5%. The amount of the invoice is $120. What is the net amount to be paid after deducting the discounts?

10. A sports jacket has been selling for $25, which allowed a 10% profit on the sales price. How much should the sales price be increased in order to guarantee a profit of 20% on the new sales price?

11. Gross sales of the Perfection Radio Shop were $4800 for the month of October. Overhead expenses amounted to $144. What per cent of gross sales was the overhead?

12. An article cost $120 and sold for $150. What per cent of the selling price was the profit? What per cent of the cost was the profit?

13. The net price of a repeating rifle is $72. If the trade discount rate was 10%, what was the list price?

14. The list price of a garden swing is $100. A trade discount rate of 20% is allowed. What additional trade discount rate should be allowed so that the net price will be $60?

15. For a month's-end sale the manager of a store reduces all the sales prices of bathing suits by 10%. If a certain type of bathing suit then sells for $8.10, what was the sales price before the sale?

16. A certain typewriter has a catalogue price of $80, and it is sold to a retailer at 10% and 5% off the list price. How much does the retailer pay for 6 typewriters?

17. A garden hose sold for $12 at a certain time, and later the price rose to $15. What per cent did the hose increase in price?

18. 8% of 300 is 24, and 10% of 400 is 40. The average of 8% and 10% is 9%. However, 9% of 700 is not equal to (8%)(300) + (10%)(400). Why not? Also, does

$$\frac{a}{100} \cdot x + \frac{b}{100} \cdot y = \frac{1}{2}\left(\frac{a}{100} + \frac{b}{100}\right)(x + y)?$$

19. If the list price of an article is subject to trade discount rates of 20% and 5%, what is the factor that can be used to multiply the list price in order to obtain the net price?

20. A jobber receives several lots of articles, all subject to trade discount rates of 25% and 10%. He wishes to sell them to a retailer at a profit of 20% of the sales price to the retailer. Find a factor that he can use to multiply the manufacturer's list price and obtain the sales price to the retailer.

21. Find the marked price of a washing machine that cost the retailer $200 less the trade discount rates of 20% and 10%, if the retailer wishes to gain 20% of the marked price after allowing a customer a discount of 10% of the marked price.

5

Exponents and Radicals

32. Positive integral exponents

When k is a positive integer, a^k is defined to be

$$a \cdot a \cdot a \cdots \text{to } k \text{ factors.}$$

Thus $\quad a^5 = a \cdot a \cdot a \cdot a \cdot a$

and $\quad 2^4 = 2 \cdot 2 \cdot 2 \cdot 2 = 16.$

The laws for operating with positive integral exponents can be expressed in the following form:

I. $\quad a^m \cdot a^n = a^{m+n}.$
II. $\quad (a^m)^n = a^{mn}.$
III. $(abc\ldots)^m = a^m b^m c^m \ldots$
IV. $\quad \left(\dfrac{a}{b}\right)^m = \dfrac{a^m}{b^m}.$
V. $\quad \dfrac{a^m}{a^n} = a^{m-n}, (m > n).$
VI. $\quad \dfrac{a^m}{a^n} = \dfrac{1}{a^{n-m}}, (m < n).$

Illustrations of these laws are:

I. $\quad a^2 \cdot a^3 = a^5.$
II. $\quad (a^2)^3 = a^6.$
III. $\quad (ab)^3 = a^3 b^3.$
IV. $\quad \left(\dfrac{a}{b}\right)^2 = \dfrac{a^2}{b^2}.$
V. $\quad \dfrac{a^5}{a^2} = a^3.$
VI. $\quad \dfrac{a^2}{a^5} = \dfrac{1}{a^3}.$

EXERCISE 1

Perform the indicated operations, using the laws for positive integral exponents:

1. $a^4 \cdot a^3$
2. $x^2 \cdot x^3 \cdot x$
3. $m^3 \cdot m^2 \cdot m^4$
4. $(1+i)^2 \cdot (1+i)^3$
5. $(1+i)^{100} \cdot (1+i)^6$
6. $2^3 \cdot 2^5$
7. $3^2 \cdot 3^4$
8. $(a^3)^3$
9. $(y^2)^4$
10. $[(1+i)^2]^3$
11. $(5^2)^3$
12. $(4^3)^4$
13. $(mn)^3$
14. $(abc)^2$
15. $(a^2b^3)^3$
16. $(xy^4)^2$
17. $\left(\dfrac{x}{y}\right)^2$
18. $\left(\dfrac{a}{b}\right)^5$
19. $\left(\dfrac{x^2y^3}{z}\right)^2$
20. $\left(\dfrac{1}{2}\right)^3$
21. $\left(\dfrac{2}{3}\right)^2$
22. $\left(\dfrac{a}{bc}\right)^4$
23. $\left(\dfrac{a^2}{b}\right)^5$
24. $\left(\dfrac{3}{5}\right)^4$
25. $\dfrac{x^8}{x^2}$
26. $\dfrac{a^5}{a^4}$
27. $\dfrac{2^4}{2^2}$
28. $\dfrac{5^3}{5^2}$
29. $\dfrac{(1+i)^{125}}{(1+i)^{25}}$
30. $\dfrac{(1+i)^{36}}{(1+i)^5}$
31. $\dfrac{(x+y)^4}{(x+y)^2}$
32. $\dfrac{m^2}{m^3}$
33. $\dfrac{r^2}{r^5}$
34. $\dfrac{m^5}{m^3}$
35. $\dfrac{3^2}{3^5}$
36. $\dfrac{4^3}{4^5}$
37. $\dfrac{a^2b^3c^5}{b^2c^2}$
38. $\dfrac{x^7y^5z^3}{x^2y^3z^2}$
39. $\dfrac{(1+i)^2}{(1+i)^{10}}$
40. $\dfrac{(a-b)^3}{(a-b)^5}$
41. $x^n \cdot x^{n+4}$
42. $a^{2n} \cdot a^{n-5}$
43. $a^{m^2-n} \cdot a^{m^2+n}$
44. $(1+i)^n \cdot (1+i)^{n+2}$
45. $(x^n)^2$
46. $[(1+i)^n]^3$
47. $(x^m)^n$
48. $\dfrac{x^{3m+2}}{x^{m-5}}$
49. $\dfrac{a^{3m+2}}{a^{m-6}}$
50. $\left(\dfrac{a^2}{b^3}\right)^m$
51. $\left(\dfrac{r^4}{s^2}\right)^{3n}$

Find the value of each of the following expressions for $x = 0.01$:

52. $1 + x$
53. $1 + 2x + x^2$
54. $1 + 3x + 3x^2 + x^3$
55. $1 + 4x + 6x^2 + 4x^3 + x^4$

Find the value of each of the following expressions for $x = 0.02$:

56. $1 + 5x$
57. $1 + 5x + 10x^2$
58. $1 + 5x + 10x^2 + 10x^3$
59. $1 + 5x + 10x^2 + 10x^3 + 5x^4$
60. $1 + 5x + 10x^2 + 10x^3 + 5x^4 + x^5$

If $i = 0.04$, find the value of:

61. $(1+i)^2$
62. $(1+i)^3$
63. $(1+i)^4$

33. Fractional exponents

According to the definition of a^k in Article 32, such an expression as $a^{\frac{1}{2}}$ has no meaning whatever. It is convenient to define $a^{\frac{1}{2}}$ in such a way that the laws for positive integral exponents given in Arti-

FRACTIONAL EXPONENTS

cle 32 hold also for fractional exponents. To do this, $a^{\frac{1}{2}}$ is defined to be a number such that
$$a^{\frac{1}{2}} \cdot a^{\frac{1}{2}} = a.$$
Likewise, $a^{\frac{1}{3}}$ is a number such that
$$a^{\frac{1}{3}} \cdot a^{\frac{1}{3}} \cdot a^{\frac{1}{3}} = a,$$
and in general if q is a positive integer $a^{\frac{1}{q}}$ is a number such that
$$a^{\frac{1}{q}} \cdot a^{\frac{1}{q}} \cdot a^{\frac{1}{q}} \cdots \text{ to } q \text{ factors} = a.$$

Another way of writing $a^{\frac{1}{2}}$ is $\sqrt{a}$, read "square root of a," and in general $a^{\frac{1}{q}}$ can be written $\sqrt[q]{a}$, read "qth root of a." Thus, the fractional exponent $\dfrac{1}{q}$ has the same meaning as the sign $\sqrt[q]{}$, which is called a **radical sign**.

Illustrations:
$$x^{\frac{1}{2}} = \sqrt{x}; \quad 25^{\frac{1}{2}} = \sqrt{25}; \quad 16^{\frac{1}{4}} = \sqrt[4]{16}; \quad 8^{\frac{1}{3}} = \sqrt[3]{8}.$$

It is shown in college algebra that any number a, except $a = 0$, has q distinct qth roots. Thus, the number 36 has two distinct square roots, $+6$ and -6.

We now adopt certain conventions which are important in our work with expressions involving fractional exponents:

1. $a^{\frac{1}{q}}$ *is positive if* a *is positive.*
2. $a^{\frac{1}{q}}$ *is negative if* a *is negative and if* q *is an odd positive integer.*
3. $a^{\frac{1}{q}}$ *is a new kind of number (imaginary number) that will be discussed in Article 72 if* a *is negative and* q *is an even positive integer.*

Illustrations of these are:

1. $16^{\frac{1}{2}} = \sqrt{16} = +4.$
   $8^{\frac{1}{3}} = \sqrt[3]{8} = +2.$
2. $(-8)^{\frac{1}{3}} = \sqrt[3]{-8} = -2.$
3. $(-4)^{\frac{1}{2}} = \sqrt{-4}$, an imaginary number.

These conventions are equivalent to an agreement to use what is called the **principal root** of a number. For example, the principal square root of 16 is $+4$, and the principal cube root of -8 is -2. When we wish to refer to both square roots of 16 we shall specifically write ± 4, or $\pm\sqrt{16}$, or $\pm 16^{\frac{1}{2}}$. Concerning the other two cube roots of -8, more can be said after imaginary numbers have been defined.

The expression $a^{\frac{p}{q}}$, where p and q are positive integers, and the fraction $\frac{p}{q}$ has been reduced to its lowest terms, is defined in such a way that

$$a^{\frac{1}{q}} \cdot a^{\frac{1}{q}} \cdot a^{\frac{1}{q}} \cdots \text{to } p \text{ factors} = a^{\frac{1}{q}+\frac{1}{q}+\frac{1}{q}+\cdots \text{ to } p \text{ factors}} = a^{\frac{p}{q}}$$

and $a^{\frac{p}{q}}$ is the pth power of $a^{\frac{1}{q}}$. That is,

$$a^{\frac{p}{q}} = (\sqrt[q]{a})^p.$$

Also, it is true that $(\sqrt[q]{a})^p = \sqrt[q]{a^p}$.
Thus, $8^{\frac{2}{3}} = (\sqrt[3]{8})^2 = (2)^2 = 4,$
and also, $8^{\frac{2}{3}} = \sqrt[3]{8^2} = \sqrt[3]{64} = 4.$

In this book, **when an expression containing literal numbers occurs under a radical sign, the expression is taken to be positive unless otherwise stated.** Thus, in $\sqrt{a+b}$, the expression $a + b$ is to be considered positive.

The following examples will illustrate the application of the laws of exponents, as stated in Article 32, to expressions involving fractional exponents.

Perform the indicated operations and express the answers with integral or fractional exponents.

Example 1. $x^{\frac{1}{2}} \cdot x^{\frac{4}{3}}$.

Solution. $\qquad x^{\frac{1}{2}} \cdot x^{\frac{4}{3}} = x^{\frac{3}{6}} \cdot x^{\frac{8}{6}} = x^{\frac{11}{6}}.$

Example 2. $(x^{\frac{1}{2}})^{\frac{3}{2}}$.

Solution. $\qquad (x^{\frac{1}{2}})^{\frac{3}{2}} = x^{\frac{3}{4}}.$

Example 3. $(xy)^{\frac{1}{3}}$.

Solution. $\qquad (xy)^{\frac{1}{3}} = x^{\frac{1}{3}} y^{\frac{1}{3}}.$

Example 4. $\left(\dfrac{x}{y}\right)^{\frac{3}{2}}$.

Solution. $\qquad \left(\dfrac{x}{y}\right)^{\frac{3}{2}} = \dfrac{x^{\frac{3}{2}}}{y^{\frac{3}{2}}}.$

Example 5. $\dfrac{x^{\frac{7}{3}}}{x^{\frac{1}{2}}}$.

Solution. $\qquad \dfrac{x^{\frac{7}{3}}}{x^{\frac{1}{2}}} = \dfrac{x^{\frac{14}{6}}}{x^{\frac{3}{6}}} = x^{\frac{11}{6}}.$

Example 6. $\dfrac{x^{\frac{1}{4}}}{x^{\frac{3}{4}}}$.

ZERO EXPONENT

Solution. $\dfrac{x^{\frac{1}{4}}}{x^{\frac{3}{4}}} = \dfrac{1}{x^{\frac{2}{4}}} = \dfrac{1}{x^{\frac{1}{2}}}.$

Example 7. Find the numerical value of $\dfrac{64^{\frac{3}{2}}}{8^{\frac{2}{3}}}$.

Solution. $\dfrac{64^{\frac{3}{2}}}{8^{\frac{2}{3}}} = \dfrac{(\sqrt{64})^3}{(\sqrt[3]{8})^2} = \dfrac{512}{4} = 128.$

EXERCISE 2

Perform the indicated operations, expressing the answers with integral or fractional exponents:

1. $a^{\frac{1}{2}} \cdot a^{\frac{1}{3}}$
2. $x^{\frac{1}{3}} \cdot x^{\frac{1}{3}}$
3. $a^{\frac{3}{7}} \cdot a^{\frac{2}{7}}$
4. $a^{1.5} \cdot a^{1.2}$
5. $m^{2.3} \cdot m^{1.4}$
6. $x^2 \cdot x^{\frac{1}{2}}$
7. $y^{\frac{1}{3}} \cdot y^3$
8. $(x^{\frac{1}{2}})^3$
9. $(2^{\frac{1}{3}})^2$
10. $(a^{\frac{1}{2}}b^{\frac{1}{2}})^2$
11. $(m^{\frac{1}{3}}n^{\frac{1}{3}})^3$
12. $(1+i)^{\frac{1}{2}} \cdot (1+i)^{\frac{1}{5}}$
13. $(1+i)^{\frac{1}{3}} \cdot (1+i)^{\frac{2}{3}}$
14. $(a+b)^{\frac{1}{2}} \cdot (a+b)^{\frac{1}{2}}$
15. $(xy)^{\frac{1}{3}}$
16. $(mn)^{\frac{1}{2}}$
17. $(abc)^{\frac{2}{3}}$
18. $(rs)^{\frac{3}{4}}$
19. $\left(\dfrac{a}{b}\right)^{\frac{1}{2}}$
20. $\left(\dfrac{ab}{c}\right)^{\frac{2}{3}}$
21. $\left(\dfrac{1}{2}\right)^{\frac{1}{2}}$
22. $\left(\dfrac{3}{4}\right)^{\frac{1}{3}}$
23. $\dfrac{a^{\frac{1}{2}}}{a^{\frac{1}{3}}}$
24. $\dfrac{x^{\frac{3}{4}}}{x^{\frac{1}{2}}}$
25. $\dfrac{y^{\frac{2}{3}}}{y^{\frac{1}{2}}}$
26. $\dfrac{x^{\frac{1}{2}}}{x^{\frac{3}{4}}}$
27. $\dfrac{a^{\frac{1}{3}}}{a^{\frac{2}{3}}}$
28. $\dfrac{a^{\frac{3}{5}}}{a}$

Find the values of the following expressions:

29. $16^{\frac{1}{2}}$ Solution: $16^{\frac{1}{2}} = \sqrt{16} = 4$
30. $8^{\frac{1}{3}}$
31. $(-8)^{\frac{1}{3}}$
32. $25^{\frac{1}{2}}$
33. $8^{\frac{2}{3}}$
34. $(-8)^{\frac{2}{3}}$
35. $27^{\frac{1}{3}}$
36. $100^{\frac{3}{2}}$
37. $64^{\frac{3}{2}}$
38. $36^{\frac{1}{2}}$
39. $\dfrac{25^{\frac{1}{2}}}{27^{\frac{1}{3}}}$
40. $\dfrac{81^{\frac{3}{2}}}{27^{\frac{1}{3}}}$
41. $\left(\dfrac{36}{81}\right)^{\frac{1}{2}}$
42. $\left(\dfrac{-8}{27}\right)^{\frac{1}{3}}$
43. $\dfrac{8^{\frac{4}{3}}}{8^{\frac{2}{3}}}$
44. $\dfrac{25}{25^{\frac{1}{2}}}$
45. $\dfrac{8^{\frac{1}{3}}}{8^{\frac{2}{3}}}$
46. $\dfrac{25^{\frac{1}{2}}}{25^{\frac{3}{2}}}$

34. Zero exponent

The expression a^0 is defined to be 1, since this definition is necessary in order that the first index law shall hold for zero exponents. Thus,
$$a^0 \cdot a^m = a^{0+m} = a^m$$
implies that $a^0 = 1$, since $1 \cdot a^m = a^m$. Here $a \neq 0$.

Illustrations:
1. $(a + b)^0 = 1$.
2. $b^0 = 1$.
3. $5^0 = 1$.

35. Negative exponents

So far, definitions have been given for positive integral exponents, fractional exponents, and zero exponents, and the laws of Article 32 hold for these kinds of exponents. It is only logical to define a^{-m}, where $m > 0$, in such a way that the same laws hold. Thus, by Law I,

$$a^m \cdot a^{-m} = a^{m-m} = a^0 = 1.$$

Hence, $\qquad a^{-m} = \dfrac{1}{a^m}, \text{ if } a \neq 0,$

since $\qquad a^m \cdot \dfrac{1}{a^m} = \dfrac{a^m}{a^m} = a^0 = 1.$

Illustrations:

1. $a^{-2} = \dfrac{1}{a^2}$.
2. $a^3 = \dfrac{1}{a^{-3}}$.
3. $a^{-\frac{1}{2}} = \dfrac{1}{a^{\frac{1}{2}}}$.

Since $a^{-m} = \dfrac{1}{a^m}$, and $a^m = \dfrac{1}{a^{-m}}$, it follows that *in a fraction any factor of the numerator can be transferred to the denominator, and any factor of the denominator can be transferred to the numerator, provided that the sign of the exponent of the factor is changed.*

Illustration:

$$\frac{a^{-3} \cdot b^4 \cdot c^{-2}}{a^5 \cdot b^{-2} \cdot c^4} = \frac{b^4 \cdot b^2}{a^5 \cdot a^3 \cdot c^4 \cdot c^2} = \frac{b^6}{a^8 \cdot c^6}.$$

Notice, however, that in the fraction

$$\frac{a + x^{-2}}{b}$$

this transfer cannot be performed on x^{-2}, since x^{-2} is not a *factor* of the numerator. In this case,

$$\frac{a + x^{-2}}{b} = \frac{a + \dfrac{1}{x^2}}{b} = \frac{ax^2 + 1}{bx^2}.$$

We assume that the definitions of fractional, zero, and negative exponents are consistent with all of the laws of exponents given in Article 32.

NEGATIVE EXPONENTS

EXERCISE 3

Perform the indicated operations, expressing the answers with positive exponents, and find the numerical value when possible:

1. 3^0
2. $a^0 \cdot a^{-2}$
3. $a^3 \cdot a^{-2} \cdot a^5$
4. $4a^2 \cdot 8a^{-2}$
5. $6x^{-3} \cdot 2x^4$
6. $(x^{-2})^3$
7. $(2^2)^{-3}$
8. $(x+y)^0 \cdot (x-y)^{-2}$
9. $\dfrac{a^{-3}}{b^{-4}}$
10. $\dfrac{x^{-2}}{x^{-5}}$
11. $\dfrac{m^{-6}}{n^{-7}}$
12. $\dfrac{8^{-1}}{8^2}$
13. $(1+i)^n \cdot (1+i)^{-n}$
14. $(1+i)^3 \cdot (1+i)^{-7}$
15. $1^{-1} + 4^{-2}$
16. $3^{-2} + 3^{-1}$
17. $(-5)^0$
18. $(a^2 + b^2 + c^2)^0$
19. $x^{-3} \cdot x^8$
20. $(x^{-2})^{-3}$
21. $(a^4)^{-2}$
22. $8^{\frac{1}{3}} - 25^{\frac{1}{2}} + 6^0 - 4^{-\frac{1}{2}}$
23. $27^{-\frac{1}{3}} + 9^{\frac{1}{2}} - 4^0$
24. $\left(\dfrac{x}{y}\right)^{-3}$
25. $\dfrac{x^{-8}}{x^{-2}}$

Express with positive exponents, and simplify:

26. $\dfrac{x^{-1} + y^{-1}}{x^{-1} - y^{-1}}$
27. $\dfrac{a^{-2} - b^{-2}}{a^{-2} + b^{-2}}$
28. $(a + b^{-2})(a - b^{-2})$
29. $\dfrac{x^{-2} - y^{-2}}{x^{-1} - y^{-1}}$
30. Show that
$$\dfrac{1}{1 - (1+i)^{-n}} - \dfrac{1}{(1+i)^n - 1} = 1.$$
31. Show that $2(1+i)^n \cdot (1+i)^{-n} = 2$.
32. If $i = 0.02$ and $n = 1$, find the value of $(1+i)^{-n}$ correct to 8 decimal places.
33. Find the value of $(1.03)^{-2}$ correct to 4 decimal places.
34. Prove that
$$\dfrac{1 - (1+i)^{-(k+m)}}{i} = \dfrac{1 - (1+i)^{-k}}{i} + (1+i)^{-k} \cdot \dfrac{1 - (1+i)^{-m}}{i}.$$
35. Prove that
$$(1+i)^{-n} \cdot \dfrac{(1+i)^n - 1}{i} = \dfrac{1 - (1+i)^{-n}}{i}.$$
36. Prove that
$$\dfrac{(1+i)^n - 1}{i} + \dfrac{1 - (1+i)^{-n}}{i} = \dfrac{1 - (1+i)^{-n}}{i}[(1+i)^n + 1].$$

37. If $i = 0.04$ and $n = 2$, find the value of $\dfrac{1 - (1 + i)^{-n}}{i}$ correct to 4 decimal places.

38. If $i = 0.02$ and $n = 1$, find the value of $\dfrac{1 - (1 + i)^{-n}}{i}$ correct to 4 decimal places.

39. If $a = \dfrac{1 - (1 + i)^{-n}}{i}$ and if $s = \dfrac{(1 + i)^n - 1}{i}$, show that
$$1/a - 1/s = i.$$

40. Show that
$$\left[\frac{(1+i)^n - 1}{i}\right]^2 = \frac{1}{i}\left\{\frac{(1+i)^{2n} - 1}{i} - 2\left[\frac{(1+i)^n - 1}{i}\right]\right\}.$$

36. Rational and irrational numbers

A **rational number** is a number that can be expressed as the quotient of two integers. Thus, $3, \frac{1}{2}$, and $\frac{2}{5}$ are rational numbers. A real number that cannot be expressed as the quotient of two integers is an **irrational number**. Thus, $\sqrt{2}, \sqrt[3]{7}$, and $8^{\frac{1}{4}}$ are irrational numbers.

Any irrational number can be enclosed between two rational numbers that differ from each other by as small a number as we please. Thus:
$$1 < \sqrt{2} < 2$$
$$1.4 < \sqrt{2} < 1.5$$
$$1.41 < \sqrt{2} < 1.42$$
$$1.414 < \sqrt{2} < 1.415$$
$$1.4142 < \sqrt{2} < 1.4143 \text{ and so on.}$$

37. Radicals

An indicated root of a number is called a **radical**. Thus $\sqrt{2}$, $\sqrt[3]{8}$ and $\sqrt[5]{x - y}$ are radicals.

The **radicand** is the number of which the root is to be taken. In $\sqrt{2}$, 2 is the radicand, and in $\sqrt{x - y}$ the radicand is $x - y$.

The number that tells what root is to be taken is the **index** of the root. In $\sqrt[3]{8}$, the index is 3, and in $\sqrt{5}$, the index is 2 (implied).

The order of a radical is given by the index of the root. Thus, $\sqrt{2}$ is of the second order, and $\sqrt[3]{8}$ is of the third order.

EXERCISE 4

In each case state the radicand, the index of the root, and the order of the radical:

1. $\sqrt{5}$
2. $\sqrt[3]{2}$
3. $\sqrt{a + b}$
4. $\sqrt{m^2 - n^2}$
5. $\sqrt[3]{a^2 b^2}$
6. $\sqrt[4]{a^3 b^2}$

7. $\sqrt{b^2 - 4ac}$ **8.** $\sqrt[5]{x^3y^4}$ **9.** $\sqrt[6]{5+x}$
10. $\sqrt[n]{P}$ **11.** $\sqrt[m]{S}$ **12.** $\sqrt[3]{x^2 - 8x}$

38. Radicals in the simplest form

An expression containing radicals is said to be in the simplest form if
    (a) *There are no fractions under the radical sign,*
    (b) *The radicand contains no factor raised to a power whose exponents equals or exceeds the index of the root,*
    (c) *The indices of the radicals are positive integers and are as small as possible,*
    (d) *There are no radicals in the denominator.*
Thus,

    (a) $\sqrt{\frac{1}{2}}$ is not in the simplest form because there is a fraction under the radical sign,

    (b) $\sqrt[3]{x^3}$ is not in the simplest form because the radicand x^3 has the exponent 3, which equals the index of the root,

    (c) $\sqrt[4]{a^2}$ is not in the simplest form because $\sqrt[4]{a^2} = a^{\frac{2}{4}} = a^{\frac{1}{2}} = \sqrt{a}$; that is, the index 4 is not as small as possible,

    (d) $\dfrac{3}{\sqrt{2}}$ is not in the simplest form, because the denominator contains a radical.

EXERCISE 5

State which of the following radicals are not in the simplest form, and give the reason for your answer, referring to (a), (b), (c), (d) above.

1. $\sqrt{\frac{2}{3}}$ **2.** $\sqrt[3]{a^3}$ **3.** $\sqrt{2}$ **4.** $\sqrt[6]{x^3}$ **5.** $\dfrac{2}{\sqrt{3}}$

6. $\sqrt{a+b}$ **7.** $\sqrt[4]{a^2b^4}$ **8.** $\sqrt{\dfrac{a}{b+c}}$ **9.** $\sqrt[3]{8}$ **10.** $\dfrac{2}{3+\sqrt{5}}$

11. $\sqrt{\frac{5}{6}}$ **12.** $\sqrt[4]{b^3c}$ **13.** $\dfrac{3}{\sqrt{5}}$ **14.** $\sqrt[6]{x^2}$

39. Operations with radicals

The coefficient of a radical may be introduced under the radical sign by raising the coefficient to a power equal to the index of the root.

Example 1. Introduce the coefficient under the radical sign: $3\sqrt{2}$.

Solution. $\qquad 3\sqrt{2} = \sqrt{3^2 \cdot 2} = \sqrt{9 \cdot 2} = \sqrt{18}.$

In the case of square roots,
$$\sqrt{ab} = (ab)^{\frac{1}{2}} = a^{\frac{1}{2}}b^{\frac{1}{2}} = \sqrt{a}\sqrt{b}.$$

This principle can be used to simplify radicals.

Example 2. Simplify $\sqrt{50}$.

Solution. $\qquad\sqrt{50} = \sqrt{25\cdot 2} = 5\sqrt{2}.$

In general, $\qquad\sqrt[k]{a^m b^n} = \sqrt[k]{a^m}\,\sqrt[k]{b^n}.$

Example 3. Simplify $\sqrt[3]{a^6 b^2}$.

Solution. $\qquad\sqrt[3]{a^6 b^2} = \sqrt[3]{a^6}\,\sqrt[3]{b^2} = a^2 \sqrt[3]{b^2}.$

Radicals containing fractions in the radicands can sometimes be simplified by a procedure known as **rationalizing the denominator**.

Example 4. Simplify $\sqrt{\tfrac{2}{3}}$.

Solution. $\qquad\sqrt{\dfrac{2}{3}} = \sqrt{\dfrac{2}{3}\cdot\dfrac{3}{3}} = \sqrt{\dfrac{6}{9}} = \dfrac{\sqrt{6}}{3} = \dfrac{1}{3}\sqrt{6}.$

Two radicals are **similar** if they are of the same order and have the same radicand. Thus, $3\sqrt{2}$ and $4\sqrt{2}$ are similar radicals, while $\sqrt{2}$ and $\sqrt[3]{2}$ are not similar, and $\sqrt{2}$ and $\sqrt{3}$ are not similar. The algebraic sum of similar radicals is the algebraic sum of their coefficients multiplied by the common radical factor.

Example 5. Add: $\quad 3\sqrt{2} - 4\sqrt{2} + 5\sqrt{2}.$

Solution. $\qquad 3\sqrt{2} - 4\sqrt{2} + 5\sqrt{2} = (3-4+5)\sqrt{2},$
$\qquad\qquad\qquad\qquad\qquad\qquad = 4\sqrt{2}.$

Example 6. Add: $\quad \sqrt{50} + \sqrt{98}.$

Solution. $\qquad \sqrt{50} + \sqrt{98} = \sqrt{25\cdot 2} + \sqrt{49\cdot 2},$
$\qquad\qquad\qquad\qquad = 5\sqrt{2} + 7\sqrt{2},$
$\qquad\qquad\qquad\qquad = 12\sqrt{2}.$

Radicals of different orders can be reduced to the same order by the use of fractional exponents reduced to the same denominator.

Example 7. Reduce $\sqrt{2}$, $\sqrt[3]{4}$ to the same order.

Solution. $\qquad \sqrt{2} = 2^{\frac{1}{2}} = 2^{\frac{3}{6}} = \sqrt[6]{2^3} = \sqrt[6]{8}.$
$\qquad\qquad \sqrt[3]{4} = 4^{\frac{1}{3}} = 4^{\frac{2}{6}} = \sqrt[6]{4^2} = \sqrt[6]{16}.$

EXERCISE 6

Introduce the coefficient under the radical sign:

1. $4\sqrt{2}$ 2. $5\sqrt{3}$ 3. $a\sqrt{5}$ 4. $x\sqrt{2}$ 5. $2\sqrt[3]{6}$
6. $3\sqrt[3]{5}$ 7. $ab\sqrt[3]{c}$ 8. $(x+y)\sqrt{7}$ 9. $2\sqrt[4]{6}$ 10. $3\sqrt[5]{2}$

Simplify the following radicals:

11. $\sqrt{75}$ 12. $\sqrt{72}$ 13. $\sqrt{32}$ 14. $\sqrt{27}$ 15. $\sqrt[3]{54}$ 16. $\sqrt[3]{16}$
17. $\sqrt[3]{24}$ 18. $\sqrt[3]{128}$ 19. $\sqrt{x^3}$ 20. $\sqrt{a^5}$ 21. $\sqrt{x^3 y^4}$ 22. $\sqrt{a^2 b^4}$

MULTIPLICATION AND DIVISION OF RADICALS

23. $\sqrt{x^5y^4}$ 24. $\sqrt{m^2n^4}$ 25. $\sqrt[3]{r^3s^4}$ 26. $\sqrt[4]{x^5}$ 27. $\sqrt{c^4}$ 28. $\sqrt[6]{b^4}$
29. $\sqrt[3]{a^5}$ 30. $\sqrt[3]{a^9b^2}$ 31. $\sqrt[4]{a^8b^2}$ 32. $\sqrt{\frac{3}{5}}$ 33. $\sqrt{\frac{4}{7}}$ 34. $\sqrt{\frac{1}{2}}$
35. $\sqrt{\frac{1}{3}}$ 36. $\sqrt{\frac{2}{5}}$ 37. $\sqrt{\frac{3}{8}}$ 38. $\sqrt{\frac{10}{7}}$ 39. $3\sqrt{\frac{1}{2}}$ 40. $5\sqrt{\frac{1}{3}}$
41. $6\sqrt{\frac{1}{5}}$ 42. $\sqrt[3]{\frac{2}{3}}$ 43. $\sqrt[3]{\frac{4}{5}}$ 44. $\sqrt[3]{\frac{1}{2}}$ 45. $\sqrt[3]{\frac{2}{5}}$ 46. $\sqrt{\frac{2}{x}}$
47. $\sqrt{\frac{3}{a}}$ 48. $\sqrt[3]{\frac{b}{c}}$

Find the algebraic sum:

49. $5\sqrt{3} + 8\sqrt{3} - 2\sqrt{3}$
50. $2\sqrt{5} - 4\sqrt{5} + 8\sqrt{5}$
51. $2\sqrt{x} + 6\sqrt{x} - 2\sqrt{x}$
52. $6\sqrt{2} - 4\sqrt{2}$
53. $\sqrt[3]{4} + 6\sqrt[3]{4}$
54. $\sqrt[3]{2} + 4\sqrt[3]{2} - 6\sqrt[3]{2}$
55. $\sqrt{24} - 4\sqrt{96}$
56. $3\sqrt{20} + 2\sqrt{45} - \sqrt{5}$
57. $\sqrt{20} + 2\sqrt{45}$
58. $\sqrt[3]{16} + 4\sqrt[3]{54}$
59. $2\sqrt[3]{48} + 5\sqrt[3]{162}$
60. $\sqrt[3]{32} + 8\sqrt[3]{162}$
61. $5\sqrt{\frac{3}{8}} - \sqrt{24} + 4\sqrt{\frac{2}{3}}$
62. $4\sqrt[3]{a^2b} + 6\sqrt[3]{8a^5b^4c^3}$

Reduce to the same order:

63. $\sqrt{2}, \sqrt[3]{3}$ 64. $\sqrt{5}, \sqrt[3]{2}$ 65. $\sqrt{a}, \sqrt[3]{b}$ 66. $\sqrt[3]{2}, \sqrt[4]{4}$
67. $\sqrt[3]{5}, \sqrt{2}$ 68. $\sqrt[3]{x}, \sqrt[4]{x}$ 69. $\sqrt{3}, \sqrt[3]{3}, \sqrt[4]{3}$ 70. $\sqrt{2}, \sqrt[3]{3}, \sqrt[4]{4}$
71. $\sqrt[3]{2}, \sqrt[6]{3}$ 72. $\sqrt[3]{x^7}, \sqrt[4]{x^5}$ 73. $\sqrt[3]{x^2}, \sqrt[4]{x^3}$ 74. $\sqrt{ab}, \sqrt[3]{x^2y}$

40. Multiplication and division of radicals

To multiply two or more radicals of the same order, simply multiply the radicands and place the product under a radical sign of the same order.

Example 1. Multiply $\sqrt{2}$ by $\sqrt{3}$.

Solution. $\qquad \sqrt{2} \cdot \sqrt{3} = \sqrt{2 \cdot 3} = \sqrt{6}.$

Example 2. Multiply $5\sqrt[3]{m^2n}$ by $4\sqrt[3]{m^2n^2}$.

Solution. $\qquad 5\sqrt[3]{m^2n} \cdot 4\sqrt[3]{m^2n^2} = 20\sqrt[3]{m^4n^3},$
$= 20mn\sqrt[3]{m}.$

To multiply two or more radicals of different orders, reduce the radicals to the same order and then proceed as above.

Example 3. Multiply $\sqrt{2}$ by $\sqrt[3]{3}$.

Solution. $\qquad \sqrt{2} = 2^{\frac{1}{2}} = 2^{\frac{3}{6}} = \sqrt[6]{2^3} = \sqrt[6]{8}.$
$\sqrt[3]{3} = 3^{\frac{1}{3}} = 3^{\frac{2}{6}} = \sqrt[6]{3^2} = \sqrt[6]{9}.$
$\sqrt[6]{8}\sqrt[6]{9} = \sqrt[6]{72}.$

Example 4. Multiply $\sqrt[3]{a^2b}$ by $\sqrt[4]{a^3b^3}$.

Solution.
$$\sqrt[3]{a^2b} = (a^2b)^{\frac{1}{3}} = (a^2b)^{\frac{4}{12}} = \sqrt[12]{(a^2b)^4} = \sqrt[12]{a^8b^4}.$$
$$\sqrt[4]{a^3b^3} = (a^3b^3)^{\frac{1}{4}} = (a^3b^3)^{\frac{3}{12}} = \sqrt[12]{(a^3b^3)^3} = \sqrt[12]{a^9b^9}.$$
$$\sqrt[12]{a^8b^4} \cdot \sqrt[12]{a^9b^9} = \sqrt[12]{a^{17}b^{13}} = ab\sqrt[12]{a^5b}.$$

Expressions containing radicals can be multiplied by using the usual rules for multiplying multinomials together with the principles stated above.

Example 5. Multiply $\sqrt{2} + \sqrt{3}$ by $\sqrt{2} - \sqrt{3}$.
Solution.
$$(\sqrt{2} + \sqrt{3})(\sqrt{2} - \sqrt{3}) = (\sqrt{2})^2 - (\sqrt{3})^2,$$
$$= 2 - 3 = -1.$$

Example 6. Multiply $2\sqrt{a} + 3\sqrt{b}$ by $5\sqrt{a} - 4\sqrt{b}$.
Solution.
$$\begin{array}{r} 2\sqrt{a} + 3\sqrt{b} \\ 5\sqrt{a} - 4\sqrt{b} \\ \hline 10a + 15\sqrt{ab} \\ -8\sqrt{ab} - 12b \\ \hline 10a + 7\sqrt{ab} - 12b. \end{array}$$

When both dividend and divisor are monomials of the same order, radicals can be divided by application of the law,
$$\frac{\sqrt[n]{a}}{\sqrt[n]{b}} = \sqrt[n]{\frac{a}{b}}.$$

Example 7. Divide $\sqrt{6}$ by $\sqrt{3}$.
Solution.
$$\frac{\sqrt{6}}{\sqrt{3}} = \sqrt{\frac{6}{3}} = \sqrt{2}.$$

Example 8. Divide $\sqrt[3]{a^2 - b^2}$ by $\sqrt[3]{a + b}$.
Solution.
$$\frac{\sqrt[3]{a^2 - b^2}}{\sqrt[3]{a + b}} = \sqrt[3]{\frac{a^2 - b^2}{a + b}} = \sqrt[3]{a - b}.$$

For purposes of computation, the division of radicals is accomplished by rationalizing the denominator.

Example 9. Divide $\sqrt{3}$ by $\sqrt{2}$.
Solution.
$$\frac{\sqrt{3}}{\sqrt{2}} = \frac{\sqrt{3}}{\sqrt{2}} \cdot \frac{\sqrt{2}}{\sqrt{2}} = \frac{\sqrt{6}}{2} = \tfrac{1}{2}\sqrt{6}.$$

Example 10. Divide $\sqrt[3]{5}$ by $\sqrt[3]{2}$.
Solution.
$$\frac{\sqrt[3]{5}}{\sqrt[3]{2}} = \frac{\sqrt[3]{5}}{\sqrt[3]{2}} \cdot \frac{\sqrt[3]{2^2}}{\sqrt[3]{2^2}} = \frac{\sqrt[3]{20}}{2} = \tfrac{1}{2}\sqrt[3]{20}.$$

Example 11. Divide $\sqrt{3} + \sqrt{5}$ by $\sqrt{3} - \sqrt{5}$.

MULTIPLICATION AND DIVISION OF RADICALS

Solution.
$$\frac{\sqrt{3}+\sqrt{5}}{\sqrt{3}-\sqrt{5}} = \frac{\sqrt{3}+\sqrt{5}}{\sqrt{3}-\sqrt{5}} \cdot \frac{\sqrt{3}+\sqrt{5}}{\sqrt{3}+\sqrt{5}},$$
$$= \frac{3+2\sqrt{15}+5}{3-5},$$
$$= \frac{8+2\sqrt{15}}{-2},$$
$$= -4 - \sqrt{15}.$$

EXERCISE 7

Perform the indicated multiplications and simplify the results:

1. $\sqrt{3} \cdot \sqrt{7}$ 2. $\sqrt{a} \cdot \sqrt{b}$ 3. $\sqrt{3} \cdot \sqrt{8}$ 4. $\sqrt{5} \cdot \sqrt{6}$ 5. $3\sqrt{2} \cdot 4\sqrt{5}$
6. $2\sqrt{3} \cdot 3\sqrt{10}$ 7. $4\sqrt{a} \cdot 2\sqrt{ab}$ 8. $\sqrt[3]{2} \cdot \sqrt[3]{5}$ 9. $\sqrt[4]{5} \cdot \sqrt[3]{3}$
10. $\sqrt{2} \cdot \sqrt[3]{4}$ 11. $\sqrt[3]{6} \cdot \sqrt{7}$ 12. $\sqrt{a} \cdot \sqrt[3]{x}$ 13. $\sqrt[3]{2} \cdot \sqrt[5]{3}$ 14. $\sqrt[4]{3} \cdot \sqrt[3]{2}$
15. $\sqrt[3]{x^2} \cdot \sqrt[4]{x^3}$
16. $(\sqrt{2}+\sqrt{5})(\sqrt{2}-\sqrt{5})$
17. $(\sqrt{7}-\sqrt{3})(\sqrt{7}+\sqrt{3})$
18. $(\sqrt{x}+\sqrt{y})(\sqrt{x}-\sqrt{y})$
19. $(\sqrt{2}+\sqrt{3})^2$
20. $(\sqrt{6}-\sqrt{5})^2$
21. $(\sqrt{m}+\sqrt{n})^2$
22. $(\sqrt{2}+\sqrt{3})(\sqrt{3}+\sqrt{5})$
23. $(2-\sqrt{5})(2+\sqrt{5})$
24. $(4+\sqrt{3})(8-\sqrt{3})$
25. $3\sqrt{3}(\sqrt{2}-\sqrt{5}+\sqrt{3})$
26. $\sqrt{5}(3\sqrt{2}-\sqrt{3}+\sqrt{6})$
27. If $x = 3 + \sqrt{7}$, find the value of $x^2 - 6x + 2$.
28. If $x = \dfrac{7+\sqrt{37}}{2}$, find the value of $x^2 - 7x + 3$.
29. If $x = \dfrac{-b+\sqrt{b^2-4ac}}{2a}$, find the value of $ax^2 + bx + c$.
30. Multiply $\dfrac{-b+\sqrt{b^2-4ac}}{2a}$ by $\dfrac{-b-\sqrt{b^2-4ac}}{2a}$.

Perform the indicated divisions, and simplify the results:

31. $\sqrt{27} \div \sqrt{3}$ 32. $\sqrt{8} \div \sqrt{2}$ 33. $\sqrt{18} \div \sqrt{3}$ 34. $\sqrt[3]{20} \div \sqrt[3]{5}$
35. $\sqrt[4]{32} \div \sqrt[4]{4}$ 36. $\sqrt{2} \div \sqrt{3}$ 37. $\sqrt{10} \div \sqrt{7}$ 38. $\dfrac{1}{\sqrt{2}}$
39. $\dfrac{2}{\sqrt{3}}$ 40. $\dfrac{1}{\sqrt{5}}$ 41. $\dfrac{2}{\sqrt[3]{4}}$ 42. $\dfrac{5}{\sqrt[3]{2}}$
43. $\sqrt{x^2y} \div \sqrt{xy}$ 44. $\sqrt[3]{a^2-b^2} \div \sqrt[3]{a-b}$ 45. $\dfrac{4}{2\sqrt{3}}$
46. $\dfrac{7}{3\sqrt{5}}$ 47. $\dfrac{2}{6+\sqrt{3}}$ 48. $\dfrac{5}{2-\sqrt{3}}$
49. $\dfrac{3+\sqrt{2}}{4-\sqrt{2}}$ 50. $\dfrac{5-\sqrt{3}}{6+\sqrt{2}}$ 51. $\dfrac{\sqrt{2}+\sqrt{6}}{\sqrt{2}-\sqrt{6}}$

52. $\dfrac{\sqrt{3} - 4}{\sqrt{2} + \sqrt{6}}$ 53. $\dfrac{\sqrt{a} + \sqrt{b}}{\sqrt{a} - \sqrt{b}}$ 54. $\dfrac{3\sqrt{2} - 2\sqrt{3}}{4\sqrt{5} - 6\sqrt{3}}$

41. Special types of equations

Some **exponential equations** can be solved by using the definitions and laws of exponents.

Example 1. Solve for x: $2^x = 32$.

Solution. $\qquad\qquad 2^x = 32.$

Since $2^5 = 32$, it follows that $x = 5$.

Example 2. Solve for x: $2^x = \frac{1}{16}$.

Solution. $\qquad 2^x = \frac{1}{16}.$

Since $\qquad 2^{-4} = \dfrac{1}{2^4} = \dfrac{1}{16}$, it follows that $x = -4$.

When the unknown is raised to a power, it is sometimes possible to solve the equation by using the laws of exponents.

Example 3. Solve for x: $x^{\frac{1}{3}} = 3$.

Solution. $\qquad\qquad x^{\frac{1}{3}} = 3.$

Raising both members of the equation to the third power,

$$(x^{\frac{1}{3}})^3 = 3^3,$$
$$x = 27.$$

Example 4. Solve for x: $x^{\frac{3}{2}} = 8$.

Solution. $\qquad\qquad x^{\frac{3}{2}} = 8.$

Raising both members to the $\frac{2}{3}$ power,

$$(x^{\frac{3}{2}})^{\frac{2}{3}} = 8^{\frac{2}{3}},$$
$$x = (\sqrt[3]{8})^2 = 4.$$

Example 5. Solve for x: $(1 + x)^{\frac{1}{3}} - 1 = S$.

Solution. $\qquad (1 + x)^{\frac{1}{3}} - 1 = S.$

Transposing the 1,

$$(1 + x)^{\frac{1}{3}} = S + 1.$$

Cubing both members,

$$1 + x = (S + 1)^3 = S^3 + 3S^2 + 3S + 1.$$

Transposing the 1,

$$x = S^3 + 3S^2 + 3S.$$

SPECIAL TYPES OF EQUATIONS

EXERCISE 8

Solve for x:

1. $3^x = 9$
2. $2^x = 8$
3. $10^x = 100$
4. $3^{x+2} = 243$
5. $5^{x-2} = 125$
6. $10^{x-1} = 1000$
7. $2^{2x-1} = 32$
8. $x^{\frac{1}{2}} = 9$
9. $2x^{\frac{1}{2}} = 5$
10. $x^{\frac{1}{3}} = 2$
11. $3x^{\frac{1}{3}} = 2$
12. $(x+1)^{\frac{1}{2}} = 6$
13. $(x-1)^{\frac{1}{3}} = 3$
14. $(1+x)^2 = 1.0404$, positive root only
15. $(1+x)^2 = 1.0609$, positive root only
16. $2^{-x} = 4$
17. $3^{-x} = \frac{1}{9}$
18. $x^{-\frac{1}{2}} = 6$
19. $x^{-\frac{1}{3}} = 2$
20. $(x-1)^{-\frac{1}{2}} = 5$
21. $(x-2)^{-\frac{1}{3}} = 4$
22. $x^{-\frac{1}{4}} = 2$
23. $x^{\frac{2}{3}} = 64$, positive root only
24. $x^{\frac{3}{4}} = 8$
25. $x^{\frac{3}{2}} = 64$
26. $(1+x)^{\frac{1}{2}} - 1 = S$
27. $S = P(1+x)^3$
28. $P = S(1+x)^{-3}$

MISCELLANEOUS EXERCISE

Find the numerical value of:

1. $3^2 + 3^0 + 9^{\frac{1}{2}} + 3^{-2}$
2. $4^{-2} - 4 - \sqrt{4} + 4^{\frac{1}{2}}$
3. $8^{\frac{2}{3}} + 9^{\frac{3}{2}} - 6^0$
4. $\dfrac{1}{\sqrt{2}} + \dfrac{3}{\sqrt{2}} - 2\sqrt{2}$
5. $4^{-\frac{3}{2}} + (\frac{1}{2})^4 - 2^{-6}$
6. $(\sqrt{8} - \sqrt{2})^2$

If $\sqrt{2} = 1.414$ and $\sqrt{3} = 1.732$, correct to 3 decimal places, find the value, to 3 decimal places, of:

7. $\sqrt{12}$
8. $\sqrt{18}$
9. $\sqrt{6}$
10. $\dfrac{1}{\sqrt{2}}$
11. $\dfrac{2}{\sqrt{3}}$
12. $\sqrt{32}$
13. $\sqrt{27}$

Solve for i:

14. $(1+i)^2 = 1.0816$, positive root only
15. $(1+i)^3 = 1.061208$
16. $\dfrac{(1+i)^2 - 1}{i} = 2.0025$
17. $\dfrac{i}{1 - (1+i)^{-1}} = 1.0025$
18. $\dfrac{i}{1 - (1+i)^{-1}} = 1.005$
19. $S = P(1+i)^5$
20. $r = (1+i)^7 - 1$

If $(1+i)^{100} = 7.24$, and if $(1+i)^{25} = 1.64$, approximately, find the value of:

21. $(1+i)^{125}$, to one decimal place
22. $(1+i)^{75}$, to two decimal places
23. $(1+i)^{225}$, to one decimal place
24. $(1+i)^{50}$, to two decimal places
25. $(1+i)^{150}$, to one decimal place

Express as radicals in the simplest form:

26. $x^{\frac{2}{3}}$
27. $7^{\frac{1}{2}}$
28. $a^{\frac{3}{2}}$
29. $x^{\frac{3}{5}}$
30. $b^{\frac{5}{3}}$
31. $3^{\frac{4}{3}}$
32. $(ab)^{-\frac{1}{2}}$

Express with positive exponents:

33. $(a+b)^{-\frac{1}{2}}$
34. $m + n^{-1}$
35. $a^{-2} + b^{-2}$
36. $\sqrt{(1+i)^{-3}}$
37. $4x^{-\frac{1}{3}}$
38. $5\sqrt[3]{x^{-5}}$
39. $3x^{-2} + 4y^{-1}$
40. $ab^{-1} + cd^{-2}$

Which of the following are rational numbers?

41. $\frac{3}{2}, \sqrt{2}, \sqrt[3]{8}$
42. $2, \frac{1}{\sqrt{2}}, 5^0$
43. $3^{-2}, \sqrt[4]{16}, \sqrt[3]{27}$
44. $1.4, 8^{\frac{2}{3}}, 6$

Rationalize the denominators:

45. $\dfrac{8}{\sqrt{2}}$
46. $\sqrt{\dfrac{12}{5}}$
47. $\dfrac{2}{\sqrt{3} - 1}$
48. $\sqrt{\dfrac{a}{b}}$
49. $\dfrac{3 + \sqrt{2}}{5 - \sqrt{2}}$
50. $\dfrac{6}{\sqrt{3}}$

6

Logarithms

42. Definition of common logarithm

If $10^x = y$, then x is said to be the **common logarithm** of the number y, and this can be written

$$x = \log y.$$

That is, the common logarithm of a number is the exponent of the power to which 10 must be raised to give that number.

The two equations $\qquad 10^x = y \qquad\qquad$ (1)
and $\qquad\qquad\qquad x = \log y \qquad\qquad$ (2)

mean exactly the same thing; and the terms logarithm and exponent are equivalent. Notice that y is positive, since 10 is positive.

The expression 10^x has a well-defined meaning when x is an integer (Article 32) and when x is a rational number (Article 33), but so far it has no meaning when x is an irrational number. Thus $10^{\sqrt{2}}$ has not yet been assigned a meaning. However, it has been pointed out that $\sqrt{2}$ is the limit of a sequence of rational numbers 1, 1.4, 1.41, 1.414, 1.4142, ... When a variable z takes this sequence of rational values, it can be shown that 10^z has a limit, and we define $10^{\sqrt{2}}$ as this limit.

In general, 10^x, with x an irrational number, is defined as the limit of 10^z as z approaches x. A precise discussion of this concept is beyond the scope of this book, but the general idea should be apparent from the foregoing description. The number 10 is called the **base** of the system of common logarithms.

We assume that, corresponding to any positive number y there exists one and only one real number x such that $10^x = y$. In other words, a positive number has one and only one logarithm. (For brevity, we shall say "logarithm" instead of "common logarithm," and later we shall discuss the significance of the adjective "common" in connection with logarithms).

We assume that the laws of exponents, as stated in Article 32, apply when irrational exponents are involved.

Logarithms are used to shorten certain arithmetical computations such as multiplication, division, extraction of roots, and raising numbers to powers. It is this fact that justifies their use.

The logarithms of powers of 10 are integers. Thus,

$$\log 1000 = 3, \text{ since } 10^3 = 1000$$
$$\log 100 = 2, \text{ since } 10^2 = 100$$
$$\log 10 = 1, \text{ since } 10^1 = 10$$
$$\log 1 = 0, \text{ since } 10^0 = 1$$
$$\log 0.1 = -1, \text{ since } 10^{-1} = 0.1$$
$$\log 0.01 = -2, \text{ since } 10^{-2} = 0.01$$
$$\log 0.001 = -3, \text{ since } 10^{-3} = 0.001$$

and so on. Notice that the logarithm of a number increases as the number increases. If a and b are positive numbers, and if $a > b$, we assume that $\log a > \log b$.

When the logarithm of a number is not an integer it can be represented, at least approximately, by a decimal fraction. Thus $\log 200 = 2.301030$, correct to six decimal places.

In general we may write the logarithm of any number in the form,

$$\log y = C + M,$$

where C is an integer, positive, negative, or zero and M is a positive number less than 1 or is zero. We call C the **characteristic** of the logarithm and M the **mantissa** of the logarithm.

In accordance with these definitions, $\log \frac{1}{2} = -.301030$, would be written $9.698970 - 10$, and hence $.698970$ is the mantissa of the logarithm of $\frac{1}{2}$, and $9 - 10$ (or -1) is the characteristic.

The following illustrations show how the characteristic and mantissa are written.

$$\log 3561. = 3.551572$$
$$\log 356.1 = 2.551572$$
$$\log 35.61 = 1.551572$$
$$\log 3.561 = 0.551572$$
$$\log 0.3561 = 9.551572 - 10$$
$$\log 0.03561 = 8.551575 - 10$$
$$\log 0.003561 = 7.551572 - 10$$

43. Significant digits

The **significant digits** of a number are the digits, reading from left to right, beginning with the first digit that is not zero and ending with the last one that is accurately specified.

SIGNIFICANT DIGITS

Thus, the significant digits of 4286 are 4, 2, 8, and 6; the significant digits of 0.003792 are 3, 7, 9, 2.

In some cases it is necessary to have additional information in order to determine the significant digits. For example, in the sum of money $400 the significant digits are 4, 0, and 0; on the other hand, when we say that the distance from the earth to the sun is 93,000,000 miles, accurate to the nearest million miles, the significant digits are 9 and 3.

The concept of significant digits does not refer to the position of the decimal point. Thus, the significant digits in the number 63.75 are 6, 3, 7, and 5.

To round off a number to n significant figures means to write an approximate value of the number that differs from the number by not more than 5 in the first neglected digit. The value of π is 3.1416, correct to five significant figures. To round this value off to four significant figures, we write 3.142, since the final 6 in 3.1416 is larger than 5. To round off 3.142 to three significant figures, we write 3.14, since the final 2 in 3.142 is less than 5. To round off a number ending in 5, we use the arbitrary rule "round off to an even number"; for example, to round off the number 2.845 to three significant digits, we write 2.84, thus making the final digit (4) an even number, while to round off 2.875 to three significant figures, we write 2.88, thus making the final digit (8) an even number.

In arithmetical computations it is necessary to distinguish between **exact numbers** and **approximate numbers.** Thus, the assets of a corporation may be exactly $25,435,247.38, or they may be stated as $25,000,000, correct to the nearest million dollars. Also, a measurement may be 24.76 inches, correct to the nearest 0.01 of an inch. Approximate numbers also arise in the case of unending decimals. Thus, $\frac{1}{7}$ may be expressed as an unending decimal; its value is 0.142857, correct to 6 significant digits, while its value correct to 5 significant digits is 0.14286.

In most of the problems of computation arising in commercial algebra and in the mathematics of finance, sums of money are involved. When a sum of money such as $5000, for example, is mentioned in the data of a problem, this shall mean *exactly* $5000. Also, if an answer is reported as $300.00, for example, this shall mean $300, correct to the nearest cent.

The logarithms of numbers are obtained by calculation, and with the exception of certain cases, such as log 100 = 2, the logarithms of numbers are approximate numbers. The logarithm of 2 is 0.301030, correct to 6 significant figures, and the logarithm of 2 is 0.3010, correct to 4 significant figures.

LOGARITHMS

Illustrations

Number	Significant Digits	Number of Significant Digits
1,324,576.	1, 3, 2, 4, 5, 7, 6	7
42,500.00	4, 2, 5, 0, 0, 0, 0	7
4,632.	4, 6, 3, 2	4
1.356	1, 3, 5, 6	4
1.0085	1, 0, 0, 8, 5	5
0.42632	4, 2, 6, 3, 2	5
0.000827	8, 2, 7	3
0.00175	1, 7, 5	3
0.01002	1, 0, 0, 2	4
500.	Additional information is needed	1, 2, or 3

EXERCISE 1

State the number of significant digits in each of the following numbers:

1. 4,324 **2.** 64 **3.** 640 **4.** 54,000 **5.** 54,000.00
6. 0.00183 **7.** 0.00015 **8.** 15.163 **9.** 432.75 **10.** 1062.7
11. 0.100634 **12.** 200.00 **13.** 1.025 **14.** 1.0375 **15.** 1.06125
16. 83,147 **17.** 0.000016 **18.** 9.16 **19.** 8,000,012 **20.** 1.06

Round off the following numbers to six significant digits:

21. 3.98908562 **22.** 1.12550881 **23.** 1.04680023 **24.** 1.24195709
25. 0.87400986 **26.** 0.25584197 **27.** 0.01505637
28. 39.93010071 **29.** 232.27925160 **30.** 2923.67123480

Round off the following numbers to five significant figures:

31. 8,206,152 **32.** 0.0816374 **33.** 455,555 **34.** 455,565
35. 455,545 **36.** 832.1674 **37.** 916.0173
38. 14.17862 **39.** 2.01863 **40.** 7.01986

44. Properties of logarithms

Since logarithms are exponents, they have certain properties based on the laws of exponents.

I. *The logarithm of a product equals the sum of the logarithms of its factors.*

Let $\quad\quad\quad\quad \log m = x$ and let $\log n = y$.
Then $\quad\quad\quad\quad 10^x = m \quad$ and $\quad 10^y = n$.
Therefore, $\quad\quad\quad 10^x \cdot 10^y = 10^{x+y} = mn$.
Hence, $\quad\quad\quad\quad \log mn = x + y$.
That is, $\quad\quad\quad\quad \log mn = \log m + \log n$. $\quad\quad\quad\quad$ (3)

CHARACTERISTIC

Similarly, $\quad \log mnp = \log m + \log n + \log p$,
and so on, for any number of factors.

   II. *The logarithm of a quotient is equal to the logarithm of the dividend minus the logarithm of the divisor.*

Let $\qquad \log m = x$ and let $\log n = y$.
Then $\qquad 10^x = m \quad$ and $\quad 10^y = n$.

Therefore $\qquad \dfrac{10^x}{10^y} = 10^{x-y} = \dfrac{m}{n}$.

Hence $\qquad \log \dfrac{m}{n} = x - y$.

That is, $\qquad \log \dfrac{m}{n} = \log m - \log n$. $\qquad$ (4)

   III. *The logarithm of* m^n *is equal to* n *times the logarithm of* m.

Let $\qquad x = \log m$.
Then $\qquad 10^x = m$.
By the laws of exponents,
$$m^n = (10^x)^n = 10^{nx}.$$
Hence, $\qquad \log m^n = nx$,
or $\qquad \log m^n = n \log m$. $\qquad$ (5)

   This law can be stated in the following form: *the logarithm of the* nth *power of a number is* n *times the logarithm of the number.* Since a root of a number can be expressed as a fractional power: *the logarithm of the real positive* nth *root of a number* m *is equal to* $\dfrac{1}{n}$ *times the logarithm of the number,* or

$$\log \sqrt[n]{m} = \dfrac{1}{n} \log m.$$

   These properties of logarithms make it possible to shorten the labor of arithmetical calculations, and they should be studied carefully and learned thoroughly.

45. Characteristic

   Tables of logarithms contain the mantissas only; the characteristic of the logarithm of a number is determined by two simple rules:

   1. *To find the characteristic of the logarithm of a number larger than 1, subtract 1 from the number of digits in the integral part of the number.*

   Thus, the number 3561 is larger than 1, and its integral part has 4 digits, so the characteristic of its logarithm is 3. The number 356.1

is larger than 1, and its integral part has 3 digits, so the characteristic of its logarithm is 2.

2. *To find the characteristic of the logarithm of a number less than 1, count the number of zeros between the decimal point and the first digit of the number and add 1 to this number. The characteristic is the negative of the number so obtained. Express this negative number in the form* $n - 10$.

Thus, since the number 0.003561 has two zeros between the decimal point and the first digit, the characteristic of its logarithm is -3, which is written $7 - 10$.

The explanation of these two rules involves the properties of the number 10, which is the base of common logarithms.

If y is a number which has n digits in its integral part, then
$$10^{n-1} \leq y < 10^n$$
and
$$n - 1 \leq \log y < n.$$
Therefore,
$$\log y = n - 1 + f,$$
where f is a positive number and less than 1. That is, f is the mantissa and $n - 1$ is the characteristic.

If y is a positive number less than 1, expressed as a decimal fraction, then we may move the decimal point ten places (or a multiple of 10) to the right, and apply Rule 1 to the integral part of the number so formed, provided that we subtract 10 (or a multiple of 10) from the resulting logarithm. Thus,
$$y = \frac{10^{10}}{10^{10}} \quad y = \frac{y_1}{10^{10}}, \text{ where } y_1 = 10^{10}y,$$
so
$$\log y = \log y_1 - \log 10^{10},$$
$$= \log y_1 - 10.$$

If two numbers contain the same sequence of digits and differ only in the position of the decimal point, their logarithms have the same mantissas, and differ only in their characteristics. Thus,
$$\log 3561 = 3.551572,$$
and
$$\log 356.1 = 2.551572.$$

The reason for this is that the two given numbers are so related that each of them is the product of the other by an integral power of 10. Thus,
$$\log 3561 = \log 356.1 + \log 10,$$
$$= \log 356.1 + 1.$$
This explains why tables of common logarithms contain only the mantissas. The person using the tables must supply the proper characteristic.

LOGARITHM OF A GIVEN NUMBER; INTERPOLATION

Illustrations:

log 4,253,000.	= 6.628695	
log 425,300.	= 5.628695	
log 42,530.	= 4.628695	
log 4,253.	= 3.628695	
log 425.3	= 2.628695	
log 42.53	= 1.628695	
log 4.253	= 0.628695	
log 0.4253	= 9.628695 − 10	
log 0.04253	= 8.628695 − 10	
log 0.004253	= 7.628695 − 10	
log 0.0004253	= 6.628695 − 10	
log 0.00004253	= 5.628695 − 10	

EXERCISE 2

State the characteristic of the logarithm of each of the following numbers:

1. 2598   2. 259.8   3. 25.98   4. 64,325   5. 123,682
6. 4,000   7. 200   8. 40   9. 23   10. 6,000,000
11. 490,000   12. 75,000   13. 4   14. 6.19   15. 2.032
16. 35.63   17. 0.982   18. 0.1764   19. 0.0134   20. 0.000632
21. 0.00014   22. 0.0450   23. 0.1625   24. 0.0125
25. 0.0550   26. 1.04   27. 1.08   28. 0.000049
29. 6.0003   30. 6.002   31. 0.0069   32. 0.00752

If log 2 = 0.301030, find the logarithms of the following numbers:

33. 20 (Solution. log 20 = 1.301030)   34. 200
35. 20,000   36. 0.002   37. 0.000020
38. 0.2   39. 0.02   40. 2,000,000

If log 2 = 0.301030, and if log 3 = 0.477121, use the properties of logarithms given in Article 44 to find the logarithms of the following numbers:

41. 6 (Solution. log 6 = log 3·2 = log 3 + log 2,
= 0.301030 + 0.477121,
= 0.778151)

42. 4   43. 9   44. 36   45. 300   46. 1.5   47. 27   48. 8
49. $\frac{2}{3}$ 50. 32   51. $2^{\frac{1}{2}}$ 52. $3^{\frac{1}{2}}$ 53. $2^{\frac{1}{3}}$ 54. 3^5
55. 5   56. 50   57. 6.75   58. 1080   59. 60,000   60. 120

46. Logarithm of a given number; interpolation

Table I in the Appendix is a six-place table of the mantissas of the logarithms of numbers.

In order to use the tables it is necessary to learn how to find the logarithm of a given number, and how to find the number that corresponds to a given logarithm.

LOGARITHMS

Example 1. Find the logarithm of 6153.

Solution. To find the logarithm of 6153, look in the column headed N (number) for 615, and read across the page to the column headed 3. Here we find the entry 789087. Notice that the first two digits 78 are not repeated in every entry, and that the decimal point is not given. The mantissa of the required logarithm is .789087. Since 6153 has 4 digits to the left of the decimal point, the characteristic is 3.

Therefore, log 6153 = 3.789087.

Example 2. Find the logarithm of 6153.4.

Solution. The logarithm of 6153.4 lies between the logarithm of 6153 and the logarithm of 6154. From the table,

$$\log 6154 = 3.789157,$$
$$\log 6153 = 3.789087.$$

The **tabular difference** between these two logarithms is 0.000070.

To find log 6153.4 we use a procedure called **interpolation,** in which we assume that the logarithms of numbers increase with the numbers according to a simple proportion. Thus:

$$1 \begin{bmatrix} & 6154.0 & & 3.789157 & \\ 94 \begin{bmatrix} 6153.4 & & & \\ 6153.0 & & 3.789087 \end{bmatrix} x \end{bmatrix} 70$$

$$\frac{x}{0.000070} = \frac{0.4}{1},$$
$$x = (0.4)(0.000070),$$
$$= 0.000028.$$

Adding this value of x to 3.789087,

$$\log 6153.4 = 3.789115.$$

The solution in Example 2 is given in detail in order to describe the method. In practice the work can be arranged briefly, as follows:

$$\frac{789157}{789087}$$
$$\overline{\quad 70 \quad}$$

$$(0.4)(70) = 28.$$
$$789087 + 28 = 789115.$$
$$\log 6153.4 = 3.789115.$$

Example 3. Find log 23.452.

Solution. Since there are two digits to the left of the decimal point, the characteristic is 1. To find the mantissa, treat the given number as if it were 2345.2, and disregard the characteristic. Using the tables,

LOGARITHM OF A GIVEN NUMBER; INTERPOLATION

$$\begin{array}{ll} \text{Number} & \text{Mantissa} \\ 2346 & 370328 \\ 2345 & \underline{370143} \\ \text{tabular difference} = & 185 \\ (0.2)(185) = 37. \\ 370143 + 37 = 370180. \\ \log 23.452 = 1.370180. \end{array}$$

Example 4. Find log 23.455.

Solution. Proceeding as in Example 3,

$$\begin{array}{ll} \text{Number} & \text{Mantissa} \\ 2346 & 370328 \\ 2345 & \underline{370143} \\ \text{tabular difference} = & 185 \\ (0.5)(185) = 92.5. \\ 370143 + 92.5 = 370235.5 = 370236. \\ \log 23.455 = 1.370236. \end{array}$$

Notice that the value 370235.5 is rounded off to 370236, making the final digit (6) an even number in accordance with the rule stated in Article 43.

Example 5. Find log 0.00918682.

Solution. By Rule 2 in Article 45, the characteristic is $7 - 10$. To find the mantissa, treat the given number as if it were 9186.82. From the tables,

$$\begin{array}{ll} \text{Number} & \text{Mantissa} \\ 9187 & 963174 \\ 9186 & \underline{963126} \\ \text{tabular difference} = & 48 \\ (0.82)(48) = 39.36 = 39. \\ 963126 + 39 = 963165. \\ \log 0.00918682 = 7.963165 - 10. \end{array}$$

EXERCISE 3

Find the logarithms of the following numbers, using Table I:

1. 1253	**2.** 4762	**3.** 18.75	**4.** 468.3
5. 9.268	**6.** 43,200	**7.** 106,000	**8.** 0.00627
9. 0.09832	**10.** 0.0005273	**11.** 0.9826	**12.** 0.7263
13. 1287.8	**14.** 2164.4	**15.** 3012.5	**16.** 234.72
17. 401.63	**18.** 23.176	**19.** 4.0187	**20.** 0.0081634
21. 0.14879	**22.** 1,963,200	**23.** 27,838	**24.** 0.00034271
25. 45,628	**26.** 7324.6	**27.** 692.48	**28.** 150.75
29. 300.24	**30.** 750.50	**31.** 41.3131	**32.** 5.89638
33. 105.782	**34.** 7.65168	**35.** 33.7025	**36.** 56.9013

47. Proportional parts: logarithm of a given number

The process of interpolation described in Article 46 is used in connection with tables of functions other than logarithms, as well as with tables of logarithms.

With Table I, however, there is a shortcut to the interpolation process afforded by the use of **proportional parts**.

Consider, for instance, Example 2 of Article 46. The problem is to find the logarithm of 6153.4, and here we show how to use proportional parts instead of the process described in Article 46.

Example 1. Find the logarithm of 6153.4

Solution. From the table,
$$\log 6154 = 3.789157,$$
$$\log 6153 = 3.789087.$$

The tabular difference is 0.000070, which may be found in the table of differences and which is written briefly as 70. When using the differences given in the tables, the student should subtract mentally the last digits of the mantissas to see whether this agrees with the last digit of the difference given in the table. In the table of proportional parts at the bottom of the page in the table, read across the page from 70 to the column headed 4. The entry found there is 28.0. This is the value of 0.4×70, that is, the multiplication has been performed and is entered in the table of proportional parts. The operation of multiplying 0.4×70 is thus eliminated by the use of the table of proportional parts.

Adding 0.000028 to 3.789087 (the logarithm of 6153), the final result is:
$$\log 6153.4 = 3.789115.$$

Example 2. Find the logarithm of 23.4526, using the table of proportional parts.

Solution. As before, the characteristic is 1. To find the mantissa, treat the number as if it were 2345.26, and prepare the form:

Number	Mantissa
2346	370328
2345	370143

The tabular difference is 185, which may be read directly from the table. In the table of proportional parts, read across the page from 185 to the column headed 2; the entry found there is 37. In the same row and in the column headed 6, we read 111.0, which should be divided by 10 and added to 37.0, giving 48.1. Adding 48 to 370143, and affixing the characteristic and inserting the decimal point, the final result is:

$$\log 23.452 = 1.370191.$$

NUMBER WHICH CORRESPONDS TO A GIVEN LOGARITHM

With a little practice, the student can locate the mantissas, find the tabular difference, use the table of proportional parts, and write the final logarithm without making any written calculations or entries other than the final result. This method of interpolating mentally is to be encouraged, since it is a timesaver.

If an entry in the table of proportional parts is, say, 59.4, it should be rounded off to 59; in the case of an entry such as 59.7, it should be rounded off to 60.

If, however, the entry is 59.5, the final logarithm should be rounded off so that its final digit is an even number. For example, if the mantissa in the table is 562055, we would have

$$\begin{array}{r} 562055 \\ 59.5 \\ \hline 562114.5, \end{array}$$

which would be rounded off to 562114, the final digit being an even number. On the other hand, if the mantissa were 562174, we would have

$$\begin{array}{r} 562174 \\ 59.5 \\ \hline 562233.5, \end{array}$$

which would be rounded off to 562234, the final digit being an even number.

EXERCISE 4

Find the logarithms of the following numbers, using the tables of proportional parts to effect the interpolation.

1. 1287.8	2. 2164.4	3. 3290.7	4. 4563.2	5. 9806.5
6. 7153.3	7. 5002.9	8. 453.62	9. 849.76	10. 77.421
11. 65.833	12. 4.1295	13. 7.0032	14. 0.91264
15. 0.80758	16. 0.076139	17. 0.061457	18. 96004
19. 0.00013476	20. 2,000,500	21. 1.06152	22. 8.64367
23. 4.10393	24. 246.217	25. 290.336	26. 136.606
27. 90.8898	28. 111.435	29. 6287.19	30. 5638.37

48. Number which corresponds to a given logarithm; interpolation

To find the number which corresponds to a given logarithm we use a method of interpolation illustrated in the following examples.

Example 1. Find N if $\log N = 2.847758$.

Solution. Disregard the characteristic for the moment. Look for 847758 in the table of mantissas. Find the number corresponding to this mantissa. In this case, the given mantissa actually is present in the table of mantissas, and the number corresponding to it is 7043. Place the decimal point in 7043 by reference to the characteristic of the given logarithm. The characteristic is 2, so there are three significant figures to the left of the decimal point. Therefore, $N = 704.3$.

Example 2. Find N if log $N = 3.156832$.

Solution. In this case, the mantissa 156832 does not appear in the table. However, it lies between 156549 and 156852. Prepare a table as follows:

$$\begin{array}{c|c} \text{Number} & \text{Mantissa} \\ \hline 1\begin{bmatrix} 1435 \\ x \begin{bmatrix} 1434 \end{bmatrix} \end{bmatrix} & \begin{bmatrix} 156852 \\ 156832 \\ 156549 \end{bmatrix} 283 \end{bmatrix} 303 \end{array}$$

Set up the proportion: $\quad \dfrac{x}{1} = \dfrac{283}{303}.$

Solve for x, rounding off to the nearest hundredth:

$$x = 0.93.$$

Annexing this decimal to 1434 gives 1434.93.

Since the characteristic of the given logarithm is 3, there are four digits to the left of the decimal point, and $N = 1434.93$.

Example 3. Find N if log $N = 5.826384$.

Solution. Disregard the characteristic for the moment and prepare an interpolation table as in Example 2.

$$\begin{array}{c|c} \text{Number} & \text{Mantissa} \\ \hline 1\begin{bmatrix} 6705 \\ x \begin{bmatrix} 6704 \end{bmatrix} \end{bmatrix} & \begin{bmatrix} 826399 \\ 826384 \\ 826334 \end{bmatrix} 50 \end{bmatrix} 65 \end{array}$$

$$\frac{x}{1} = \frac{50}{65},$$

$x = 0.77$, correct to nearest hundredth.

Without regard to the given characteristic, the number would be 6704.77. Since the characteristic is 5, there are six digits to the left of the decimal point. Hence $N = 670,477$.

Example 4. Find N if log $N = 7.516388 - 10$.

Solution. Proceeding as in Examples 2 and 3:

$$\begin{array}{c|c} \text{Number} & \text{Mantissa} \\ \hline 1\begin{bmatrix} 3284 \\ x \begin{bmatrix} 3283 \end{bmatrix} \end{bmatrix} & \begin{bmatrix} 516403 \\ 516388 \\ 516271 \end{bmatrix} 117 \end{bmatrix} 132 \end{array}$$

$$\frac{x}{1} = \frac{117}{132},$$

$x = 0.89$, to nearest hundredth.

NUMBER CORRESPONDING TO A GIVEN LOGARITHM 93

The number without regard to characteristic is 3283.89. Since the characteristic is 7 − 10, there are 2 zeros between the decimal point and the first significant figure to the right of the decimal point. Therefore, $N = 0.00328389$.

The number which corresponds to a given logarithm is called an **antilogarithm**.

EXERCISE 5

Find the number which corresponds to the given logarithm, using interpolation when necessary.

1. 2.561101	**2.** 8.876276 − 10	**3.** 9.372544 − 10
4. 5.934751	**5.** 3.168943	**6.** 2.827354
7. 4.434826	**8.** 1.143285	**9.** 0.928643
10. 9.178642 − 10	**11.** 8.326497 − 10	**12.** 7.016436 − 10
13. 6.945678 − 10	**14.** 1.806944	**15.** 3.500000
16. 1.765431	**17.** 7.216348	**18.** 6.502030
19. 2.650837 − 10	**20.** 5.109643 − 10	

49. Number corresponding to a given logarithm, by use of a table of proportional parts

As in the case of finding the logarithm of a given number, there is a short cut to the problem of interpolation in finding the number corresponding to a given logarithm, based on the tables of proportional parts.

Example 1. Find the number N corresponding to $\log N = 3.156832$, using the tables of proportional parts.

Solution. Disregard the characteristic for the moment and look for 156832 in the table of mantissas. It does not occur in the table, but it lies between 156549 and 156852. Prepare the form:

Number	Mantissa
1435	156852
	156832
1434	156549

Perform the subtraction: 156832
 156549
 ———
 283

The tabular difference is 303 according to the table. We need only verify the terminal digit to see that this is correct.

In the table of proportional parts, read across the page from 303 to the entry nearest to 283, but less than 283. The entry in this case is 272.7. At the top of the column containing 272.7 is 9. Subtract

272.7 from 283 obtaining 10.3. Multiplying by 10 we have 103. Now look in the same row (303 row) to find an entry as near to 103 as possible. We find 90.9 in the column marked 3. That is, the quotient $\frac{283}{303}$ is 0.93, correct to the nearest hundredth. Affixing 93 to the number 1434 gives 143493. Finally, determining the decimal point from the value of the given characteristic, which is 3 in this problem,

$$N = 1434.93.$$

The use of the table of proportional parts eliminates the operation of dividing 283 by 303 and rounding off the quotient to the nearest hundredth.

EXERCISE 6

Find the number corresponding to the given logarithm, using the tables of proportional parts.

1. 0.026058
2. 0.025306
3. 2.973817
4. 3.240960
5. 0.009945
6. 0.153596
7. 3.724144
8. 1.146287
9. 4.856268
10. 9.016034 − 10
11. 8.476532 − 10
12. 7.816004 − 10
13. 5.276028
14. 5.379982 − 10
15. 1.408928
16. 9.816437 − 10
17. 8.701659 − 10
18. 2.551430
19. 2.500000
20. 3.411689

50. Multiplication and division, using logarithms

Logarithms can be used to shorten the labor of problems involving multiplication and division. By formula (3) in Article 44,

$$\log m + \log n = \log mn.$$

That is, the sum of the logarithms of two numbers is equal to the logarithm of the product of the two numbers.

Example 1. Multiply 1254 by 4.246.

Solution.
$$\begin{aligned}
\log 1254 &= 3.098298 \\
\log 4.246 &= 0.627980 \\
\log N &= 3.726278 \\
N &= 5324.49
\end{aligned}$$

Example 2. Multiply: (345.6)(42.89)(7532).

Solution.
$$\begin{aligned}
\log 345.6 &= 2.538574 \\
\log 42.89 &= 1.632356 \\
\log 7532 &= 3.876910 \\
\log N &= 8.047840 \\
N &= 111{,}645{,}000
\end{aligned}$$

MULTIPLICATION AND DIVISION, USING LOGARITHMS

In each of these two examples, the sum of the logarithms of the factors is equal to the logarithm of the answer, and the answer is the number corresponding to the logarithm of the answer.

By formula (4) in Article 44,
$$\log m - \log n = \log \frac{m}{n}.$$

That is, the difference of the logarithms of two numbers is equal to the logarithm of the quotient of the two numbers.

Example 3. Divide 4350 by 216.482.

Solution.
$$\log 4350 = 3.638489$$
$$\log 216.482 = 2.335422$$
$$\log N = 1.303067$$
$$N = 20.0940.$$

In Example 3 we subtract the logarithms of the given numbers; the remainder is the logarithm of the answer, and the answer is the number corresponding to the logarithm of the answer.

Problems involving both multiplication and division can be solved by combining the methods shown above. Notice that in a certain sense the use of logarithms changes multiplication to addition and changes division to subtraction.

A special case of formula (4) is:
$$\log \frac{1}{x} = \log 1 - \log x = 0 - \log x = -\log x.$$

Thus, the logarithm of the reciprocal of a number is equal to the negative of the logarithm of the number.

The logarithm of the reciprocal of a number is called the **cologarithm** of the number. Thus,
$$\operatorname{colog} x = \log \frac{1}{x} = \log 1 - \log x = 0 - \log x.$$

To find the cologarithm of a number, subtract the logarithm of the number from zero. Since $10 - 10 = 0$, the work can be arranged as in the following example.

Example 4. Find the cologarithm of 8.653.

Solution.
$$\log 1 = 10.000000 - 10$$
$$\log 8.653 = \underline{0.937167}$$
$$\operatorname{colog} 8.653 = 9.062833 - 10.$$

Example 5. Use logarithms to find the value of:
$$\frac{22.83 \times 4.065}{1.628 \times 14.50}.$$

Solution.
$$\log 22.83 = 1.358506$$
$$\log\ 4.065 = \underline{0.609061}$$
$$\log \text{ numerator} = 1.967567$$
$$\log\ 1.628 = 0.211654$$
$$\log 14.50 = \underline{1.161368}$$
$$\log \text{ denominator} = 1.373022$$

$\log N = \log \text{ numerator} - \log \text{ denominator} = 0.594545,$
$N = 3.93138.$

It is a good idea to prepare a table of entries first and fill in the logarithms afterward. Thus in Example 5, the table of entries would be:

$$\log 22.83 =$$
$$\log\ 4.065 = \underline{\qquad}$$
$$\log \text{ numerator} =$$
$$\log\ 1.628 =$$
$$\log 14.50 = \underline{\qquad}$$
$$\log \text{ denominator} =$$
$$\log N =$$
$$N =$$

The use of cologarithms makes it possible to arrange the table of entries in Example 5 as follows:

$$\log 22.83\ \ = 1.358506$$
$$\log\ \ 4.065\ \ = 0.609061$$
$$\text{colog}\ \ 1.628\ \ = 9.788346 - 10$$
$$\text{colog}\ 14.50\ \ = 8.838632 - 10$$
$$\log N = 20.594545 - 20$$
$$N = 3.93138.$$

EXERCISE 7

Perform the indicated multiplications and divisions, using Table I.

1. 234.6×80.75
2. $5{,}678 \times 1{,}432$
3. 78.63×24.17
4. 8.063×7.952
5. 1.063×0.4378
6. $14{,}500 \times 0.0062463$
7. $0.07365 \times 1{,}580.8$
8. $23{,}080 \times 1{,}050.6$
9. $2{,}560 \times 0.18676$
10. 624.75×1.065
11. $4386 \div 1427$
12. $9002 \div 1.009$
13. $853.13 \div 1.7525$
14. $623.872 \div 1.0614$
15. $739.25 \div 2.78631$
16. $23.875 \div 4.06568$
17. $78.3242 \div 94.721$
18. $65{,}430.3 \div 14{,}672.6$
19. $199.20 \div 2268.75$
20. $46.253 \div 50.7545$
21. $0.152143 \times 593.25 \times 169.50$
22. $432.22 \times 0.008556 \times 1.06789$
23. $14{,}500 \times 3.0075 \times 227.907$
24. $43{,}118.1 \times 0.0165 \times 2.45344$
25. $1.1935 \times 0.0148363 \times 0.1701$
26. $\dfrac{453 \times 472.6 \times 0.08172}{634.783}$
27. $\dfrac{1.065 \times 84.75 \times 13.25}{8.008 \times 0.0162}$
28. $\dfrac{0.0954 \times 6.015 \times 32}{5.107 \times 8.693 \times 115}$

USE OF LOGARITHMS IN POWERS AND ROOTS

29. $\dfrac{43.150 \times 65 \times 0.00928}{73.2 \times 11.8 \times 0.01341}$ 30. $\dfrac{156.254}{1.008 \times 1.0065}$

51. Use of logarithms in powers and roots

By formula (5) in Article 44,

$$n \log m = \log m^n.$$

For example, $\quad 8 \log 2 = \log 2^8.$

This property can be used to calculate the value of a power of a number.

Example 1. Find the value of 3.24^6.

Solution.
$$\log 3.24 = 0.510545$$
$$6 \log 3.24 = 3.063270.$$

Since the logarithm of 3.24, given above, may be in error by as much as 0.0000005 due to rounding off, 6 log 3.24 may be in error by as much as 6(0.0000005) or 0.0000030. Thus we are certain of accuracy to only 5 significant places. We then have,

$$(3.24)^6 = 1156.8.$$

In certain types of problems in mathematics of finance, it is necessary to calculate the values of expressions such as $(1+i)^n$, where i is a rate of interest. In using logarithms the expression $n \log (1+i)$ is involved and hence the error in $\log (1+i)$ is multiplied by n. In general, multiplication by n reduces the accuracy by as many places as there are digits in n. The use of Table II, a seven-place table of mantissas from 10000 to 11009, will give more accurate results for such problems.

Example 2. Find the value of 1.063^{24}.

Solution. $\quad \log 1.063 = 0.0265333$, from Table II.
$\quad\quad\quad\quad\quad 24 \log 1.063 = 0.6367992.$

Since the accuracy may be cut two places in this example, we use only 5 places in the logarithm; however, it is usual to use 6 places to find the antilogarithm and then round off to 5 significant figures. Following this procedure we have

$$1.063^{24} = 4.3331 \text{ from Table II}.$$

Example 3. Multiply: 4850×1.063^{24}.

Solution.
$$\log 4850 = 3.685742$$
$$\log 1.063^{24} = 0.636799$$
Adding $\quad\quad\quad\quad \log N = \overline{4.322541}.$

Rounding off to 4 significant figures,

$$N = 21.016.$$

98 LOGARITHMS

Example 4. Multiply: 4850×1.063^{-24}.

Solution.
$$4850 \times 1.063^{-24} = 4850 \times \frac{1}{1.063^{24}},$$
$$= \frac{4850}{1.063^{24}}.$$

$$\log 4850 = 3.685749$$
$$\log 1.063^{24} = 0.636799$$

Subtracting, $\log N = \overline{3.048943}$

Rounding the answer off to 4 places we have

$$N = 119.3.$$

In Example 4, notice that multiplication by 1.063^{-24} is equivalent to division by 1.063^{24}.

Since $a^{\frac{p}{q}} = \sqrt[q]{a^p}$, as defined in Article 33, logarithms can be used to extract roots.

Example 5. Find the square root of 327.8.

Solution.
$$\sqrt{327.8} = (327.8)^{\frac{1}{2}}.$$
$$\log 327.8 = 2.515609,$$
$$\tfrac{1}{2} \log 327.8 = 1.257804,$$
$$\sqrt{327.8} = 18.1052.$$

Example 6. Find the cube root of 327.8.

Solution.
$$\sqrt[3]{327.8} = (327.8)^{\frac{1}{3}}.$$
$$\log 327.8 = 2.515609,$$
$$\tfrac{1}{3} \log 327.8 = 0.838536,$$
$$\sqrt[3]{327.8} = 6.89503.$$

While logarithms can be used to effect multiplication, division, raising to powers, and extracting roots, they cannot be used to effect additions and subtractions. The following example illustrates what can be done in such cases:

Example 7. Find the value of $\dfrac{(1.0125)^{18} - 1}{0.0125}$.

Solution.
$$\log 1.0125 = 0.0053950 \text{ (from Table II)}.$$
$$18 \log 1.0125 = 0.097110,$$
$$1.0125^{18} = 1.2506,$$

where only 5 significant figures are retained since the logarithm of 1.0125 was multiplied by a two-digit number, thus cutting the accuracy from seven places to five places.

$$1.0125^{18} - 1 = 0.2506,$$
$$\log (1.0125^{18} - 1) = 9.398981 - 10,$$
$$\log 0.0125 = 8.096910 - 10,$$
$$\log N = 1.302071.$$
$$N = 20.05.$$

EXPONENTIAL EQUATIONS

It should be noted that only four significant figures are retained in the answer. In a series of multiplications or divisions with approximate numbers, the answer should be given to not more significant figures than the least accurate of the various components used to obtain the answer.

EXERCISE 8

Use logarithms to find the value of:

1. 34.2^3 2. 1.68^7 3. 0.0243^4 4. 8.246^3 5. 432.7^2
6. 4.065^8 7. 16.246^3 8. 2.5061^4 9. 0.168582^3 10. 25.8243^3

Use Tables I and II to find the value of:

11. 1.02^{15} 12. 1.055^{16} 13. 1.043^8 14. 1.027^{24} 15. 1.012^{36}
16. 1.016^{-5} 17. 1.068^{-8} 18. 1.072^{-16} 19. 1.0556^{-12} 20. 1.0415^{-18}

Perform the indicated operations, using Tables I and II:

21. 4925×1.062^{25} 22. $385.60 \times 1.0416^{20}$ 23. 87.65×1.072^{30}
24. 1736×1.066^{8} 25. 4500×1.083^{16} 26. 5250×1.092^{-12}
27. 4800×1.078^{-10} 28. $3750.46 \times 1.0483^{-6}$
29. $68{,}500 \times 1.0415^{-30}$ 30. $785.75 \times 1.028^{-30}$

Use logarithms to find the values of the indicated roots:

31. $\sqrt{16.84}$ 32. $\sqrt{9.82}$ 33. $\sqrt{432.7}$
34. $\sqrt{18{,}412}$ 35. $\sqrt{0.1673}$ 36. $\sqrt[3]{260}$
37. $\sqrt[3]{42.78}$ 38. $\sqrt[3]{1.06482}$
39. $\sqrt[3]{4286}$ 40. $\sqrt[3]{0.0148}$

Use logarithms to find the value of the following expressions. Use Table II in Problems 46–50.

41. $1.04^{\frac{1}{3}}$ 42. $1.06^{\frac{2}{3}}$ 43. $1.07^{\frac{3}{4}}$ 44. $1.05^{\frac{1}{6}}$
45. $1.082^{\frac{1}{4}}$ 46. $\dfrac{(1 + 0.06)^{18} - 1}{0.06}$
47. $\dfrac{(1 + 0.024)^{16} - 1}{0.024}$ 48. $\dfrac{1 - (1 + 0.046)^{-20}}{0.046}$
49. $\dfrac{1 - (1 + 0.038)^{-10}}{0.038}$ 50. $\dfrac{(1 + 0.0636)^{20} - 1}{0.0636}$

52. Exponential equations; another type of equation

Logarithms can be used to solve certain types of equations in which the unknown appears as an exponent.

Example 1. Solve for x: $1.04^x = 1.5$.

Solution. $1.04^x = 1.5$.

Taking logarithms of both members of the equation,

$$\log 1.04^x = \log 1.5.$$

Since $\log m^n = n \log m$,

$$x \log 1.04 = \log 1.5.$$

Dividing both members by $\log 1.04$,

$$x = \frac{\log 1.5}{\log 1.04}.$$

Therefore,

$$x = \frac{0.176091}{0.0170333}, \text{ (using Table II for log 1.04)}.$$

The division can be effected by logarithms,

$$\log 0.176091 = 9.245737 - 10$$
$$\log 0.0170333 = 8.231299 - 10$$
$$\log x = 1.014438.$$
$$x = 10.3380.$$

Example 2. Solve for x: $1.05^x = \frac{3000}{2546}$.

Solution.
$$1.05^x = \frac{3000}{2546}.$$

$$\log 1.05^x = \log \frac{3000}{2546},$$

$$x \log 1.05 = \log 3000 - \log 2546,$$

$$x = \frac{\log 3000 - \log 2546}{\log 1.05},$$

$$= \frac{3.477121 - 3.405858}{0.0211893},$$

$$= \frac{0.071263}{0.0211893}.$$

$$\log 0.071263 = 8.852864 - 10$$
$$\log 0.0211893 = 8.326117 - 10$$
$$\log x = 0.526747.$$
$$x = 3.36316.$$

The student should observe the difference in meaning between $\frac{\log a}{\log b}$ and $\log \frac{a}{b}$; the former represents the quotient of the logarithms of two numbers, and the latter represents the logarithm of the quotient of two numbers.

EXPONENTIAL EQUATIONS

Example 3. Solve for x: $280 = 360\,(1.02)^{-x}$.

Solution.
$$280 = 360\,(1.02)^{-x},$$
$$\frac{280}{360} = 1.02^{-x},$$
$$\frac{360}{280} = 1.02^{x},$$
$$\log \frac{360}{280} = \log 1.02^{x},$$
$$\log \frac{360}{280} = x \log 1.02,$$
$$\frac{\log 360 - \log 280}{\log 1.02} = x,$$
$$\frac{2.556303 - 2.447158}{0.0086002} = x,$$
$$\frac{0.109145}{0.0086002} = x.$$

This division can be effected by logarithms:
$$\log 0.109145 = 9.038004 - 10$$
$$\log 0.0086002 = 7.934508 - 10$$
$$\log x = 1.103496.$$
$$x = 12.691.$$

Another type of equation, not of the exponential type, can be solved by logarithms. This type occurs frequently in problems of mathematics and finance, and it will be illustrated by examples:

Example 4. Solve for x: $(1 + x)^5 = 1.24$.

Solution.
$$(1 + x)^5 = 1.24.$$
Taking the logarithms of both members of the equation,
$$\log (1 + x)^5 = \log 1.24.$$
By formula (5) of Article 44,
$$5 \log (1 + x) = \log 1.24.$$
Therefore
$$\log (1 + x) = \frac{\log 1.24}{5},$$
$$\log (1 + x) = \frac{0.093422}{5} = 0.018684,$$
$$1 + x = 1.04396,$$
$$x = 0.04396.$$

Example 5. Solve for x: $2000 = 800\,(1 + x)^{30}$.

Solution.

$$2000 = 800(1+x)^{30}$$
$$\log 2000 = \log 800(1+x)^{30},$$
$$\log 2000 = \log 800 + 30 \log(1+x),$$
$$\log 2000 - \log 800 = 30 \log(1+x),$$
$$\frac{\log 2000 - \log 800}{30} = \log(1+x),$$
$$\frac{3.301030 - 2.903090}{30} = \log(1+x),$$
$$0.013265 = \log(1+x),$$
$$1.03101 = 1 + x,$$
$$0.03101 = x.$$

EXERCISE 9

Solve for x:

1. $1.02^x = 2$
2. $1.06^x = 2$
3. $1.05^x = 1.5$
4. $1.01^x = 3$
5. $1.025^x = 6.50$
6. $1.035^x = 7.25$
7. $2500(1.03)^x = 3150$
8. $1785(1.02)^x = 2168$
9. $1.07^x = \dfrac{8100}{6450}$
10. $1.03^x = \dfrac{5166}{4287}$
11. $1.02^{-x} = 0.98$
12. $1.06^{-x} = 0.75$
13. $\dfrac{1.028^x - 1}{0.028} = 30.43$
14. $\dfrac{1 - 1.026^{-x}}{0.026} = 21.5$
15. $(1+x)^{19} = 2$
16. $(1+x)^{16} = 1.534$
17. $(1+x)^{28} = \dfrac{4000}{3000}$
18. $(1+x)^{40} = \dfrac{5500}{1800}$
19. $2800 = 2400(1+x)^{18}$
20. $2200 = 860(1+x)^{42}$

53. Other bases for logarithms

In Article 42 it was pointed out that the number 10 is the base of the system of common logarithms. Numbers other than 10 can be used as the base of a system of logarithms; in fact any positive number, except 1, can be used for this purpose.

Consider a system of logarithms with the number 2 as the base. Then,

$$\log_2 4 = 2 \text{ because } 2^2 = 4,$$
$$\log_2 8 = 3 \text{ because } 2^3 = 8,$$
$$\log_2 16 = 4 \text{ because } 2^4 = 16, \text{ and so on.}$$

Two of the main advantages of using 10 as the base are that:
1. The characteristic is easily determined.
2. The mantissa is the same for all numbers having the same sequence of digits.

CALCULATION OF LOGARITHMS

Another base of great importance is the number e, where $e = 2.71828$, approximately. A more accurate value is

$$e = 2.718281828459045,$$

which is correct to 16 significant digits.

Logarithms to the base e are usually called **natural** logarithms, and are sometimes called **Napierian logarithms,** after their inventor, John Napier. Natural logarithms are used extensively in higher mathematics. Logarithms to the base 10 are sometimes called Briggsian logarithms, after their inventor, Henry Briggs.

The relation between the common logarithm of a number and its natural logarithm is given by

$$\log N = 0.434329 \log_e N,$$

where 0.434329 is the value of $\log_{10} e$.

The number e can be defined by the unending series

$$e = 1 + \frac{1}{1} + \frac{1}{1 \cdot 2} + \frac{1}{1 \cdot 2 \cdot 3} + \frac{1}{1 \cdot 2 \cdot 3 \cdot 4} + \frac{1}{1 \cdot 2 \cdot 3 \cdot 4 \cdot 5} + \cdots,$$

but a complete discussion of the number e, and the reasons why natural logarithms are useful, is beyond the scope of this book.

54. Calculation of logarithms

The natural logarithm of a number n can be calculated by substituting the value of n in the unending series.

$$\log_e n - \log_e(n-1) = \frac{1}{n} + \frac{1}{2n^2} + \frac{1}{3n^3} + \cdots$$

where $n > +1$, and $n < -1$.

The common logarithm of the number can be obtained by multiplying the natural logarithm by 0.434329. (A more accurate value, correct to 8 significant digits, is 0.43429448.)

Example. Calculate the common logarithm of 3.

Solution. Instead of letting $n = 3$, use $n = 10$. Then ...

$$\log_{10} 10 - \log_{10} 9 = 0.434329 \left(\frac{1}{10} + \frac{1}{2(10)^2} + \frac{1}{3(10)^3} + \cdots \right),$$

$$= 0.434329 \,(0.1 + 0.005 + 0.000333 +$$
$$0.000025 + 0.000002 + 0.000000167 + \cdots).$$

$$1 - \log_{10} 9 = 0.0457575,$$
$$1 - \log_{10} 3^2 = 0.0457575,$$
$$1 - 2 \log_{10} 3 = 0.0457575,$$
$$2 \log_{10} 3 = 0.9542425,$$
$$\log_{10} 3 = 0.477121.$$

MISCELLANEOUS EXERCISE

1. Since $3^2 = 9$, what is the logarithm of 9 to the base 3?
2. Since $2^5 = 32$, what is the logarithm of 32 to the base 2?
3. What is the common logarithm of 1? 10? 100? $\frac{1}{10}$?

If $\log 8 = 0.903090$ and $\log 5 = 0.698970$, find the logarithms of the following numbers, using only these two logarithms and the properties of logarithms in Article 44:

4. 40   5. 25   6. 1.6   7. 9.625   8. $\sqrt{5}$ 9. 2   10. 200

11. Find x to 4 significant digits if $\log x = 9.407129 - 10$.
12. Find i to 3 significant digits if $(1 + i)^{-10} = 0.8203$.
13. Using the properties of logarithms, find x if $\log x = \log 3 + \log 4$.
14. Find the value of x to 5 significant digits if $\log x = 3.820613$.
15. Compute the value of $\dfrac{(\sqrt{165})(\sqrt[3]{82})}{45^2}$ by logarithms, to 4 significant figures.
16. Write in the logarithmic form the equation $y = 10^x$.
17. Find the value of $S = P(1 + i)^n$ if $P = 400$, $i = 0.05$, $n = 8$.
18. Find the value of $P = S(1 + i)^{-n}$ if $S = 590.98$, $i = 0.05$, $n = 8$.
19. Solve for x: $3^{x+2} = 5$.
20. Find the value of $\dfrac{(1 + i)^n - 1}{i}$ if $i = 0.04$, $n = 10$.

7

Simple Interest and Discount

55. Simple interest

The following definitions are basic in the discussion of simple interest:

1. **Interest** is the sum received (or paid) for the use of capital. Interest and capital are expressed in terms of units of money.
2. The sum borrowed (or loaned) is called the **principal.**
3. The **time** is the number of years or fraction of a year, for which the principal is borrowed (or loaned).
4. The **rate of interest** is the quotient obtained by dividing the interest per unit of time by the principal, and is expressed as a decimal or as a per cent.
5. The **amount** is the sum of the principal and the interest.

For example, if a man borrows $100 for two years at 6%, the principal is $100, the time is two years, and the rate of interest is 6%.

The following symbols are used for these fundamental quantities:

P = principal in dollars (or other units of money)
n = time in years
i = rate of interest in decimal form
I = interest in dollars (or other units of money)
S = amount in dollars (or other units of money).

The definitions of interest and amount lead to the following formulas:

$$I = Pni, \qquad (1)$$
and, $$S = P + I. \qquad (2)$$

Substituting Pni for I in (2) yields $S = P + Pni$, or

$$S = P(1 + ni). \qquad (3)$$

These formulas can be used to calculate the interest on a stated principal for a given time at a given rate, and to find the amount.

Interest computed in this way is called simple interest, as contrasted with compound interest, which will be discussed in a later chapter.

Example 1. Find the simple interest on $200 for 3 years at 5%.

Solution. Since $I = Pni$, we have
$$I = (200)(3)(0.05),$$
$$= \$30.$$

Example 2. Find the simple interest on $500 for 2 months at 6%, and find the amount.

Solution. Using formula (1),
$$I = (500)(\tfrac{2}{12})(0.06),$$
$$= \$5.$$
Since $\quad\quad\quad\quad\quad S = P + I,$
then $\quad\quad\quad\quad\quad S = 500 + 5,$
$$= \$505.$$

This second result may have been obtained by using formula (3). We obtain
$$S = 500[1 + (\tfrac{2}{12})(0.06)],$$
$$= \$505.$$

It is helpful to use a line graph to illustrate the conditions of the problem. The line graph for Example 2 is:

$500	2 months	
P	6%	S

When the amount, S, has been calculated, it is placed above the S in the line graph. The graph emphasizes the fact that $500 at the beginning of the two-month period is equivalent to $505 at the end of that period if interest is figured at 6%.

Formulas (1), (2), and (3) are the basic formulas for problems involving simple interest. Sometimes it is necessary to solve for quantities other than I or S in these formulas, that is, to change the subjects of the formulas. Thus, the basic formula, $I = Pni$, can be written

$$P = \frac{I}{ni}, \quad n = \frac{I}{Pi}, \quad i = \frac{I}{Pn}.$$

The formula, $S = P(1 + ni)$, can be written

$$P = \frac{S}{1 + ni},$$

or it can be solved for n or i. The student should practice the changing of the subjects of these formulas as an exercise in algebra.

SIMPLE INTEREST

Example 3. A principal of $3000 earns $120 in interest in 1 year. What is the interest rate?

Solution. First method. From the formula, $I = Pni$, we obtain the formula:

$$i = \frac{I}{Pn},$$

hence, $$i = \frac{120}{(3000)(1)} = 0.04,$$

which, in per cent form, is expressed as 4%.

Second method. By substituting directly in $I = Pni$ we have,

$$120 = (3000)(1)(i),$$

or $$\frac{120}{(3000)(1)} = i,$$

so $$0.04 = i.$$

Example 4. How much should a person lend at 5% in order to have $645 at the end of $1\frac{1}{2}$ years?

Solution. The line graph is as follows:

	$1\frac{1}{2}$ years	$645
P	5%	S

First method. From the formula, $S = P(1 + ni)$, we have

$$P = \frac{S}{1 + ni}.$$

Therefore $$P = \frac{645}{1 + (1\frac{1}{2})(.05)},$$
$$= \$600.$$

Second method. By substituting directly in formula (3),

$$645 = P[1 + (1\frac{1}{2})(1.05)],$$
or $$645 = P(1.075).$$

Hence $$P = \frac{645}{1.075},$$
$$= \$600.$$

EXERCISE I

1. Find the interest on $5000 for 2 years at 5%, and find the amount.
2. Calculate the simple interest on $2400 for 3 years at 7%.
3. If $n = 2$ years, $P = \$875$, and $i = 0.05$, find I and S.
4. If $n = \frac{1}{4}$ year, $P = \$450$, and $i = 0.045$, find I and S.
5. Find the interest on $280 for 4 months at $4\frac{1}{2}$%.
6. Mr. W. C. Smith borrows $300 from Mr. A. L. Johnson for 8 months at 6%. How much does he pay Mr. Johnson at the end of 8 months?
7. Calculate the amount, if the principal is $1350, the time is 6 months, and the rate is $5\frac{1}{4}$%.

SIMPLE INTEREST AND DISCOUNT

8. Mr. R. C. Agnew lends $400 for 1 year and 3 months at $6\frac{1}{2}\%$. How much does he receive at the end of that time?

9. What is the interest on $325 for 1 year and 4 months at 5%?

10. Find the amount of $225 in 4 months at 6%.

11. If the principal is $400 and the interest is $4 for 3 months, find the rate.

12. What principal will amount to $4680 in 8 months at 6%?

13. If $P = \$350$ and $I = \$15.75$ for 1 year, find i.

14. Solve $S = P(1 + ni)$ for n; for i.

15. Find the principal if the amount is $2257.50 at the end of 1 year and 6 months.

16. What principal will amount to $252.13 in 5 months at 4%?

17. What is the rate if $280 amounts to $284.20 in three months?

18. The sum of $4000 is invested for 9 months at 5%. What is the amount?

19. Mr. R. B. Atkins invests some of his money in bonds that pay $3\frac{1}{2}\%$ interest. If he receives $43.75 per month from the investment how much did he invest in the bonds?

20. In what time will $800 earn $4 at 6%?

56. Methods of counting time.

In the formulas $I = Pni$ and $S = P(i + ni)$, n is the time in years.

If the time is expressed in days, there are two methods of counting the number of days, and the two methods are called **exact time** and **approximate time**.

In exact time, the exact number of days between the two given dates is used. For example, to count the exact time from May 4 to November 20, we can proceed as follows:

May	27 days	$(31 - 4)$
June	30 days	
July	31 days	
August	31 days	
September	30 days	
October	31 days	
November	20 days	
Total	200 days.	

Observe that we do not count the first day (May 4), but we do count the last day (November 20). Thus the time from May 4 to May 5 is one day, the time from May 4 to May 6 is 2 days and so on.

Special consideration must be given to February in leap years. For example, the time from February 3, 1948 to March 10, 1948 is:

February	26 days
March	10 days
Total	36 days.

METHODS OF COUNTING TIME

An alternate method of computing the exact number of days between two given dates is based on the use of Table III.

To find the exact number of days from May 4 to November 20, locate May 4 in the table. There we find that May 4 is the 124th day of the year. Next, locate November 20 in the table; it is the 324th day of the year. Subtracting, $324 - 124 = 200$, the exact number of days from May 4 to November 20. For leap years, the number of each day is one greater than the number found in the table for dates after February 28.

Sometimes approximate time is used instead of exact time. In this case it is assumed that each month has 30 days. To find the approximate time from May 4 to November 20, we proceed as follows:

May	26 days $(30 - 4)$
June	30 days
July	30 days
August	30 days
September	30 days
October	30 days
November	20 days
Total	196 days.

We observe that the approximate time in this case is less than the exact time, which is usually the case, although in some cases the two are equal.

Another way of finding approximate time is to subtract as follows:

$$11 - 20 \text{ (November 20)}$$
$$\underline{5 - 4} \text{ (May 4)}$$
$$6 - 16.$$

The approximate time is 6 months and 16 days, and since we assume that each month has 30 days, the approximate time is $6(30) + 16 = 196$ days. Likewise to find the approximate time from August 28, 1946 to January 3, 1948, we first write

$$1948 - 1 - 3 \text{ (January 3, 1948)}$$
$$1946 - 8 - 28 \text{ (August 28, 1946)},$$

and then change this to the following, and subtract:

$$1947 - 12 - 33 \text{ (January 3, 1940)}$$
$$\underline{1946 - 8 - 28} \text{ (August 28, 1946)}$$
$$1 - 4 - 5.$$

The approximate time is 1 year, 4 months, and 5 days or $360 + 4(30) + 5 = 485$ days.

EXERCISE 2

Find the exact time, using Table III:
1. From May 15 to July 2
2. From March 26 to June 16
3. From January 29 to August 5
4. From December 10 to December 31
5. From March 16, 1947 to February 10, 1948
6. From May 28, 1945 to June 5, 1948
7. From February 6, 1946 to December 2, 1946
8. From June 24, 1947 to February 3, 1948
9. From January 10, 1948 to July 8, 1948
10. From November 30, 1947 to April 6, 1948

Find the approximate time:
11. From March 11 to November 2
12. From May 1 to December 8
13. From August 28 to October 3
14. From August 28 to October 31
15. From July 5 to November 7
16. From January 2, 1946 to March 8, 1948
17. From October 30, 1946 to January 2, 1948
18. From July 26, 1947 to February 10, 1948
19. From June 15, 1945 to August 7, 1947
20. From August 2, 1947 to May 9, 1948

57. Ordinary and exact interest

Simple interest is used chiefly for short-term obligations. If the time is measured in days, there are two kinds of simple interest; one is called **ordinary simple interest,** and the other is called **exact simple interest.**

In ordinary simple interest, a year is considered to be 360 days; in exact simple interest, a year is considered to be 365 days.

Since there are two ways of counting time — exact time and approximate time — and two kinds of simple interest — ordinary simple and exact simple interest — four different cases may arise:

1. Ordinary simple interest, with exact time.
2. Ordinary simple interest, with approximate time.
3. Exact simple interest, with exact time.
4. Exact simple interest, with approximate time.

Generally, the first method above is more favorable for the creditor than any of the other methods, since the exact time is greater than,

ORDINARY AND EXACT INTEREST

or equal to, the approximate time, and ordinary interest is greater than exact interest for the same time, as will be shown presently.

Of the four methods of computing simple interest, it can be said that the first method is used most extensively by far, followed by the others in the order given above. In fact the fourth method is seldom used, excepting by agreement between individuals. If nothing is said or implied to the contrary, it is understood that ordinary simple interest will be calculated with exact time, and also that exact simple interest will be computed in the same way.

We begin with a discussion and comparison of ordinary and exact simple interest.

Let
- t = number of days
- P = principal
- i = rate of interest
- I_o = ordinary simple interest
- I_e = exact simple interest.

Since $I = Pni$, where n is the time in years, it follows that

$$I_o = \frac{Pti}{360}, \qquad (4)$$

and

$$I_e = \frac{Pti}{365}. \qquad (5)$$

Example 1. Find the ordinary simple interest on $300 for 30 days at 4%.

Solution. By formula (4), $I_o = \frac{Pti}{360}$,

hence
$$I_o = \frac{(300)(30)(0.04)}{360},$$
$$= \$1.00.$$

Example 2. Find the exact simple interest on $300 for 30 days at 4%.

Solution. By formula (5), $I_e = \frac{Pti}{365}$,

hence
$$I_e = \frac{(300)(30)(0.04)}{365},$$
$$= \$0.99.$$

Observe that I_e is less than I_o for the above two examples. Comparison of formulas (4) and (5) shows that, for the same values of P, t, i, the value of I_o is obtained by dividing the product Pti by 360, and I_e is obtained by dividing the same product by 365. Hence I_e is is less than I_o.

SIMPLE INTEREST AND DISCOUNT

The exact relation between I_e and I_o can be obtained as follows:

$$\frac{I_e}{I_o} = \frac{\dfrac{Pti}{365}}{\dfrac{Pti}{360}} = \frac{360}{365} = \frac{72}{73}, \qquad (6)$$

that is, $\qquad I_e = \dfrac{72}{73} I_o = I_o - \dfrac{1}{73} I_o.$ $\qquad\qquad (7)$

Thus, to compute the exact simple interest we may compute the ordinary simple interest and then reduce this amount by $\frac{1}{73}$ of itself.

Example 3. Find the ordinary simple interest on $400 for 90 days at 5%; find the exact simple interest.

Solution. $\qquad I_o = \dfrac{Pti}{360} = \dfrac{(400)(90)(0.05)}{360},$

$\qquad\qquad = \$5.00.$

$\qquad I_e = I_o - \dfrac{1}{73} I_o = 5 - \dfrac{1}{73}(5) = 5 - 0.07,$

$\qquad\qquad = \$4.93.$

The following examples will illustrate how ordinary and exact simple interest can be calculated for either exact or approximate time.

Example 4. Find the ordinary simple interest on $500 at 4% from March 2, 1948 to May 6, 1948, using exact time.

Solution. Using Table III, the exact time from March 2, 1948 to May 6, 1948 is 65 days.

$$I_o = \frac{Pti}{360} = \frac{(500)(65)(0.04)}{360},$$
$$= \$3.61.$$

Example 5. Find the ordinary simple interest on $1000 at 5% from March 16, 1948 to June 6, 1948, using the approximate time.

Solution. The approximate time from March 16, 1948 to June 6, 1948 can be found as follows:

$\qquad\qquad 1948 - 6 - 6$ (June 6, 1948)
$\qquad\qquad 1948 - 3 - 16$ (March 16, 1948)

which can be changed to

$\qquad\qquad 1948 - 5 - 36$
$\qquad\qquad \underline{1948 - 3 - 16}$
$\qquad\qquad\qquad\quad 2 - 20.$

The approximate time is 2 months and 20 days, or $2(30) + 20 = 80$ days.

$$I_o = \frac{Pti}{360} = \frac{(1000)(80)(0.05)}{360},$$
$$= \$11.11.$$

ORDINARY AND EXACT INTEREST

Example 6. Find the exact simple interest on $800 at 6% from May 8, 1947 to November 6, 1947, using the exact time.

Solution. From Table III the exact time from May 8, 1947 to November 6, 1947 is 182 days.

$$I_e = \frac{Pti}{365} = \frac{(800)(182)(0.06)}{365}.$$

Using logarithms for the computation, we have

$$I_e = \$23.93.$$

Example 7. Find the exact simple interest on $600 at 5% from January 3, 1947 to December 10, 1947, using approximate time.

Solution. The approximate time may be found as follows:

$$\begin{array}{r} 1947 - 12 - 10 \quad (\text{December 10, 1947}) \\ 1947 - 1 - 3 \quad (\text{January 3, 1947}) \\ \hline 11 - 7. \end{array}$$

The approximate time is 11 months and 7 days, or $11(30) + 7 = 337$ days. Hence

$$I_e = \frac{Pti}{365} = \frac{(600)(337)(0.05)}{365}.$$

Using logarithms for the computation,

$$I_e = \$27.70.$$

When ordinary simple interest is computed with exact time, the method is commonly called the **Banker's Rule**.

In applications of simple interest in practical business situations, ordinary simple interest by the Banker's Rule is used if nothing is said, or implied, to the contrary. If other methods are to be used it is necessary to specify exactly which method and whether approximate or exact time is to be used.

EXERCISE 3

Find the ordinary simple interest, using the exact time (Banker's Rule); also find the exact simple interest, using the exact time:

1. $P = \$800$, $i = 0.06$; from May 3, 1947 to November 30, 1947
2. $P = \$1600$, $i = 0.05$; from March 6, 1948 to April 28, 1948
3. $P = \$500$, $i = 0.07$; from March 26, 1947 to January 9, 1948
4. $P = \$300$, $i = 0.06$; from June 6, 1947 to February 15, 1948
5. $P = \$900$, $i = 0.045$; from August 10, 1947 to March 30, 1948

Find the ordinary simple interest, using the approximate time; also find the exact simple interest, using the approximate time:

6. $P = \$2400$, $i = 6\%$; from March 3, 1946 to October 15, 1946
7. $P = \$150$, $i = 0.05$; from January 18, 1946 to January 10, 1947

8. $P = \$850$, $i = 0.04$; from March 2, 1948 to May 1, 1948

9. $P = \$1200$, $i = 4\frac{1}{2}\%$; from May 10, 1948 to July 3, 1948

10. $P = \$1500$, $i = 5\%$; from November 20, 1947 to May 2, 1948

11. Calculate the exact simple interest corresponding to the ordinary simple interest $80.75.

12. Calculate the ordinary simple interest corresponding to the exact simple interest $43.87.

13. The sum of $10,000 is invested at 5% from June 6, 1947 to December 18, 1947. Calculate the simple interest by each of the methods of Article 57.

14. The sum of $5000 is invested at 4% from June 12, 1947 to January 11, 1948. Calculate the interest by each of the methods of Article 57.

15. Find the ordinary and exact simple interest on $100 for 90 days at 5%.

16. Find the ordinary and exact simple interest on $100 for 60 days at 4%.

17. Show that the ordinary simple interest on P dollars for 60 days at 6% is $0.01P$ dollars.

18. Show that the ordinary simple interest on P dollars for 6 days at 6% is $0.001P$ dollars.

19. Show that $I_o = I_e + \frac{1}{72} I_e$.

20. Show that $I_o = \frac{73}{72} I_e$.

58. Sixty-day, 6% method for ordinary simple interest. Simple interest table.

Consider the computation of ordinary simple interest on a principal of P dollars for 60 days at 6%. Since $I_o = \dfrac{Pti}{360}$, we have

$$I_o = \frac{P(60)(0.06)}{360} = 0.01P. \qquad (8)$$

Example 1. Find the ordinary simple interest on $680 for 60 days at 6%.

Solution. Substituting in $I_o = 0.01P$, we have
$$I_o = (0.01)(680) = \$6.80.$$

Observe that since in this case $I_o = 0.01P$, the interest can be found by simply moving the decimal point two places to the left.

This method, with suitable modifications, can be used to simplify the calculation in many problems in simple interest, other than those for a 60-day period and other than those for which the rate is 6%. The following examples will illustrate the types of modification possible:

Example 2. Find the ordinary simple interest on $680 for 90 days at 6%.

Solution.   Interest on $680 for 60 days at 6%   6.80
Interest on $680 for 60 days at 3%
(one-half of the above)   3.40
Interest on $680 for 90 days at 6% $10.20.

Example 3. Find the ordinary simple interest on $680 for 60 days at 4%.

Solution.
Interest on $680 for 60 days at 6%	6.80
Interest on $680 for 60 days at 2%	2.27
Interest on $680 for 60 days at 4%	$4.53

In this solution, the interest at 2% is obtained by multiplying the interest at 6% by $\frac{1}{3}$, since 2% = $\frac{1}{3}$ of 6%. The interest at 4% is then obtained by subtracting the interest at 2% from the interest at 6%. The same result could be obtained by multiplying the interest at 6% by $\frac{2}{3}$, since 4% = $\frac{2}{3}$ of 6%.

Example 4. Find the ordinary simple interest on $680 for 82 days at 5%.

Solution.
Interest on $680 for 60 days at 6%	6.80
Interest on $680 for 20 days at 6%	2.27
Interest on $680 for 2 days at 6%	0.23
Interest on $680 for 82 days at 6%	9.30
Interest on $680 for 82 days at 1%	1.55
Interest on $680 for 82 days at 5%	$7.75

In this solution, notice that the interest for 20 days is $\frac{1}{3}$ of the interest for 60 days, the interest for 2 days is $\frac{1}{10}$ of the interest for 20 days, and the interest at 1% is $\frac{1}{6}$ of the interest at 6%.

Another special method of computing simple interest is by the use of specially prepared tables, of which Table IV is an example. Table IV gives the amount of ordinary and exact simple interest on 1000 at 1%.

Example 5. Find the ordinary and exact simple interest on $500 for 123 days at 3%.

Solution. From Table IV:
Ordinary interest on 1000 for 120 days at 1% =	3.3333333
Ordinary interest on 1000 for 3 days at 1% =	0.0833333
Ordinary interest on 1000 for 123 days at 1% =	3.4166666
Ordinary interest on 1000 for 123 days at 3% =	10.2499998
Ordinary interest on 500 for 123 days at 3% =	$5.12

Similarly, the exact interest by Table IV is found to be $5.05.

EXERCISE 4

Use the sixty-day, 6% method to find the simple interest on:

1. $460 for 90 days at 6%
2. $860 for 60 days at 4%
3. $950 for 120 days at 6%
4. $1200 for 30 days at 6%
5. $1000 for 30 days at 8%
6. $240 for 300 days at 6%
7. $650 for 15 days at 6%
8. $720 for 18 days at 6%
9. $800 for 36 days at 5%
10. $400 for 74 days at 6%
11. $200 for 93 days at 6%
12. $500 for 235 days at 6%

13. $600 for 312 days at 4% **14.** $900 for 345 days at 3%
15. $490 for 274 days at 3% **16.** $620 for 125 days at $7\frac{1}{2}$%

17. Find a short cut for computing the ordinary simple interest for 80 days at 9%.

18. Find a short cut for computing the ordinary simple interest for 90 days at 4%.

19. Find a short cut for computing the ordinary simple interest for 75 days at 5%.

20. Find a short cut for computing the ordinary simple interest for 120 days at $4\frac{1}{2}$%.

Use Table IV to find the ordinary and exact simple interest on:

21. $250 for 87 days at 5% **22.** $500 for 53 days at 6%
23. $125 for 61 days at 7% **24.** $2400 for 235 days at 2%

59. Present value and simple discount

The **present value** of a sum of money S, due in n years, is the principal P which must be invested now to amount to S in n years. If the rate of interest is i, then P can be found by substitution in the formula,

$$S = P(1 + ni).$$

It may be more convenient to have this formula solved for P, giving

$$P = \frac{S}{1 + ni}, \qquad (9)$$

which is the formula for the present value of S, at rate i and for time n.

The relation between P and S can be shown in the line diagram:

```
              n years
─────────────────────────────
P              i            S
```

Notice particularly that P refers to a sum of money at a certain date, and S refers to a sum of money in the future, with respect to the given date. That is, P refers to the present value and S refers to the future value.

The present value of $106 due in 1 year at 6% simple interest is $100, since $100 invested now at 6% will amount to $106 due in 1 year. In this case the line diagram is:

```
  $100        1 year        $106
─────────────────────────────────
   P             6             S
```

Example 1. Find the present value of $500 due in $1\frac{1}{2}$ years at 5% simple interest.

PRESENT VALUE AND SIMPLE DISCOUNT

Solution. The line graph is:

$$\overline{\underset{P}{}\underset{5\%}{\overset{1\frac{1}{2}\text{ years}}{}}\underset{S}{\overset{\$500}{}}}$$

Since formula (9) gives the present value, P, in terms of S, n, and i, we have

$$P = \frac{500}{1 + (1\frac{1}{2})(0.05)} = \frac{500}{1.075}.$$

By the use of logarithms,

$$P = \$465.12.$$

The **simple discount** on S is defined to be the difference $S - P$. Observe that the simple discount on S is equal to the simple interest on P for the same length of time. Observe also that in Example 1, $465.12 *now* is equivalent to $500 in *$1\frac{1}{2}$ years*, if money is worth 5%.

The phrase "to discount S for n years at a simple interest rate i" means to find the present value of S which is due at the end of n years, with the assumption that money can be invested at the simple interest rate i. The phrase "money is worth a certain per cent" means that money can be invested at that rate.

Example 2. Discount $800 for 2 years at 4% simple interest. What is the simple discount?

Solution. The line diagram is:

$$\overline{\underset{P}{}\underset{4\%}{\overset{2\text{ years}}{}}\underset{S}{\overset{\$800}{}}}$$

$$P = \frac{S}{1 + ni} = \frac{800}{1 + (2)(0.04)},$$
$$= \$740.74,$$

which is the required present value. The simple discount is

$$S - P = 800 - 740.74 = \$59.26.$$

EXERCISE 5

1. Find the present value of $2000 due in 2 years if money is worth 5%.

2. What is the present value of a debt of $500 due in 6 months if money can be invested at 4%?

3. Discount $900 for 8 months at 6% simple interest.

4. What is the present value, at 3%, of a debt of $1200 due in 10 months? What is the simple discount?

5. An investor expects to receive a dividend of $600 in 6 months. What is the present value of the dividend if money is worth 5%?

6. Mr. Carl Allen is given the choice of paying $3000 cash or $3300 at the end of a year for a home site. If money is worth 5%, which is the better proposition?

7. In a business transaction, Mr. Charles Brown agreed to pay Mr. A. M.

Carlson $4000 at the end of 9 months. If money is worth 5%, what should Mr. Brown pay now to cancel the debt? If money is worth 6%, what should he pay?

8. Compare the present values of $1000 due in 1 year at the rates 4%, 5%, and 6%.

9. Compare the present values of $1000 at 6% due in 1 year, 2 years, and 3 years.

10. Miss Gloria Dickinson is to receive $2000 from her parents on January 1, 1948. What is the value of this sum on June 1, 1947, if money is worth 4%? Use exact time and ordinary simple interest.

11. Using exact time and ordinary simple interest, how much is $500, due on November 10, 1948, worth on April 5, 1948 if interest is computed at 3%?

12. In buying a sloop, Mr. G. H. James is offered a price of $8000 cash or $8120 in 6 months. Which is more advantageous to Mr. James, if money is worth 3%?

13. On June 5, Mr. Dillon agrees to pay Mr. Wells $3000 on December 5. Find the value of this obligation on September 1, if money is worth 4%. Use the exact time and ordinary interest.

14. An obligation for $2000 dated today is due in 9 months. Find the value of this obligation 2 months from now, if money is worth 3%.

15. Mr. John Matthews receives a consignment of goods from the Owl Manufacturing Co. The company asks Mr. Matthews to pay $800 in 60 days, and Mr. Matthews offers to pay cash. From the standpoint of the company, what should they be willing to accept, assuming that they can invest their money at 4%?

60. Present value of a debt that bears interest

Suppose that A borrows P dollars from B and agrees to pay it back in 1 year with simple interest at the rate i. To be more specific, suppose that A borrows $100 from B and agrees to pay it back in 1 year with simple interest at 5%. In this case, $100 is the face value of the debt and $105 is the maturity value of the debt. The term of the debt is 1 year and the maturity date is 1 year from the date of the debt.

If A borrows $100 and agrees to repay $100 plus interest at 5% at the end of 1 year, it is possible that B may wish to find the present value of $105 at an interest rate different from 5%. In this case the present value of $105 at this different interest rate will not be equal to the face value of the debt, which is $100.

Example 1. A receives $1000 from B on January 8 and signs an agreement to pay $1000 plus simple interest at 5% at the end of 6 months. What is the face value of the debt? What is the maturity value? What is the term of the debt? What is the maturity date? If B can invest his money at 4%, what is the present value of the maturity value?

PRESENT VALUE OF A DEBT THAT BEARS INTEREST 119

Solution. Face value = $1000.
Maturity value = $P(1 + ni) = 1000[1 + (\frac{1}{2})(0.05)]$,
= $1025.
Term = 6 months.

Therefore, maturity date is July 8.

$$\text{Present value} = P = \frac{S}{1 + ni}.$$

$$P = \frac{1025}{1 + (\frac{1}{2})(0.04)},$$

= $1004.90.

In this example, two line diagrams will illustrate the situation. In finding the maturity value, the line diagram is

$1000	6 months	
P	5%	S

In finding the present value of the maturity value, the line diagram is

	6 months	$1025
P	4%	S

Example 2. What is the present value at 6% on March 1 of a debt of $800 due 6 months after February 1, if the debt bears interest at 4%?

Solution. To find the maturity value of the debt, the line diagram is:

$800	6 months	
P	4%	S

$S = P(1 + ni)$.
$S = 800[1 + (\frac{1}{2})(0.04)]$,
= 800(1.02),
= $816.

To find the present value of the maturity value, the line diagram is:

	5 months	$816
P	6%	S

$$P = \frac{S}{1 + ni} = \frac{816}{1 + (5/12)(0.06)},$$

= $796.10.

A line diagram that combines the two parts and shows the results is:

```
        |     6 months       |
        |       4%           |
        |                    |
        |    |  5 months  |  |
        |    |    5%      |  |
      Feb. 1  Mar. 1        Aug. 1
      $800   $796.10        $816
```

To find the present value of an interest-bearing debt:
1. Find the maturity value of the debt.
2. Find the present value of the maturity value.

EXERCISE 6

1. A. C. Atkins borrows $1000 on July 2 from R. W. Jones and signs an agreement to pay back the $1000 plus interest at 5% on October 5. What is the face value of the debt? What is its term? What is the maturity value? What is the present value of the debt on July 2 for a person who can invest his money at 4%?

2. Find the present value of a debt of $2000 bearing interest at 4% for 90 days if money is worth 3%.

3. Find the present value at 3% of a debt of $500 for 6 months bearing interest at 5%.

4. The Reliable Hardware Co. owes $1500 to the Ace Manufacturing Corporation, the debt maturing in 6 months with interest at 6%. Find the present value of the obligation if money is worth 5%.

5. What is the present value at 5% on June 12 of a debt of $900 due 8 months after April 12, if the debt bears interest at 6%? Use approximate time.

6. A debt of $1000 with interest at 6% is due in 8 months. Find the present value of the debt if money can be invested at 3%.

7. Solve for i:

$$P = \frac{S}{1 + ni}.$$

8. A. R. Robinson agrees to pay M. C. Smith $500 plus interest at 4% in 4 months. Find the maturity value of the debt. Find the value of the debt 1 month before its due date, if money can be invested at 3%.

9. A debt of $600 bears interest at 4% and is due in 6 months. Find the present value if money is worth 4%.

10. Find the present value of $2000 due in 35 days with interest at 6%, if money is worth 4%.

61. Bank discount

Banks commonly make short-term loans for which the borrower is required to sign a written agreement promising to pay a fixed sum of money at some future date. Such an agreement is called a **note**. The specified sum of money to be repaid is called the **face** of the note. The bank deducts from the face a certain per cent of it to determine the amount actually to be given to the borrower. The sum the borrower actually receives is called the **proceeds** of the note and the per cent used in figuring the deduction is called the **discount rate**. The amount of the deduction is called the **discount** and is commonly called the **bank discount**. The length of time that the note runs is called its **term**.

Example 1. John Smith signs a note for $200 due in 1 year. If the bank uses a discount rate of 6%, find the proceeds.

BANK DISCOUNT

Solution. The amount of the deduction, or discount, is

$$(0.06)(200) = \$12.00.$$

Hence $200 - 12.00 = \$188$
is the sum of money, or proceeds, received by Mr. Smith.

The discount rate must not be confused with the interest rate. Thus, in the above problem, Mr. Smith receives $188 for which he pays $12 for its use for one year. Hence the interest rate he pays is

$$i = \frac{12}{188} = 0.0638 \text{ or } 6.38\% \text{ approximately.}$$

To develop the general formulas, let

D = bank discount
S = maturity value
n = term in years
d = discount rate, expressed as a decimal
P_b = proceeds.

Then $\qquad D = Snd,$ (10)
and $\qquad P_b = S - D.$
Hence $\qquad P_b = S - Snd = S(1 - nd).$ (11)

The **maturity value** of a note is the amount needed to cancel the note when it becomes due. Hence the maturity value of a noninterest bearing note is its face value. The maturity value of an interest-bearing note is equal to the sum of the face value and the amount of the interest. If the term of the note is expressed in months, it is customary to use a 12-month year. If the term of the note is expressed in days, it is customary to use a 360-day year.

Example 2. A note due on September 2 and dated March 2 was discounted on June 4. Find the proceeds, if the maturity value of the note is $1000 and the bank discount rate is 6%.

Solution. The exact number of days from June 4 to September 2, from Table III, is 90 days. We apply the formulas above as we would for a note made on June 4 and due in 90 days. Hence $S = 1000$, $n = \frac{90}{360} = \frac{1}{4}$, $d = 0.06$. We use formula (11) to find the proceeds P_b.

$$P_b = S(1 - nd) = 1000[1 - \tfrac{1}{4}(0.06)] = 1000(1 - 0.015),$$
$$= 1000(0.985) = \$985.00.$$

Example 3. A note for $2000 dated April 10 is due in 60 days and bears interest at 4%. If it is discounted on May 15 by a bank at a discount rate of 6%, find the proceeds.

SIMPLE INTEREST AND DISCOUNT

Solution.
$$\text{Interest on } \$2000 \text{ for } 60 \text{ days at } 4\% = (2000)(\tfrac{60}{360})(0.04),$$
$$= \$13.33.$$
Maturity value of note $= 2000 + 13.33 = \$2013.33$.
Due date (60 days from April 10) is June 9.
Exact number of days from May 15 to June 9 is 25 days.

We note that $S = 2013.33$, $n = \tfrac{25}{360}$, $d = 0.06$. The proceeds may be obtained as follows:
$$P_b = S(1 - nd) = 2013.33[1 - \tfrac{25}{360}(0.06)],$$
$$= \$2004.94.$$

If the proceeds of a non-interest bearing note are known, the face value of the note can be found. Solving the equation in (11) for S,

$$S = \frac{P_b}{1 - nd}. \tag{12}$$

Example 4. A 90-day note was discounted by a bank at a discount rate of 4%. The proceeds of the note were $1485. Assuming that the note is non-interest bearing, find its face value.

Solution. By use of formula (12) the face value S is
$$S = \frac{P_b}{1 - nd} = \frac{1485}{1 - \tfrac{90}{360}(0.04)} = \frac{1485}{1 - 0.01} = \frac{1485}{0.99},$$
$= \$1500.00$, which is the face value of the note.

EXERCISE 7

Find the proceeds of each of the following non-interest bearing notes:

1. Face value, $1500; date, May 16; term, 90 days; discount rate, 6%; date of discount, May 16.

2. Face value, $300; date, April 3; term, 1 year; discount rate, 8%; date of discount, April 3.

3. Face value, $500; date, January 16; term, 8 months; discount rate, 7%; date of discount, January 16.

4. Face value, $400; date, September 10; term, 60 days; discount rate, 6%; date of discount, October 10.

5. Face value, $1200; date, March 20; term, 270 days; discount rate, 6%; date of discount, August 5.

Find the proceeds of each of the following interest-bearing notes:

6. Face value, $1000; date, July 8; term, 90 days; interest rate, 4%; discount rate, 6%; date of discount, August 6.

7. Face value, $700; date, November 2; term, 270 days; interest rate, 5%; discount rate, 7%; date of discount, December 10.

8. Face value, $4000; date, February 11; term, 6 months; interest rate, 6%; discount rate, 5%; date of discount, May 29.

PROMISSORY NOTES

9. Face value, $8000; date, March 23; term, 1 year; interest rate, 6%; discount rate, 5%; date of discount, October 5.

10. Face value, $900; date, May 7; term, 90 days; interest rate, $5\frac{1}{2}\%$; discount rate, $6\frac{1}{2}\%$; date of discount, June 6.

11. George Johnson wishes to receive $500 in cash as the proceeds of a 6-months note at a bank whose discount rate is 7%. What loan should he request?

12. Mrs. Nancy Jones wishes to receive $1000 as the proceeds of a note at the bank. How much should she promise to pay at the end of 1 year if the discount rate is 6%?

13. Mr. A. C. Morley signs a 6-months note at a bank, in which he agrees to pay $500 at the end of 6 months. If the discount rate is $5\frac{1}{2}\%$, how much cash does he actually receive?

14. A student receives $752 cash as the proceeds of a note for 1 year, at the end of which time he agrees to pay the bank $800. Find the bank's discount rate.

15. A non-interest bearing note is dated January 7, and is payable 8 months after date. It is discounted on January 7 at 6%. If the discount is $36, find the face value of the note.

62. Promissory notes

A **promissory note** is a written promise made by one person to another and signed by the **maker,** in which the maker agrees to pay a certain sum of money on a certain fixed future date. The note may or may not bear interest. See Figures 1 and 2.

```
$500.00                    Los Angeles, Calif.    June 20    1948
         Six months         after date       I        promise to pay
to the order of              John R. Robinson
         Five hundred and 00/100                                Dollars
Payable at     Los Angeles
Due     Dec. 20, 1948              Arthur H. Gates
```

FIG. 1

In Fig. 1, Arthur H. Gates is the **drawer** of the note, John R. Robinson is the **drawee;** the **term** of the note is six months; the date of the note is June 20, 1948; the **face** of the note is $500.00; the **maturity date** is December 20, 1948; and the **maturity value** of the note is $500.00, which is the same as the face value, since the note bears no interest.

John R. Robinson has the right to sell the note to a third party at any time before the note is paid.

Example 1. John R. Robinson takes the note in Fig. 1 to the First Union Bank on August 2, 1948 and the bank discounts it at 8%. How much does Mr. Robinson receive from the bank?

Solution. The maturity date is December 20, 1948.

The date of discount is August 2, 1948.

The exact number of days from August 2, 1948 to December 20, 1948 is 140 days, from Table III.

$P_b = S(1 - nd)$,
$S = \$500$, $n = \frac{140}{360}$, $d = 0.08$,
$P_b = \$500[1 - \frac{140}{360}(0.08)]$,
= \$484.44, amount Mr. Robinson receives from the bank.

$1000.00   Detroit, Mich.   May 2   1948

___Ninety days___ after date ___I___ promise to pay

to the order of ___Walter M. Byrd___

___One thousand and $\frac{00}{100}$_____ Dollars

Payable at ___Detroit___

Value received with interest at ___6___ per cent.

George C Farrar

FIG. 2

EXERCISE 8

For the promissory note in Fig. 1:

1. How much would Mr. John R. Robinson receive from a bank that discounts the note on September 2, 1948 at a discount rate of 6%?

2. How much would Mr. Robinson receive from a bank that discounts the note on November 3, 1948 at a discount rate of 6%?

3. How much would Mr. Robinson receive from a bank that discounts the note on November 3, 1948 at a discount rate of 7%?

For the promissory note in Fig. 2:

4. Who is the drawer? the drawee?

5. What is the term of the note? the date of the note? the maturity date?

6. What is the face value of the note? the maturity value?

7. If Mr. Byrd sells the note to a bank that discounts it on June 18, 1948 at a discount rate of 6%, how much would he receive from the bank?

8. If Mr. Byrd sells the note to a bank that discounts it on June 18, 1948 at a discount rate of 8%, how much would he receive from the bank? How much would he receive if the discount rate was 4%?

9. If Mr. Byrd sells the note to the First Union Bank on June 2, 1948 at a discount rate of 7%, and if the First Union Bank then sells it to a Federal Reserve Bank on July 10 at a rediscount rate of 4%, how much does the First Union Bank receive from the Federal Reserve Bank, if the Federal Reserve Bank uses a 365-day year in computing its discount?

10. John L. McCarthy signs a note promising to pay H. K. Sullivan $500 in 90 days, with interest at 4%. Mr. Sullivan takes the note to a bank 30 days before it is due, and the bank discounts it at 6%. The bank immediately sends the note to a Federal Reserve Bank that rediscounts the note at 3%. What are the proceeds to the bank?

63. Drafts and trade acceptances

A **draft** is a written order, signed by the drawer, requiring the drawee to pay to the payee a certain sum of money at a certain future date. If the drawee accepts the obligation he writes "accepted" on the draft and returns it to the drawer. See Figs. 3, 4 for examples of drafts. A **trade acceptance** is a draft that arises from the sale of merchandise.

```
$600.00                  Chicago, Illinois     March 3, 1948
Ninety days after sight          Pay to the order of
               First Union Bank, Chicago, Illinois
Six hundred and 00/100                                  Dollars
Value received and charge to the account of
Perfection Radio Shop
Chicago, Illinois
Accepted  March 5, 1948            John P. Macy
```

FIG. 3

In Fig. 3, the **drawer** is Mr. John P. Macy, the **drawee** is the Perfection Radio Shop, the **payee** is the First Union Bank, and the term of the draft is ninety days and begins on March 5, 1948 (the date of acceptance). This is an example of a sight draft, and it is a trade acceptance. On March 5, 1948 this draft becomes a promissory note payable to the First Union Bank by the Perfection Radio Shop.

In Fig. 4, the **drawer** is A. C. Turpin, the **drawee** is R. M. McLellan, the **payee** is A. C. Turpin, and the term of the draft is sixty days and begins on April 9, 1948. This is a **time draft** or **after date draft**.

SIMPLE INTEREST AND DISCOUNT

This draft becomes a promissory note on April 9, 1948 payable to A. C. Turpin by R. M. McClellan.

$1000.00　　　　　　　　*Philadelphia, Penn.*　　*April 9,* 1948

Sixty days after date　　Pay to the order of　　　*myself*

One thousand and $\frac{00}{100}$　　　　　　　　　　　　　　　　Dollars

Value received and charge to the account of　A. C. Turpin

To　*R. M. McClellan*　　　　Accepted _____

　　　Philadelphia, Penn.

FIG. 4

Another type of draft is a bank draft, but this type does not ordinarily involve discounts. A **bank draft** is simply an order written by one bank directing another bank to pay a certain sum of money to a certain person on demand.

EXERCISE 9

For the draft in Fig. 3:

1. What are the proceeds if Mr. Macy sells the draft to a bank on April 15 1948, the bank's discount rate being 6%?

2. What are the proceeds if Mr. Macy sells the draft to a bank on May 2, 1948, if the bank's discount rate is $6\frac{1}{2}\%$?

For the draft in Fig. 4:

3. What are the proceeds if Mr. Turpin transfers the draft to a bank on May 9, 1948, if the bank's discount rate is $5\frac{1}{2}\%$?

4. What are the proceeds if Mr. Turpin transfers the draft to a bank on April 9, 1948, if the bank's discount rate is 7%?

5. What are the proceeds if Mr. Turpin takes the draft to a bank 10 days before the due date, if the bank's discount rate is 6%?

64. Comparison of discount at a discount rate and discount at a simple interest rate

The essential difference between discount at a discount rate and discount at an interest rate can be illustrated by the following two examples:

Example 1. Find the proceeds and discount on a note for $1000 due in 1 year without interest if a discount rate of 6% is used.

Solution.　　　$P = S(1 - nd) = 1000[1 - 1(0.06)]$,
　　　　　　　　　$= 1000(0.94) = \$940.$

COMPARISON OF INTEREST RATE AND DISCOUNT RATE

Hence the discount D is
$$D = 1000 - 940 = \$60,$$
which may have been obtained by taking 6% of $1000.

Example 2. Find the present value and discount of $1000 due in 1 year using an interest rate of 6%.

Solution. The present value P is given by
$$P = \frac{S}{1+ni} = \frac{1000}{1+(1)(0.06)} = \frac{1000}{1.06},$$
$$= \$943.40.$$

Hence the discount is $1000 - 943.40 = \$56.60$.

Notice that the calculation is easier for finding the discount at a discount rate. Also notice that if the same per cent is used for a discount rate and an interest rate, the discount obtained by using the discount rate is the larger.

Discounting at a discount rate is used mainly for short-term obligations. Suppose that the note in Example 1 was due in 30 years, instead of 1 year. Then,
$$P = 1000[1 - (30)(0.06)],$$
$$= 1000(1 - 1.80),$$
$$= 1000(-0.80),$$
$$= -\$800.$$

That is, for long terms the method of discounting at a discount rate leads to absurd results.

65. Comparison of interest rate and discount rate

Since
$$S = \frac{P_b}{1-nd}$$
from formula (12) in Article 61, it follows that P_b dollars will amount to S dollars in n years at a discount rate of d per cent. The amount of interest earned in n years is therefore
$$S - P_b = \frac{P_b}{1-nd} - P_b,$$
$$= \frac{P_b - P_b(1-nd)}{1-nd},$$
$$= \frac{P_b nd}{1-nd}.$$

The amount of interest earned in 1 year is given by
$$\frac{P_b nd}{1-nd} \div n = \frac{P_b nd}{1-nd} \cdot \frac{1}{n} = \frac{P_b d}{1-nd}.$$

The amount of interest earned by $1 in 1 year is

$$\frac{P_b d}{1-nd} \div P_b = \frac{P_b d}{1-nd} \cdot \frac{1}{P_b} = \frac{d}{1-nd}.$$

But the amount of interest earned by $1 in 1 year is exactly the definition of the rate of simple interest, so

$$i = \frac{d}{1-nd}. \tag{13}$$

In this formula we assume that the denominator $1 - nd$ is greater than zero, since, if it were not, the formula would lead to absurd results. Also, $1 - nd$ is always less than 1, since n and d are positive. Therefore i is always greater than d, and i increases with n if d is held fixed.

Example 1. Find the interest rate if a bank discounts a note for 60 days at a discount rate of 6%.

Solution.
$$i = \frac{d}{1-nd}.$$

$$d = 0.06; \quad n = \frac{60}{300} = \frac{1}{6}.$$

$$i = \frac{0.06}{1 - (\tfrac{1}{6})(0.06)} = \frac{0.06}{1 - 0.01} = \frac{0.06}{0.99}, \text{ or } 6.06\%$$

correct to three significant figures as a per cent.

Formula (13) can be solved for d in terms of i, as follows:

$$i = \frac{d}{1-nd}.$$

Clearing of fractions,

$$i(1 - nd) = d.$$

Simplifying the left member of this equation,

$$i - ind = d.$$

Transposing and factoring,

$$d(1 + ni) = i.$$

Dividing both members of this equation by $(1 + ni)$,

$$d = \frac{i}{1+ni}. \tag{14}$$

Formula (14) can be used to find the discount rate when the rate of interest is given.

COMPARISON OF INTEREST RATE AND DISCOUNT RATE

Example 2. A bank wishes to earn 8% in discounting a 90-day note. At what discount rate should the bank discount the note?

Solution.
$$d = \frac{i}{1+ni}.$$

$$i = 0.08; \quad n = \frac{90}{360} = \frac{1}{4}.$$

Hence,
$$d = \frac{0.08}{1 + (\tfrac{1}{4})(0.08)},$$

$$= \frac{0.08}{1 + 0.02} = \frac{0.08}{1.02} \quad \text{or} \quad 7.84\%,$$

correct to three significant figures as a per cent.

EXERCISE 10

1. What simple interest rate is equivalent to a discount rate of 6% if the term of discount is 60 days? 90 days?
2. What discount rate is equivalent to a simple interest rate of 6% if the term is 60 days? 90 days?
3. A bank discounts a note of $1000 for 6 months at a discount rate of 7%. Find the rate of simple interest it is charging in this case.
4. A man signs a note at a bank promising to pay $500 at the end of 6 months. The bank gives him $482.50 in cash on the day he signs the note. What is the bank's discount rate? What rate of interest is the bank charging?
5. What does formula (13) become if $n = 1$?
6. What does formula (14) become if $n = 1$?
7. In formula (13), let $d = 0.06$, and compute the values of i for $n = \frac{1}{12}$, $\frac{1}{6}, \frac{1}{3}, \frac{1}{4}, \frac{1}{2}, 1$.
8. In formula (14), let $i = 0.06$, and compute the values of i for $n = \frac{1}{12}$, $\frac{1}{6}, \frac{1}{3}, \frac{1}{4}, \frac{1}{2}, 1$.
9. If $200 due in 6 months is discounted at a discount rate of 5%, what is the corresponding interest rate?
10. Solve formula (14) for i in terms of n and d.
11. A bank discounts small 1-year loans at a discount rate of 5%. What rate of interest is the bank earning?
12. On a short-term note for a small amount of money, a discount rate of 8% corresponds to an interest rate of $8\frac{1}{3}\%$. What is the term of the note?
13. On notes for 1 year, find the interest rates corresponding to discount rates of 4%, 5%, 6%, 7%, and 8%.
14. Find the interest rates corresponding to a discount rate of 6% on notes whose terms are 30 days, 60 days, 90 days, and 6 months, respectively.
15. John L. McCarthy wishes to obtain $1000 cash as the proceeds of a 6-month note at a bank. If the bank's discount rate is 8%, how much should he ask to borrow? What is the interest rate that the bank is charging?

16. E. H. Buchanan received $837.25 as the proceeds of a 90-day note. The face of the note was $900. What was the discount rate? What was the rate of interest charged?

17. M. R. McBride wishes to receive $500 as the proceeds of a 60-day loan at a bank whose discount rate is 5%. How much should he ask to borrow? A friend will lend him the money at a 5% interest rate. How much would he save if he borrowed from his friend?

18. Solve formula (14) for n.

19. A note for $2000, bearing simple interest at 6%, is due in 9 months. What is the value of this debt 3 months before it is due? If the note were discounted at a discount rate of 5% at the latter date, what would be the proceeds of the note?

20. If $d = 0.06$ in formula (12), what values of n will make P_b negative?

66. Partial payments

Consider a debt on a certain date at a specified rate of interest. It is possible to retire the debt by making payments at equal or unequal intervals of time before the due date. In such a case the creditor should allow credit for interest on each payment made before the due date. With short-term obligations there are two commonly used methods of computing the interest allowed on these partial payments, known as the **United States Rule** and the **Merchants' Rule.** We illustrate the methods by examples.

UNITED STATES RULE. **Example 1.** A note for $2000 bears interest at 6%. It is dated March 10, 1948. Payments of $500 each are made at the end of each thirty days after March 10. Find the balance due on July 8, 1948.

Solution.

Original debt, March 10, 1948	$2000.00
Interest on $2000 for 30 days	10.00
Amount due on April 9	$2010.00
Deduct first payment, April 9	500.00
Balance due on April 9	$1510.00
Interest on $1510 for 30 days	7.55
Amount due on May 9	$1517.55
Deduct second payment, May 9	500.00
Balance due on May 9	$1017.55
Interest on $1017.55 for 30 days	5.09
Amount due on June 8	$1022.64
Deduct third payment, June 8	500.00
Balance due on June 8	$ 522.64
Interest on $522.64 for 30 days	2.61
Amount due on July 8	$ 525.25
Deduct fourth payment, July 8	500.00
Balance due on July 8	$ 25.25

MERCHANTS' RULE. **Example 2.** Use the same data as in Example 1, assuming the debt will be completely paid off after 120 days.

Solution.

Original debt, March 10, 1948		$2000.00
Interest on $2000 for 120 days, from March 10 to July 8		40.00
Value of note on July 8		$2040.00
First payment, April 9	$500.00	
Interest on $500 for 90 days	7.50	507.50
Balance		$1532.50
Second payment, May 9	$500.00	
Interest on $500 for 60 days	5.00	505.00
Balance		$1027.50
Third payment, June 8	$500.00	
Interest on $500 for 30 days	2.50	502.50
Balance		$ 525.00
Fourth payment, July 8	$500.00	500.00
Balance due on July 8		$ 25.00

Notice that the United States Rule favors the creditor, and the Merchants' Rule favors the debtor.

In the United States Rule, the first partial payment is applied to the payment of the interest due on the principal from the date of the debt to the date of the first partial payment, and the excess of the payment over this interest is applied to the reduction of the principal. The second partial payment is applied to the payment of the interest due on the reduced principal from the date of the first payment to the date of the second payment, and the excess of the second payment over this interest is used to again reduce the principal. Similar statements apply to the rest of the partial payments.

In the event that a certain partial payment is less than the amount of interest due at the time the payment is made, the principal is not reduced, but instead the interest is computed to the time of the next payment. Then, if the sum of both payments exceeds the interest due, the sum of the two payments is used to pay the interest due and the remainder is used to reduce the principal.

In the Merchants' Rule, the original principal draws interest from the date of the debt to the date of the final payment that extinguishes the debt. Interest is computed on each partial payment from the date of the payment to the final date on which the debt is settled.

Example 3. A 6% note for $1000, dated June 15, 1949, calls for two repayments of $25 each, the first at the end of 180 days, and the second at the end of the next 30 days followed by payments of $300 each at the end of 30-day periods. Using the United States Rule, what additional payment must be made at the time of the fifth payment to pay off the debt?

Solution.

Original debt on June 15, 1949	$1000.00
Interest for 180 days at 6%	$ 30.00
First payment of $25, made on Dec. 12, not sufficient to cover interest.	
Interest for 210 days, (180 + 30) days at 6%	$ 35.00
Amount due on Jan. 11, 1950	$1035.00
Deduct the sum of the first and second payments on Jan. 11	$ 50.00
Balance due on Jan. 11, 1950	$ 985.00
Interest for 30 days at 6%	$ 4.93
Amount due on Feb. 10, 1950	$ 989.93
Deduct third payment	$ 300.00
Balance due on Feb. 10, 1950	$ 689.93
Interest for 30 days at 6%	$ 3.45
Amount due Mar. 12, 1950	$ 693.38
Deduct fourth payment	$ 300.00
Balance due on Mar. 12, 1950	$ 393.38
Interest for 30 days at 6%	$ 1.97
Amount due on April 11, 1950	$ 395.35
Deduct fifth payment	$ 300.00
Balance due on April 11, 1950	$ 95.35

Hence the debt may be paid off completely by making this payment of $95.35.

EXERCISE 11

Solve the following problems by both the United States Rule and the Merchants' Rule:

1. A note for $5000 bears interest at 6%. It is dated April 2, 1948. Payments of $1000 each are made at the end of each 30 days. Find the amount on August 30, 1948 which will pay off the debt.

2. A 6% note for $8000 is repaid in partial payments as follows: $1000 at the end of the 2nd month; $500 at the end of the third month; $2000 at the end of the 5th month; $3000 at the end of the 6th month; $1000 at the end of the 7th month; and a final payment at the end of the 8th month. What is the amount of the last payment?

3. A note for $6000 at 4% is dated March 20, 1948. Partial payments are made as follows: $500 on April 16; $1200 on June 3; $1700 on June 23; $2000 on August 15. How much must be paid on September 14 to retire the debt?

4. An automobile sells for $2500 cash. A buyer receives $800 for his old car and agrees to pay $80 per month, with the first payment due one month after the date of purchase. If the interest rate is 12%, what is the balance due after 12 payments have been made?

5. A house and lot cost $25,000. The buyer pays $15,000 cash and agrees to pay $3000 at the end of each 6 months, with interest at 6%. How much should he pay at the time of the third payment to retire the debt?

6. A debt of $5000 bearing interest at the rate of 7% from August 1, 1948 is to be paid off by four payments of $25 each, followed by payments of $1000. Each payment is to be made at the end of 30-day periods. What extra payment at the time of the sixth payment will retire the debt?

67. Equation of value

A sum of money has different values at different times and at different interest rates. For example, if money is worth 6%, the sums "$100 today" and "$106 one year from now" are equivalent sums.

Consider a debt of $100 due at some specified future date. To find its value at the rate i, n years after the due date, multiply $100 by $(1 + ni)$; to find its value n years before the due date, divide $100 by $(1 + ni)$. [See formula (3) and formula (9)].

Example 1. A debt of $100 is due 8 months from now. If money is worth 6%, find its value (a) 12 months from now, (b) 6 months from now.

Solution. Consider the line diagram:

```
                          (b)        $100.00                    (a)
   |    |    |    |    |    |    |    |    |    |    |    |
   0    1    2    3    4    5    6    7    8    9   10   11   12
```

(a) $n = \frac{4}{12} = \frac{1}{3}$, $i = 0.06$.

Hence, since the value wanted is after the due date,

$100 [1 + \frac{1}{3}(0.06)] = \$100 (1.02) = \$102$, value 12 months from now.

(b) $n = \frac{2}{12} = \frac{1}{6}$, $i = 0.06$. In this case the value wanted is at a time prior to the due date, so,

$$\frac{100}{1 + \frac{1}{6}(0.06)} = \frac{100}{1.01} = \$99.01, \text{ value 6 months from now.}$$

In this example, "$100 in 8 months," "$102 in 12 months," and "$99.01 in 6 months" are equivalent sums of money if money is worth 6%.

Example 2. A debt of $1000 due in 5 months bears interest at 5%. If money is worth 6%, find its value (a) 9 months from now, (b) 3 months from now.

Solution. Consider the line diagram:

```
                   (b)        $1020.83              (a)
   |    |    |    |    |    |    |    |    |
   0    1    2    3    4    5    6    7    8    9
```

SIMPLE INTEREST AND DISCOUNT

$1000 \left[1 + \frac{5}{12}(0.05)\right] = 1000\left(\frac{49}{48}\right) = \$1020.83$, maturity value of the debt.

(a) $n = \frac{4}{12} = \frac{1}{3}$; $i = 0.06$.
$1020.83 \left[1 + \frac{4}{12}(0.06)\right] = 1020.83(1.02)$,
$= \$1041.25$, value 9 months from now.

(b) $n = \frac{2}{12} = \frac{1}{6}$; $i = 0.06$.
$$\frac{1020.83}{1 + \frac{1}{6}(0.06)} = \frac{1020.83}{1.01} = \$1010.72, \text{ value 3 months from now.}$$

In this example, "$1000 in 5 months," "$1020.83 in 9 months," and "$1010.72 in 3 months" are equivalent sums of money if money is worth 6%.

An **equation of value** is an equation that expresses the equivalence of two sets of obligations on a specified date and at a specified interest or discount rate. The equivalence is dependent on the date selected to express the equation. The date selected for the equivalence is called the **focal date**.

Example 3. A man owes two debts: $1000 due in 6 months and $500 due in 3 months. He wishes to discharge the debts by a single payment 5 months hence. Find the amount of the single payment, if money is worth 6% and if the focal date is 5 months hence.

Solution. Consider the line diagram:

```
                    $500 (debt)    focal  $1000 (debt)
                         |         date        |
    |    |    |    |     |    |     |     |
    0    1    2    3     4    5     6
                                    |
                                    x (payment)
```

The equation of value is:
$$x = 500\left[1 + \frac{2}{12}(0.06)\right] + \frac{1000}{1 + \frac{1}{12}(0.06)},$$
$$= 500(1.01) + \frac{1000}{1.005},$$
$$= 505 + 995.02,$$
$$= \$1500.02.$$

Example 4. Use the same data as Example 3, but focal date 6 months hence.

Solution. Consider the line diagram:

```
                    $500 (debt)         $1000 (debt)
                         |                    |
    |    |    |    |     |    |     |     |
    0    1    2    3     4    5     6
                                          |
                                          focal date
                                    x (payment)
```

EQUATION OF VALUE

The equation of value is:
$$x[1 + \tfrac{1}{12}(0.06)] = 500[1 + \tfrac{3}{12}(0.06)] + 1000.$$
Simplifying $\quad 1.005x = 500(1.015) + 1000 = 1507.50,$
or $\quad x = \$1500.00.$

Notice that the date selected for the focal date makes a difference in the amount of the single payment necessary to discharge both debts. For short terms this difference is small. When compound interest is used, the same payment is obtained for any choice of focal date. This will be explained in a later chapter.

Example 5. A man owes two debts: $100 due in 8 months, and $800 due in 12 months. He wishes to discharge these debts by two payments: $500 at the end of 6 months and another payment at the end of 11 months. How much should the second payment be, if money is worth 6% and the debts and payments are focalized at 11 months?

Solution. Consider the line diagram:

```
                                        $100 (debt)         $800
                                                           (debt)
                                                    focal
                                                    date
  |   |   |   |   |   |   |   |   |   |   |   |   |
  0   1   2   3   4   5   6   7   8   9  10  11  12
                          $500 (payment)    x (payment)
```

Equation of value:
$$x + 500\left[1 + \tfrac{5}{12}(0.06)\right] = \frac{800}{1 + \tfrac{1}{12}(0.06)} + 100\left[1 + \tfrac{3}{12}(0.06)\right].$$

Simplifying, $\quad x + 512.50 = 796.02 + 101.50,$
whence $\quad x = \$385.02,$ amount of the second payment.

EXERCISE 12

1. A. C. Jones owes $1000 due in 9 months. If money is worth 4% find the value of this debt (a) 2 months hence, (b) 1 year from now.

2. George R. White owes the Perfection Radio Shop $500 due in 8 months. If the radio shop can invest its money at 3%, find the value of this debt (a) 6 months hence, (b) 10 months hence.

3. Walter M. Smith signed a promissory note for $400 plus interest at 6%, the debt being payable in 1 year to the Acme Hardware Co. If the Acme Hardware Co. can invest its money at 4%, what is the value of this debt 6 months before it is due?

4. Find the sum of the values of $400 due in 3 months and $500 due in 6 months if money is worth 6%. (Use "now" as the focal date).

5. Find the sum of the values of $1000 due in 5 months and $2000 due in 8 months, if money is worth 8%, and if the sums are focalized 1 year from the present date. Find the sum if the amounts are focalized 6 months from the present date.

6. A person owes $800 due in 6 months and $1200 due in 8 months. Find the single payment made in 10 months that will retire both debts, if money is worth 6%. Use 10 months from the present as the focal date.

7. A person owes $500 due in 1 year and $1000 due in 15 months. Find the single payment that can be made 18 months hence and that will discharge both debts, if money is worth 6%. Use 18 months from the present as the focal date. Find the payment if money is worth 5%.

8. Malcolm L. Baker owes a wholesaler $400 due in 3 months, $600 due in 4 months, and $800 due in 6 months. He makes a payment of $900 at the end of 5 months. How much should he pay in 6 months in order to retire the debts, if money is worth 4%? Use 6 months from the present as the focal date.

9. A man owes $1200 due in 8 months. He desires to discharge the debt by making two equal payments at the end of 6 months and 9 months, respectively. How much should these payments be, if money is worth 5%? Use 9 months from now as the focal date.

68. Equation of time

Consider the following problem:

Example 1. A debt of $100 is due in 60 days and a debt of $200 is due in 90 days. Find the date on which a single payment of $300 will retire both debts.

Solution. The line diagram is:

$100 (debt) $200 (debt)

| | |
0 (focal date)   60 days t days   90 days

$300 (payment)

Choose the present time as the focal date, and discount the amounts to the present, using a discount rate.

The equation of value is:

$$300\left[1 - \frac{t}{360}d\right] = 100\left[1 - \frac{60}{360}d\right] + 200\left[1 - \frac{90}{360}d\right],$$

which reduces to:

$$300 - 300\left(\frac{t}{360}\right)d = 100 - 100\left(\frac{60}{360}\right)d + 200 - 200\left(\frac{90}{360}\right)d,$$

or

$$300\left(\frac{t}{360}\right)d = 100\left(\frac{60}{360}\right)d + 200\left(\frac{90}{360}\right)d.$$

EQUATION OF TIME

Multiplying both members of this equation by 360, and dividing by d,
$$300t = 100(60) + 200(90),$$
and finally,
$$t = \frac{100(60) + 200(90)}{300},$$
$$= 80 \text{ days.}$$

If we use literal numbers P_1 and P_2 for the two debts and n_1 and n_2 for the number of years in the due dates of these debts, the line diagram becomes:

```
           P₁                           P₂ (debt)
|_____|_____|_____|
0          n₁          n            n₂
|
focal date            (P₁ + P₂) payment
```

The single payment is $(P_1 + P_2)$ and its due date is n years from now. Let the focal date be taken at the present time. Using a discount rate the time equation is:
$$P_1(1 - n_1 d) + P_2(1 - n_2 d) = (P_1 + P_2)(1 - nd).$$
Simplifying,
$$P_1 - P_1 n_1 d + P_2 - P_2 n_2 d = P_1 - P_1 nd + P_2 - P_2 nd,$$
whence
$$n(P_1 + P_2) = P_1 n_1 + P_2 n_2,$$
so
$$n = \frac{P_1 n_1 + P_2 n_2}{P_1 + P_2}.$$

If the focal date is chosen at any time after the due date of the first debt, the value of n will be dependent upon the discount rate. However, for the usual cases that arise, n varies very little with the choice of the focal date and the discount rate.

The student may easily obtain the above formula if he uses for focal date the time n_2 and instead of a discount rate he uses a simple interest rate. Again if any time is used for a focal date prior to n_2 the value of n becomes dependent upon the focal date chosen and upon the interest rate involved.

The value of n obtained is called the **equated time,** and the corresponding date is called the **equated date.**

In general, if there are k debts designated by $P_1, P_2, \ldots, P_k$, due in $n_1, n_2, \ldots, n_k$ years, respectively, these debts can be discharged by a single payment of $(P_1 + P_2 + \cdots + P_k)$ dollars made in n years, where
$$n = \frac{n_1 P_1 + n_2 P_2 + \cdots + n_k P_k}{P_1 + P_2 + \cdots + P_k}. \tag{15}$$

This formula will give the exact value of n if:

(1) A discount rate is used and the focal date is any date not subsequent to the due date of the first debt.

(2) An interest rate is used and the focal date is any date not prior to the due date of the last debt.

In all other cases the answer for n is approximate.

The values of $n_1, n_2, \ldots, n_k$ can be in any unit of time, provided that they are all in the same unit, and the value of n will be expressed in this common unit.

Example 2. Find the time at which a single payment of \$600 will discharge debts of \$100, \$200, and \$300 due in 3 days, 60 days, and 90 days, respectively.

Solution.
$$P_1 = 100, \quad P_2 = 200, \quad P_3 = 300.$$
$$n_1 = 30, \quad n_2 = 60, \quad n_3 = 90.$$
$$n = \frac{P_1 n_1 + P_2 n_2 + P_3 n_3}{P_1 + P_2 + P_3},$$
$$= \frac{100(30) + 200(60) + 300(90)}{100 + 200 + 300},$$
$$= 70 \text{ days.}$$

If the debts bear interest, the maturity values of the debts must be used in formula (15) for $P_1, P_2, \ldots, P_k$, and the single payment will be the sum of these maturity values. If we use $S_1, S_2, \ldots, S_k$ to represent these maturity values, formula (15) becomes

$$n = \frac{S_1 n_1 + S_2 n_2 + \cdots + S_k n_k}{S_1 + S_2 + \cdots + S_k}. \tag{16}$$

Example 3. A man owes \$100 plus interest at 6% due in 60 days and \$200 plus interest at 6% due in 90 days. What is the value of the single payment necessary to discharge both debts, and what is its due date?

Solution.
$$S_1 = P_1(1 + n_1 i).$$
$$P_1 = 100; \quad n_1 = \tfrac{60}{360}; \quad i = 0.06.$$
$$S_1 = 100[1 + \tfrac{60}{360}(0.06)],$$
$$= 100(1.01) = 101.00.$$
$$S_2 = P_2(1 + n_2 i).$$
$$P_2 = 200; \quad n_2 = \tfrac{90}{360}; \quad i = 0.06.$$
$$S_2 = 100[1 + \tfrac{90}{360}(0.06)],$$
$$= 100(1.015) = 101.50.$$
$$n = \frac{S_1 n_1 + S_2 n_2}{S_1 + S_2}.$$
$$n = \frac{101(60) + 101.50(90)}{101 + 101.50},$$
$$= 75 \text{ days.}$$

EQUATION OF TIME

EXERCISE 13

1. Debts of $500 and $1000 are due in 30 days and 90 days, respectively. If a single payment of $1500 is made to discharge both of these debts, find the time when the payment should be made.

2. William Walker owes the National Mfg. Co. debts of $300, $800, and $1200 due in 15 days, 30 days, and 90 days, respectively. He desires to discharge these three debts by a single payment of $2300. On what date should he make this payment?

3. The Center Street Grocery Store bought merchandise from a wholesaler as follows: $1000 on May 1, $1500 on June 10, $800 on July 1. Payments were made as follows: $500 on June 1, and $900 on June 20. Find the equated date for the balance.

4. R. C. Jones bought machine tools from the Apex Tool Co. as follows: August 2, $300, n/10; $500, September 23, n/30. Find the equated date for a single payment of $800 to discharge both debts.

5. The Union Drug Co. owes $800 due on March 10 and pays $400 on March 20. At what date would the balance of $400 settle the account? At 5% how much interest should the Union Drug Co. pay if it settles its account on May 2?

6. The following account is to be settled by a single payment equal to the difference between the sum of the debts and the sum of the payments already made. On what date should this single payment be made?

> Debts: $200 due on May 1
> $500 due on June 1
> $700 due August 12
> $1000 due September 3.
> Payments: $1600 on May 13
> $600 on May 18.

7. The Perfection Radio Shop owes its wholesaler the following debts:

> $300 due in 3 months with interest at 5%,
> $800 due in 6 months with interest at 6%,
> $1000 due in 8 months with interest at 4%.

Assuming that money is worth 6%, what single payment is necessary to discharge these debts 10 months from now?

8. The account of the Reliable Hardware Co. with its wholesaler is as follows:

Debts		Payments Made	
May 10, 1948	$900	May 30, 1948	$400
June 18, 1948	$1000	August 1, 1948	$500
September 20, 1948	$1500	October 10, 1948	$1100
November 13, 1948	$2000		

On what day should the balance be paid in order that no interest be due?

If the interest rate is 5%, how much should the company pay on December 10, 1948 to settle the account?

9. Raymond Ellis owes $500 due in 3 months with interest at 6%, and $1000 due in 9 months with interest at 4%. What is the equated date for retiring both of these debts with a single payment? What is the amount of the payment? If payment is made 1 month after the equated date, and if the interest rate is 5%, what is the amount of the payment?

10. Using a line diagram and the equation of value, derive the formula

$$n = \frac{P_1 n_1 + P_2 n_2 + P_3 n_3}{P_1 + P_2 + P_3}$$

(a) with n_3 as the focal date, using an interest rate, (b) with the present as the focal date, using a discount rate.

69. Installment buying

For short-term obligations, simple interest is usually employed even though slightly different results are obtained by different choices of focal dates.

Consider the following problem:

Example 1. A customer buys an article whose cash price is $100. He pays $10 down and $10 at the end of each month for 10 months. Find the interest rate.

Solution. Use the time of the last payment as the focal date.

```
   $10  $10  $10  $10  $10  $10  $10  $10  $10  $10
    |    |    |    |    |    |    |    |    |    |
 ───┼────┼────┼────┼────┼────┼────┼────┼────┼────┼───
    0    1    2    3    4    5    6    7    8    9   10
    |                                              |
  $90                                          focal date
```

The balance due is the cash price less the down payment or $100 - 10 = 90$. Hence the equation of value is:

$$90(1 + \tfrac{10}{12}i) = 10(1 + \tfrac{9}{12}i) + 10(1 + \tfrac{8}{12}i) + \cdots + 10.$$

Simplifying,

$$90 + \tfrac{900}{12}i = 100 + \tfrac{450}{12}i,$$

or

$$\tfrac{450}{12}i = 10,$$

whence

$$i = \tfrac{120}{450}, \text{ or } 26\tfrac{2}{3}\%.$$

To generalize this problem, let

C = cash price
D = down payment
R = monthly payment
n = number of monthly payments
i = interest rate.

INSTALLMENT BUYING

The line diagram is:

```
        R    R    R    R    R        R     R    R
        |    |    |    |    |        |     |    |
  ──────┼────┼────┼────┼────┼── ─── ─┼─────┼────┼──
  0     1    2    3    4    5       n-2   n-1   n
  |                                              |
  C - D                                    focal date
```

If all amounts are focalized at the end of n months, the equation of value is:

$$(C - D)\left(1 + \frac{n}{12}i\right) = R\left[1 + \frac{(n-1)}{12}i\right] + R\left[1 + \frac{(n-2)}{12}i\right] + \cdots + R,$$

which reduces to

$$(C - D) + (C - D)\frac{n}{12}i = nR + R\left[\frac{n(n-1)}{24}\right]i,$$

whence
$$i = \frac{24(nR - C + D)}{n(2C - 2D - nR + R)}. \tag{17}$$

A formula in more common use than that given above is obtained by using the present time as focal date and by assuming that a discount rate is approximately equivalent to an interest rate. We set up the formula designating the approximate interest rate by the symbol for a discount rate.

```
  focal
  date    R    R    R    R        R     R
   |      |    |    |    |        |     |
  ─┼──────┼────┼────┼────┼── ─── ─┼─────┼──
   0      1    2    3    4       n-1    n
   |
  C - D
```

$$C - D = R\left(1 - \frac{1}{12}d\right) + R\left(1 - \frac{2}{12}d\right) + R\left(1 - \frac{3}{12}d\right) + \cdots$$
$$+ R\left[1 - \frac{(n-1)}{12}d\right] + R\left[1 - \frac{n}{12}d\right],$$

$$C - D = nR - R\left(\frac{n}{2}\right)\left(\frac{n+1}{12}\right)d,$$

or
$$d = \frac{24(nR - C + D)}{n(n+1)R}. \tag{18}$$

142   SIMPLE INTEREST AND DISCOUNT

Example 2. Find the discount rate involved in Example 1 as an approximation to the interest rate.

Solution. Using a line graph with focal date at the present time, we have

```
focal
date   10   10   10   10   10   10   10   10   10   10
 |      |    |    |    |    |    |    |    |    |    |
─┼──────┼────┼────┼────┼────┼────┼────┼────┼────┼────┼──
 0      1    2    3    3    4    5    6    8    9    10
 |
$90
```

$$90 = 10\left(1 - \frac{d}{12}\right) + 10\left(1 - \frac{2}{12}d\right) + 10\left(1 - \frac{3}{12}d\right) + 10\left(1 - \frac{4}{12}d\right)$$
$$+ 10\left(1 - \frac{5}{12}d\right) + 10\left(1 - \frac{6}{12}d\right) + 10\left(1 - \frac{7}{12}d\right) + 10\left(1 - \frac{8}{12}d\right)$$
$$+ 10\left(1 - \frac{9}{12}d\right) + 10\left(1 - \frac{10}{12}d\right).$$

$$90 = 100 - \frac{550}{12}d.$$

$$d = \frac{(10)(12)}{550},$$

$$= 0.21\tfrac{9}{11} \quad \text{or} \quad 21\tfrac{9}{11}\%.$$

A third formula is obtained by assuming an average time of $\frac{n+1}{2}$ months for each payment. Thus in Example 1, the average time $\frac{1+2+3+4+5+6+7+8+9+10}{10} = \frac{55}{10} = 5.5$ months, which may be obtained by substituting $n = 10$ in $\frac{n+1}{2}$. We argue that $C - D$, the outstanding debt, carried forward at interest for the average time is equivalent to the total paid in interest, namely, $nR - (C - D)$. Hence,

$$(C - D)\frac{\frac{n+1}{2}}{12} i = nR - (C - D),$$

from which we obtain,

$$i = \frac{24(nR + D - C)}{(n+1)(C - D)}. \tag{19}$$

In formula (19) notice that nR represents the sum of the monthly payments expressed in dollars, and D is the down payment, so the

INSTALLMENT BUYING

quantity $nR + D - C$ represents the difference between the cash price and the amount actually paid; that is, it represents the **carrying charge**. Also notice that in the denominator of the right member of formula (19) the quantity $C - D$ represents the difference between the cash price and the down payment; that is, it represents the unpaid balance. Thus formula (19) becomes

$$i = \frac{24 \times \text{carrying charge}}{(n+1) \times \text{unpaid balance}}.$$

Example 3. Work Example 1, using formula (19).

Solution. $C = 100$, $D = 10$, $R = 10$, $n = 10$.

$$i = \frac{24(nR + D - C)}{(n+1)(C - D)},$$

$$= \frac{24[10(10) + 10 - 100]}{(10+1)(100 - 10)},$$

$$= 0.24\tfrac{8}{33}, \text{ or } 24\tfrac{8}{33}\%.$$

In the installment-buying problem, the carrying charge is often figured as a per cent of the outstanding debt. Thus if this per cent is 5% per year on an outstanding debt of $600 the carrying charge for the year is $30, for two years it is $60 and so on. The installment payment is obtained by dividing the sum of the outstanding debt and the carrying charge by the number of payments. This is commonly called the *r%* **plan** where r is the per cent used in figuring the carrying charge for the year.

Example 4. An article is listed for sale at $400 cash. It is sold for $50 down under the 6% plan with 12 monthly installment payments. Find the carrying charge, the monthly payments and the interest rate involved using the method of formula (19).

Solution. The outstanding debt is $400 − $50 or $350. The carrying charge is 6% of $350 or $21. This added to $350 gives $371. This is divided by 12 to give the installment payment which is $30.92. Substituting in formula (19), $C = 400$, $D = 50$, $R = 30.92$, $n = 12$, we have,

$$i = \frac{24[12(30.92) + 50 - 400]}{(12+1)(400 - 50)},$$

$$= 0.11\tfrac{1}{13}, \text{ or } 11\tfrac{1}{13}\%.$$

Example 5. A car costing $2000 cash is sold under the 6% plan for $500 down, followed by 18 monthly payments. Find the carrying charge, the monthly payment, and the interest rate involved, using formula (19).

Solution. The balance due is $1500. The carrying charge for a year is $(1500)(0.06) = \$90$, hence for $1\frac{1}{2}$ years it is $(90)(1\frac{1}{2}) = \$135$. The installment payment is

$$\frac{1500 + 135}{18} = \$90.83.$$

Hence, by formula (19),

$$i = \frac{24[18(90.83) + 500 - 2000]}{19(2000 - 500)},$$

$$= \frac{24(135)}{19(1500)},$$

$$= 0.11\tfrac{7}{19}, \text{ or } 11\tfrac{7}{19}\%.$$

EXERCISE 14

1. A customer buys a radio, the cash price of which is $300. He pays $20 down and $30 per month for 10 months. Find the rate of interest (a) by formula (17), and (b) by formula (18).

2. The cash price of a refrigerator is $200. The down payment is $50 and the carrying charge is figured by the 6% plan. If twelve monthly payments are to be made, find the monthly payments and the rate of interest, using formula (19).

3. An article is listed for $100 cash. The time-payment plan consists of a $10 down payment and four monthly payments of $25 each. Find the interest rate using each of the three methods.

4. A company offers $100 loans under the 5% plan. If the loan is to be repaid in six monthly installments find the amount of each payment and find the rate of interest, using formula (18).

5. A car selling for $2000 is sold for $500 down and the balance in eighteen monthly payments including a carrying charge figured by the 6% plan. What is the amount of each installment and what is the interest rate involved, if figured by formula (17)?

MISCELLANEOUS EXERCISE

1. Find the simple interest and amount of a principal of $200 for 9 months at 5%.

2. If the principal is $1600 and the simple interest for 1 year is $48, what is the interest rate?

3. In how many months will a principal of $800 amount to $821.33 at 4%?

4. Find the principal, if the amount is $947.25 in $1\frac{1}{2}$ years at $3\frac{1}{2}\%$.

5. Find the exact time from April 2, 1947 to January 15, 1948.

6. Find the approximate time from June 16, 1946 to February 3, 1948.

7. Find the ordinary and exact simple interest on $1000 for 185 days at 4%.

8. Calculate the interest on $500 at 3% from May 1, 1947 to November 15, 1947, using the Bankers' Rule.

INSTALLMENT BUYING

9. Use the 60-day 6% method for finding the interest on $400 for 135 days at 3%.

10. Compute the present value of $2000 due in 6 months at 5%.

11. Discount $1000 for 1 year using (a) a simple interest rate of 5%, and (b) a discount rate of 5%.

12. A debt of $500 plus interest at 6% is due in 1 year. Find the present value of this debt if money is worth 5%.

13. Mrs. R. A. Baker borrows $500 from a bank. The bank gives her $473.75 and she signs a note in which she agrees to pay the bank $500 at the end of 9 months. What is the bank's discount rate? What is the rate of interest on this loan?

14. Solve for d:
$$P_b = S(1 - nd).$$

15. Which is more profitable, to lend money for 60 days at 5.55% interest or to discount notes for 60 days at a discount rate of $5\frac{1}{2}$%?

16. A 60-day trade acceptance for $300, dated March 3, is discounted at $4\frac{1}{2}$% on April 2. Find the proceeds.

17. In a promissory note Arthur Millikan promises to pay Edward H. Fields the sum of $1500 with interest at 5%. The note is dated August 1 and the term is 90 days after date. Find the maturity value of the note. If Edward H. Fields takes the note to the First Union Bank on August 28 and the bank discounts the note at 6%, how much does Mr. Fields receive from the bank?

18. Solve for n: $i = \dfrac{d}{1 - nd}$.

19. A note for $1000 bears interest at 5%, and is dated January 1, 1947. Payments of $200 each are made at the end of each 30 days. (a) Find the balance due on March 6, 1947, by the United States Rule. (b) Using the Merchants' Rule, find the balance due at the time of the 5th payment if the debt is to be paid off completely at that time.

20. A debt of $200 is due 9 months hence. Find its value (a) 3 months hence, and (b) 12 months hence, if money is worth 6%.

21. A man has two debts: $300 due in 6 months and $1000 due in 9 months. Find the single payment that will retire both debts 8 months hence, if money is worth 5%, and if the focal date is 8 months hence.

22. Mr. A. T. Keller owes $200 due in 5 months and $400 due in 11 months. On what date can he retire both debts by a single payment of $600 if money is worth 5%?

23. The cash price of an automobile is $2500. A down payment of $500 is accepted. Payments are made at the end of each month for 18 months. Find the amount of each monthly payment, and find the rate of interest, using formula (18), if the 6% plan is used.

24. Malcolm Atkins buys a $500 bond on May 2, 1948 and sells it on December 10, 1948. If the bond pays 4% interest, how much interest was earned, if a 30-day month, 360-day year is assumed?

25. How long will it take $750 to amount to $800 at 6%, using the Bankers' Rule? Give the answer in days.

26. Find the discount on a 90-day, 5%, $1000 note dated March 10, 1948 at 6%. What are the proceeds of the note? If the bank sends the note to a Federal Reserve Bank on April 18, 1948, where it is rediscounted at 5%, what are the proceeds to the bank?

27. The cash price of a chair is $80. It can be purchased by a series of 10 payments of $8.50 each. If the payments are made at the end of each month, what is the interest rate, by formula (18)?

28. In purchasing an outboard motor, the customer is given the choice of $200 cash or $210 in 60 days. What rate of interest does the latter choice imply?

29. An invoice states that $1000 is due at the end of 60 days, but 4% cash discount is allowed for immediate payment. At what rate of interest could the debtor borrow money in order to take advantage of the discount?

30. Suppose that you need approximately $1000 for 6 months. A bank offers to discount your note for $1000 at 6%, while an individual will lend you $1000 if you will repay it with interest at $6\frac{1}{2}\%$. Which offer carries the higher interest rate?

31. The debts $P_1, P_2, \ldots, P_k$ are due in $n_1, n_2, \ldots, n_k$ years, respectively, and payments of $B_1, B_2, \ldots, B_r$ (where $B_1 + B_2 + \cdots + B_r < P_1 + P_2 + \cdots + P_k$) are made in $m_1, m_2, \ldots, m_r$ years respectively. Show that a single payment of $(P_1 + P_2 + \cdots + P_k) - (B_1 + B_2 + \cdots + B_r)$ can be used to discharge the balance of the debt in n years, where

$$n = \frac{(P_1 n_1 + P_2 n_2 + \cdots + P_k n_k) - (B_1 m_1 + B_2 m_2 + \cdots + B_r m_r)}{(P_1 + P_2 + \cdots + P_k) - (B_1 + B_2 + \cdots + B_r)}.$$

32. Debts of $100, $200, and $300 are due in 30 days, 45 days, and 90 days, respectively. Payments of $150, $50, and $100 are made in 15 days, 30 days, and 45 days, respectively. Find the time that the single payment of $300 can be made to discharge the balance of the debt.

8

Quadratic Equations

70. Typical form

A **quadratic equation** is an equation in one unknown of the form

$$ax^2 + bx + c = 0 \qquad (1)$$

where a, b, and c do not involve x and $a \neq 0$.

Illustrations. The following are examples of quadratic equations:

$$5x^2 + 7x - 3 = 0.$$
$$3x^2 + 7x = 0.$$
$$x^2 - 16 = 0.$$

When a quadratic equation is arranged as in (1) it is said to be in the **typical form**. A quadratic equation such as

$$3x^2 = 8x - 2$$

can be put in the typical form by transposing, to yield

$$3x^2 - 8x + 2 = 0,$$

which is in the typical form.

EXERCISE 1

Arrange the following quadratic equations in the typical form, and select the values of a, b, and c.

1. $3x^2 - 8x + 7 = 0$
2. $5x^2 + 9x - 2 = 0$
3. $8x^2 = 11x - 2$
4. $x^2 + 10x = 3$
5. $x^2 + x = -4$
6. $3x = 5x^2 - 7$
7. $4 = x^2 - 6x$
8. $6x^2 - 8x = 0$
9. $3x^2 + 7x = 0$
10. $x^2 = 9x$
11. $3x^2 - 2 = 0$
12. $x^2 = 25$
13. $6 - 3x = x^2$
14. $7 = 8x^2$
15. $x^2 + px + q = 0$
16. $mx^2 + nx + k = 0$
17. $nx^2 - mx = 0$
18. $(k+1)x^2 - (5k+6)x - 3 = 0$
19. $x^2 + (2x - 3)^2 = 4x$
20. $(x - 3)(3x + 2) = 0$

71. Special or incomplete quadratics

If b or c is zero in
$$ax^2 + bx + c = 0$$
the quadratic equation is said to be **incomplete**. Thus,
$$5x^2 + 8x = 0,$$
and
$$3x^2 - 16 = 0,$$
are incomplete quadratics.

Suppose that $c = 0$. Then the quadratic equation becomes
$$ax^2 + bx = 0.$$
The left member of this equation can be factored to give
$$x(ax + b) = 0.$$
The two factors are x and $ax + b$. Since any value of x that makes either factor zero will satisfy the equation, we have
$$x = 0,$$
and
$$ax + b = 0.$$
From $ax + b = 0$,
$$ax = -b,$$
$$x = -\frac{b}{a}.$$
Thus, the two roots are $x = 0$ and $x = -\frac{b}{a}$.

Example 1. Solve for x: $\quad 5x^2 - 8x = 0$.
Solution. $\quad\quad\quad\quad 5x^2 - 8x = 0.$
Factoring the left member of the equation,
$$x(5x - 8) = 0.$$
Setting each factor equal to zero and solving for x,
$$x = 0,$$
$$x = \tfrac{8}{5}.$$

Example 2. Solve for x: $\quad 3x^2 = 16x$.
Solution. $\quad\quad\quad\quad 3x^2 = 16x.$
Transposing, $\quad\quad 3x^2 - 16x = 0.$
Factoring, $\quad\quad\quad x(3x - 16) = 0.$
Solving for x, $\quad\quad x = 0,$ and $x = \tfrac{16}{3}.$

Check: Substituting $x = 0$ in $3x^2 = 16x$ we have $3(0)^2 = 16(0)$, or $0 = 0$. Likewise, using $x = \tfrac{16}{3}$, we have,
$$3\left(\frac{16}{3}\right)^2 = 16\left(\frac{16}{3}\right),$$
$$\frac{256}{3} = \frac{256}{3}.$$

IMAGINARY NUMBERS

Notice that in Example 2 we do not divide both members of the equation by x. To do so would result in losing the root $x = 0$, for we would obtain only $x = \frac{16}{3}$.

When $b = 0$ in the quadratic equation
$$ax^2 + bx + c = 0,$$
the equation has the form
$$ax^2 + c = 0.$$
The discussion of this form will be postponed until Article 73.

EXERCISE 2

Solve the following incomplete quadratics for x, and check:

1. $7x^2 - 9x = 0$
2. $6x^2 + 11x = 0$
3. $x^2 - 9x = 0$
4. $x^2 + 6x = 0$
5. $5x^2 + 10x = 0$
6. $7x^2 = 5x$
7. $x^2 = 4x$
8. $7x - x^2 = 0$
9. $x - x^2 = 0$
10. $x = 3x^2$

72. Imaginary numbers

The square of any real number, positive or negative, is a positive number. Thus,
$$(3)^2 = 9 \quad \text{and} \quad (-3)^2 = 9.$$

The square root of a negative number cannot, therefore, be a real number; it is called an **imaginary number**. Thus,
$$\sqrt{-3} \quad \text{and} \quad \sqrt{-4}$$
are imaginary numbers.

The imaginary number $\sqrt{-1}$ occurs so often that a special symbol is used for it, namely, i. That is,
$$\sqrt{-1} = i.$$

Any imaginary number involves the product of a real number and i. Thus,
$$\sqrt{-4} = \sqrt{4}\sqrt{-1} = 2i,$$
$$\sqrt{-3} = \sqrt{3}\sqrt{-1} = \sqrt{3}i.$$

To add, subtract, or multiply with imaginary numbers we make two agreements:

1. *Replace $\sqrt{-a}$ ($a > 0$) by $i\sqrt{a}$ and operate with i as with any other literal number.*
2. *Replace i^2 by -1.*

A number of the form
$$a + bi$$

QUADRATIC EQUATIONS

where a and b are real numbers and $i = \sqrt{-1}$ is called a **complex number**. For example,

$$3 + 4i,\ 5 - 6i,\ \text{and } 3 - \sqrt{7}i$$

are complex numbers.

If $a = 0$, $a + bi$ reduces to the form bi, which is sometimes called a **pure imaginary number**.

Example 1. Add $2 + 5i$ to $8 - 9i$.

Solution. Treating i as a literal number, we have

$$(2 + 5i) + (8 - 9i) = 10 - 4i.$$

Example 2. Subtract $3 + 5\sqrt{-2}$ from $8 - \sqrt{-8}$.

Solution. These numbers can be written in the following forms:

$$3 + 5\sqrt{-2} = 3 + 5\sqrt{2}i \quad \text{and} \quad 8 - \sqrt{-8} = 8 - 2\sqrt{2}i.$$

Hence

$$(8 - \sqrt{-8}) - (3 + 5\sqrt{-2}) = (8 - 2\sqrt{2}i) - (3 + 5\sqrt{2}i) = 5 - 7\sqrt{2}i.$$

Example 3. Multiply $(5 + i)$ by $(5 - i)$, replacing i^2 by -1 in the product.

Solution. $(5 + i)(5 - i) = 25 - i^2 = 25 - (-1) = 25 + 1 = 26$.

Example 4. Multiply $3 + 4i$ by $5 - 6i$.

Solution.
$$(3 + 4i)(5 - 6i) = 15 + 2i - 24i^2,$$
$$= 15 + 2i + 24,$$
$$= 39 + 2i.$$

EXERCISE 3

Which of the following are imaginary numbers, and which are real numbers?

1. $\sqrt{7}$ **2.** $\sqrt{-5}$ **3.** $\sqrt{16}$ **4.** $-\sqrt{25}$ **5.** $\sqrt{-9}$ **6.** $\sqrt{-36}$

Express the following imaginary numbers in the form $i\sqrt{a}$, where $a > 0$ and $i = \sqrt{-1}$:

7. $\sqrt{-16}$ **8.** $\sqrt{-64}$ **9.** $\sqrt{-100}$ **10.** $\sqrt{-6}$ **11.** $\sqrt{-3}$
12. $\sqrt{-b},\ (b > 0)$

Perform the indicated operations, giving the answers in the form $a + bi$:

13. $(2 + 3i) + (8 - 3i)$
14. $(2 - 4i) + (3 - 2i)$
15. $(-6 + 4i) + (-8 - 2i)$
16. $(-3 - 4i) + (-8 - i)$
17. $(2 + i) - (3 + 5i)$
18. $(8 + 2i) - (9 + 3i)$
19. $(3 + 5i) - (6 + 5i)$
20. $(4 - 2i) - (4 + 3i)$
21. $(4 + i)(4 - i)$
22. $(6 - i)(6 + i)$
23. $(3 + 4i)(3 - 4i)$
24. $(5 + 8i)(7 - 2i)$
25. $(x + bi)(x - bi)$
26. $(2 + \sqrt{-3})(2 - \sqrt{-3})$

INCOMPLETE QUADRATICS, WITH b = 0   151

27. $(6 - \sqrt{-4})(6 + \sqrt{-4})$ 28. $(7 - \sqrt{-5})(7 + \sqrt{-5})$
29. $(7 + 5i)(8 - 3i)$ 30. $(7 + 2\sqrt{-2})(3 - 2\sqrt{-3})$

73. Incomplete quadratics, with b = 0

Consider the quadratic equation
$$ax^2 + c = 0.$$
Transposing, $\quad ax^2 = -c.$

Dividing both members by a, we get $x^2 = \dfrac{-c}{a}.$

Whence, $\quad x = \pm \sqrt{\dfrac{-c}{a}}.$

If $\dfrac{c}{a}$ is positive, $\sqrt{\dfrac{-c}{a}}$ is an imaginary number; if $\dfrac{c}{a}$ is negative, $\sqrt{\dfrac{-c}{a}}$ is a real number.

Example 1. Solve $x^2 - 16 = 0.$
Solution. $\quad\quad\quad\quad\quad x^2 = 16.$
$$x = \pm 4.$$
Check: Substituting ± 4 in $x^2 - 16 = 0$ gives.
$$(\pm 4)^2 - 16 = 0,$$
$$16 - 6 = 0,$$
$$0 = 0.$$

Example 2. Solve $x^2 + 16 = 0$ for x.
Solution. $\quad\quad x^2 + 16 = 0.$
$$x^2 = -16,$$
$$x = \pm \sqrt{-16} = \pm 4i.$$
Check: Substituting $\pm 4i$ in $x^2 + 16 = 0$ gives:
$$(\pm 4i)^2 + 16 = 0,$$
$$16i^2 + 16 = 0.$$
Since $i^2 = -1$ we have $\quad -16 + 16 = 0,$
$$0 = 0.$$

Notice that we use both the positive and negative values of the square root in these examples. We do this since both solutions satisfy the given equation.

EXERCISE 4

Solve for x and check:

1. $x^2 - 25 = 0$ 2. $x^2 + 25 = 0$ 3. $3x^2 + 48 = 0$
4. $5x^2 - 125 = 0$ 5. $x^2 = 100$ 6. $x^2 = 625$

7. $x^2 = -100$
8. $5 + x^2 = 0$
9. $x^2 - 6 = 0$
10. $3x^2 - 17 = 0$
11. $4x^2 + 15 = 0$
12. $9 = x^2$
13. $-3 = x^2$
14. $8 + x^2 = 0$
15. $12 - x^2 = 0$

74. Solution by factoring

Sometimes a complete quadratic equation can be solved by factoring.

Example 1. Solve for x: $x^2 - 7x + 12 = 0$.

Solution.
$$x^2 - 7x + 12 = 0.$$
$$(x - 4)(x - 3) = 0,$$
$$x - 4 = 0,$$
$$x = 4.$$
$$x - 3 = 0,$$
$$x = 3.$$

The roots are 4, 3.

Check:
$$4^2 - 7(4) + 12 = 0, \quad 3^2 - 7(3) + 12 = 0,$$
$$16 - 28 + 12 = 0, \quad 9 - 21 + 12 = 0,$$
$$28 - 28 = 0, \quad 21 - 21 = 0,$$
$$0 = 0. \quad 0 = 0.$$

Example 2. Solve for x: $12x^2 + 13x - 14 = 0$.

Solution.
$$12x^2 + 13x - 14 = 0.$$
$$(3x - 2)(4x + 7) = 0,$$
$$3x - 2 = 0,$$
$$3x = 2,$$
$$x = \tfrac{2}{3}.$$
$$4x + 7 = 0,$$
$$4x = -7,$$
$$x = \frac{-7}{4}.$$

The roots are $\frac{2}{3}, \frac{-7}{4}$.

Check:
$$12\left(\tfrac{2}{3}\right)^2 + 13\left(\tfrac{2}{3}\right) - 14 = 0, \quad 12\left(\tfrac{-7}{4}\right)^2 + 13\left(\tfrac{-7}{4}\right) - 14 = 0,$$
$$12\left(\tfrac{4}{9}\right) + 13\left(\tfrac{2}{3}\right) - 14 = 0, \quad 12\left(\tfrac{49}{16}\right) + 13\left(\tfrac{-7}{4}\right) - 14 = 0,$$
$$\tfrac{16}{3} + \tfrac{26}{3} - 14 = 0, \quad \tfrac{147}{4} - \tfrac{91}{4} - 14 = 0,$$
$$\tfrac{42}{3} - 14 = 0, \quad \tfrac{56}{4} - 14 = 0,$$
$$0 = 0. \quad 0 = 0.$$

SOLUTION BY COMPLETING THE SQUARE

EXERCISE 5

Solve by factoring, and check by substitution:

1. $x^2 + 6x + 8 = 0$
2. $x^2 + 9x + 14 = 0$
3. $x^2 - 7x + 10 = 0$
4. $x^2 - 6x + 8 = 0$
5. $x^2 + 11x + 18 = 0$
6. $x^2 + 4x - 21 = 0$
7. $x^2 - 6x - 16 = 0$
8. $x^2 - 7x - 18 = 0$
9. $x^2 + 6x - 27 = 0$
10. $x^2 - 9x + 20 = 0$
11. $2x^2 + 13x + 15 = 0$
12. $2x^2 + 9x + 7 = 0$
13. $3x^2 + 13x + 4 = 0$
14. $2x^2 - 9x + 9 = 0$
15. $4x^2 - 8x + 3 = 0$
16. $2x^2 - 5x - 12 = 0$
17. $10x^2 - 13x - 3 = 0$
18. $6x^2 + 13x - 28 = 0$
19. $2x^2 - 15x = 8$
20. $6x^2 = 6 - 5x$

75. Solution by completing the square

A quadratic equation may be solved by **completing the square**.

Example 1. Solve by completing the square: $x^2 + 8x + 12 = 0$.

Solution. $$x^2 + 8x + 12 = 0.$$

Transposing the constant term (the term not containing x),
$$x^2 + 8x = -12.$$

Adding "the square of half the coefficient of x" to both members,
$$x^2 + 8x + (\tfrac{1}{2} \cdot 8)^2 = -12 + (\tfrac{1}{2} \cdot 8)^2,$$
$$x^2 + 8x + 16 = -12 + 16 = 4.$$

Factoring the left member, which is now a perfect square,
$$(x + 4)^2 = 4.$$

Extracting the square roots,
$$x + 4 = \pm 2.$$

Whence, $$x = -6, -2.$$

Check:

$(-6)^2 + 8(-6) + 12 = 0,$ $(-2)^2 + 8(-2) + 12 = 0,$
$36 - 48 + 12 = 0,$ $4 - 16 + 12 = 0,$
$48 - 48 = 0,$ $16 - 16 = 0,$
$0 = 0.$ $0 = 0.$

Example 2. Solve by completing the square: $x^2 + 8x + 2 = 0$.

Solution.
$$x^2 + 8x + 2 = 0.$$
$$x^2 + 8x = -2,$$
$$x^2 + 8x + 16 = -2 + 16 = 14,$$
$$(x + 4)^2 = 14,$$
$$x + 4 = \pm \sqrt{14},$$
$$x = -4 + \sqrt{14},$$
$$x = -4 - \sqrt{14}.$$

Check: $(-4 + \sqrt{14})^2 + 8(-4 + \sqrt{14}) + 2 = 0,$
$16 - 8\sqrt{14} + 14 - 32 + 8\sqrt{14} + 2 = 0,$
$30 - 32 + 2 = 0,$
$32 - 32 = 0,$
$0 = 0.$

The other root can be checked similarly.

Example 3. Solve by completing the square: $3x^2 + 2x + 5 = 0$.

Solution. $3x^2 + 2x + 5 = 0.$
$3x^2 + 2x = -5,$
$x^2 + \frac{2}{3}x = -\frac{5}{3},$
$x^2 + \frac{2}{3}x + \frac{1}{9} = -\frac{5}{3} + \frac{1}{9} = -\frac{14}{9},$
$\left(x + \frac{1}{3}\right)^2 = -\frac{14}{9},$
$x + \frac{1}{3} = \pm\sqrt{-\frac{14}{9}} = \pm\frac{\sqrt{14}}{3}i,$
$x = -\frac{1}{3} + \frac{\sqrt{14}}{3}i,$
$x = -\frac{1}{3} - \frac{\sqrt{14}}{3}i.$

Check: $3\left(-\frac{1}{3} + \frac{\sqrt{14}}{3}i\right)^2 + 2\left(-\frac{1}{3} + \frac{\sqrt{14}}{3}i\right) + 5 = 0,$
$\frac{3}{9} - \frac{6\sqrt{14}}{9}i + \frac{14}{3}i^2 - \frac{2}{3} + 2\frac{\sqrt{14}}{3}i + 5 = 0,$
$\frac{1}{3} - \frac{14}{3} - \frac{2}{3} + 5 = 0,$
$-5 + 5 = 0,$
$0 = 0.$

The other root can be checked similarly.

EXERCISE 6

Supply the missing term to make these expressions perfect squares.

1. $x^2 + 10x + ()$
2. $x^2 + 6x + ()$
3. $x^2 + 12x + ()$
4. $x^2 + 14x + ()$
5. $x^2 + 16x + ()$
6. $x^2 + 4x + ()$
7. $x^2 + 2x + ()$
8. $x^2 + 7x + ()$
9. $x^2 - 9x + ()$
10. $x^2 - 12x + ()$
11. $x^2 - 5x + ()$
12. $x^2 - 18x + ()$
13. $x^2 - 19x + ()$
14. $x^2 - x + ()$
15. $x^2 - \frac{1}{2}x + ()$
16. $x^2 + \frac{1}{3}x + ()$
17. $x^2 - \frac{2}{3}x + ()$
18. $x^2 - \frac{1}{5}x + ()$
19. $x^2 + \frac{1}{4}x + ()$
20. $x^2 + \frac{3}{7}x + ()$

SOLUTION BY QUADRATIC FORMULA

Solve by completing the square:

21. $x^2 + 8x + 15 = 0$ **22.** $x^2 + 6x + 8 = 0$ **23.** $x^2 + 10x + 21 = 0$
24. $x^2 - 12x + 20 = 0$ **25.** $x^2 - 11x + 24 = 0$ **26.** $x^2 - 7x + 10 = 0$
27. $x^2 + 8x + 4 = 0$ **28.** $x^2 + 6x + 1 = 0$ **29.** $x^2 - 5x + 2 = 0$
30. $x^2 - 10x + 3 = 0$ **31.** $6x^2 - x - 1 = 0$ **32.** $4x^2 - 8x + 3 = 0$
33. $5x^2 - 6x + 1 = 0$ **34.** $3x^2 + 2x - 4 = 0$ **35.** $2x^2 - 8x + 3 = 0$
36. $4x^2 + 2x + 7 = 0$ **37.** $x^2 + 3x + 9 = 0$ **38.** $3x^2 - 3x + 5 = 0$
39. $x^2 + x + 4 = 0$ **40.** $x^2 + 2x + 5 = 0$

76. Solution by quadratic formula

Consider the general quadratic equation:

$$ax^2 + bx + c = 0.$$

Apply the method of completing the square to solve for x:

$$ax^2 + bx = -c,$$

$$x^2 + \frac{b}{a}x = -\frac{c}{a},$$

$$x^2 + \frac{b}{a}x + \frac{b^2}{4a^2} = \frac{b^2}{4a^2} - \frac{c}{a} = \frac{b^2 - 4ac}{4a^2},$$

$$\left(x + \frac{b}{2a}\right)^2 = \frac{b^2 - 4ac}{4a^2},$$

$$x + \frac{b}{2a} = \frac{\pm\sqrt{b^2 - 4ac}}{2a},$$

$$x = \frac{-b \pm \sqrt{b^2 - 4ac}}{2a}. \qquad (2)$$

This result is known as the **quadratic formula.** It states that the roots of

$$ax^2 + bx + c = 0$$

are

$$x = \frac{-b + \sqrt{b^2 - 4ac}}{2a},$$

and

$$x = \frac{-b - \sqrt{b^2 - 4ac}}{2a}.$$

The formula (2) can be used to solve quadratic equations, by substituting the values of a, b, and c in (2).

Example 1. Solve $4x^2 - 8x + 3 = 0$ by the quadratic formula.

Solution.
$$4x^2 - 8x + 3 = 0.$$
$$a = 4, \ b = -8, \ c = 3,$$

$$x = \frac{-b \pm \sqrt{b^2 - 4ac}}{2a},$$

$$= \frac{8 \pm \sqrt{64 - 4(4)(3)}}{8},$$
$$= \frac{8 \pm \sqrt{16}}{8} = \frac{8 \pm 4}{8},$$
$$= \frac{3}{2}, \frac{1}{2}.$$

Example 2. Solve $x^2 + 6x + 2 = 0$ by the quadratic formula.

Solution.
$$x^2 + 6x + 2 = 0.$$
$$a = 1, b = 6, c = 2.$$
$$x = \frac{-b \pm \sqrt{b^2 - 4ac}}{2a}.$$
$$x = \frac{-6 \pm \sqrt{36 - 4(1)(2)}}{2},$$
$$= \frac{-6 \pm \sqrt{28}}{2} = \frac{-6 \pm 2\sqrt{7}}{2},$$
$$= -3 + \sqrt{7}, \quad -3 - \sqrt{7}.$$

Example 3. Solve $x^2 + 2x + 9 = 0$ by the quadratic formula.

Solution.
$$x^2 + 2x + 9 = 0.$$
$$a = 1, b = 2, c = 9.$$
$$x = \frac{-b \pm \sqrt{b^2 - 4ac}}{2a}.$$
$$x = \frac{-2 \pm \sqrt{4 - 4(1)(9)}}{2},$$
$$= \frac{-2 \pm \sqrt{-32}}{2} = \frac{-2 \pm 4\sqrt{-2}}{2},$$
$$= -1 + 2\sqrt{2}i, \quad -1 - 2\sqrt{2}i.$$

EXERCISE 7

Solve by the quadratic formula:

1. $x^2 + 7x + 10 = 0$
2. $x^2 + 11x + 18 = 0$
3. $x^2 + 6x + 9 = 0$
4. $x^2 - 10x + 25 = 0$
5. $x^2 + 12x + 20 = 0$
6. $x^2 - 13x + 36 = 0$
7. $3x^2 - 16x + 15 = 0$
8. $3x^2 - 8x + 4 = 0$
9. $5x^2 - 6x + 1 = 0$
10. $12x^2 - 29x + 15 = 0$
11. $x^2 + 8x + 4 = 0$
12. $x^2 + 9x + 3 = 0$
13. $x^2 + 10x + 1 = 0$
14. $3x^2 + 8x + 2 = 0$
15. $4x^2 + 9x - 3 = 0$
16. $x^2 + x - 8 = 0$
17. $x^2 + 7x - 2 = 0$
18. $5x^2 - 16x - 2 = 0$
19. $x^2 + 2x + 9 = 0$
20. $x^2 + x + 8 = 0$
21. $x^2 + 3x + 10 = 0$
22. $x^2 - 4x + 16 = 0$
23. $3x^2 + 2x + 5 = 0$
24. $2x^2 - 8x + 1 = 0$
25. $4x^2 + 7x + 2 = 0$

77. Summary: Solution of quadratic equations

Incomplete quadratic equations of the form
$$ax^2 + c = 0$$
should be solved by transposing and extracting the square root, as in Article 73.

Incomplete quadratic equations of the form
$$ax^2 + bx = 0$$
should be solved by factoring, as in Article 71.

Complete quadratic equations of the form
$$ax^2 + bx + c = 0$$
should be solved by:

1. *Factoring, if the factors are easily determined.*
2. *Quadratic formula, if they are not factorable, or if the factors cannot easily be recognized.*

The method of completing the square is used chiefly to derive the quadratic formula.

Sometimes the solution of equations involving fractions leads to the solution of a quadratic equation. For example, the equation
$$\frac{5}{x+2} + \frac{2}{x-3} = 7$$
becomes, on clearing of fractions,
$$5(x-3) + 2(x+2) = 7(x+2)(x-3),$$
which reduces to
$$7x^2 - 14x - 31 = 0$$

EXERCISE 8

Solve for x:

1. $5x^2 + 9x = 0$
2. $x^2 = -25$
3. $x^2 + 17x = 0$
4. $x^2 - 11x + 30 = 0$
5. $x^2 + x + 3 = 0$
6. $3x^2 = x - 4$
7. $4 - x = x^2$
8. $4x^2 = x$
9. $3x^2 - 15 = 0$
10. $x^2 + 10x + 16 = 0$
11. $x^2 + 2 = 7x$
12. $3x^2 = 2x - 4$
13. $x^2 = 2x$
14. $(x+1)(x-3) = 0$
15. $\frac{x+1}{x-2} = \frac{x+3}{5}$
16. $\frac{6}{x-2} = \frac{x+3}{4}$
17. $\frac{6}{x} = \frac{x}{2}$
18. $\frac{x}{2} + \frac{1}{x} = 3$
19. $\frac{x-1}{3} + \frac{1}{x-2} = \frac{1}{2}$
20. $\frac{3x-1}{x+5} = \frac{x-6}{x-5} + 4$

78. Theorems concerning the roots of quadratic equations

Theorem I. *If r is a root of the quadratic equation,*
$$ax^2 + bx + c = 0$$
then $x - r$ is a factor of $ax^2 + bx + c$, and if $x - r$ is a factor of $ax^2 + bx + c$, then r is a root of the equation $ax^2 + bx + c = 0$.

This theorem, together with Theorem II, will be stated without proof.

Theorem II. *A quadratic equation has two and only two roots.*

Theorem III. *The sum of the roots of the quadratic equation*
$$ax^2 + bx + c = 0$$
is equal to $-\dfrac{b}{a}$.

Proof:
$$r_1 = \frac{-b + \sqrt{b^2 - 4ac}}{2a},$$
$$r_2 = \frac{-b - \sqrt{b^2 - 4ac}}{2a}.$$

Therefore,
$$r_1 + r_2 = \frac{-b + \sqrt{b^2 - 4ac}}{2a} + \frac{-b - \sqrt{b^2 - 4ac}}{2a} = \frac{-2b}{2a} = -\frac{b}{a}.$$

Theorem IV. *The product of the roots of the quadratic equation*
$$ax^2 + bx + c = 0$$
is equal to $\dfrac{c}{a}$.

Proof:
$$r_1 = \frac{-b + \sqrt{b^2 - 4ac}}{2a},$$
$$r_2 = \frac{-b - \sqrt{b^2 - 4ac}}{2a}.$$

$$r_1 r_2 = \left(\frac{-b + \sqrt{b^2 - 4ac}}{2a}\right)\left(\frac{-b - \sqrt{b^2 - 4ac}}{2a}\right),$$
$$= \frac{b^2 - (b^2 - 4ac)}{4a^2},$$
$$= \frac{4ac}{4a^2},$$
$$= \frac{c}{a}.$$

Theorem V. *The roots of the quadratic equation*
$$ax^2 + bx + c = 0$$

ROOTS OF QUADRATIC EQUATIONS

are (1) *real and equal if* $b^2 - 4ac = 0$,
(2) *real and unequal if* $b^2 - 4ac > 0$,
(3) *imaginary if* $b^2 - 4ac < 0$.

Proof: Since
$$x = \frac{-b \pm \sqrt{b^2 - 4ac}}{2a}$$
the nature of the roots depends on the value of $b^2 - 4ac$.

If $b^2 - 4ac = 0$, we have
$$x = \frac{-b}{2a},$$
in which case the roots are real and equal.

If $b^2 - 4ac > 0$, then $\sqrt{b^2 - 4ac}$ is a real number, and the two real roots are
$$r_1 = \frac{-b + \sqrt{b^2 - 4ac}}{2a},$$
and
$$r_2 = \frac{-b - \sqrt{b^2 - 4ac}}{2a},$$
which are unequal.

If $b^2 - 4ac < 0$, then $b^2 - 4ac$ is negative and $\sqrt{b^2 - 4ac}$ is the square root of a negative number, which is an imaginary number.

The quantity $b^2 - 4ac$ is called the **discriminant** of the quadratic equation $ax^2 + bx + c = 0$.

Example 1. Form the quadratic equation with roots 3, -4.

Solution. $(x - 3)(x + 4) = 0$.
$x^2 + x - 12 = 0$.

Example 2. Find the sum of the roots and the product of the roots of the quadratic equation $3x^2 + 7x - 4 = 0$.

Solution. $3x^2 + 7x - 4 = 0$.
$a = 3, b = 7, c = -4$.
$$\text{Sum of the roots} = -\frac{b}{a} = -\frac{7}{4}.$$
$$\text{Product of roots} = \frac{c}{a} = -\frac{4}{3}.$$

Example 3. Without solving for x, describe the nature of the roots of the quadratic equation $3x^2 + 7x - 2 = 0$, by calculating the value of the discriminant.

Solution. $3x^2 + 7x - 2 = 0$.
$a = 3, b = 7, c = -2$,
$b^2 - 4ac = (7)^2 - 4(3)(-2) = 49 + 24 = 73$.

Thus, $b^2 - 4ac > 0$, so the roots are real and unequal.

EXERCISE 9

Form the quadratic equation whose roots are:

1. $3, 8$
2. $4, 7$
3. $-2, 3$
4. $3, -5$
5. $-6, -9$
6. $\frac{1}{2}, 3$
7. $-4, \frac{2}{3}$
8. $\frac{1}{3}, \frac{2}{5}$
9. $\frac{3}{4}, -\frac{4}{7}$
10. $2 + \sqrt{3}, 2 - \sqrt{3}$
11. $4 - \sqrt{5}, 4 + \sqrt{5}$
12. $\dfrac{2 - \sqrt{5}}{3}, \dfrac{2 + \sqrt{5}}{3}$
13. $\frac{1}{3} - \frac{1}{3}\sqrt{6}, \frac{1}{3} + \frac{1}{3}\sqrt{6}$
14. $2 - i, 2 + i$
15. $3 - 4i, 3 + 4i$

Find the sum of the roots and the product of the roots:

16. $x^2 - 9x + 3 = 0$
17. $x^2 + 5x - 4 = 0$
18. $x^2 + 9x + 11 = 0$
19. $3x^2 - 5x + 6 = 0$
20. $5x^2 - 3x + 2 = 0$
21. $2x^2 + 7x + 8 = 0$
22. $x^2 + 8x - 15 = 0$
23. $4x^2 - 15x + 7 = 0$
24. $x^2 + x + 1 = 0$
25. $6x^2 - 6x + 13 = 0$

Without solving for x, describe the nature of the roots of the following equations:

26. $x^2 + 10x + 25 = 0$
27. $3x^2 + 7x + 2 = 0$
28. $x^2 + 2x + 12 = 0$
29. $5x^2 - 8x + 2 = 0$
30. $x^2 - 6x + 9 = 0$
31. $x^2 - 14x + 49 = 0$
32. $3x^2 - 6x + 1 = 0$
33. $4x^2 + 16x - 2 = 0$
34. $5x^2 - x + 12 = 0$
35. $6x^2 - 6x + 3 = 0$
36. $4x^2 + 20x + 25 = 0$
37. $25x^2 - 30x + 9 = 0$
38. $x^2 + x + 7 = 0$
39. $x^2 + 8x - 4 = 0$
40. $x^2 + 2x - 16 = 0$

79. Problems leading to quadratic equations

Sometimes a stated problem leads to a quadratic equation, the solutions of which furnish the solutions of the problem. In some cases one of the roots of the quadratic equation is rejected as meaningless in reference to the statement of the problem.

Example 1. The sum of two numbers is 18 and their product is 80. Find the numbers.

Solution. Let $x =$ one of the numbers, and
$18 - x =$ the other number.
Then
from which
$$x(18 - x) = 80,$$
$$18x - x^2 = 80,$$
$$x^2 - 18x + 80 = 0,$$
$$(x - 10)(x - 8) = 0,$$
$$x = 8, 10, \quad \text{the two roots.}$$

Using the root $x = 8$ as one of the numbers, we find that the other number is $18 - x = 18 - 8 = 10$.

Using the root $x = 10$ as one of the numbers, we find the other number is $18 - x = 18 - 10 = 8$. Therefore, the second root of the quadratic gives the same pair of numbers as given by the first, and hence no new solution of the problem results.

Check: $8 + 10 = 18,$ $\quad 8(10) = 80,$
$\qquad\qquad\quad 18 = 18.$ $\qquad\quad 80 = 80.$

Example 2. A dealer sold a number of radio sets for $800. If he had sold 10 more sets at $5 less per set he would have received $1050. How many sets did he sell, and what was the price of each set?

Solution. Let $x =$ number of sets sold, and

$$\frac{800}{x} = \text{number of dollars in the price of each set.}$$

Then
$$(x + 10)\left(\frac{800}{x} - 5\right) = 1050.$$

Multiplying both members by x,
$$(x + 10)(800 - 5x) = 1050x,$$
$$800x - 5x^2 + 8000 - 50x = 1050x,$$
$$-5x^2 - 300x + 8000 = 0,$$
$$x^2 + 60x - 1600 = 0,$$
$$(x + 80)(x - 20) = 0,$$
$$x = 20, \text{ number of sets sold,}$$
and $\dfrac{800}{x} = 40,$ number of dollars in the price of each set.

The root $x = -80$ is discarded.

Check: $(20 + 10)(40 - 5) = (30)(35) = 1050.$

EXERCISE 10

1. The sum of two numbers is 11 and their product is 30. Find the numbers.
2. The sum of two numbers is 48 and their product is 432. What are the numbers?
3. What numbers differing by 6 have a product of 160?
4. A rectangular lot is 90 feet longer than it is wide. Its area is 9000 square feet. What are the dimensions?
5. A dealer sold a number of electric clocks for $600. If he had sold 12 more at $3 less per clock he would have received a total of $24 more. How many clocks did he sell, and what was the selling price of each clock?
6. In the formula
$$S = \frac{n}{2}[2a + (n - 1)d]$$
$S = 38$, $a = 5$, and $d = 3$. Solve for n, retaining the positive answer only.
7. Find two consecutive positive integers whose product is 182.
8. The sum of a number and its reciprocal is 4. Find the number.
9. A man sold some shares of stock for $5000. Later, when the price dropped $10 per share, he used the money to buy 25 more shares than he had sold. How many shares did he sell?
10. In the formula $S = P(1 + i)^2$, find i if $S = 112.36$, $P = 100$.

MISCELLANEOUS EXERCISE

Solve for y:
1. $y^2 + 8y + 15 = 0$
2. $y^2 - 9y = 0$
3. $y = 10y^2$
4. $3y^2 - 9y + 2 = 0$
5. $4y^2 = y - 3$
6. $y^2 - 17 = 0$
7. $y^2 + 49 = 0$
8. $\dfrac{y+1}{y-3} = \dfrac{y+7}{y-2}$
9. $\dfrac{3}{y} = \dfrac{y}{27}$
10. $4 + \dfrac{1}{y} = y + 2$

11. Solve by completing the square: $x^2 + px + q = 0$.

12. Find the sum of the roots and the product of the roots of the quadratic equation, $x^2 + px + q = 0$.

13. Substitute $\dfrac{-b + \sqrt{b^2 - 4ac}}{2a}$ for x in the equation $ax^2 + bx + c = 0$ and show that it satisfies the equation.

14. Solve for n in terms of S, a, and d:

$$S = \dfrac{n}{2}[2a + (n-1)d].$$

15. Determine by inspection the sum of the roots and the product of the roots: $rx^2 + sx + t = 0$.

Reduce the following expressions to the form $a + bi$, where $i = \sqrt{-1}$, and $i^2 = -1$:

16. $\dfrac{3 + \sqrt{-4}}{2}$
17. $\dfrac{-10 + \sqrt{-20}}{2}$
18. $\dfrac{15 + \sqrt{-17}}{3}$

19. $(2 + 3i)(2 - 3i)$
20. $(m + ni)(m - ni)$

Determine the nature of the roots from the value of the discriminant:
21. $x^2 + 22x + 121 = 0$
22. $9x^2 - 24x + 16 = 0$
23. $x^2 - 9x + 3 = 0$
24. $x^2 + 2x + 12 = 0$
25. $x^2 + 3x + 4 = 0$

Form the quadratic equation with roots:
26. $-3, -9$
27. $-2, -2$
28. $\sqrt{-3}, -\sqrt{-3}$
29. $2 + \sqrt{5}, 2 - \sqrt{5}$
30. $\dfrac{-m + \sqrt{m^2 - 4n}}{2}, \dfrac{-m - \sqrt{m^2 - 4n}}{2}$

Solve each of the following equations by (a) factoring, (b) completing the square, and (c) quadratic formula:
31. $x^2 - 5x + 6 = 0$
32. $x^2 - 9x + 8 = 0$
33. $15x^2 - 8x + 1 = 0$
34. $x^2 - 16x + 64 = 0$
35. $6x^2 + 7x - 6 = 0$

9

Graphical Representation

80. Functions

A **constant** is a symbol that represents the same number throughout a given problem or discussion. In the equation
$$y = x + 8$$
the number 8 is a constant. In the formula for the area of a circle
$$A = \pi r^2$$
π is a constant; its value is 3.1416, correct to five significant figures.

A **variable** is a symbol that may represent different numbers in a given problem or discussion. In the equation
$$y = x + 8$$
the literal numbers x and y are variables. In the formula
$$A = \pi r^2$$
A and r are variables.

If two variables are so related that when a value of one is given, a corresponding value of the other is determined, the second variable is called a **function** of the first variable. In the equation
$$y = x + 8,$$
if $x = 2$, then $y = 10$; if $x = 3$, then $y = 11$, and so on. In this equation y is said to be a function of x.

The expression $x + 8$, represented by y in the above equation, is a function of x, since its value is determined when a value is assigned to x. In general, any expression involving a single variable x is a function of x. Thus, $x^2 - 5x + 6$, $x^3 - \frac{1}{x}$, and $\frac{x+2}{x-1}$ are functions of x. The student should note that the function $x^3 - \frac{1}{x}$ is not defined at $x = 0$, since division by zero is not permissible. Likewise the function $\frac{x+2}{x-1}$ is not defined at $x = 1$.

EXERCISE 1

In each case find the value of y corresponding to the given values of x.

1. $y = x - 9; x = -3, 0, 4$
2. $y = x + 6; x = -2, 0, 7$
3. $y = x^2; x = -2, -1, 0, 1, 2$
4. $y = -x^2; x = -2, -1, 0, 1, 2$
5. $y = -x^3; x = -2, -1, 0, 1, 2$
6. $y = x^2 - 5x; x = -1, 0, 1, 3, 5, 7$
7. $y = -x^2 + 6; x = -3, -2, -1, 0, 1, 2$
8. $y = 3x^2 - x + 2; x = -3, -2, -1, 0, 1, 2$
9. $y = -x^2 + 6x - 8; x = -2, -1, 0, 1, 2, 3, 4, 5$
10. $y = x^3 - 6x^2; x = -2, -1, 0, 1, 2$
11. $y = \log x; x = 2, 3, 4$
12. $y = 2^x; x = -2, -1, 0, 1, 2$
13. $y = 3^x; x = -2, -1, 0, 1, 2$
14. $y = (1 + x)^3; x = 0.02, 0.03$
15. $y = (1 + x)^2; x = 0.02, 0.03$
16. $y = (1.06)^x; x = 1, 2, 3$
17. $y = (1.04)^x; x = 1, 2, 3$
18. $y = \dfrac{1}{x}; x = -2, -1, 0, 1, 2$
19. $y = \dfrac{x}{x+1}; x = -2, -1, 0, 1, 2$
20. $y = \dfrac{x-2}{x}; x = -2, -1, 0, 1, 2$

81. Rectangular coordinate system

Let $X'X$ and $Y'Y$ be a pair of perpendicular lines in a plane intersecting at O. See Fig. 5.

Fig. 5

Consider $X'X$ and $Y'Y$ to be number scales with the zero point of each at O. Let the positive numbers on $X'X$ be represented by points on $X'X$ beginning at O and proceeding towards the right, as shown in Fig. 5, and let the negative numbers on $X'X$ be represented by points on $X'X$ beginning at O and proceeding in decreasing algebraic value towards the left. Likewise, let the positive numbers on $Y'Y$ be represented by points above O, and the negative numbers on $Y'Y$ by points below O, as indicated in Fig. 5.

Consider the point P in the plane of $X'X$ and $Y'Y$. The point P can be represented by an ordered pair of numbers. Suppose that P is 3 units to the right of $Y'Y$ and 2 units above $X'X$. Then the ordered pair of numbers (3, 2) locates the point P with respect to the reference lines $X'X$ and $Y'Y$.

The reference line $X'X$ is called the **X-axis,** the reference line $Y'Y$ is called the **Y-axis,** and the point O is called the **origin.** The number representing the perpendicular distance from any point P to the X-axis is called the **ordinate** of the point P, and the number representing the perpendicular distance from a point P to the Y-axis is called the **abscissa** of the point P. Together, the ordinate and abscissa of a given point P are called the **coordinates** of the point P.

Thus, for the point P in Fig. 5, the abscissa of P is 3, its ordinate is 2, and its coordinates are 3, 2. The abscissa is always given first, and the ordinate is given second.

Such a scheme for locating points in a plane is called a **rectangular coordinate system.**

To every point P in the plane there corresponds a pair of ordered numbers, and to every pair of ordered numbers there corresponds a point P in the plane.

When a point P is located in the above manner it is said to be plotted. Coordinate paper, ruled in squares, is used for convenience in plotting points.

The X-axis and Y-axis divide the plane into four regions. These regions are called **quadrants,** and are numbered as in Fig. 6.

	Y	
Second Quadrant $(-,+)$		First Quadrant $(+,+)$
X'	O	X
$(-,-)$ Third Quadrant		$(+,-)$ Fourth Quadrant
	Y'	

Fig. 6

In Fig. 6 the signs of the coordinates in the four quadrants are given.

Example. Plot the points (2, 4), (0, 3), (− 5, 1), (− 2, 0), (− 5, − 3), (0, − 2), (3, − 4), (5, 0), (0, 0).

Solution. Since the first number indicated for each point represents the distance from the Y-axis and the second the distance from the X-axis, the required points are as indicated in Fig. 7.

FIG. 7

EXERCISE 2

1. Plot the points (5, 8), (− 5, 8), (− 5, − 8), (5, − 8).
2. Plot the points (6, 0), (0, 0), (− 3, 0), (0, − 4).
3. Draw the triangle whose vertices are (− 2, 4), (6, 2), and (5, − 3).
4. Draw the square whose vertices are (4, 6), (− 4, 6), (− 4, − 6), and (4, − 6).
5. Plot the points (0, 3), (1, 4), (2, 5), and (3, 6). Is it possible to draw a straight line through these points?
6. Plot the following points as accurately as you can: (0, 0), (1, 0.1), (2, 0.4), (3, 0.9), (4, 1.6), (5, 2.5), (6, 3.6), (7, 4.9), (8, 6.4) (9, 8.1), (10, 10). Draw a smooth curve that passes through these points.
7. Plot the following points: (0, 1), (2, 3), (4, 1), (5, 5), (7, 4), (8, 7), (10, 5). Join the points successively by line segments.
8. Where are all points whose ordinate is 6?
9. Where are all points whose abscissa is 4?
10. Where are all points whose distance from the origin is 5?

82. Linear function

The function
$$mx + b, \quad m \neq 0$$

LINEAR FUNCTION

is called a **linear function**. Here m and b represent constants and x is a variable. Thus $3x + 5$, $x - 4$, and $6x$ are examples of linear functions.

The graph of
$$y = mx + b$$
is a straight line. By the graph of a function we mean the set of all points whose coordinates satisfy the equation representing the functions. That is, the graph of $y = 3x + 5$, for example, is the set of all points whose coordinates satisfy the equation $y = 3x + 5$.

To draw the graph of a linear function, such as $y = 3x + 5$, we assign values to x, compute the corresponding values of y, plot the points represented by these pairs of values of x and y, and draw a straight line through the points. See Fig. 8. Since two points determine a straight line, only two points are necessary to determine the graph of a linear function.

x	-4	-3	-2	-1	0	1
y	-7	-4	-1	2	5	8

Fig. 8

An equation of the form
$$Ax + By + C = 0$$
is called a **linear equation**, if A and B are not both zero.

GRAPHICAL REPRESENTATION

If $B \neq 0$, this equation can be put in the form

$$y = -\frac{A}{B}x - \frac{C}{B}$$

which is in the form $y = mx + b$.

If $B = 0$, the equation becomes

$$Ax + C = 0$$

and the graph of this equation is a straight line parallel to the Y-axis. Thus, the graph of $Ax + By + C = 0$ is a straight line.

EXERCISE 3

Draw the graphs:

1. $y = 2x + 8$ 2. $y = 3x + 4$ 3. $y = -5x + 2$ 4. $y = -6x + 3$
5. $y = 4x$ 6. $y = 2x$ 7. $y = -x$ 8. $y = -2x$ 9. $y = 2$
10. $y = -5$ 11. $x = 3$ 12. $x = -4$ 13. $2x + y = 7$
14. $3x + 4y = 6$ 15. $x + 2y - 8 = 0$ 16. $-x + 3y - 4 = 0$
17. $5x - 4y + 20 = 0$ 18. $x = 3y - 2$
19. $x = 5y + 10$ 20. $y = 0.2x + 6.4$
21. Plot the graph of $S = P(1 + ni)$ for $P = 10$ and $i = 0.06$, using $n = 0, 1, 2, 3, 4$.
22. Plot the graph of $S = P(1 + ni)$ for $P = 10$ and $n = 1$, using $i = 0$, 0.02, 0.04, 0.06.

83. Quadratic function

The function

$$ax^2 + bx + c, \quad a \neq 0,$$

is called a **quadratic function**. Here a, b, and c are constants and x is a variable. Thus, $3x^2 + 7x + 8$, $x^2 - 6x$, $5x^2 + 6$, and $8x^2$ are examples of quadratic functions.

The graph of

$$y = ax^2 + bx + c, \quad a \neq 0,$$

is a curve called a **parabola**.

Example 1. Draw the graph of $y = x^2 - 6x + 8$.

Solution. Prepare a table of values by assigning numerical values to x and computing the corresponding values of y.

x	-2	-1	0	1	2	3	4	5	6	7	8
y	24	15	8	3	0	-1	0	3	8	15	24

Plot these points and draw a smooth curve through them. See Fig. 9.

QUADRATIC FUNCTION

[Graph of $y = x^2 - 6x + 8$]

FIG. 9

In this example notice that the graph crosses the X-axis at $x = 2$ and $x = 4$, which are the roots of the quadratic equation $x^2 - 6x + 8 = 0$; that is, these are the values of x for which $y = 0$.

The graph of $y = ax^2 + bx + c$ will intersect the X-axis when $y = 0$; that is, the abscissas of the points of the intersection will be given by the roots of $ax^2 + bx + c = 0$. The graph may intersect the X-axis in two distinct points, it may be tangent to X-axis, or it may not touch the X-axis. These three possibilities depend upon the nature of the roots of $ax^2 + bx + c = 0$.

Recall, from Theorem V in Article 78, that the roots of a quadratic equation may be classified as

1. *real and unequal,* 2. *real and equal,* 3. *imaginary.*

These three cases are illustrated graphically in Fig. 10.

```
I  : y = x² − 6x + 8
II : y = x² − 6x + 9
III: y = x² − 6x + 10
```

Fig. 10

For I, $x^2 - 6x + 8 = 0$ when $x = 2$ and $x = 4$, so that the roots are real and unequal, and the graph of $y = x^2 - 6x + 8$ intersects the X-axis in two distinct points, at (2, 0) and (4, 0). For II, $x^2 - 6x + 9 = 0$ when $x = 3$ and $x = 3$, so the roots are real and equal, and the graph of $y = x^2 - 6x + 9$ is tangent to the X-axis at (3, 0). For III, $x^2 - 6x + 10 = 0$ for $x = 3 + i$ and $x = 3 - i$, so that the roots are imaginary and the graph of $y = x^2 - 6x + 10$ does not intersect the X-axis.

The graph of $y = ax^2 + bx + c$ opens upward if $a > 0$, as in Figs. 9 and 10. If $a < 0$, the graph of $y = ax^2 + bx + c$ opens downward, as in Fig. 11.

Example 2. Draw the graph of $y = -x^2 + 6x - 8$.

Solution. Proceed as in Example 1.

x	− 2	− 1	0	1	2	3	4	5	6	7	8
y	− 24	− 15	− 8	− 3	0	1	0	− 3	− 8	− 15	− 24

QUADRATIC FUNCTION

$y = -x^2 + 6x - 8$

FIG. 11

Consider the equation
$$y = ax^2 + bx + c.$$
Completing the square in x,
$$y = a\left(x^2 + \frac{b}{a}x + \frac{b^2}{4a^2}\right) + \frac{4ac - b^2}{4a},$$
or
$$y = a\left(x + \frac{b}{2a}\right)^2 + \frac{4ac - b^2}{4a}.$$

If $a > 0$, $x = -\dfrac{b}{2a}$ makes the value of y a **minimum,** and the minimum value of y is $\dfrac{4ac - b^2}{4a}$.

If $a < 0$, $x = -\dfrac{b}{2a}$ makes the value of y a **maximum,** and the maximum value of y is $\dfrac{4ac - b^2}{4a}$.

In problems, the numerical value of x obtained from $x = -\dfrac{b}{2a}$ can be substituted in the given function to obtain the minimum or maximum value of y.

Example 3. Find the lowest point of the parabola $y = x^2 - 6x + 8$.

Solution.
$$y = x^2 - 6x + 8.$$
$$a = 1, b = -6, c = 8.$$

The minimum value of y occurs when $x = -\dfrac{b}{2a} = -\dfrac{-6}{2(1)} = 3$. When $x = 3$, $y = 3^2 - 6(3) + 8 = -1$. The lowest point is therefore $(3, -1)$.

Example 4. Find the highest point of the parabola $y = -x^2 + 12x - 20$.

Solution.
$$y = -x^2 + 12x - 20.$$
$$a = -1, b = 12, c = -20.$$

The maximum value of y occurs when $x = -\dfrac{b}{2a} = -\dfrac{12}{2(-1)} = 6$. When $x = 6$, $y = -(6)^2 + 12(6) - 20 = 16$. The highest point is therefore $(6, 16)$.

EXERCISE 4

Draw the graphs:

1. $y = x^2$ 2. $y = 3x^2$ 3. $y = \tfrac{1}{4}x^2$ 4. $y = -x^2$ 5. $y = -3x^2$
6. $y = x^2 + 8x$ 7. $y = x^2 - 9x$ 8. $y = 3x^2 - 12x$
9. $y = 5x^2 + 2x$ 10. $y = x^2 - 7x + 14$ 11. $y = x^2 + 6x + 8$
12. $y = -3x^2 + 18x$ 13. $y = -5x^2 + 6x - 2$ 14. $y = -4x^2 - 16x$
15. $y = x^2 + 4$ 16. $y = x^2 - 9$ 17. $y = 3x^2 - 21$

Draw on the same axes:

18. $y = x^2$, $y = 3x^2$, $y = \tfrac{1}{3}x^2$
19. $y = x^2 - 5x + 3$, $y = x^2 - 5x + 8$, $y = x^2 - 5x + 12$
20. $y = x^2 - 6x$, $y = x^2 - 8x$
21. $y = x^2 - 8x + 12$, $y = x^2 - 8x + 16$, $y = x^2 - 8x + 20$
22. In the formula $S = P(1 + i)^n$, let $P = 10$ and let $n = 2$. Draw the graph. Include in your table of values the values of S for $i = 0$, 0.02, 0.04, 0.06, 0.08. Use different scales on the S and i axes.
23. In the formulas $S = P(1 + i)^n$ and $S = P(1 + ni)$, let $P = 10$ and let $n = 2$. Draw the graphs for both formulas on the same set of axes. Include in your table of values the values of S for $i = 0$, 0.02, 0.04, 0.06, 0.08. Use different scales on the S and i axes.

LOGARITHMIC AND EXPONENTIAL FUNCTIONS

24. The cost C of producing x radio sets per week is $(40 + 2x + \frac{1}{8}x^2)$ dollars. Plot the graph. Include in your table of values the values of C for $x = 0, 1, 2, 3, 4, 5, 6, 7, 8, 9, 10$.

25. Plot the graph of $y = (100 + x)(10 - 0.1x)$.

Find the highest (or lowest) point of each of the following parabolas, and draw the graphs:

26. $y = x^2 - 6x$ **27.** $y = -x^2 + 8x$ **28.** $y = x^2 + 6x + 12$
29. $y = -3x^2 + 24x - 14$ **30.** $y = -12x^2 + 6x - 2$

84. Logarithmic and exponential functions

Consider the function

$$y = \log x.$$

Using a table of mantissas, and the rules for characteristics, we obtain the following table of values:

x	$\log x$
0.01	-2.000000
0.1	-1.000000
0.5	-0.698970
1	0
2	0.301030
3	0.477121
4	0.602060
5	0.698970
.	.
.	.
.	.
10	1

Plotting these points gives the graph of the logarithmic function, in Fig. 12.

Notice the following features of this graph:

1. There is no logarithm of a negative number, that is, no portion of the curve exists to the left of the Y-axis.

2. The curve intersects the X-axis at the point $(1, 0)$; that is $\log 1 = 0$.

3. The logarithm of a number can be made smaller algebraically than any negative number chosen, by taking the number close enough to zero; that is, the curve approaches closer and closer to the Y-axis as x proceeds form $x = 1$ toward $x = 0$, but the curve never touches the Y-axis.

174   GRAPHICAL REPRESENTATION

[Graph of $y = \log x$]

Fig. 12

4. The curve rises gradually as x increases from $x = 1$ to larger and larger values of x, but it never ceases to rise; that is, $\log b > \log a$ if $b > a$.

By means of the graph of $y = \log x$ a graphical interpretation can be given to the process of interpolation.

Consider the problem of finding $\log 2000.4$ by interpolation.

$$1\left[0.4\begin{bmatrix}\log 2001 & 3.301247 \\ \log 2000.4 & \\ \log 2000 & 3.301030\end{bmatrix}d\right]0.000217$$

The proportion is:

$$\frac{d}{0.000217} = \frac{0.4}{1}.$$

Consider the graph of this portion of the curve of the logarithmic function. See Fig. 13, which is greatly magnified and distorted to emphasize the point.

Linear interpolation may be thought of as a process of substituting a straight line segment AED for the curved segment AFD of the logarithmic curve. By similar triangles,

$$\frac{BE}{CD} = \frac{AB}{AC}.$$

But $BE = d,$
           $CD = 3.301247 - 3.301030 = 0.000217,$
           $AB = 2000.4 - 2000 = 0.4.$

So $AC = 2001 - 2000 = 1$,

$$\frac{d}{0.000217} = \frac{0.4}{1},$$

which is the proportion used in interpolation.

Fig. 13

Now the value of d is BE on Fig. 13, which, when added to AH ($= BG$) gives GE as the approximate ordinate to the curve. Notice

Fig. 14

that the true ordinate to the curve is GF, which is slightly larger than GE, the value obtained by interpolation.

Actually, the curvature is so slight between A and D that the straight line approximation is eminently suitable as an approximation to the true value.

Because of the definition of a common logarithm, the two equations

$$y = \log x \quad \text{and} \quad x = 10^y$$

are equivalent. They state that y is the logarithm of x to the base 10, or that y is the exponent of the power to which 10 must be raised to give x; these two statements have exactly the same meaning.

Consider the equation

$$y = 10^x$$

This is an **exponential equation.** Comparing it with $x = 10^y$, we notice that the x and y have been interchanged. The graph of $y = 10^x$ is shown in Fig. 14.

This graph is similar to the graph of $y = \log x$, except that the x and y have been interchanged.

In the mathematics of finance it is shown that P dollars invested

Fig. 15

at 6% interest compounded annually for x years will amount to S dollars, where
$$S = P(1.06)^x.$$
Let $P = 1$; then: $S = 1.06^x.$

This is an exponential equation; its graph for $x \geq 0$ is shown in Fig. 15.

x	0	1	10	20	30	40	50
S	1	1.06	1.79	3.21	5.74	10.29	18.42

EXERCISE 5

1. Plot the graph of $y = \log x$. Include in your table of values the values of y for $x = 1, 10, 20, 30, 40, 50, 60, 70, 80, 90, 100$. Use different scales for the X, Y axes.

2. Find, by linear interpolation, the logarithm of 25 from $\log 20$ and $\log 30$. Illustrate by a diagram, and compare the result with $\log 25$ from the table of logarithms.

3. Draw the graph of $y = 2^x$. Include in your table of values the values of y for $x = 0, 1, 2, 3, 4$.

4. On the same set of axes draw the graphs of $y = 2^x$ and $y = 3^x$. Include in your table of values the values of y for $x = 0, 1, 2, 3, 4$.

5. Draw the graph of $S = P(1 + i)^n$ for $P = 10$, $i = 0.06$, using $n = 0, 1, 2, 3$. Use different scales on the S, i axes.

6. In the formula $S = P(1.06)^x$ let $S = 1$; then $P = \dfrac{1}{(1.06)^x} = (1.06)^{-x}.$
Plot the graph. Include in your table of values the values of P for $x = 0, 1, 10, 20, 30, 40, 50$.

85. Other functions

The systematic study of the graphs of functions is undertaken in analytic geometry. In this article we shall consider only a few cases and treat them only briefly.

Example 1. Plot the graph of $y = x^3$.

Solution. Prepare a table of values:

x	-3	-2	-1	0	1	2	3
y	-27	-8	-1	0	1	8	27

Draw the graph. See Fig. 16.

GRAPHICAL REPRESENTATION

FIG. 16

Example 2. Plot the graph of $y = x^3 - 2x^2 - 8x$.

Solution. Prepare a table of values.

x	-3	-2	-1	0	1	2	3	4	5
y	-21	0	5	0	-9	-16	-15	0	35

Draw the graph. See Fig. 17.

Example 3. Plot the graph of $y = \dfrac{10}{x}$.

Solution. Prepare a table of values:

x	-10	-5	-2	-1	0	1	2	5	10
y	-1	-2	-5	-10	Undefined	10	5	2	1

Draw the graph. See Fig. 18.

FIG. 17

FIG. 18

EXERCISE 6

Draw the graphs:
1. $y = \frac{1}{8}x^3$
2. $y = x^3 + 18x$
3. $y = x^3 + 2x^2 - 15x$
4. $y = x^2 + \frac{1}{x}$; positive values of x only
5. $y = x^3 + \frac{1}{x}$; positive values of x only
6. $y = +\sqrt{x}$
7. $y = \frac{20}{x}$
8. $y = \frac{x}{x+5}$
9. $y = \frac{x-3}{x}$
10. $y = x^3 - 24x^2$
11. $y = 2^{-x}$
12. $y = 1.02^{-x}$
13. $y = \frac{100}{x^2}$
14. $y = x^2 + \frac{100}{x^2}$
15. $y = 10x + \frac{1}{x}$

86. Graphical solution of a system of linear equations

Consider the system of linear equations
$$x + y = 16,$$
$$x - y = 4.$$

Fig. 19

GRAPHICAL SOLUTION OF A SYSTEM OF LINEAR EQUATIONS

The graph of each of these equations is a straight line. Each equation is satisfied by an unlimited number of pairs of values of x and y. Thus, $x + y = 16$ is satisfied by the pairs of values of x and y (0, 16), (1, 15), (2, 14), (3, 13), and so on. Also, $x - y = 4$ is satisfied by the pairs of values (0, $-$ 4), (1, $-$ 3), (2, $-$ 2), and so on. Out of all of these pairs of values there is one pair that satisfies both equations, namely, $x = 10$ and $y = 6$. Algebraically, these values can be obtained by solving the equations simultaneously. Graphically, this pair of values indicates the point of intersection of the graphs of the two straight lines that represent these equations. See Fig. 19.

Consider the pair of equations

$$x + y = 16,$$
$$x + y = 8.$$

There is no pair of values of x and y that satisfies both of these equations. Graphically, this signifies that the graphs of the two equations are two parallel lines. See Fig. 20.

Fig. 20

Consider the pair of equations

$$x + y = 16,$$
$$2x + 2y = 32.$$

There is an unlimited number of pairs of values of x and y that satisfy both of these equations. Graphically, this signifies that the graphs of the equations are coincident straight lines. See Fig. 21.

Fig. 21

If a pair of linear equations in two unknowns has a single solution — that is, if their graphs intersect in a single point — the equations are said to be **consistent**. If a pair of linear equations in two unknowns have no solution — that is, if their graphs are two paralled lines — the equations are said to be **inconsistent**. If a pair of linear equations in two unknowns have an unlimited number of solutions — that is, if their graphs are coincident straight lines — the equations are said to be **equivalent** or **dependent**.

EXERCISE 7

Find the solutions (if they exist) of the following pairs of equations by plotting their graphs:

1. $x + y = 10,$
   $2x + y = 180$

2. $x - y = 10,$
   $x + y = 6$

3. $3x + 2y = 15,$
   $2x + 3y = 45$

FITTING CURVES TO DATA: STRAIGHT LINES 183

4. $3x + y = 9,$
$3x + y = 12$
5. $x - 4y = 6,$
$2x - 8y = 12$
6. $5x + 2y = 20,$
$x - 4y = -18$
7. $x + 2y = 7,$
$x + 2y = 3$
8. $x + y = 5,$
$x - y = 15$
9. $x + 8y = 10,$
$2x + 16y = 20$
10. $3x - y = 7,$
$x + 8y = 5$

87. Fitting curves to data: straight lines

Sometimes there is no known equation relating the pairs of values of two variables; all that is available is a set of pairs of corresponding values of the variables, obtained by experiment or by observation. These given pairs of corresponding values are called **empirical data.**

Suppose that the data are plotted and the graph appears to be nearly a straight line. The problem then arises of finding the equation of a straight line that approximately fits the data. There are several ways of doing this.

The quickest and easiest method is to draw a line that appears to fit the given data, select two points on this line, and find the equation of the line through these two points. This equation will approximately represent, or fit, the given data. This is called the **method of selected points.** We illustrate the method by an example.

Example 1. Find the equation of a line that approximately fits the following data, using the method of selected points.

x	2	3	5	6	8	10
y	2	4	7	6	8	11

Solution. Plot the given points on graph paper. See Fig. 22. Draw a straight line that nearly fits these points. On this line select two points, say (3, 4) and (10, 11). Substitute these two pairs of values for x and y in the equation
$$y = mx + b.$$
We obtain:
$$4 = m(3) + b,$$
$$11 = m(10) + b.$$
Solve these two equations for m and b. We obtain $m = 1$ and $b = 1$. The equation of the line is
$$y = x + 1.$$

This is the equation of a line that nearly fits the given data. Notice that the result depends on the judgment of the person who draws the straight line that approximates the data.

Another method of solving this same type of problem is called

FIG. 22

the **method of averages.** We illustrate the method as applied to the previous example:

Example 2. Using the data of Example 1, find the equation of a line that approximately fits the given data.

Solution. Separate the data into two groups:

x	2	3	5
y	2	4	7

x	6	8	10
y	6	8	11

Substitute each pair of values for x and y in the equation

$$y = mx + b,$$

keeping the resulting equations in two groups, and add:

$$\begin{aligned} 2 &= m(2) + b \\ 4 &= m(3) + b \\ \underline{7 &= m(5) + b} \\ 13 &= 10m + 3b \end{aligned} \qquad \begin{aligned} 6 &= m(6) + b \\ 8 &= m(8) + b \\ \underline{11 &= m(10) + b} \\ 25 &= 24m + 3b \end{aligned}$$

This procedure yields the two equations:

$$10m + 3b = 13,$$
$$24m + 3b = 25.$$

FITTING CURVES TO DATA: STRAIGHT LINES 185

Solving for m and b,
$$m = \tfrac{6}{7}, \ b = \tfrac{31}{21}.$$
Therefore,
$$y = \tfrac{6}{7}x + \tfrac{31}{21}$$
is the equation of a line that approximately fits the given data.

Notice that this method does not depend on sketching in a line that seems to fit the data, as was the case in the method of selected points. Also, notice that all of the data enter into the calculation of m and b. On the other hand, this method takes more time to obtain the final result, and if the data were numerous, it would entail a great deal of arithmetic.

If there are an odd number of equations, we agree to place the larger number of equations in the second group.

There is a third method which, in the opinion of statisticians and others, gives the line of best fit. This method is known as the **method of least squares.** We illustrate the method by applying it to the same data as before.

Example 3. Using the data in Example 1, find the equation of a line that best fits the data, by the method of least squares.

Solution. Substitute each of the given pairs of values of x and y in the equation $y = mx + b$, arrange the results in a single column, and add:

$$
\begin{aligned}
2 &= m(2) + b \\
4 &= m(3) + b \\
7 &= m(5) + b \\
6 &= m(6) + b \\
8 &= m(8) + b \\
\underline{11} &= \underline{m(10) + b} \\
38 &= 34m + 6b
\end{aligned}
$$

Multiply each of these equations by the coefficient of m in that equation, arrange the results in a single column, and add:

$$
\begin{aligned}
4 &= 4m + 2b \\
12 &= 9m + 3b \\
35 &= 25m + 5b \\
36 &= 36m + 6b \\
64 &= 64m + 8b \\
\underline{110} &= \underline{100m + 10b} \\
261 &= 238m + 34b
\end{aligned}
$$

Solving the equations

$$238m + 34b = 261,$$
$$34m + 6b = 38$$

for m and b, we obtain
$$m = \tfrac{137}{136} \text{ and } b = \tfrac{5}{8},$$
so that the final equation is
$$y = \tfrac{137}{136}x + \tfrac{5}{8}.$$

The theory of this method is beyond the scope of this book and will not be reproduced here. It may be sufficient to say that this method gives the best fit in the sense that the sum of the squares of the distances from each of the given points to this line is a minimum. The method of least squares is justifiable when the accuracy of the data and the use to be made of the resulting equation demand the best method possible.

In summary, we list the three answers to the same problem as obtained by three different methods:

1. $y = x + 1$ (method of selected points)
2. $y = \tfrac{6}{7}x + \tfrac{31}{21}$ (method of averages)
3. $y = \tfrac{137}{136}x + \tfrac{5}{8}$ (method of least squares).

EXERCISE 8

Find the equation of a line that approximately fits the following data. Use all three methods and compare the results:

1.

x	3	4	5	6
y	8	10	11	13

2.

x	0	5	10	15
y	12	9	7	4

3.

x	0	2	4	6	8	10
y	3	5	10	12	16	19

4.

x	0	1	2	3	4
y	0	5	10	16	21

5. A retail storekeeper, while studying the effect on gross sales of increasing the number of salespeople, accumulated the following data, where x represents the number of salespeople and y represents gross sales per week.

x	20	22	23	25
y	30,000	32,000	34,000	35,000

FITTING CURVES TO DATA: PARABOLAS

Use the method of averages to find the equation of the line that approximately fits these data, and from the equation calculate the gross sales corresponding to 24 salespeople.

6. An owner of a motel keeps a record of number of guests per day, x, and total expenditures per day, y. The data are:

x	36	43	47	52	58
y	58	69	75	82	90

Using the method of selected points, find the equation of a line that approximately fits these data. Use the equation to estimate the expenditure corresponding to 50 guests.

7. A man who owns a fleet of trucks keeps a record of number of trucks in operation, x, versus number of ton-miles of pay load moved in one day, y. The data are:

x	32	38	40	43	47
y	800	940	990	1060	1180

Using the method of averages, find the equation of a line that approximately fits these data. Use the equation to estimate the number of ton-miles corresponding to 45 trucks in operation.

8. Use the method of averages and the method of least squares to find the equation of a line that approximately fits these data:

x	1	2	3
y	8	11	14

Explain your results.

88. Fitting curves to data: parabolas

Sometimes empirical data are plotted on graph paper and the points seem to lie on a curve, which may be a portion of a parabola of the type $y = ax^2 + bx + c$.

To fit a parabola to a set of given data, we may sketch a curve that approximately fits the data, select three points on this curve, substitute the three pairs of values of x and y in the equation $y = ax^2 + bx + c$, and solve the resulting three equations in three unknowns for a, b, and c. This gives the equation of a parabola that approximately fits the data, and the parabola can be plotted from its equation. This is called the method of selected points.

Example 1. Fit a parabola of the type $y = ax^2 + bx + c$ to the data:

x	0	2	4	6
y	16	23	24	15

Solution. Plot these points on graph paper, and draw a smooth curve that approximately fits these points. See Fig. 23.

From the sketch select three pairs of values of x and y. Suppose that these selected points are (0, 16), (1, 20), and (5, 22). Substitute these pairs of values for x and y in $y = ax^2 + bx + c$, arrange the results in a column, and solve for a, b, c:

$$16 = a(0) + b(0) + c$$
$$20 = a(1) + b(1) + c$$
$$22 = a(25) + b(5) + c$$

Solving for a, b, and c we obtain $a = -0.7$, $b = 4.7$, $c = 16$. Therefore, the equation of a parabola that approximately fits these data is

$$y = -0.7x^2 + 4.7x + 16.$$

Instead of using the method of selected points we may use the method of averages. To do this, substitute the pairs of values of x and y in the given data in the equation $y = ax^2 + bx + c$, arrange the results in three groups, and add. Solve the resulting three equations in three unknowns for a, b, and c. This gives the equation of a parabola that approximately fits the given data. We illustrate the method by applying it to the data of Example 1:

Example 2. Using the data of Example 1, find the equation of a parabola that approximately fits the data by the method of averages.

Solution. Substituting the given values of x and y in the equation $y = ax^2 + bx + c$, arranging in three groups, and adding, we obtain:

$16 = a(0) + b(0) + c, \quad 23 = a(4) + b(2) + c, \quad 24 = a(16) + b(4) + c$
$ \underline{15 = a(36) + b(6) + c.}$
$ 39 = a(52) + b(10) + 2c.$

Notice that in this example, because of the small number of given points, we have to add only two equations. We put the last two equations in the third group; this was arbitrary. Now, solving the equations

$$c = 16,$$
$$4a + 2b + c = 23,$$
$$52a + 10b + 2c = 39,$$

for a, b, and c we obtain $a = -0.875$, $b = 5.25$, $c = 16$. The equation of a parabola that approximately fits these data is

$$y = -0.875x^2 + 5.25x + 16.$$

FITTING CURVES TO DATA: PARABOLAS

FIG. 23

The method of least squares is applicable here, also. We illustrate by applying the method to the data of Example 1.

Example 3. Using the data of Example 1, find the equation of a parabola that fits the data by the method of least squares.

Solution. Substitute each pair of the given values of x and y in the equation $y = ax^2 + bx + c$, arrange in a single column, and add:

$$
\begin{aligned}
16 &= a\,(0) + b(0) + c \\
23 &= a\,(4) + b(2) + c \\
24 &= a(16) + b(4) + c \\
\underline{15 &= a(36) + b(6) + c} \\
78 &= 56a\;\; + 12b + 4c
\end{aligned}
$$

Multiply each of these equations by the coefficient of b in the equation, arrange in a single column, and add:

$$\begin{aligned} 0 &= 0 + 0 + 0 \\ 46 &= 8a + 4b + 2c \\ 96 &= 64a + 16b + 4c \\ 90 &= 216a + 36b + 6c \\ \hline 232 &= 288a + 56b + 12c \end{aligned}$$

Multiply each of the first set of equations by the coefficient of a in that equation, arrange in a single column, and add:

$$\begin{aligned} 0 &= 0 + 0 + 0 \\ 92 &= 16a + 8b + 4c \\ 384 &= 256a + 64b + 16c \\ 540 &= 1296a + 216b + 36c \\ \hline 1016 &= 1568a + 288b + 56c \end{aligned}$$

Solving the equations

$$56a + 12b + 4c = 78,$$
$$288a + 56b + 12c = 232,$$
$$1568a + 288b + 56c = 1016,$$

for a, b, and c, we obtain

$$a = -1,$$
$$b = 5.9,$$
$$c = 15.8.$$

Therefore, the equation of the parabola is

$$y = -x^2 + 5.9x + 15.8.$$

In summary, we list here the three different results for the data of Example 1 by the three different methods:

1. $y = -0.7x^2 + 4.7x + 16$ (selected points)
2. $y = -0.875x^2 + 5.25x + 16$ (averages)
3. $y = -x^2 + 5.9x + 15.8$ (least squares).

EXERCISE 9

Find the equation of a parabola of the type $y = ax^2 + bx + c$ that approximately fits the following data. Use all three methods and compare the results.

1.

x	0	1	2	3
y	1	2	0	-3

FITTING CURVES TO DATA: PARABOLAS

2.

x	0	1	2	3	4	5
y	0	1	0	-3	-7	-14

3.

x	1	2	5
y	3	3	39

4.

x	0	3	7	10
y	6	10	12	11

5. The cost of producing x vacuum cleaners per week is y dollars, where x and y are as follows:

x	0	5	10	20
y	50	58	70	105

Find the equation of a parabola that approximately fits these data, using the method of selected points.

6. Find the equation of a parabola of the type $y = ax^2 + bx + c$ that approximately fits the following data, using the method of least squares:

x	0	1	2	3
y	0	20	37	44

MISCELLANEOUS EXERCISE

1. Plot the graph of $3x + 4y = 12$.
2. On the same set of axes plot the graphs of $y = x + 8$ and $y = \frac{1}{2}x^2$, and locate the points of intersection.
3. On the same set of axes plot the graphs of $y = x$, $y = x^2$, $y = x^3$.
4. Draw the graph of $y = x^2 - 8x$ and find the lowest point of the parabola.
5. Plot the graph of $y = \log x$ for $x = 0.5, 1, 5, 10, 15, 20, 25$.
6. Plot the graph of $y = \dfrac{36}{x^2}$.
7. Plot the graph of $y = x^2 - \dfrac{10}{x}$ for positive values of x.
8. Solve the equations
$$3x + 5y = 28,$$
$$2x + 8y = 28,$$
and draw the graphs.

9. Which of the following systems of equations are inconsistent?

(a) $3x + y = 9,$
$2x + y = 9$

(b) $3x + y = 9,$
$6x + 2y = 18$

(c) $3x + y = 9,$
$3x + y = 10$

10. Estimate the roots of $x^2 + 4x + 2 = 0$ by drawing the graph of $y = x^2 + 4x + 2$.

11. Draw the graph of $y = \pm \sqrt{25 - x^2}$. Include in your table of values the values of y for $x = \pm 5, \pm 4, \pm 3, \pm 1, 0$.

12. (a) Find the distance from the point $(5, 2)$ to the point $(8, 6)$.

(b) Show that the distance from the point (x_1, y_1) to the point (x_2, y_2) is $\sqrt{(x_2 - x_1)^2 + (y_2 - y_1)^2}$.

13. Plot the graphs of $y = \tfrac{1}{2}x$, $y = x$, and $y = 2x$ on the same set of axes.

14. If y varies directly as x, then $y = kx$. If $x = 20$ when $y = 2$, find the value of k, and draw the graph of $y = kx$ for positive values of x.

15. If y varies inversely as x, then $y = \dfrac{k}{x}$. If $x = 30$ when $y = 3$, find the value of k, and draw the graph of $y = \dfrac{k}{x}$ for positive values of x.

16. Plot the graph of $P = \dfrac{S}{1 + ni}$ for $S = 1$ and $i = 0.04$, using $n = 0, 1, \cdots, 10$. Choose suitable scales on the P, n axes.

17. On the same set of axes, plot the graphs of $y = x^2 - 2$, $y = x^2$, $y = x^2 + 2$. From the graphs, what can you say of the roots of the quadratic equations $x^2 - 2 = 0$, $x^2 = 0$, and $x^2 + 2 = 0$?

10

Progressions: Binomial Theorem

89. Arithmetical progressions

An **arithmetical progression** is a sequence of numbers each of which differs from the immediately preceding one by a constant called the **common difference**. For example:

$$1, 3, 5, 7, 9, \cdots$$

is an arithmetical progression with the common difference 2. Also,

$$25, 20, 15, 10, \cdots$$

is an arithmetical progression with the common difference -5, and

$$\tfrac{1}{4}, \tfrac{1}{2}, \tfrac{3}{4}, 1, \tfrac{5}{4}, \cdots$$

is an arithmetical progression with the common difference $\tfrac{1}{4}$.

The numbers of the sequence are called the **terms** of the progression.

In general, we let a stand for the first term of an arithmetical progression, d, the common difference, n the number of terms under consideration in a given problem, l the nth or last term considered, and s the sum of n terms of the sequence.

Then $a, d, n, l,$ and s are called the **elements** of the arithmetical progression.

Consider the first four terms of the arithmetical progression

$$2, 4, 6, 8, 10, 12, \cdots.$$

Then $a = 2, d = 2, n = 4, l = 8,$ and $s = 20$.

In the arithmetical progression

$$25, 20, 15, \cdots$$

consider the first six terms. Then $a = 25, d = -5, n = 6, l = 0,$ and $s = 75$.

90. Relations among the elements

Consider the problem of finding a formula for the **nth or last term**, or last term considered, of an arithmetical progression. We have:

$$a = \text{first term}$$
$$a + d = \text{second term}$$
$$a + 2d = \text{third term}$$
$$a + 3d = \text{fourth term}$$
$$\cdots$$
$$a + (n-1)d = n\text{th term.}$$

Thus,
$$l = a + (n-1)d. \tag{1}$$

Example 1. Find the 25th term of the arithmetical progression
$$1, 3, 5, \cdots.$$

Solution. $\quad a = 1, d = 2, n = 25.$
$$l = a + (n-1)d.$$
$$l = 1 + (25-1)2,$$
$$= 1 + (24)2,$$
$$= 1 + 48,$$
$$= 49, \text{ the 25th term.}$$

Example 2. Find the 14th term of the arithmetical progression
$$25, 20, 15, \cdots.$$

Solution. $\quad a = 25, d = -5, n = 14.$
$$l = a + (n-1)d.$$
$$l = 25 + (14-1)(-5),$$
$$= 25 + (13)(-5),$$
$$= 25 - 65,$$
$$= -40, \text{ the 14th term.}$$

Consider the problem of finding the sum of the first n terms of an arithmetical progression. The sum of an arithmetical progression may be written

$$s = a + (a+d) + (a+2d) + \cdots + (l-2d) + (l-d) + l.$$

Also,
$$s = l + (l-d) + (l-2d) + \cdots + (a+2d) + (a+d) + a.$$

Adding,
$$2s = (a+l) + (a+l) + (a+l) + \cdots + (a+l) + (a+l) + (a+l).$$

Now there are exactly n of these quantities $(a+l)$, so
$$2s = n(a+l).$$

Dividing both members of this equation by 2,

$$s = n\frac{(a+l)}{2}. \qquad (2)$$

Notice that this formula states that the **sum of n terms** of an arithmetical progression is equal to the product of the number of terms by the arithmetical average of the first and last terms.

Example 3. Find the sum of the first 15 terms of the arithmetical progression

$$8, 11, 14, \cdots.$$

Solution.
$$a = 8, d = 3, n = 15.$$
$$l = a + (n-1)d,$$
$$l = 8 + (15-1)3,$$
$$= 50.$$
$$s = n\frac{(a+l)}{2}.$$
$$s = 15\frac{(8+50)}{2},$$
$$= 435.$$

Formulas (1) and (2) can be combined to give

$$s = n\frac{(a+l)}{2},$$
$$= n\frac{[a + a + (n-1)d]}{2},$$
$$= \frac{n}{2}[2a + (n-1)d]. \qquad (3)$$

Sometimes formula (2) is preferable to formula (3), and vice versa. The decision as to which of these two formulas to use in a certain problem depends upon the data given in the problem.

Example 4. Find the sum of the first 10 terms of the arithmetical progression

$$23, 19, 15, \cdots.$$

Solution.
$$a = 23, d = -4, n = 10.$$
$$s = \frac{n}{2}[2a + (n-1)d],$$
$$= \frac{10}{2}[46 + 9(-4)],$$
$$= 50.$$

An arithmetical progression has five elements: a, d, n, l, s. If any three of these elements are given, the remaining two elements can be found from equations (1), and either (2) or (3).

Example 5. Given $l = 78$, $n = 20$, $d = 4$; find a and s.

Solution.
$$l = a + (n - 1)d.$$
$$78 = a + (20 - 1)4.$$

Solving,
$$a = 2.$$
$$s = n\frac{(a + l)}{2}.$$
$$s = 20\frac{(2 + 78)}{2},$$
$$= 800.$$

Example 6. Given $a = 3$, $d = 5$, $s = 819$; find n and l.

Solution.
$$s = \frac{n}{2}[2a + (n - 1)d].$$
$$819 = \frac{n}{2}[6 + (n - 1)5].$$
$$5n^2 + n - 1638 = 0.$$
$$n = 18, -\frac{91}{5}.$$

We reject the root $-\frac{91}{5}$ since n stands for the number of terms and is necessarily positive, so $n = 18$.
$$l = a + (n - 1)d.$$
$$l = 3 + (18 - 1)5,$$
$$= 88.$$

EXERCISE 1

Find l and s for the following arithmetical progressions:

1. 3, 6, 9, $\cdots$ to 12 terms
2. 2, 7, 12, $\cdots$ to 8 terms
3. 5, 10, 15, $\cdots$ to 100 terms
4. 2, 4, 6, $\cdots$ to 1000 terms
5. 8, 6, 4, $\cdots$ to 50 terms
6. 17, 13, 9, $\cdots$ to 16 terms
7. $\frac{1}{4}, \frac{1}{2}, \frac{3}{4}, \cdots$ to 25 terms
8. $\frac{1}{3}, \frac{2}{3}, 1, \cdots$ to 30 terms
9. $\frac{5}{12}, \frac{1}{3}, \frac{1}{4}, \cdots$ to 22 terms
10. $\frac{7}{8}, \frac{5}{8}, \frac{3}{8}, \cdots$ to 43 terms
11. 0.125, 0.250, 0.375, $\cdots$ to 8 terms
12. 0.50, 1.00, 1.50, $\cdots$ to 4 terms
13. Given $l = 48$, $n = 10$, $d = 5$; find a and s.
14. Given $n = 8$, $d = 6$, $l = 44$; find a and s.
15. Given $s = 133$, $a = 1$, $d = 6$; find n and l.
16. Given $s = \frac{77}{4}$, $a = \frac{1}{2}$, $d = \frac{1}{4}$; find n and l.
17. Given $d = 5$, $n = 100$, $s = 26250$; find a and l.
18. Given $n = 40$, $d = -2$, $s = 2440$; find a and l.
19. Given $s = 99$, $l = -1$, $d = -3$; find a and n.
20. Given $s = 255$, $l = 10$, $d = \frac{1}{5}$; find a and n.
21. Given $a = 37$, $n = 28$, $s = 2170$; find d and l.
22. Given $a = \frac{47}{3}$, $n = 15$, $s = 165$; find d and l.
23. A man buys a radio for $400. He agrees to pay $100 cash, and the

balance in weekly installments of $10 with interest of $\frac{1}{5}\%$ per week on each unpaid balance. How much interest does he pay?

24. A man buys an electric washing machine for $300. He pays $100 cash, and the remainder in 10 monthly payments of $20 each. If he agrees to pay $\frac{1}{2}\%$ interest per month on all unpaid balances, in addition to the monthly $20 payments, how much interest does he pay?

25. Find the sum of the arithmetical progression $\frac{1}{12} + \frac{2}{12} + \cdots + \frac{12}{12}$.

26. How many integers are there between 1 and 1000 that are multiples of 17?

91. Arithmetical means

The first and last terms of an arithmetical progression are called the **extremes,** and the intervening terms are called the **means.** For example, in the arithmetical progression

$$3, 5, 7, 9, 11, 13,$$

the extremes are 3 and 13, and the means are 5, 7, 9, 11.

If the extremes of an arithmetic progression are given, it is possible to insert any given number of means between the extremes by using equation (1) to find the common difference.

Example 1. Insert six arithmetical means between 2 and 24.

Solution. $a = 2, l = 24, n = 8.$
$l = a + (n - 1)d.$
$24 = 2 + (8 - 1)d.$
$d = \frac{22}{7}.$

The progression, with the means inserted, is

$$2, \tfrac{36}{7}, \tfrac{58}{7}, \tfrac{80}{7}, \tfrac{102}{7}, \tfrac{124}{7}, \tfrac{146}{7}, 24.$$

Example 2. Insert three arithmetical means between 2 and 24.

Solution. $a = 2, l = 24, n = 5.$
$l = a + (n - 1)d.$
$24 = 2 + (5 - 1)d.$
$d = \tfrac{11}{2}.$

The arithmetical progression, with the means inserted, is

$$2, \tfrac{15}{2}, \tfrac{26}{2}, \tfrac{37}{2}, 24.$$

EXERCISE 2

1. Insert four arithmetical means between 3 and 18.
2. Insert five arithmetical means between 3 and 18.
3. Insert one arithmetical mean between 6 and 23.
4. Insert one arithmetical mean between 11 and 48.

5. Insert three arithmetical means between -2 and 30.
6. Insert four arithmetical means between -10 and 20.
7. Insert five arithmetical means between $-\frac{1}{2}$ and $\frac{1}{2}$.
8. Insert seven arithmetical means between 10 and -6.
9. If the first term of an arithmetical progression is x and the fourth term is y, find the second and third terms.
10. If the first term of an arithmetical progression is 16 and the fourth term is 20.5, find the second and third terms.

92. Geometrical progressions

A **geometrical progression** is a sequence of numbers in which the quotient obtained by dividing any term by the term immediately preceding it is equal to a constant. This constant quotient is called the **common ratio**; and is denoted by the letter r.

As in arithmetical progressions, we let a = first term, n = number of terms being considered, l = nth or last term being considered, and s = sum of n terms.

Examples of geometric progressions are:

$$2, 4, 8, \cdots \quad \text{(common ratio} = 2\text{)},$$
$$6, -18, 54, \cdots \quad \text{(common ratio} = -3\text{)},$$
$$\tfrac{1}{2}, \tfrac{1}{4}, \tfrac{1}{8}, \cdots \quad \text{(common ratio} = \tfrac{1}{2}\text{)}.$$

93. Relations among the elements

Consider the problem of finding a formula for the nth or last term of a given geometrical progression. We have:

$$a = \text{first term},$$
$$ar = \text{second term},$$
$$ar^2 = \text{third term},$$
$$ar^3 = \text{fourth term},$$
$$\cdots$$
$$ar^{n-1} = n\text{th or last term}.$$

Therefore the desired formula is

$$l = ar^{n-1}. \tag{4}$$

Example 1. Find the 5th term of the geometrical progression

$$2, 4, 8, \cdots.$$

Solution. $\qquad a = 2, r = 2, n = 5.$
$$l = ar^{n-1},$$
$$l = 2(2)^{5-1},$$
$$= 2(2)^4,$$
$$= 32.$$

RELATIONS AMONG THE ELEMENTS 199

Example 2. Find the 6th term of the geometrical progression
$$\tfrac{1}{2}, \tfrac{1}{4}, \tfrac{1}{8}, \cdots.$$

Solution. $a = \tfrac{1}{2}, r = \tfrac{1}{2}, n = 6.$
$$l = ar^{n-1}.$$
$$l = \tfrac{1}{2}(\tfrac{1}{2})^{6-1},$$
$$= \tfrac{1}{2}(\tfrac{1}{2})^{5},$$
$$= \tfrac{1}{64}.$$

Example 3. Find the 7th term of the geometrical progression
$$2, -6, 18, \cdots.$$

Solution. $a = 2, r = -3, n = 7.$
$$l = ar^{n-1}.$$
$$l = 2(-3)^{7-1},$$
$$= 2(-3)^{6},$$
$$= 1458.$$

Example 4. Given $l = 64, a = 4, r = 2$; find n.

Solution.
$$l = ar^{n-1}.$$
$$64 = 4(2)^{n-1},$$
$$16 = 2^{n-1}.$$
But $2^4 = 16,$
so $n - 1 = 4,$
and $n = 5.$

Consider the problem of finding the **sum of the first n terms** of a geometrical progression. We have:
$$s = a + ar + ar^2 + \cdots + ar^{n-1},$$
and $$rs = ar + ar^2 + ar^3 + \cdots + ar^{n},$$
Subtracting, $s - rs = a - ar^n,$
Whence $s(1 - r) = a(1 - r^n),$
and finally, $$s = a\frac{1 - r^n}{1 - r} = a\frac{r^n - 1}{r - 1}. \qquad (5)$$

Example 5. Find the sum of the first 5 terms of the geometrical progression
$$3, 6, 12, \cdots.$$

Solution. $a = 3, r = 2, n = 5.$
$$s = a\frac{r^n - 1}{r - 1}.$$
$$s = \frac{3(2^5 - 1)}{2 - 1},$$
$$= 93.$$

Example 6. Find the sum of the first 4 terms of the geometric progression:
$$\tfrac{1}{3}, \tfrac{1}{6}, \tfrac{1}{12}, \cdots.$$

Solution. $a = \tfrac{1}{3},\ r = \tfrac{1}{2},\ n = 4.$

$$s = a\frac{1 - r^n}{1 - r}.$$

$$s = \frac{\tfrac{1}{3}[1 - (\tfrac{1}{2})^4]}{1 - \tfrac{1}{2}},$$

$$= \tfrac{5}{8}.$$

Formulas (4) and (5) can be combined to give

$$s = a\frac{r^n - 1}{r - 1},$$

$$= \frac{ar^n - a}{r - 1},$$

Therefore, $\qquad s = \dfrac{rl - a}{r - 1} = \dfrac{a - rl}{1 - r}.$ \hfill (6)

Example 7. Find the sum of the six terms of the geometrical progression

$$6,\ 12,\ 24,\ 48,\ 96,\ 192.$$

Solution. $a = 6,\ r = 2,\ l = 192.$

$$s = \frac{rl - a}{r - 1}.$$

$$s = \frac{(2)(192) - 6}{2 - 1},$$

$$= 378.$$

EXERCISE 3

Find l and s for the following geometrical progressions:

1. $2, 6, 18, \cdots$ to 6 terms
2. $4, 8, 16, \cdots$ to 6 terms
3. $10, 40, 160, \cdots$ to 5 terms
4. $100, 50, 25, \cdots$ to 7 terms
5. $7, -14, 28, \cdots$ to 8 terms
6. $40, -20, 10, \cdots$ to 5 terms
7. $\tfrac{1}{2}, \tfrac{1}{4}, \tfrac{1}{8}, \cdots$ to 9 terms
8. $\tfrac{2}{3}, \tfrac{2}{9}, \tfrac{2}{27}, \cdots$ to 5 terms
9. $1.03, 1.03^2, 1.03^3, \cdots$ to 4 terms, to 5 significant figures
10. $1.02, 1.02^2, 1.02^3, \cdots$ to 4 terms, to 5 significant figures
11. Find the sum of

$$100 + 100(1.05) + 100(1.05)^2 + 100(1.05)^3$$

to 5 significant figures, if $1.05^4 = 1.2155062.$

12. Show that

$$1 + (1 + i) + (1 + i)^2 + \cdots + (1 + i)^{n-1}$$

is equal to

$$\frac{(1 + i)^n - 1}{i}.$$

GEOMETRICAL MEANS

13. Show that
$$(1 + i)^{-1} + (1 + i)^{-2} + (1 + i)^{-3} + \cdots + (1 + i)^{-n}$$
is equal to
$$\frac{1 - (1 + i)^{-n}}{i}.$$

14. Find the sum of the geometrical progression
$$8, 16, 32, \ldots, 1024.$$

15. Find the sum of the geometrical progression
$$3, 9, 27, \ldots, 729.$$

16. Find the seventh term of a geometrical progression whose first term is $\frac{1}{2}$ and whose fourth term is $\frac{27}{2}$.

17. What is the eighth term of a geometrical progression if the first term is 9 and the third term is 36?

94. Geometrical means

The first and last terms of a geometrical progression are called the **extremes,** and the intervening terms are called the **geometrical means.**

We can insert a given number of geometrical means between two given numbers by first finding the common ratio by equation (4).

Example 1. Insert three geometrical means between 12 and 192.

Solution. $a = 12,\ l = 192,\ n = 5.$
$$l = ar^{n-1},$$
$$192 = 12(r)^{5-1},$$
$$16 = r^4,$$
$$r = \pm 2 *$$

The corresponding geometrical progressions are
$$12, 24, 48, 96, 192$$
and
$$12, -24, 48, -96, 192,$$
and the corresponding geometrical means are
$$24, 48, 96$$
and
$$-24, +48, -96.$$

Example 2. Find the geometrical mean of 9 and 729.

Solution. $a = 9,\ l = 729,\ n = 3.$
$$l = ar^{n-1},$$
$$729 = 9(r)^{3-1},$$
$$81 = r^2,$$
$$r = \pm 9.$$

* Notice that we use only the real roots of 16, disregarding the imaginary roots.

The geometrical progressions are
$$9, 81, 729$$
and
$$9, -81, 729$$
and the geometrical means are $+81$ and -81, respectively.

EXERCISE 4

Insert 3 geometrical means between:
1. 4 and 64
2. 2 and 512
3. 5 and 405
4. $\frac{1}{2}$ and $\frac{1}{32}$
5. -10 and $-\frac{5}{8}$
6. 128 and 2048.
7. Insert 5 geometrical means between 1 and $\frac{729}{64}$.
8. Insert 4 geometrical means between 1 and 1024.
9. Find the positive geometrical mean between 1 and 2.
10. Find the positive geometrical mean between 4 and 16.

95. Infinite geometrical progressions

Formula (5) in Article 93 can be written
$$s = \frac{a(1-r^n)}{1-r} = \frac{a}{1-r} - \frac{ar^n}{1-r}.$$
If $-1 < r < 1$, then r^n can be made to differ from zero by as small a positive number as we please if we take n large enough. In this case $\frac{ar^n}{1-r}$ can be made to differ from zero by as small a positive number as we please by taking n large enough, and we write
$$s_\infty = \frac{a}{1-r}. \tag{7}$$

Example 1. Find s_∞ for the geometrical progression
$$1, \tfrac{1}{2}, \tfrac{1}{4}, \cdots.$$
Solution. $r = \frac{1}{2}$, so r lies between -1 and $+1$. Here $a = 1$, so
$$s_\infty = \frac{1}{1-\frac{1}{2}} = \frac{1}{\frac{1}{2}} = 2.$$

A geometrical progression with $-1 < r < 1$ has a "sum" which is given by (7). In the above example, the "sum" of the infinite geometrical progression $1, \frac{1}{2}, \frac{1}{4}, \cdots$ is 2 in the sense that the sum of n terms can be made to differ from 2 by as small a positive number as we please by taking n large enough.

Formula (7) can be used to convert a **repeating decimal** to a common fraction. See Example 2.

Example 2. To what common fraction is the repeating decimal $0.535353\cdots$ equivalent?

Solution. $0.535353 = 0.53 + 0.0053 + 0.000053 + \cdots$.
$$a = 0.53, r = 0.01.$$

$$s_\infty = \frac{a}{1-r}.$$

$$s_\infty = \frac{0.53}{1-0.01},$$

$$= \frac{0.53}{0.99},$$

$$= \frac{53}{99}.$$

EXERCISE 5

Find s_∞ for the following infinite geometrical progressions:

1. $1, \frac{1}{3}, \frac{1}{9}, \cdots$
2. $1, \frac{1}{4}, \frac{1}{16}, \cdots$
3. $2, 1, \frac{1}{2}, \cdots$
4. $5, 2\frac{1}{2}, 1\frac{1}{4}, \cdots$
5. $1, \frac{2}{3}, \frac{4}{9}, \cdots$
6. $10, 2, \frac{2}{5}, \cdots$
7. $-8, 4, -2, \cdots$
8. $\frac{23}{100}, \frac{23}{10,000}, \frac{23}{1,000,000}, \cdots$
9. $\frac{3}{10}, \frac{3}{100}, \frac{3}{1000}, \cdots$
10. $\frac{8}{5}, -1, \frac{5}{8}, \cdots$

96. Binomial theorem; positive integral index

Consider the following expansions of the binomial $a + x$:

$(a + x)^0 = 1$
$(a + x)^1 = a + x$
$(a + x)^2 = a^2 + 2ax + x^2$
$(a + x)^3 = a^3 + 3a^2x + 3ax^2 + x^3$
$(a + x)^4 = a^4 + 4a^3x + 6a^2x^2 + 4ax^3 + x^4$
$(a + x)^5 = a^5 + 5a^4x + 10a^3x^2 + 10a^2x^3 + 5ax^4 + x^5.$

Let n be the exponent of the power to which the binomial is raised. Then we notice that:

1. *The first term is* a^n.
2. *The second term is* $na^{n-1}x$.
3. *The exponents of* a *begin with* n *and decrease by 1 from term to term.*
4. *The exponents of* x *increase from zero in the first term* $(x^0 = 1)$ *to* n *in the last term, the increase being by 1 from term to term.*
5. *If in any term the numerical coefficient of the term be multiplied by the exponent of* a *and divided by the exponent of* x *increased by 1, the result is the coefficient of the next term.*
6. *There are* n + 1 *terms in the expansion.*

It can be proved that these observations hold for any positive integral value of n, so

$$(a + x)^n = a^n + na^{n-1}x + \frac{n(n-1)}{2!}a^{n-2}x^2$$
$$+ \frac{n(n-1)(n-2)}{3!}a^{n-3}x^3 + \cdots$$
$$+ \frac{n(n-1)\cdots(n-r+2)}{(r-1)!}a^{n-r+1}x^{r-1}$$
$$+ \cdots + x^n, \tag{8}$$

where $2! = 1\cdot 2$, $3! = 1\cdot 2\cdot 3$, and in general $r! = 1\cdot 2\cdot 3 \cdots r$. (Note: $r!$ is read "r factorial.")

Formula (7) is called the **binomial formula**. The theorem (whose proof we omit here) that justifies the expansion, according to the rules listed above, for all positive integral values of n, is called the **binomial theorem**.

In (7) no restriction is placed on a and x. For example, in the term $(2m^3 - 6n^2)^5$, $a = 2m^3$ and $x = -6n^2$.

Example 1. Expand $(x + y)^8$.

Solution.
$(x + y)^8 = x^8 + 8x^7y + 28x^6y^2 + 56x^5y^3 + 70x^4y^4 + 56x^3y^5 + 28x^2y^6$
$+ 8xy^7 + y^8.$

Example 2. Expand $(2x - 3y)^4$.

Solution.
$(2x - 3y)^4 = (2x)^4 + 4(2x)^3(-3y) + 6(2x)^2(-3y)^2 + 4(2x)(-3y)^3$
$+ (-3y)^4 = 16x^4 - 96x^3y + 216x^2y^2 - 216xy^3 + 81y^4.$

EXERCISE 6

Expand by the binomial theorem:

1. $(a + x)^{10}$ 2. $(m + n)^5$ 3. $(x + y)^6$ 4. $(c + d)^7$
5. $(a - x)^4$ 6. $(r - s)^9$ 7. $(a + 2x)^5$ 8. $(2m + n)^4$
9. $(2c + 3d)^6$ 10. $(4x - 3y)^4$ 11. $(x^2 - 2y)^3$ 12. $(3a + b^2)^4$
13. $(a^2x - by^2)^5$ 14. $(3b^2 + 4c^3)^3$ 15. $(x + 3)^5$

Write the first four terms in the expansion of:

16. $(a + b)^{20}$ 17. $(x + y)^{16}$ 18. $(a + x)^{12}$
19. $(m - n)^{25}$ 20. $(x + 2)^{18}$

97. General term of the binomial formula

The rth term of the expansion of $(a + x)^n$ is

$$\frac{n(n-1)(n-2)\cdots(n-r+2)}{(r-1)!}a^{n-r+1}x^{r-1}. \tag{9}$$

COMPUTATIONS BY THE BINOMIAL FORMULA

Example 1. Find the 5th term of the expansion of $(a + x)^{16}$.

Solution. In $(a + x)^{16}$, $n = 16$, and for the 5th term $r = 5$. The 5th term is

$$\frac{16 \cdot 15 \cdot 14 \cdot 13}{4!} a^{12} x^4.$$

Example 2. Find the middle term of $(a + x)^{16}$.

Solution. In the expansion of $(a + x)^{16}$ there are 17 terms. The middle term is therefore the 9th term. The 9th term, by formula (9), is

$$\frac{16 \cdot 15 \cdot 14 \cdot 13 \cdot 12 \cdot 11 \cdot 10 \cdot 9}{8!} a^8 x^8.$$

The rth term of the expansion is sometimes called the general term. In applying formula (8) to find the rth term of $(a + x)^n$ notice that:

1. The exponent of x is 1 less than the number of the term; that is, it is $r - 1$.
2. The exponent of a is the difference between n and the exponent of x; that is, it is $n - (r - 1)$.
3. The factorial in the denominator of the coefficient is the factorial of $r - 1$, which agrees with the exponent of x.
4. There are the same number of factors in the numerator of the coefficient as in the denominator of the coefficient.

EXERCISE 7

Find the indicated term in the expansions of the following binomials:

1. $(a + x)^{20}$; the 6th term
2. $(x + d)^{20}$; the 17th term
3. $(m - 2)^{30}$; the 8th term
4. $(c + d)^8$; the middle term
5. $(a + 3)^{10}$; the middle term
6. $(x + y)^{18}$; the next to last term
7. $(3x^2 - 4y)^{12}$; the 10th term
8. $(a + b)^{30}$; the 5th term
9. $(ax + b)^{40}$; the 6th term
10. $(x + y)^{99}$; the 4th term

98. Computations by the binomial formula

The binomial formula can be used to compute the values of certain types of numerical expressions. If the terms of the expansion decrease rapidly in numerical value, a good approximation can sometimes be obtained by retaining only the first four terms of the expansion.

Example 1. Find the numerical value of $(31)^4$ by the binomial formula.

Solution.

$$31^4 = (30 + 1)^4 + (30)^4 + 4(30)^3(1) + 6(30)^2(1)^2 + 4(30)(1)^3 + (1)^4,$$
$$= 810{,}000 + 4(27{,}000) + 6(900) + 4(30) + 1,$$
$$= 810{,}000 + 108{,}000 + 5{,}400 + 120 + 1,$$
$$= 923{,}521.$$

Example 2. Use four terms of the binomial expansion to find an approximate value of $(1.01)^7$.

Solution.

$$(1.01)^7 = (1 + 0.01)^7.$$

$$(1 + 0.01)^7 = (1)^7 + 7(1)^6(0.01) + \frac{7 \cdot 6}{1 \cdot 2}(1)^5(0.01)^2 + \frac{7 \cdot 6 \cdot 5}{1 \cdot 2 \cdot 3}(1)^4(0.01)^3 + \cdots$$

$$= 1 + 0.07 + 0.0021 + 0.000035 + \cdots$$
$$= 1.072.$$

EXERCISE 8

Expand by the binomial formula to find the exact value of:

1. $(41)^3$ 2. $(39)^3$ 3. $(59)^4$ 4. $(22)^3$
5. $(99)^4$ 6. $(101)^5$ 7. $(12)^4$ 8. $(98)^3$

Use four terms of the binomial expansion to find the approximate values of the following expressions, correct to four significant figures:

9. $(1.01)^4$ 10. $(1.01)^6$ 11. $(1.02)^8$
12. $(1.02)^{10}$ 13. $(1.04)^5$ 14. $(1.03)^6$
15. $(1.01)^{20}$ 16. $(1.06)^{10}$ 17. $(0.99)^4$
18. $(0.98)^5$ 19. $(0.97)^8$ 20. $(1.05)^{10}$

99. Binomial theorem; negative and fractional indices

It can be proved that for negative and fractional values of n,

$$(a + x)^n = a^n + na^{n-1}x + \frac{n(n-1)}{2!}a^{n-2}x^2 + \cdots,$$

but in these cases the number of terms is unlimited, and the number x must lie between $-a$ and $+a$.

Example 1. Expand $(1 + x)^n$ by the binomial theorem.

Solution.

$$(1 + x)^n = (1)^n + n(1)^{n-1}x + \frac{n(n-1)}{2!}(1)^{n-2}x^2 + \frac{n(n-1)(n-2)}{3!}(1)^{n-3}x^3 + \cdots$$

$$= 1 + nx + \frac{n(n-1)}{2!}x^2 + \frac{n(n-1)(n-2)}{3!}x^3 + \cdots.$$

In Example 1, the expansion is valid for values of x that lie between -1 and $+1$.

Example 2. Find an approximation to the value of $(1 + i)^{-10}$ for $i = 0.02$, by using the first four terms of the binomial expansion.

Solution.

$$(1+i)^{-10} = (1)^{-10} + (-10)(1)^{-11}i + \frac{(-10)(-11)}{2!}(1)^{-12}i^2$$
$$+ \frac{(-10)(-11)(-12)}{3!}(1)^{-13}i^3 + \cdots,$$
$$= 1 - 10i + 55i^2 - 220i^3 + \cdots.$$

If $i = 0.02$, then

$$(1.02)^{-10} = 1 - 10(0.02) + 55(0.0004) - 220(0.000008) + \cdots,$$
$$= 1 - 0.20 + 0.0220 - 0.001760 + \cdots,$$
$$= 0.82, \text{ which is the required approximation.}$$

Example 3. Find an approximation to the value of $\sqrt{102}$ by the binomial theorem.

Solution. $\sqrt{102} = (100 + 2)^{\frac{1}{2}}$.

$$(100+2)^{\frac{1}{2}} = (100)^{\frac{1}{2}} + \frac{1}{2}(100)^{-\frac{1}{2}}(2) + \frac{(\frac{1}{2})(-\frac{1}{2})}{2!}(100)^{-\frac{3}{2}}(2)^2 + \cdots,$$
$$= 10 + \frac{1}{2(10)}(2) + \left(-\frac{1}{8}\right)\left(\frac{1}{1000}\right)(4) + \cdots,$$
$$= 10 + 0.1 - 0.0005 + \cdots,$$
$$= 10.10.$$

An alternate procedure is as follows:

$$(100+2)^{\frac{1}{2}} = 10\left(1 + \frac{1}{50}\right)^{\frac{1}{2}} = 10\left\{1 + \frac{1}{2}\left(\frac{1}{50}\right) + \frac{\frac{1}{2}(-\frac{1}{2})}{2}\left(\frac{1}{50}\right)^2 + \cdots\right\},$$
$$= 10\{1 + 0.01 - 0.00005 + \cdots\},$$
$$= 10.10.$$

EXERCISE 9

In each of the following problems, compute an approximate value using the first four terms of the proper binomial expansion:

1. $(1.01)^{-10}$
2. $(1.01)^{-6}$
3. $(1.02)^{-8}$
4. $(1.03)^{-4}$
5. $(1.02)^{\frac{1}{12}}$
6. $(1.03)^{\frac{1}{12}}$
7. $(1.06)^{-5}$
8. $(1.05)^{-5}$
9. $(1.04)^{\frac{1}{6}}$
10. $(1.04)^{\frac{1}{12}}$
11. $\sqrt{103}$
12. $\sqrt{98}$
13. $\sqrt{50}$
14. $\sqrt{38}$
15. $\sqrt[3]{128}$
16. $\sqrt[3]{65}$
17. $\sqrt[3]{63}$
18. $\sqrt[3]{7}$
19. $\sqrt[3]{998}$
20. $(630)^{\frac{3}{4}}$.

Expand to four terms and simplify:

21. $(1+x)^{\frac{3}{2}}$
22. $(1-x)^{\frac{3}{2}}$
23. $(1+x)^{-8}$
24. $(1+x)^{-10}$
25. $(1-x)^{-3}$
26. $(1-3x^2)^{\frac{1}{2}}$

27. $(1 - 4y^2)^{\frac{1}{2}}$
28. $(1 + i)^{\frac{1}{12}}$
29. $(1 + i)^{-20}$
30. $(1 + i)^{-\frac{1}{2}}$

MISCELLANEOUS EXERCISE

The following progressions are either arithmetical progressions or geometrical progressions. State which type each one is:

1. 3, 12, 21, $\cdots$
2. 4, 12, 36, $\cdots$
3. $-10, 5, -2\frac{1}{2}, \cdots$
4. $16, -4, -24, \cdots$

Find the 50th term and the sum of 50 terms:

5. 2, 9, 16, $\cdots$
6. 100, 94, 88, $\cdots$
7. $2i, 4i, 6i, \cdots$
8. $i, 3i, 5i, \cdots$

Find the 5th term and the sum of the 5 terms:

9. 7, 49, 343, $\cdots$
10. $\frac{1}{3}, \frac{1}{9}, \frac{1}{27}, \cdots$
11. $-8, 4, -2, \cdots$
12. $1, 1 + i, (1 + i)^2, \cdots$
13. $1 + i, (1 + i)^3, (1 + i)^5, \cdots$
14. $1, (1 + i)^{-1}, (1 + i)^{-2}, \cdots$

Find the arithmetical mean and the geometrical mean between:

15. 6 and 8
16. 5 and 20
17. 4 and 36
18. x and y
19. $\frac{1}{2}$ and $\frac{1}{18}$
20. -4 and -16

21. If the numbers $a_1, a_2, a_3, \cdots$ form an arithmetical progression, then the reciprocals of these numbers: $\dfrac{1}{a_1}, \dfrac{1}{a_2}, \dfrac{1}{a_3}, \cdots$ are said to form a harmonical progression. Which of the following progressions are harmonical progressions:

(a) $\frac{1}{2}, \frac{1}{4}, \frac{1}{8}, \cdots$
(b) $2, \frac{6}{5}, \frac{6}{7}, \cdots$
(c) $3, 9, 27, \cdots$

22. Find the value of the repeating decimal $0.4232323\cdots$ by using the formula $s_\infty = \dfrac{a}{1 - r}$.

23. Find three numbers in geometrical progression whose sum is 65 and whose product is 3375.

24. How many terms of the arithmetical progression $2, 9, 16, \cdots$ must be taken in order that their sum is 335?

25. A man pays $10,000 for a machine. At the end of each year its value is 80% of its value one year prior to that time. What is this value at the end of 5 years?

26. The population of a certain city at the end of each year is 5% more than its population one year prior to that time. If its present population is 30,000 and if it continues to grow at the same rate, what will its population be five years from now?

27. Find a formula for the sum of the first n integers $1, 2, 3, \cdots$.
28. Find a formula for the sum of the first n even integers $2, 4, 6, \cdots$.
29. Find a formula for the sum of the first n odd integers $1, 3, 5, \cdots$.

Expand by the binomial theorem:

30. $(x+y)^4$ **31.** $(a-5b)^4$ **32.** $(1+i)^5$ **33.** $\left(\dfrac{x}{y}+a\right)^4$

Write the first four terms in the expansion of:

34. $(1+i)^{-m}$ **35.** $(1+i)^{\frac{1}{6}}$ **36.** $(1.03)^{-20}$

Use the binomial theorem to find:

37. $\sqrt{82}$ **38.** $\sqrt[3]{9}$

Write the term involving x^8 in the expansion of:

39. $(a+x)^{12}$ **40.** $(a+x)^{10}$ **41.** $(x+y)^{16}$ **42.** $(x^2-a)^6$

11

Permutations and Combinations; Probability

100. A fundamental principle

*If a certain event can happen in **m** ways, and if, after this event has occurred, another event can happen in **n** ways, then both events can happen in **mn** ways, in the order given.*

Example 1. Five bus lines operate between cities A and B. In how many ways can a person go from A to B, and return on a different bus line?

Solution. There are five choices in going from A to B. For each of these five choices there are four choices for the return trip, since the return is to be on a different bus line. Altogether there are $5 \times 4 = 20$ different ways of making the trip as specified. If we name the bus lines a, b, c, d, e the trip from A to B and return may be made in any one of the following twenty ways:

ab	ba	ca	da	ea
ac	bc	cb	db	eb
ad	bd	cd	dc	ec
ae	be	ce	de	ed

In each case the first letter represents the bus line taken in going from A to B and the second letter represents the bus line taken for the return trip, from B to A.

Example 2. How many arrangements of the letters a, b, c can be made, if repetitions are allowed?

Solution. There are three choices for the first letter, namely, a, b or c. Corresponding to each of these, there are three choices for the second letter, since repetitions are allowed. There are therefore $3 \times 3 = 9$ choices for the first two letters, by virtue of the **fundamental principle.** Corresponding to each of these nine choices, there are three choices for the third letter, since repetitions are allowed. The total number of arrangements in this case is therefore $9 \times 3 = 27$.

The actual arrangements are:

aaa	baa	caa
aab	bab	cab
aac	bac	cac
aba	bba	cba
abb	bbb	cbb
abc	bbc	cbc
aca	bca	cca
acb	bcb	ccb
acc	bcc	ccc

EXERCISE 1

1. There are five hotels in a certain city. Two men arrive in the city and wish to stay at different hotels. In how many ways can this be done?

2. How many numbers of three digits each can be formed from the numbers 2, 3, and 7, repetitions being allowed?

3. In how many ways can four books be arranged on a shelf in a library?

4. A man can travel from city A to city B by airplane, railroad, or automobile. He can make the return trip by railroad or automobile. In how many different ways can he make the trip?

5. How many license plates with numbers of four digits each can be issued, using the digits 0 to 9 inclusive, if 0 cannot be used as the first digit?

6. An automobile is made in four body types and five choices of color for each body type. How many models are necessary to exhibit all possible choices of body types and color schemes?

7. Three speakers are to deliver addresses on a program. In how many different orders can they be assigned places?

8. From a collection of flags, of which four are red, four are white, four are blue, and four are green, how many signals can be given by arranging four of the different-colored flags on a flagpole?

9. In how many ways can a man distribute a first prize, a second prize, and a third prize among four boys, assuming that no boy can win more than one prize?

10. Five persons apply for two positions. In how many ways can the two positions be filled, provided that a person can fill only one position?

11. How many arrangements of the letters a, b, c, d can be made, if repetitions are allowed?

12. In a certain organization there are four candidates for president and three for vice-president. In how many ways can the two positions be filled?

101. Permutations

Consider the collection of letters a, b, c, d. Any arrangement of all of these letters in a certain order is called a **permutation** of the letters taken four at a time. The complete list of all of these permutations is:

abcd	bacd	cabd	dabc
abdc	badc	cadb	dacb
acdb	bcad	cbad	dbac
acbd	bcda	cbda	dbca
adbc	bdac	cdab	dcab
adcb	bdca	cdba	dcba

We can think of this in terms of the fundamental principle of Article 100. Suppose that the four blank squares

□   □   □   □

represent the positions of the letters a, b, c, d, and consider the problem of filling these blanks. There are four choices for the first blank square, namely, the letters $a, b, c,$ and d. After this one has been filled, three choices remain for the second blank square, namely, the three letters remaining in a, b, c, d after one of them has been used to fill the first blank square. After the first two squares have been filled there are two choices remaining for the third square, and finally there is only one choice for the last square.

Thus, the first square can be filled in 4 ways, the second in 3 ways, the third in 2 ways, and the last square can be filled in 1 way. By the fundamental principle of Article 100 the four squares can be filled in

$$\boxed{4} \times \boxed{3} \times \boxed{2} \times \boxed{1} = 24 \text{ ways.}$$

The permutations of the letters a, b, c, d taken two at a time are

ab	ba	ca	da
ac	bc	cb	db
ad	bd	cd	dc

In general, the number of permutations of n things taken n at a time is designated by $_nP_n$, and

$$_nP_n = n! \tag{1}$$

Example 1. Find the number of permutations of the letters a, b, c, d, e taken five at a time.

Solution. $_5P_5 = 5! = 120.$

The number of permutations of n things taken r at a time, where $r \leq n$, is denoted by $_nP_r$, and

$$_nP_r = n(n-1)(n-2) \cdots (n-r+1). \tag{2}$$

PERMUTATIONS

Example 2. Calculate the values of $_6P_2$ and $_6P_4$.

Solution. By formula (2)
$$_6P_2 = 6 \cdot 5 = 30,$$
and
$$_6P_4 = 6 \cdot 5 \cdot 4 \cdot 3 = 360.$$

In using formula (2), notice that:
(1) n denotes the first factor in the product,
(2) r denotes the number of factors in the product, and
(3) each factor after the first is one less than the preceding factor.

Thus, in $_6P_4 = 6 \cdot 5 \cdot 4 \cdot 3$, the first factor in the product is 6, the number of factors is 4, and each factor after the first is one less than the preceding factor.

In formula (2), multiply the right member by $(n-r)!$ and divide by the same quantity. The result is

$$_nP_r = \frac{n!}{(n-r)!}. \tag{3}$$

Formula (3) gives an alternate method of calculating the value of $_nP_r$.

Example 3. Calculate the value of $_7P_3$ by formula (3).

Solution. Using formula (3),
$$_7P_3 = \frac{7!}{(7-3)!} = \frac{7!}{4!} = \frac{\cancel{1 \cdot 2 \cdot 3 \cdot 4} \cdot 5 \cdot 6 \cdot 7}{\cancel{1 \cdot 2 \cdot 3 \cdot 4}},$$
$$= 210.$$

EXERCISE 2

1. Calculate the values of $_5P_3$ and $_5P_4$.

2. How many permutations of the numbers 1, 2, 3, 4, 5 are possible, taking 2 numbers at a time?

3. How many different five digit numbers can be formed out of the 9 digits 1, 2, 3, $\cdots$, 9 if each digit can be used only once in each 5 digit number?

4. Calculate the values of $_6P_3$ and $_7P_3$.

5. In how many different orders can six horses finish in a horse race, provided that there are no ties?

6. How many permutations of the letters a, b, c, d, e, f are possible if five letters are taken at a time?

7. A baseball team has four pitchers and three catchers. How many batteries can be selected, each battery consisting of a pitcher and a catcher?

8. How many 3-digit numbers can be formed from the digits 1, 2, 3, 4, 5 if each digit may be used only once in each 3-digit number?

9. Write the letters a, b, c in six different arrangements of three letters each.

10. There are three highways from A to B, two highways from B to C, and five highways from C to D. In how many ways can one travel from A to D?

102. Permutations of things not all different

Consider the set of letters a, a, a, b, b. Here we have five letters, of which three are alike and different from the others, and two are alike and different from the others. If all five letters were different, there would be $_5P_5 = 5!$ permutations of the five letters taken five at a time. If there are three a's, these three a's can be arranged in $3!$ ways and if there are two b's, these b's can be arranged in $2!$ ways, and together the a's and b's can be arranged in $3!\,2!$ ways. These arrangements of the a's and b's among themselves will contribute only one arrangement to the total, so if we let x represent the number of permutations of a, a, a, b, b taken five at a time we must have

$$3!\,2!\,x = 5!,$$

so that
$$x = \frac{5!}{3!\,2!} = 10.$$

In general, if there are n letters, of which r_1 are alike and different from the others, r_2 are alike and different from the others, and so on, and if $r_1 + r_2 + \cdots + r_n = n$, then the number of permutations is given by

$$\frac{n!}{r_1!\,r_2!\cdots r_n!}. \tag{4}$$

Example. Find the number of permutations of the eight letters a, a, a, b, b, c, c, c taken eight at a time.

Solution. Here $n = 8$, $r_1 = 3$, $r_2 = 2$, $r_3 = 3$.

Therefore there are

$$\frac{8!}{3!\,2!\,3!} = 560$$

permutations in this case.

EXERCISE 3

1. How many permutations can be made from the letters a, a, b, b, c, c if six letters are used at a time?

2. Write the ten arrangements of the letters a, a, a, b, b, each arrangement consisting of five letters.

3. Calculate the value of $\dfrac{6!}{4!\,2!}$.

4. How many different arrangements can be made of the letters in the word *algebra* if seven letters are used in each arrangement?

5. How many different arrangements of eleven letters each can be made of the letters in the word *Mississippi?*

6. Write the six arrangements of the letters a, a, b, b, using four letters at a time.

COMBINATIONS

7. In a set of 9 objects, 4 are alike and are different from the others. In how many orders can these objects be arranged?

8. In how many ways can the letters of the word *abacadabra* be arranged if all ten letters are used in each arrangement?

9. A man owns three copies of a certain book and two copies of another book. In how many ways can these five books be arranged on a shelf?

10. In how many orders can the four numbers 1, 3, 3, 1 be arranged, taken all at a time?

103. Combinations

In permutations the arrangement depends on the order of the things selected. That is, the permutation *abc* is different from the permutation *bac*.

A **combination** of n objects taken r at a time is a set of r of the objects taken with no regard to the order of the objects in the set.

Thus, the combinations of the four letters a, b, c, d taken two at a time are

$$\begin{array}{ccc} ab & bc & cd \\ ac & bd & \\ ad & & \end{array}$$

Consider the problem of finding the number of combinations of n things taken r at a time. Represent this number by $_nC_r$. Then each of these combinations is a set of r dissimilar things, which can be arranged among themselves in $r!$ different ways. Therefore $_nC_r \cdot r!$ is the total number of permutations of n things taken r at a time, so

$$_nC_r \cdot r! = {_nP_r},$$

whence $\qquad _nC_r = \dfrac{_nP_r}{r!} = \dfrac{n(n-1)(n-2) \cdots (n-r+1)}{r!}.$ \qquad (5)

Multiplying the numerator and denominator of the right member of formula (5) by $(n - r)!$ we have another formula for $_nC_r$, namely

$$_nC_r = \frac{n!}{r!\,(n-r)!}. \qquad (6)$$

We define $0!$ to be 1.

Notice that formulas (5) and (6) are equivalent for all permissible values of r.

Example 1. Find the number of committees of three persons each that can be formed from a group of six persons.

Solution. This is a problem in combinations, rather than permutations, since the order makes no difference. That is, a committee of Smith, Jones, and

Robinson would be the same as a committee of Jones, Smith, and Robinson.

$$_6C_3 = \frac{6 \cdot 5 \cdot 4}{1 \cdot 2 \cdot 3} = 20.$$

Therefore 20 committees of three persons each can be selected from a group of six persons.

Example 2. In how many ways can a committee consisting of three Republicans and three Democrats be selected from a group of five Republicans and seven Democrats?

Solution. Three Republicans can be selected from five Republicans in $_5C_3$ ways, and three Democrats can be selected from seven Democrats in $_7C_3$ ways, so the committee can be selected in

$$_5C_3 \cdot {_7C_3} = 350 \text{ ways.}$$

EXERCISE 4

1. How many committees of four persons each can be formed from a group of seven persons?
2. Write the four combinations of the letters a, b, c, d taken three at a time.
3. Compute the value of $_8C_5$ by formula (5) and by formula (6).
4. Compute the value of $_4C_1 + {_4C_2} + {_4C_3} + {_4C_4}$.
5. Four persons meet and each person shakes hands with each of the others. How many handshakes are there?
6. How many different sums of money can be formed from a penny, a nickel, a dime, a quarter, and a half-dollar, if two coins are taken at a time?
7. A group of people consists of ten men and eight women. How many committees of five persons can be selected from this group, if each committee is to consist of three men and two women?
8. Show that $_nC_r = {_nC_{n-r}}$.
9. Use the formula in Problem 8 to evaluate $_6C_5$, $_8C_6$, and $_{52}C_{50}$.
10. Compute the value of $_5C_5 + {_5C_3} + {_5C_1}$.
11. In how many different ways can two white balls be drawn from a bag containing six white balls?
12. Show that $_6C_2 + {_6C_3} = {_7C_3}$.

104. Binomial coefficients

In the expansion of $(a + x)^n$ by the binomial formula, in Article 97, notice that the coefficient of the rth term is

$$\frac{n(n-1)(n-2) \cdots (n-r+1)}{(r-1)!}.$$

But this is exactly equal to $_nC_{r-1}$, by formula (5) in Article 103.

Therefore the binomial formula can be written

$$(a+x)^m = a^n + {_nC_1}a^{n-1}x + {_nC_2}a^{n-2}x^2 + \cdots + {_nC_{r-1}}a^{n-r+1}x^{r-1} + \cdots + {_nC_n}x^n.$$

105. A priori probability

Suppose that a bag contains five white balls and four black balls. If one ball is drawn at random, what is the probability that the ball drawn is black?

There are nine balls in the bag and four of them are black, so we say that the probability of drawing a black ball is $\frac{4}{9}$. In general, if a certain event can happen in h ways and it can fail to happen in f ways, and if each of the $h+f$ ways it can happen or fail is equally likely, then we define the **probability** that it will happen to be $p = \dfrac{h}{h+f}$, and we define the probability that it will fail to be $q = \dfrac{f}{h+f}$.

Notice that the sum of the probability that the event will happen and the probability that it will fail is

$$p + q = \frac{h}{h+f} + \frac{f}{h+f} = \frac{h+f}{h+f} = 1.$$

Thus a probability of 1 represents certainty. Also, a probability of 0 represents certain failure.

This type of probability is called **a priori probability,** since it depends upon an analysis of the situation before the event takes place.

Example. From a bag containing four black balls and five white balls, two balls are drawn at random. (a) What is the probability that they are both black? (b) That they are both white? (c) That one is white and one is black?

Solution. (a) Since 2 black balls may be selected from 4 black balls in $_4C_2 = 6$ ways and 2 balls may be selected from 9 balls in $_9C_2 = 36$ ways, the probability of drawing two black balls is

$$\frac{6}{36} = \frac{1}{6}.$$

(b) Likewise, the probability of drawing 2 white balls is

$$\frac{_5C_2}{_9C_2} = \frac{10}{36} = \frac{5}{18}.$$

(c) The probability of drawing a white ball and a black ball is

$$\frac{_5C_1 \cdot {_4C_1}}{_9C_2} = \frac{20}{36} = \frac{5}{9}.$$

EXERCISE 5

1. A coin is tossed once. What is the probability of throwing heads?
2. A bag contains three white balls, six black balls, and four red balls. One ball is drawn from the bag. What is the probability that it is white? black? red?

3. What is the probability of throwing an ace in one throw of a die? an ace or a deuce?

4. A deck of 52 cards contains four aces. If one card is drawn from the deck, what is the probability that it is an ace?

5. A deck of 52 cards contains 13 hearts. If one card is drawn, what is the probability that it is a heart? What is the probability that it is not a heart?

6. In a certain raffle the tickets are numbered from 1 to 10, inclusive. If a person buys two tickets, and if one of the ten tickets wins a prize, what is the probability that this person will win the prize?

7. A certain algebra class consists of 20 boys and 14 girls. One member of the class is chosen by lot. What is the probability that the student chosen is a boy?

8. If the probability of winning a certain game is $\frac{2}{15}$, what is the probability of losing the game?

9. Ten cards are numbered consecutively from 1 to 10. One card is drawn. What is the probability that the number on it is an even number?

10. If two coins are tossed, what is the probability that both will be heads?

11. From a bag containing three red balls and four white balls, three balls are drawn at random. What is the probability that (a) all three balls are red? (b) all three balls are white? (c) two balls are red and one ball is white?

12. From a group of people consisting of five men and three women, two persons are selected at random. What is the probability that (a) both are men? (b) both are women? (c) one is a man and the other is a woman?

106. Independent events, mutually exclusive events, and dependent events

Two or more events are said to be **independent** if the occurrence or non-occurrence of any one of them is not affected by the occurrence or non-occurrence of any of the rest of the events.

For example, suppose that a bag contains three white balls and four black balls. If one of the balls is drawn from the bag, the probability that it will be white is $\frac{3}{7}$. If the ball so drawn is replaced, and then a second drawing is made, the probability that a white ball will be drawn on the second drawing is again $\frac{3}{7}$. The two drawings in this case are independent.

On the other hand, if the ball first drawn is not replaced, the probability of drawing a white ball on the second drawing depends on the color of the ball obtained on the first drawing. In this case, the two drawings are not independent events.

*The probability that all of a set of **independent** events will occur is equal to the product of the probabilities of the separate events.*

Take the case of the two drawings from a bag containing three white balls and four black balls. Here the probability of obtaining a white ball on both drawings is $\frac{3}{7} \times \frac{3}{7} = \frac{9}{49}$, if the ball first drawn is replaced before the second drawing is made. Notice that the number of favorable cases in the first drawing is 3, and corresponding to each of these favorable cases there are 3 favorable cases on the second drawing. By the fundamental principle of Article 100 there are $3 \times 3 = 9$ ways in which the favorable event can occur. Similarly, for the total number of cases there are $7 \times 7 = 49$ ways in which the drawing can be made. This line of reasoning can be extended to any number of independent events.

If two or more events are such that only one of them can occur, the events are said to be **mutually exclusive** events.

Suppose that a bag contains three white balls, four black balls, and five red balls. If one drawing is made, the drawing of a white ball and the drawing of a black ball at the same time are mutually exclusive events. Both of these events cannot happen at the same time.

*The probability that one or another of a set of **mutually exclusive** events will occur is the sum of the probabilities of the separate events.*

Thus, in drawing one ball from a bag containing three white balls, four black balls, and five red balls, the probability of drawing either a white ball or a red ball is $\frac{3}{12} + \frac{4}{12} = \frac{7}{12}$. Observe that the number of favorable cases is $3 + 4 = 7$, and the total number of cases is 12.

In solving problems of this type, which involve several events, the first step is to decide whether the events are independent or mutually exclusive.

Two or more events are said to be **dependent** if the occurrence of one of them affects the occurrence of the others. For example, if a bag contains three white balls and four black balls, and if a ball is drawn and this ball is not replaced before a second drawing of one ball is made, the probability of drawing a white (or black) ball on the second drawing depends upon the color of the ball drawn in the first drawing. If p_1 denotes the probability that a certain event will happen, and if p_2 denotes the probability that a certain second event will happen after the first has happened, then the probability that both of these events will happen in the order given is the product $p_1 p_2$, and similarly for more than two dependent events.

EXERCISE 6

1. A bag contains six black balls and three white balls. A ball is drawn and then replaced in the bag, after which a second ball is drawn. What is the probability that both balls drawn are black?

2. If the probability that A will live ten years is $\frac{8}{9}$ and the probability that B will live ten years is $\frac{7}{8}$, what is the probability that both will live ten years?

3. A bag contains five white balls, five red balls, and six black balls. If one drawing is made, what is the probability that the ball drawn is either red or black?

4. A deck of 52 cards contains four aces and four kings. If one card is drawn from the deck, what is the probability that it will be either an ace or a king?

5. A coin is tossed five times. What is the probability of throwing heads on all five tosses?

6. A bag contains ten cards marked with the numbers 1 to 10. A card is drawn and then it is replaced in the bag, after which a second drawing is made. What is the probability that the first number drawn is even and the second number drawn is odd?

7. The probability that A will live to be 60 is $\frac{5}{6}$, and the probability that B will live to be 60 is $\frac{7}{8}$. What is the probability that both will live to be 60? What is the probability that neither will live to be 60?

8. A bag contains four white balls and six black balls. Two balls are drawn from the bag at the same time. What is the probability that either one of two balls is white and the other is black?

9. Five coins are tossed at once. What is the probability that all five will be tails?

10. The probabilities that A, B, and C will live to be 70 are $\frac{9}{10}$, $\frac{8}{9}$, and $\frac{7}{8}$, respectively. What is the probability that A and B will live to be 70 but C will not?

11. A bag contains three white balls and three red balls. A ball is drawn and is not replaced. If a second drawing of one ball is made, what is the probability that both balls are white?

12. In Problem 11, what is the probability that the first ball is white and the second is red?

107. Empirical probability

The a priori probability of throwing heads in a single throw of a coin is $\frac{1}{2}$. This does not mean that in 50 throws of a coin exactly 25 will be heads. However, as the number of throws increases, the ratio of the number of heads to the number of throws will approach $\frac{1}{2}$.

In general, if h represents the number of times an event has occurred and n equals the number of trials made, then we define

$$p = \frac{h}{n} \cdot {}^* \tag{7}$$

* Some writers define empirical probability to be $\lim\limits_{n \to \infty} \frac{h}{n}$.

This type of probability is called **empirical** or **a posteriori** probability. The determination of empirical probabilities depends upon the collection of experimental data. In addition to the collection of data, it is important to select a set of homogeneous events, and it is customary to select a random sample of this set of homogeneous events. The study of homogeneity and random samples is not simple; such studies are in the field of advanced mathematical statistics, and will not be pursued here.

108. Mortality table

A **mortality table** can be thought of as a record of lives and deaths of a large group of people. Thus, the American Experience Table of Mortality, first published in 1868, starts with a basic group of 100,000 persons alive at age 10. The table records the number alive at each of the ages 10, 11, 12, $\cdots$, 96, where 96 is the upper limit of the table. This table was constructed from actual life experience during the years from 1843 to 1858 and hence does not represent very accurately the mortality experience at the present time. In fact, the present-day expectancy of life is much better than it was when the American Experience Table was made. The first major change in mortality tables by the insurance companies since the adoption of the American Experience Table in 1868 came on January 1, 1948, when a new table called the **Commissioners 1941 Standard Ordinary Table** (CSO) came into use by practically all the insurance companies in the United States. The CSO table was first published in 1941 and is based on life experience from 1930–1940. The table represents far better the actual mortality experience of people at the present time. Table XII of this text is the CSO table.

In the first column on the left is a list of ages starting at 0, designated by the symbol x. Thus $x = 30$ refers to the age 30. In the second column, the symbol l_x refers to the number of individuals alive at age x; for example, $l_{32} = 917{,}880$, is the number of individuals alive at age 32. The third column is headed d_x, where d_x stands for the number of individuals dying between the ages x and $x + 1$; for example, $d_{32} = 3598$ is the number of individuals dying between age 32 and age 33. The fourth column is headed $1000q_x$. Here q_x represents the probability that a person aged x will die between age x and $x + 1$; for example, $q_{32} = 0.00392$, and this is the probability that a person aged 32 will die between age 32 and age 33. Notice that the table gives $1000q_x$, so in this column for $x = 32$ is the entry 3.92 which is 1000 times the value 0.00392.

For a given value of l_x, it is easy to find d_x and q_x, because
$$d_x = l_x - l_{x+1}$$
and
$$q_x = \frac{d_x}{l_x}.$$

Some of the probabilities that can be obtained from the mortality table, together with the symbols used to designate them, are:

1. The probability that a person aged x will die between age x and age $x + 1$:
$$q_x = \frac{d_x}{l_x}. \tag{8}$$

2. The probability that a person aged x will live at least one year:
$$p_x = \frac{l_{x+1}}{l_x}. \tag{9}$$

3. The probability that a person aged x will be alive at age $x + n$:
$$_np_x = \frac{l_{x+n}}{l_x}. \tag{10}$$

4. The probability that a man aged x will die within n years:
$$_nq_x = 1 - {}_np_x = 1 - \frac{l_{x+n}}{l_x} = \frac{l_x - l_{x+n}}{l_x}. \tag{11}$$

5. The probability that a person aged x will die within the year after he attains age $x + n$.
$$_nq_x = \frac{d_{x+n}}{l_x}. \tag{12}$$

The following examples will illustrate how probabilities of living and dying can be computed on the basis of empirical probability as recorded in a mortality table. The answers to some of these examples are given to two significant figures, and this is done simply to give the reader an approximate value of the probability that is easy to visualize.

Example 1. Find the number of persons living at age 18.

Solution. $\qquad l_{18} = 955,942.$

Example 2. Find the number of persons dying between age 18 and age 19.

Solution. $\qquad d_{18} = 2199.$

Example 3. Find the probability that a person aged 18 will die between age 18 and 19.

Solution. $\quad 1000 q_{18} = 2.30.$
$\qquad q_{18} = 0.00230$, correct to 3 significant figures.

MORTALITY TABLE

Example 4. Find the probability that a person aged 18 will live at least one year.

Solution. $p_{18} = 1 - q_{18} = 1 - 0.00230,$
$= 0.998$, correct to 3 significant figures.

Example 5. Find the probability that a person aged 18 will be alive at age 75.

Solution. $_{57}p_{18} = \dfrac{l_{75}}{l_{18}} = \dfrac{315,982}{955,942},$
$= 0.33$, correct to 2 significant figures.

Example 6. Find the probability that a person 18 will die within 57 years.

Solution. $_{57}q_{18} = 1 - {}_{57}p_{18},$
$= 1 - \dfrac{315,982}{955,942},$
$= 0.67.$

Example 7. Find the probability that a person aged 18 will live 57 years and will die in the following year.

Solution
$_{57}q_{18} = \dfrac{28,009}{955,942},$
$= 0.029.$

Example 8. A man is 45 years old and his son is 15 years old. Find the probability that both will be alive at the end of 20 years.

Solution. The probability that the man will be alive at the end of 20 years is

$_{20}p_{45} = \dfrac{l_{65}}{l_{45}} = \dfrac{577,882}{852,554},$
$= 0.68.$

Likewise the probability that the son will be alive at the end of 20 years is

$_{20}p_{15} = \dfrac{l_{35}}{l_{15}} = \dfrac{906,554}{962,270} = 0.94.$

Hence $_{20}p_{45} \cdot {}_{20}p_{15} = (0.68)(0.94) = 0.64,$

which is the probability that both father and son will be alive at the end of 20 years.

EXERCISE 7

The following problems refer to Table XII:

1. Find the number of individuals living at age 20; at age 30; at age 40.
2. Find l_{15}, l_{45}, l_{75}.
3. Verify: $d_{20} = l_{20} - l_{21}$, and in general $d_x = l_x - l_{x+1}$.
4. Find d_{20} and d_{80}.
5. Calculate the probability that a person whose age is 25 will live to be 80.
6. Calculate the probability that a person age 20 will live to be 80.

7. Find the probability that an individual whose age is 22 will live 20 years.

8. A boy whose age is 10 is to receive an inheritance at age 21. What is the probability that he will live to receive it?

9. What is the probability that a person whose age is 20 will die between age 20 and age 21?

10. What is the probability that a person whose age is 21 will die in the year after he is 45?

11. A man whose age is 23 is to receive a retirement income beginning at age 65. What is the probability that he will live to receive the first payment?

12. Verify: $l_{21} - l_{25} = d_{21} + d_{22} + d_{23} + d_{24}$.

13. What is the probability that two persons, each age 30, will both live to reach the age of 60?

14. One person's age is 20 and another's age is 25. What is the probability that neither will live to be 60?

15. A man's age is 35 and his son's age is 10. What is the probability that both will be alive at the end of 20 years?

16. A man's age is 32 and his son's age is 8. What is the probability that the son will be alive at the end of 40 years and the father will not?

17. What is the probability that a man whose age is 70 will live 10 years? What is the probability that he will not live 10 years? What is the sum of these two probabilities?

18. Find the probability that a person aged 60 will live at least one year.

19. Three persons are aged 45, 30, and 27, respectively. Find the probability that all three will be alive at the end of 20 years. What is the probability that at least one of them will be alive at the end of 20 years?

20. Two persons are 20 and 25 years old, respectively. What is the probability that both will live 30 years and die in the following year?

109. Mathematical expectation

Suppose that 100 tickets are sold in a raffle and a single prize of $100 is offered. If a person buys one ticket, then his probability of winning is $\frac{1}{100}$ and his mathematical expectation is said to be $\frac{1}{100}$ ($100) = $1. That is, $1 is the fair price to pay for one ticket.

In general, if the probability of winning M is p, then the **mathematical expectation E**, is defined as

$$E = pM. \qquad (13)$$

EXERCISE 8

1. What is the mathematical expectation if the probability of winning a prize of $100 is $\frac{1}{1000}$?

2. Tickets numbered 1 to 25 are sold for $1 each. There is a single prize of $20. If a man buys two tickets, what is his mathematical expectation?

3. A bag contains seven white balls and three black balls. A prize of $1 is offered for drawing a black ball. What should a man pay for a single trial?

4. A man buys one ticket in a lottery in which 100,000 tickets are sold. There is a single prize of $50,000. What should he pay for his ticket?

5. A man is to receive $36 if he throws an ace in one throw of a die. What should he pay for the privilege of throwing?

6. There are 36 cards in a bag, numbered from 1 to 36, and in addition there is one blank card. A fee of $1 is charged for drawing one card, and a prize of $36 is offered if a preselected number is drawn. What is the mathematical expectation of a person who makes one trial? How much will he lose on each trial, in the long run?

110. Expectation of life

We have shown how to find the probability that an individual aged x will live to the age of $x + n$. Now we consider this question: on the average, how many years may an individual aged x expect to live? For example, an individual aged 25 may, on the average, expect to live how many years?

Consider the group of people aged x, as given in the mortality table. There are l_x individuals in this group. Of these, l_{x+1} individuals will live 1 year, l_{x+2} individuals will live 2 years, and so on to the end of the table. That is, the number of complete years lived by the l_x individuals, being considered, is given by

$$l_{x+1} + l_{x+2} + l_{x+3} + \cdots \text{ to the end of the table.}$$

The *average* number of *complete* years lived by the l_x individuals is therefore

$$e_x = \frac{l_{x+1} + l_{x+2} + l_{x+3} + \cdots \text{ to the end of the table}}{l_x}. \quad (14)$$

The value of this result, designated by the symbol e_x, is called the **curtate expectation of life at age x**. Note that e_x is stated in years.

Under the assumption that the deaths in a given year are uniformly distributed throughout the year, the average number of years lived by the l_x individuals will be given by

$$\overset{\circ}{e}_x = \tfrac{1}{2} + e_x. \quad (15)$$

The value of this result, designated by the symbol $\overset{\circ}{e}_x$, is called the **complete expectation of life at age x**.

Example 1. Find the curtate expectation of life for a person aged 90. What is his complete expectation of life?

Solution. We have

$$e_{90} = \frac{l_{91} + l_{92} + l_{93} + l_{94} + l_{95} + l_{96} + l_{97} + l_{98} + l_{99}}{l_{90}}.$$

From Table XII we have

$$e_{90} = \frac{15{,}514 + 10{,}833 + 7327 + 4787 + 3011 + 1818 + 1005 + 454 + 125}{21{,}577},$$

$$= \frac{44{,}874}{21.577},$$

$$= 2.08, \text{ the curtate expectation of life.}$$

To find the complete expectation of life, we have from formula (15)

$$\overset{\circ}{e}_{90} = \tfrac{1}{2} + e_{90} = 0.5 + 2.08,$$
$$= 2.58.$$

EXERCISE 9

Find the curtate expectation of life and the complete expectation of life for each of the following ages:

1. 98   2. 97   3. 95   4. 92   5. 85   6. 99

MISCELLANEOUS EXERCISE

1. The Greek alphabet contains 24 letters. How many fraternities can be named if three letters are to be used in each name, and if repetitions are allowed; if, for example, Alpha Alpha Alpha can be used?

2. In how many different orders can eight people sit in a row of eight seats?

3. Calculate the values of $_4P_1$, $_3P_1$, $_2P_1$, and $_1P_1$.

4. Calculate the values of $_4P_2$, $_3P_2$, and $_2P_2$.

5. Make a list of the six possible permutations of the letters a, b, c, taken three at a time.

6. How many combinations of the letters a, b, c are there, if three letters are to be taken at a time?

7. Compute the value of $_4C_1 + {_4C_2} + {_4C_3} + {_4C_4}$.

8. Write the four permutations of the letters, a, a, a, b taken four at a time.

9. If three balls are drawn from a bag containing six white balls and five black balls, what is the probability that one of the balls is white and the other two are black?

10. If the probability that a certain event will occur in one trial is p, it can be shown that the probability that the event will occur exactly r times in n trials is $_nC_r p^r q^{n-r}$, where $q = 1 - p$. If a coin is tossed ten times, what is the probability that heads will occur exactly three times?

11. How many committees of three persons can be selected from a group of four men and four women, if at least one member of the committee must be a woman?

12. If the probabilities that two independent events will occur are $\tfrac{2}{3}$ and $\tfrac{1}{5}$, respectively, what is the probability that neither event will occur?

13. Find the probability that a person aged 20 will die between the ages of 60 and 65.

EXPECTATION OF LIFE

14. A man and his wife are 23 and 22 years old, respectively, on their wedding day. What is the probability that they will live to celebrate their golden wedding anniversary?

Show that:

15. $_n|q_x = {_n}p_x - {_{n+1}}p_x$

16. $_nq_x = 1 - {_n}p_x$

17. $l_x = d_x + d_{x+1} + d_{x+2} + \cdots$ to end of table

18. $l_x - l_{x+n} = d_x + d_{x+1} + d_{x+2} + \cdots + d_{x+n-1}$

19. $_{n-1}|q_x = {_{n-1}}p_x - {_n}p_x$

20. $_np_x = p_x \cdot p_{x+1} \cdot p_{x+2} \cdot \cdots \cdot p_{x+n-1}$

12

Statistics

111. Preliminary remarks

Statistics includes the collection, classification, analysis, and interpretation of data. The field of statistics is a broad one; in this chapter we shall merely introduce a few of the simpler concepts and methods of statistics.

Collected data are essentially numbers, and may be exact or approximate. Data may be presented in their entirety, or they may be subdivided into groups. One of the main purposes of the analysis of data is to compute the values of certain numbers that will in a restricted sense represent the entire data, at least for purposes of comparing two or more sets of data. The interpretation of the results of this analysis of statistical data is in part subjective and is a task that requires experience, judgment, caution, and integrity.

112. Arithmetical mean

Consider the set of k numbers $x_1, x_2, x_3, \ldots, x_k$. The **arithmetical mean** of this set of numbers is defined to be

$$M = \frac{x_1 + x_2 + x_3 + \cdots + x_k}{k} = \frac{\Sigma x}{k}. \tag{1}$$

Here the Greek Σ is a summation symbol, and Σx denotes "the sum of the x's."

Example 1. The grades on a final examination in algebra were: 96, 95, 92, 92, 91, 90, 89, 88, 88, 88, 87, 86, 85, 85, 83, 82, 77, 76, 75, 74, 74, 73, 60, 58, 55, 54, 53, 52, 52, 50, 48, 48, 45. Find the arithmetical mean of these grades.

Solution. The sum of the grades is 2441. The number of grades is 33. The arithmetical mean is $\frac{2441}{33} = 73\frac{32}{33}$, or 74, correct to the nearest integer.

The arithmetical mean is often called simply the average. Thus, in Example 1, the average grade is 74.

Sometimes a set of data consists of a set of numbers, some of which are repeated several times. Consider, for example, the set of data

ARITHMETICAL MEAN

3, 3, 3, 3, 4, 4, 5, 5, 5, 5, 5, 5. Here the number 3 occurs four times, the number 4 occurs twice, and the number 5 occurs six times. In this case we say that the **frequency** of the number 3 is four, the frequency of the number 4 is two, and the frequency of the number 5 is six. Sometimes the word **weight** is used in this sense instead of the word frequency.

If we let y_1 = frequency of x_1, y_2 = frequency of x_2, and so on, we have in general,

$$M = \frac{x_1 y_1 + x_2 y_2 + \cdots + x_k y_k}{y_1 + y_2 + \cdots y_k},$$

$$= \frac{\Sigma xy}{\Sigma y}. \qquad (2)$$

Example 2. Find the arithmetical mean of the numbers, 3, 3, 3, 3, 4, 4, 5, 5, 5, 5, 5, 5.

Solution. $$M = \frac{3(4) + 4(2) + 5(6)}{4 + 2 + 6} = \frac{50}{12} = 4\frac{1}{6}.$$

The type of mean illustrated in formula (2) and Example 2 is called a weighted average, or weighted arithmetical mean. Sometimes data are weighted with numbers that are not frequencies. For example, the grades for a student may be 85, 80, 88, and 84, but the grade 84 may be a grade on a final examination, which might be weighted with the number 2 in order to emphasize the importance of the final examination in determining the semester grade.

The difference $x_1 - M$ is called the **deviation** of x_1 from the mean, the difference $x_2 - M$ is called the deviation of x_2 from the mean, and in general $x_i - M$ is called the deviation of x_i from the mean. It can be shown that the sum of the deviations of $x_1, x_2, x_3, \cdots, x_k$ from the mean of these data is zero.

For example, if the data are x_1, x_2, x_3 then the mean is $\frac{x_1 + x_2 + x_3}{3}$, and the sum of the deviations of x_1, x_2, x_3 from the mean is

$$x_1 - \frac{x_1 + x_2 + x_3}{3} + x_2 - \frac{x_1 + x_2 + x_3}{3} + x_3 - \frac{x_1 + x_2 + x_3}{3} = 0.$$

EXERCISE 1

1. A golfer made the following scores: 80, 78, 81, 76. Find the arithmetical mean of his scores, correct to the nearest integer.

2. A salesman earned the following commissions per week over a period of six weeks: $60, $82, $30, $44, $50, $28. Find the arithmetical mean of his weekly commissions.

3. On a long trip in an automobile, a motorist drove 300 miles, 420 miles, 250 miles, 450 miles, and 290 miles on successive days. Find the average number of miles per day for these days.

4. The heights of five players on a basketball team are 5 ft. 10 in., 6 ft. 2 in., 5 ft. 11 in., 6 ft. 1 in., and 6 ft. 3 in. Find the average height.

5. Gross sales of a clothing store for four successive weeks were: $12,000; $15,000; $9000; $18,000. Find the average weekly gross sales.

6. Find the average of the following numbers: 8, 8, 9, 9, 9, 10, 11, 11, 11, 12, 12, 12, 12, 13, 14, 14, 14.

7. Find the arithmetical mean of the following numbers: 20, 20, 20, 20, 30, 30, 40, 40, 40.

8. In a certain experiment, the following observations, and their frequencies, were obtained:

Observations	Frequencies
18.12	2
18.16	4
18.17	5
18.18	8
18.19	6
18.21	4
18.25	3

Find the arithmetical mean of this set of observations, correct to four significant figures.

9. Find the arithmetical mean of the numbers 10, 20, 30, 40, 50 and verify the fact that the sum of the deviations of the data from the mean is zero.

10. In a certain office the weekly salaries of the employees, together with the number of employees receiving each salary, are given by the table:

Salary	Frequency
$60	8
$65	10
$70	17
$80	12
$90	6

Find the average weekly salary, correct to the nearest dollar.

11. A student's grades on a series of examinations are 80, 84, 92, 88, 86, 90. These grades are assigned weights of 1, 1, 2, 1, 1, and 4, respectively. Find the weighted average of the grades.

12. The gross sales of a men's wear store for the first five months of 1948 were:

Month	Jan.	Feb.	Mar.	Apr.	May
Gross sales	$20,000	$30,000	$45,000	$40,000	$35,000

Losses due to bad accounts, worthless checks, and so on in these months amounted to 1%, ½%, 1%, ½%, and 1% of the gross sales, respectively. What was the average amount lost per month? Can the per cents be averaged and the result multiplied by the total gross sales to obtain the average loss?

113. Median, mode, and geometrical mean

The **median** of a set of numbers is the middle number when the numbers are arranged in order of magnitude.

Example 1. Find the median and the arithmetical mean of the numbers 23, 26, 28, 30, 31, 33, 34.

Solution. The median, or middle number, is 30. The arithmetical mean, or average, is $29\frac{2}{7}$.

If the set contains an even number of entries, there is no middle number in the set. In this case, we arbitrarily agree to select the average of the two numbers in the middle.

Example 2. Find the median of the numbers 15, 18, 19, 21, 23, 26.

Solution. The two middle numbers are 19 and 21. Their average is $\frac{19 + 21}{2} = 20$. The median is 20.

Notice that the selection of the median requires little or no computation. In general, the median of a set of numbers is different from the arithmetical mean, although they may be equal in some cases. The median divides the set of numbers in two parts in such a way that there are as many numbers in the given set less than the median as there are in the given set greater than the median.

Sometimes the medians of the two parts, into which the median separates the given data, are found. These are called **quartiles**. In Example 1, the lower part consists of the numbers 23, 26, 28 and the middle number here is 26, so that we call 26 the first quartile. Similarly, the upper part consists of the numbers 31, 33, 34 and the middle number is 33, so we call 33 the third quartile. The median of the entire set of numbers, 30, could be called the second quartile. Quartiles divide the given set of data into four equal or nearly equal parts. In like manner, **percentiles** are defined as those numbers that divide the set of data into one hundred equal parts, and are sometimes used if the data are numerous.

The **mode** of a set of numbers is the number that occurs most frequently.

Example 3. Find the mode of the numbers 98, 96, 95, 95, 95, 80, 80, 73.

Solution. The number 95 occurs more frequently than any other number in the set, so 95 is the mode.

Sometimes a mode is defined to be a number that occurs more frequently than the numbers immediately preceding or following it. In this case a set of numbers may have more than one mode. We shall restrict ourselves to consideration of cases with a single mode.

The **geometrical mean** of a set of k numbers $x_1, x_2, x_3, \ldots, x_k$ is defined to be the positive kth root of the product of the numbers. Thus,

$$\text{G. M.} = \sqrt[k]{x_1 x_2 x_3 \ldots x_k}. \tag{3}$$

Example 4. Find the geometrical mean of the numbers 6, 12, 24.

Solution. The geometrical mean is given by

$$\begin{aligned} \text{G. M.} &= \sqrt[3]{(6)(12)(24)}, \\ &= \sqrt[3]{1728}, \\ &= 12. \end{aligned}$$

EXERCISE 2

1. Find the median of the numbers 17, 10, 9, 8, 19, 13, 15, 11, 6.

2. Find the median of the numbers 42, 46, 48, 51.

3. Find the mode: 6, 16, 33, 33, 33, 41, 72, 80.

4. Find the geometrical mean: 12, 36, 108.

5. Find (a) the arithmetical mean, (b) the median, and (c) the mode of the following set of numbers: 5, 10, 15, 25, 30, 35, 50, 50, 50, 50, 60, 60, 60, 65.

6. Find (a) the arithmetical mean, (b) the median, and (c) the mode of the numbers 100, 100, 100, 0.

7. The batting averages of the members of a baseball squad were: 0.190, 0.202, 0.213, 0.256, 0.273, 0.280, 0.285, 0.286, 0.288, 0.291, 0.292, 0.293, 0.295, 0.298, 0.304, 0.310, 0.320, 0.340. Find (a) the arithmetical mean and (b) the median.

8. The heights of a group of men, together with the frequencies of each height, are:

Height in inches	Frequency
62	3
63	7
64	10
65	20
66	32
67	54
68	60
69	75
70	58
71	47
72	38
73	21
74	12

Find (a) the median height, and (b) the modal height.

9. Find the arithmetical mean and the median of the numbers (a) 10, 15, 20, (b) 10, 15, 20, 800.

10. Find (a) the median, and (b) the mode of the set of numbers 1, 1, 1, 3, 4, 6.

11. Find the first quartile, median, and third quartile of the numbers 3, 8, 16, 24, 63, 84, 92, 98, 102, 115, 120, 123, 131, 142, 156.

12. The population of the United States, to the nearest million, for the years indicated was:

Year	1860	1870	1880	1890	1900	1910	1920	1930	1940
Population	31	39	50	63	76	92	106	123	132

Find the first quartile, median, and third quartile.

114. A comparison

The terms arithmetical mean, median, mode, and geometrical mean have been defined and can be calculated for a given set of data. The interpretation of these terms and in general, their uses in comparing sets of data is a matter that requires experience, judgment, caution, and in many cases additional information. A few examples will illustrate some of the significant features of these statistical concepts.

Consider the annual incomes of four men, as follows: $2000; $2000; $2000; and $100,000. The arithmetical mean is $26,500; the median is $2000; and the mode is $2000. In this case, the mean gives a misleading conception of the data in the sense that the income of the "average" man in this group is actually $2000. The mode usually is a good indication of the type in the sense that it gives the number that occurs most frequently, and is therefore "typical" of the data.

As a second illustration, consider the numbers 1, 1, 1, 10, 100, 100, 100. The arithmetical mean is $44\frac{5}{7}$ and the median is 10. Notice that the presence of a few very small and a few very large numbers does not affect the median much, since the median is simply the middle number. For example, the set of numbers 7, 8, 9, 10, 11, 12, 13 has the same median, 10, as the previous set, but in this case the average is 10 instead of $44\frac{5}{7}$, as it was in the previous set. The presence of very small, very large, or very small and very large numbers in a set has a decided influence on the arithmetical mean.

When a set of numbers is such that each number bears the same ratio to the preceding number, as in the case of geometrical progressions, the geometrical mean is often used instead of the arithmetical mean. Consider the set of numbers 4, 12, 36. The arithmetical mean is $\frac{4 + 12 + 36}{3} = 14$, and the geometrical mean is $\sqrt[3]{(4)(12)(36)} = \sqrt[3]{1728} = 12$. The number 12 represents the set better than the number 14 in the sense that it is a member of the set, and the ratio of 12 to 4 is equal to the ratio of 36 to 12. In statistical data, the ratio of successive numbers is seldom constant, but this ratio may be approximately constant.

Examples such as those given above emphasize the fact that the investigator must select those statistical constants that best represent the data at hand. The matter of interpreting the results of statistical analysis is the final step in the investigation, and it is here that experience and judgment play an important role.

Consider, finally, the batting averages of two baseball players for 3 years, which are .250, .300, and .350 for one player, and .299, .300, and .301 for the other player. In both cases, the arithmetical mean is .300 and the median is .300. However, there is a difference between the data that the mean and the median do not reveal. The deviations from the arithmetical mean are greater in the first case than in the second case. The second player is more *consistent* than the first player. There is, then, a need for statistical constants other than the arithmetical mean and median.

115. Aids to computation

In some cases it is expeditious to "change the origin" of a set of numbers. For example, in calculating the arithmetical mean of a given set of numbers, it sometimes helps to select a tentative arithmetical mean, find the average of deviations of the data from this tentative mean, and finally apply this average to the tentative mean as a correction to obtain the true mean. In this procedure it is necessary to use the algebraic signs of the deviations.

Example 1. Find the arithmetical mean of the numbers 101, 102, 104, 106, 109.

Solution. Select 100 as a tentative mean. The deviations of the original numbers from this tentative mean are 1, 2, 4, 6, and 9. The arithmetical mean of these deviations is

$$\frac{1 + 2 + 4 + 6 + 9}{5} = 4.4.$$

Adding 4.4 to 100 gives 104.4, which is the arithmetical mean of the original set of numbers.

Example 2. Find the arithmetical mean of the numbers 98, 96, 95, 93, 91, 90, 89, 88, 86, 85, 80, 75.

Solution. Select 90 as a tentative mean. The deviations are 8, 6, 5, 3, 1, 0, −1, −2, −4, −5, −10, −15 respectively. The average of the deviations is −1⅙. The true mean is 90 − 1⅙ = 88⅚.

In some cases, it saves computation to select a different unit of measurement and apply the method of Example 2, after which the result is transformed to the original unit of measurement. Consider the following illustration:

Illustration

Data (x)	Frequencies (y)	Deviations (d)	dy
14.5	2	−2	−4
15.0	13	−1	−13
15.5	28	0	0
16.0	15	1	15
16.5	4	2	8
	$\Sigma y = 62$		$\Sigma dy = 6$

Select 15.5 as a tentative mean, and 0.5 as the unit of measurement. Then the entries in the column of deviations may be computed as follows. The measurement 14.5 deviates 14.5 − 15.5 from the tentative mean. This deviation is −1, but if 0.5 is used as the unit of measurement this deviation becomes $-\frac{1}{0.5} = -2$. In like manner, the other entries in the column of deviations may be verified by the student.

The unit correction is $\frac{\Sigma dy}{\Sigma y} = \frac{6}{62}$. The true mean is given by

$$M = 15.5 + 0.5 \left(\frac{6}{62}\right),$$
$$= 15.55, \text{ to four significant figures.}$$

EXERCISE 3

1. Find the arithmetical mean: 1012, 1048, 1052, 1078, 1080.
2. Find the arithmetical mean: 2521, 2523, 2527, 2530, 2532.
3. Find the arithmetical mean: 995, 997, 997, 998, 999, 1000, 1001, 1001, 1002, 1004.
4. Find the arithmetical mean, correct to three significant figures:

Observations	Frequencies
23.5	1
24.0	3
24.5	8
25.0	15
25.5	10
26.0	5
26.5	2

5. Find the arithmetical mean: 75, 76, 77, 77, 78, 79, 80, 81, 81, 82, 83, 84, 85.

6. Find the arithmetical mean, correct to four significant figures:

Observations	Frequencies
210.1	35
210.2	40
210.3	50
210.4	55
210.5	45
210.6	30

7. In the following set of data, use 28.60 as a tentative mean, use 0.15 as the unit of measurement, and find the arithmetical mean correct to four significant figures:

Data	Frequencies
28.15	10
28.30	10
28.45	20
28.60	40
28.75	50
28.90	30

8. In the following set of measurements use 98.65 as a tentative mean, use 0.01 as the unit of measurement, and find the arithmetical mean correct to five significant figures:

Measurements	Frequencies
98.63	3
98.64	7
98.65	12
98.66	23
98.67	11

9. In the following set of data, use 95.48 as a tentative mean, use 0.12 as the unit of measurement, and find the arithmetical mean correct to four significant figures:

Data	Frequencies
95.24	10
95.36	20
95.48	20
95.60	10
95.72	10
95.84	5
95.96	1

116. Frequency distributions; histograms

Consider the following set of observations and their corresponding frequencies:

x	y
4.98	1
5.00	2
5.12	2
5.24	2
5.36	4
5.41	6
5.43	7
5.52	8
5.64	7
5.76	6
5.83	5
5.95	5
6.00	2
6.15	2
6.22	1

Instead of using the data as given, it may be desirable to separate the observations into groups. The groups are called **classes.** For example, it is possible to separate this set of observations into classes based on ranges of x as follows: 4.9–5.1, 5.1–5.3, 5.3–5.5, 5.5–5.7, 5.7–5.9, 5.9–6.1, 6.1–6.3. The range of x in each case is 0.2, and this is called the **class interval.** The middle value in each class interval is called the **class mark** of that interval, and in this case the class marks are 5.0, 5.2, 5.4, 5.6, 5.8, 6.0, 6.2.

Arrange the data as follows:

Class marks	Frequencies
5.0	3
5.2	4
5.4	17
5.6	15
5.8	11
6.0	7
6.2	3

This set of pairs of values of class marks and corresponding frequencies, ordered with respect to size of class marks, is called a

frequency distribution. Naturally, the size of class intervals is arbitrary, and a variety of groupings is possible with the same set of observations. Consider the pair of values 5.2, 4 in the above frequency distribution. This does not mean that there were 4 observations of 5.2 in the original set. It does mean that there were 4 observations in the range 5.1 to 5.3 in the original set.

The pairs of values of class marks and frequencies in the frequency distribution can be plotted as a set of rectangles, as in Fig. 24. Such a diagram is called a *rectangular histogram*.

Fig. 24

One of the reasons for changing a given set of observations and their frequencies into a frequency distribution is that it serves to reduce the labor of computing the arithmetical mean and other statistical constants, with little loss in accuracy. In the example given above, the arithmetical mean of the original set is 5.59, correct to three significant figures, and the arithmetical mean of the frequency distribution with class interval of 0.2 is 5.6.

EXERCISE 4

1. Consider the following set of observations: 28.1, 31.2, 35.9, 36.1, 37.1, 37.3, 37.3, 38.2, 38.4, 39.1, 39.3, 39.7, 40.1, 40.2, 40.3, 41.6, 41.8, 42.2, 42.3. Classify these data into groups with class marks (a) 28, 30, 32, 34, 36, 38, 40, 42 and (b) 30, 34, 38, 42. Compute the arithmetical mean in each case, correct to three significant figures.

FREQUENCY DISTRIBUTIONS; HISTOGRAMS

2. Construct a rectangular histogram for the following set of classified data:

Class mark	Frequency
50	5
60	15
70	50
80	25
90	5

3. The following frequency distribution gives the weights of 374 men students in a college:

Weight in pounds	Frequency
116–120	1
121–125	2
126–130	5
131–135	8
136–140	16
141–145	20
146–150	24
151–155	30
156–160	38
161–165	49
166–170	38
171–175	34
176–180	31
181–185	27
186–190	21
191–195	18
196–200	10
201–205	2

Reclassify these data into groups with class marks 120, 130, $\cdots$, 200. Compute the average weight from the new distribution, correct to the nearest pound.

4. The annual salaries of 33 individuals working in a certain department of a manufacturing concern for 1947 were: $3150, $3175, $3180, $3190, $3205, $3215, $3240, $3260, $3280, $3310, $3340, $3350, $3375, $3390, $3405, $3450, $3475, $3510, $3570, $3610, $3750, $3820, $3840, $3850, $3920, $3925, $3925, $3970, $4050, $4120, $4180, $4250. Classify these salaries, using class marks of $3200, $3400, $3600, $\cdots$, $4200. Compute the average salary, using this frequency distribution, correct to three significant figures.

5. Draw a rectangular histogram for the following set of classified data:

x	y
1000–1999	400
2000–2999	650
3000–3999	900
4000–4999	2000
5000–5999	1500
6000–6999	1000
7000–7999	750
8000–8999	500
9000–9999	200

6. In the expansion of the binomial $(a + b)^4$ the number of the term can be taken to be a class mark and the numerical coefficient of the term can be thought of as the corresponding frequency. The following frequency distribution results:

No. of the term (Class mark)	1	2	3	4	5
Coefficient (Frequency)	1	4	6	4	1

Draw the rectangular histogram for this distribution.

117. Frequency curves

A smooth curve drawn through the points represented by corresponding pairs of values of class marks and frequencies is called a **frequency curve**. The frequency curve for the data represented in the histogram of Fig. 24 is shown in Fig. 25.

A frequency curve of particular interest is the so-called **normal frequency curve**. The equation of the normal frequency curve is

$$y = ce^{-h^2 x^2} \qquad (3)$$

where $e = 2.718$ approximately (the base of natural logarithms), c is the ordinate for $x = 0$ and is the maximum ordinate, and h is a constant. The curve is symmetrical with respect to the Y-axis. The general shape of the curve for a particular pair of values of c and h is shown in Fig. 26.

An extended discussion of the properties of the normal frequency curve and the assumptions underlying it is beyond the scope of this book, but a few remarks concerning it may be apropos.

If the coefficients of the expansion of the binomials $(a + b)$, $(a + b)^2$, $(a + b)^3$, $\cdots$, $(a + b)^n$ are plotted as ordinates using the number of the term as the abscissa, and if the corresponding rec-

FIG. 25

tangular histogram is plotted for each value of n, then the histogram will approach the shape of the normal frequency curve as n increases without limit.

If a large number of careful readings of a certain dimension is made by a given measuring instrument, and if the deviations of these readings from their mean are recorded as abscissas, using the frequencies of the deviations as ordinates, then a smooth curve drawn through the plotted points will approximate a normal frequency curve of the type shown in Fig. 26. On the other hand, a curve showing the distribution of incomes of individuals by age groups in a given community may differ greatly from a normal frequency curve.

The normal frequency curve of formula (3) is known by many different names, some of which are: bell-shaped curve, normal curve of error, Gaussian curve of error, probability curve, biological curve, normal distribution curve, and grade curve.

118. Standard deviation

Consider the set of data x_1, x_2, x_3, ..., x_k. If the arithmetical mean of these k data is designated by M, the **standard deviation**,

Fig. 26

σ (sigma), is defined to be:

$$\sigma = \sqrt{\frac{(x_1 - M)^2 + (x_2 - M)^2 + (x_3 - M)^2 + \cdots + (x_k - M)^2}{k}}. \quad (4)$$

Example 1. Find the standard deviation for the data 1, 2, 3, 4, 5.

Solution. The arithmetical mean is 3. The deviations of the data from the mean are $-2, -1, 0, 1$, and 2, respectively. The sum of the squares of these deviations is $(-2)^2 + (-1)^2 + (0)^2 + (1)^2 + (2)^2 = 10$. The number of data is 5. Therefore

$$\sigma = \sqrt{\tfrac{10}{5}} = \sqrt{2} = 1.4, \text{ correct to two significant figures.}$$

The standard deviation is a measure of the extent to which a set of data deviates from their arithmetical mean. Thus for no deviation $\sigma = 0$.

Example 2. Compute the standard deviation for the set of data 9, 10, 11 and for the set of data 5, 10, 15. Compare the results.

Solution. For the first set of data,

$$\sigma = \sqrt{\frac{(9-10)^2 + (10-10)^2 + (11-10)^2}{3}} = 0.82,$$

to two significant figures.

STANDARD DEVIATION

For the second set of data,

$$\sigma = \sqrt{\frac{(5-10)^2 + (10-10)^2 + (15-10)^2}{3}} = 4.1,$$

to two significant figures. Although the arithmetical mean in both cases is 10, the larger value of σ in the second case shows that the second set of data deviates from the mean more than does the first set.

The standard deviation is called a **measure of dispersion,** while the arithmetical mean, median, and geometric mean are called **measures of central tendency.**

When the data are given as a table of observations and frequencies, the arithmetic involved in computing the standard deviation can be arranged in tabular form, as in the solution of Example 3.

Example 3. Compute the standard deviation of the following set of data:

Observations	2	4	6	8	10
Frequencies	1	5	10	4	2

Solution. The arithmetic mean is 6.1, to two significant figures:

x	y	$x - M$	$(x-M)^2 y$
2	1	-4.1	16.81
4	5	-2.1	22.05
6	10	-0.1	0.10
8	4	1.9	14.44
10	2	3.9	30.42
	$\Sigma y = 22$		$\Sigma(x-M)^2 y = 83.82$

$$\sigma = \sqrt{\frac{83.82}{22}} = 2.0, \text{ to two significant figures.}$$

EXERCISE 5

1. Compute the standard deviations of the two sets of data
   (a) 98, 99, 100, 101, 102   (b) 80, 90, 100, 110, 120

correct to three significant figures. Compare the results.

2. Compute the standard deviation of the data:

Observations	Frequencies
1	5
2	20
3	10

correct to two significant figures.

3. Compute the standard deviation of the data:

Observations	Frequencies
1	1
2	5
3	10

correct to two significant figures. Compare this with the answer to Problem 2.

4. Compute the arithmetical mean, median, mode, geometrical mean, and standard deviation of the data: 10, 10, 15, 100.

5. The batting averages of two baseball players for 1945, 1946, and 1947 were 0.280, 0.300, 0.305 and 0.290, 0.300, 0.310, respectively. Compute the arithmetical means for the two players, and compare the standard deviations.

6. Five freshmen made the following scores on an intelligence test: 90, 100, 120, 140, 150. Five sophomores made the following scores on the same test: 80, 110, 130, 140, 140. Compare the means and the standard deviations.

MISCELLANEOUS EXERCISE

1. Find the arithmetical mean of the numbers 16, 23, 38, 46, 54, 65.

2. Arrange the following numbers in the form of a frequency distribution and calculate the arithmetical mean: 3, 4, 4, 4, 5, 5, 5, 5, 6, 6, 6, 7, 7, 7, 7, 7, 8, 8, 8, 8, 9, 9, 10, 10.

3. Compute the arithmetical mean of $a, a + d, a + 2d, \cdots, a + (n - 1)d$.

4. Using 80 as a tentative mean, list the deviations from the mean, and find the arithmetical mean, of the numbers, 70, 72, 72, 74, 74, 76, 78, 79, 80, 81, 81, 83, 84, 85, 86, 87.

5. Use 1010.0 as a tentative mean, use 0.5 as the unit of measurement, and compute the arithmetical mean of the numbers 1007.5, 1008.0, 1008.5, 1008.5, 1008.5, 1009.0, 1009.0, 1009.5, 1009.5, 1010.0, 1010.0, 1010.5, 1010.5, 1011.0, 1011.0, 1011.0, 1011.5, 1012.0, 1012.5, 1012.5.

6. Show that the sum of the deviations of the numbers a, b from their mean is zero.

7. Consider the numbers $x_1, x_2, \cdots$. Show that $\Sigma(x_i - M)^2 = \Sigma x_i^2 - \dfrac{(\Sigma x_i)^2}{n}$, where i takes on the values 1 and 2, M is the arithmetical mean of x_1, x_2, and $n = 2$. (Note: This relation is also true for $i = 1, 2, 3, \cdots, n$.)

8. The maximum temperatures at a certain location on each day for a week were 80°, 81°, 83°, 86°, 84°, 85°, 82°. Find the average maximum temperature and the median maximum temperature.

9. Using logarithms, calculate the geometrical mean of the numbers 2.0, 4.1, 8.0, 16.2, and 32.3, correct to three significant figures.

STANDARD DEVIATION

10. Show that the logarithm of the geometrical mean of a given set of numbers is the arithmetical mean of the logarithms of the numbers.

11. Find the median and mode of the numbers 17, 17, 18, 18, 18, 19, 19, 19, 19, 20, 21, 22, 23.

12. On a certain farm the production of potatoes in bushels for certain years was as follows:

Year	No. Bushels
1940	2032
1941	2615
1942	2900
1943	3016
1944	3120
1945	2800
1946	2600

Find the average yield for this seven-year period, correct to three significant figures.

13. A bowler made the following scores in five consecutive games: 200, 180, 210, 170, 240. Another bowler made the scores 160, 190, 200, 210, 200. Compute their average scores, and the standard deviations of the two sets of scores, to three significant figures.

14. Plot the points (1,1), (2,7), (3,21), (4,35), (5,35), (6,21), (7,7), (8,1). Draw a smooth curve through the points. Use a scale in which the length representing one unit on the Y-axis equals one-tenth the length representing one unit on the X-axis. What sort of curve do you have?

15. Draw a rectangular histogram for the following set of classified data:

Class marks	Frequencies
5	8
10	14
15	26
20	44
25	28
30	16
35	10

16. The value $\dfrac{100\sigma}{M}$ is called the **coefficient of variation**. Compute the coefficient of variation for each of the two sets of data 18, 19, 20, 21, 22 and 28, 29, 30, 31, 32. Compare the standard deviations, and also compare the coefficients of variation. Report the results to three significant figures.

17. Calculate the standard deviation of the two numbers a, b.

18. Using the following approximate values of e^{-x^2}, plot the graph of $y = e^{-x^2}$.

x	0	0.1	0.2	0.3	0.4	0.5	0.6	0.7	0.8
y	1	0.99	0.96	0.91	0.85	0.78	0.70	0.61	0.53

0.9	1.0	1.1	1.2	1.3	1.4	1.5	1.6
0.44	0.37	0.30	0.24	0.18	0.14	0.11	0.08

Use appropriate scales on the x, y axes.

13

Compound Interest and Compound Discount

119. Preliminary concepts and definitions

In the chapter on simple interest, it was learned that the interest earned on an investment which pays simple interest is directly proportional to the number of years for which the investment is made. Thus, an investment of $300 at 5% simple interest, made for 3 years, earns $15 per year, or a total of $45. The amount due the investor at the end of three years would be $300 + $45 or $345.

In the above investment, let us assume that a new arrangement for interest payments has been made whereby the interest earned during any year is added to the principal for that year and that interest is computed on the new principal for the succeeding year. The amount due the investor at the end of three years may then be computed as follows.

Principal invested	$300.00
Interest rate expressed as a decimal	0.05
Interest earned during the first year	$ 15.00
New principal is $300.00 + $15.00 or	$315.00
	0.05
Interest earned during the second year	$ 15.75
New principal is $315.00 + $15.75 or	$330.75
	0.05
Interest earned during the third year	$ 16.54

New principal, which is the amount due the investor at the end of three years, is $330.75 + $16.54 or $347.29.

Thus, $47.29 is earned on the investment under this plan in place of the $45 earned as simple interest under the original arrangement, where the $2.29 difference represents the interest earned on interest under the second plan. The difference between the amount and the original principal in this illustration is called the **compound interest** earned on $300 in 3 years.

Although compound interest may always be computed as indicated, the arithmetical work becomes increasingly tedious as the number of times interest is added to principal increases. A careful examination of the illustration above will give us a clue to a simplified method for computing compound interest. It will be noted that the amount at the end of the first year is $315 = $300 + $15; or, since $15 = $300(0.05), this amount equals $300 + $300(0.05), or $300(1.05). Likewise, the amount at the end of the second year may be written $300(1.05) + $300(1.05)(0.05), or $300(1.05)^2, and in like manner, the amount at the end of three years is $300(1.05)^3. It should be noted that these amounts form a geometrical progression (see Article 92) whose common ratio is equal to (1.05), and hence the amount after n years would be the nth term or $300(1.05)^n. In this form, the computation may be carried out by means of logarithms, by use of the binomial expansion, or by use of a previously constructed table of powers of (1.05).

120. The compound amount formula

For the purpose of clarity in discussing the general problem of compound interest, let us agree to use the following representation of the various quantities involved:

P = the principal,
n = the number of interest periods,
i = the interest rate *per period* expressed in decimal form,
S = the compound amount of P at the end of n interest periods,
I = the compound interest earned on P.

Let us now consider the general problem of investing a sum of money P at compound interest for n periods at the rate of i per period. The interest on P for one period is Pi, hence the amount at the end of the first period is

$$P + Pi \text{ or } P(1 + i).$$

As in the illustration given above, we note that the amount at the end of one period is obtained by multiplying the principal by the factor $(1 + i)$. Hence $P(1 + i)$, the new principal at the beginning of the second period, amounts to

$$P(1 + i)(1 + i) \text{ or } P(1 + i)^2$$

at the end of the second period. In like manner, the amount at the end of the third period is

$$P(1+i)^2(1+i) \text{ or } P(1+i)^3$$

and so on. Since the amounts $P(1+i)$, $P(1+i)^2$, $P(1+i)^3$, $\ldots$ form a geometrical progression, the amount at the end of the nth period is the nth term of this progression. Hence (see Article 93) we have that the **compound amount** is

$$S = P(1+i)^n. \tag{1}$$

It follows immediately that the compound interest is given by the following formula:

$$I = S - P. \tag{2}$$

The following example is used to show the various methods of computing the values of the amount, S, and the compound interest.

Example 1. Find the compound amount and the compound interest on $500 invested at 3% per year for 15 years.

Solution 1. By use of the table of amounts at compound interest.

The principal, P, is $500, the interest rate, i, expressed as a decimal, is 0.03, and the number of periods, n, is 15. Hence, substituting in the formula (1), we have

$$S = \$500(1.03)^{15}.$$

In Table V, Amount of 1 at Compound Interest, are found the values of $(1+i)^n$ for various interest rates listed across the top of the page and for consecutive values of n arranged in vertical columns on either side of the page. *If the principal is represented by a single digit followed by zeros, or by a number for which a short-cut multiplication scheme exists, the actual value of the amount should be read from the proper table. Otherwise, the multiplication should be done by logarithms.* This particular problem is best done without the use of logarithms, hence we have

$$S = \$500(1.5579674) = \$778.98,$$

where the value 1.5579674 was read from page 302 of Table V in the column headed by 3% and in the row marked 15. The multiplication was carried out by first multiplying by 1000 (by moving the decimal point three places to the right), followed by division by 2. The answer is correct to the nearest cent.

Hence the compound interest is

$$I = S - P = 778.98 - 500 = \$278.98.$$

Solution 2. By the use of logarithms entirely.

If a table of compound amounts is not available or if the required quantity does not appear in the table, logarithms may be used as follows:

250 COMPOUND INTEREST AND COMPOUND DISCOUNT

$$\log S = \log 500$$
$$+ 15 \log (1.03) = 15(1.0128372) \text{ or}$$

	2.698970
	0.192558
	2.891528

from which we obtain,

$$S = \$778.98.$$

It should be noted that the 7-place logarithm table was used to find the value of log (1.03) to insure accuracy in the 6th place of the logarithm.

Example 2. Find the compound amount and the compound interest on $2783.65 for $3\frac{1}{2}$ years if interest is computed on the basis of 1% each half-year.

Solution. Since interest is computed on the half-yearly basis we have $n = 7$ and $i = 0.01$. Hence,

$$S = 2783.65 \, (1.01)^7.$$

By the use of logarithms, we have

$$\log S = \log 2783.65$$
$$+ \log (1.01)^7$$

	3.444614
	0.030250
	3.474864

from which $\qquad S = \$2984.45.$

The compound interest is

$$I = 2984.45 - 2783.65,$$
$$= \$200.80.$$

Hereafter in this book compound interest should be used in all problems unless otherwise stated or implied.

EXERCISE 1

Find the compound amount and the compound interest in each of the following problems:

Prob. no.	Principal	Interest rate	No. of years at interest
1.	$500	4% per year	18
2.	$2500	$3\frac{1}{2}$% per year	10
3.	$1750	6% per year	20
4.	$3765	$2\frac{3}{4}$% per year	15
5.	$5000	2% each half-year	4
6.	$1000	$1\frac{1}{2}$% each half-year	12
7.	$1300	1% each quarter-year	50
8.	$2000	$\frac{7}{12}$% each quarter-year	13

9. A building and loan association pays interest on deposits at the rate of 3% per year. Find the amount of a deposit of $5000 at the end of 15 years.

NOMINAL AND EFFECTIVE RATES OF INTEREST

10. A savings bank pays interest on deposits at the rate of 1% each half-year. A deposit of $2500 will amount to how much in 12 years?

11. Six years ago a trust fund amounting to $5387.86 was invested at the rate of $3\frac{1}{3}$% per year. Find the value of the fund now.

12. A boy inherits $24,560.80 on his 15th birthday.* Under the specifications of the will, the money is to be placed in a trust fund which earns interest at the rate of 2% every 6 months and is to be made available to the heir when he is 21 years old. What amount does the boy have on his 21st birthday?

13. Find the value of $(1.002)^{10}$, accurate to six significant places.

14. Find the value of $(1.003)^{15}$, accurate to five significant places.

15. Mr. Jones signs a note for $500 payable at the end of 8 years. The note bears interest at the rate of 5% payable at the end of each year. After making three interest payments, Mr. Jones obtains from his creditor permission to stop the annual interest payments. In place of these payments, the creditor requires compound interest for the balance of the life of the note. What payment must Mr. Jones make when the note is due?

16. If Mr. Jones, in Problem 15, defaults on the first 3 interest payments but agrees to make all the others, how much would he have to pay to clear his indebtedness at the due date of the note, assuming the creditor requires compound interest on the defaulted payments?

17. Show that $(1 + i)^n$, where n is greater than 100, may be computed from a compound amount table for which the maximum value of n is 100. (Hint: Recall that $a^n \cdot a^m = a^{n+m}$.)

18. Find the compound amount of $287.50 for 125 years at $1\frac{1}{2}$%.

19. During the past 10 years, a city of 55,638 people has increased in population by 6% per year. Assuming the rate of increase is the same for the next 10 years, find the approximate population of this city at the end of 10 years.

20. Assuming that a town of 5000 will decrease in population at the rate of 1% per year, what will its population be 50 years from now?

121. Nominal and effective rates of interest

It is customary in business to quote interest rates on a yearly basis irrespective of how often the interest is added to the principal. Thus, if interest at 2% is added to the principal every 6 months, the quoted rate is two times 2% or 4%. Similarly, if interest at $\frac{1}{2}$% is added every month, the quoted rate is 6%. In general, if interest at the rate i is added to the principal m times per year at equal intervals of time, the **quoted rate**, j, is mi. The rate, j, is called the **nominal rate of interest** and is usually expressed as a per cent. Whenever a nominal rate is given, it should be accompanied by a

---
* In this book, "birthday" is used in the sense of "anniversary of birth." Thus a person is one year old on his first birthday, 15 years old on his 15th birthday, and so on.

statement giving the number of times interest is added to the principal during the year. Thus in the first of our two previous examples, where 2% is added to the principal every 6 months, we say that the nominal rate is 4% compounded, or converted, two times per year or semiannually. The interest period is frequently called the **conversion period.** Thus in this example, we have a conversion period of 6 months.

Referring again to the nominal rate of 4% converted semiannually, we see that $1 amounts to $1.02 at the end of the first conversion period. At the end of the second 6 months, $1.02 amounts to 1.02 + (1.02)(0.02) or $1.0404. Hence the interest earned on $1 in one year is $0.0404 and we see that an interest rate of 4.04% converted annually will earn the same on $1 in one year as a nominal rate of 4% converted semiannually. Two rates which earn the same interest in a given length of time are said to be **equivalent.** The rate of interest, converted annually, equivalent to a given nominal rate, is called the **effective rate.** Thus in the above example the effective rate equivalent to 4% converted semiannually is 4.04%.

Let us consider now the general problem of finding the effective rate of interest, r, equivalent to a nominal rate, j, converted m times a year. Let the interest rate for the conversion period of $\frac{1}{m}$th of a year be i. Then since $j = mi$ and since there are exactly m conversion periods in the year, the amount of 1 at the interest rate of $i = \frac{j}{m}$ per period is $1\left(1 + \frac{j}{m}\right)^m$. But at an effective rate of r, 1 amounts to $1 + r$ in one year. In order that the two rates be equivalent,

$$1 + r = \left(1 + \frac{j}{m}\right)^m, \tag{3}$$

or
$$r = \left(1 + \frac{j}{m}\right)^m - 1. \tag{4}$$

Solving equation (3) for j we have

$$j = m\left[(1 + r)^{\frac{1}{m}} - 1\right], \tag{5}$$

which is the nominal rate of interest converted m times a year that is equivalent to an effective rate of r.

Example 1. Find the effective rate of interest equivalent to a nominal rate of 6% converted (a) semiannually, (b) quarterly, (c) monthly.

Solution. A nominal rate of 6% converted semiannually means that 3% is added to the principal at the end of each half-year. Hence, since there are two

NOMINAL AND EFFECTIVE RATES OF INTEREST

interest periods in the year, 1 amounts to $1(1.03)^2$ in one year. At the effective rate r, 1 amounts to $1 + r$ in one year and we have

$$1 + r = (1.03)^2.$$

Using Table V,
$$1 + r = 1.060900,$$
$$r = 0.060900.$$

This result might have been obtained by use of formula (4). We list this result and the answers for (b) and (c) below in tabular form, for comparison:

	Nominal rate	Number of conversion periods per year	Equivalent effective rate
a	6%	2	6.0900%
b	6%	4	6.1364%
c	6%	12	6.1678%

Example 2. Find the nominal rate compounded quarterly, equivalent to an effective rate of 5%.

Solution. By use of formula (3) or by direct reasoning, we have

$$1.05 = \left(1 + \frac{j}{4}\right)^4,$$

or,
$$1 + \frac{j}{4} = (1.05)^{\frac{1}{4}}.$$

From Table X, we find that $(1.05)^{\frac{1}{4}} = 1.0122722$; hence

$$1 + \frac{j}{4} = 1.0122722,$$

or,
$$\frac{j}{4} = 0.0122722,$$
$$j = 0.0490888, \text{ or } 0.049089$$

since the result may not be accurate to more than five significant figures. We might have substituted directly in formula (5) for this answer.

Example 3. Find the nominal rate of interest converted monthly equivalent to a nominal rate of 8% converted quarterly.

Solution. Neither formula (4) nor (5) can be used for this problem, but the principle used in setting up formula (3) may be employed. In one year, 1 amounts to $(1.02)^4$ at the nominal rate of 8% converted quarterly. At a nominal rate of j, compounded monthly, 1 amounts to

$$\left(1 + \frac{j}{12}\right)^{12} = (1.02)^4,$$

or
$$1 + \frac{j}{12} = (1.02)^{\frac{1}{3}}.$$

Using logarithms, we have

$$\log\left(1 + \frac{j}{12}\right) = \frac{1}{3}\log 1.02 = 0.0028667 \text{ (using Table II)},$$

whence
$$j = 0.0795,$$

the nominal rate converted monthly equivalent to a nominal rate of 8% converted quarterly.

EXERCISE 2

Determine m, the number of conversion periods per year, and i, the interest rate for the conversion period.

Prob. no.	Interest rate	m	i
1.	3% converted semiannually		
2.	5% converted quarterly		
3.	8% converted monthly		
4.	4% converted annually		
5.	12% converted semimonthly		
6.	4% converted bimonthly		

7. Find the effective rate equivalent to 3% converted semiannually.

8. Find the nominal rate, converted quarterly, equivalent to 7% effective.

9. Find the nominal rate, converted monthly, equivalent to 5% effective.

10. Find the effective rate equivalent to 2% compounded bimonthly.

11. Find the nominal rate, converted quarterly, equivalent to 6% converted semiannually.

12. Find the nominal rate, converted monthly, equivalent to 4% converted semiannually.

13. An investment company wishes to earn an average of 4.9% nominal, converted monthly, on its funds. Would an investment, which pays 5%, converted annually, give a yield greater than, equal to, or less than the average?

14. A yield of 3% effective for 10 years is equivalent to what simple interest rate for this period?

15. The simple interest rate on the United States Savings bonds at the time of World War II was $3\frac{3}{5}$%. These bonds mature in 10 years; all interest is payable at the due date. What was the equivalent compound interest rate converted monthly?

122. Interest for a fractional part of a period

The exponent, n, used in the derivation of the compound amount formula, is an integer and hence any meaning that may be attached to the formula for fractional values of n must be defined. However, the business practice of using simple interest for fractional parts of periods makes it unnecessary to use the formula for fractional values of n.

Example. Find the amount of $2500 for $8\frac{3}{4}$ years if interest is computed at 4% converted semiannually.

COMPOUND AMOUNT AT CHANGING RATES

Solution. The interest period is one-half year; hence $8\frac{3}{4}$ years is equivalent to $17\frac{1}{2}$ periods. Hence the amount at the end of 17 periods at 2% per period is

$$2500(1.02)^{17} = \$3500.60.$$

Using simple interest, the amount of \$3500.60 for $\frac{1}{2}$ period is

$$S = 3500.60 \left[1 + \tfrac{1}{2}(0.02)\right],$$
$$= \$3535.61.$$

EXERCISE 3

1. Find the amount of \$5374 for $15\frac{1}{2}$ years if interest is computed at 6%, converted annually.
2. Find the amount of \$8750 for $9\frac{1}{4}$ years if interest is computed at 4%, compounded semiannually.
3. A note for \$500 dated March 1, 1949 is to be paid, together with compound interest at 6% converted quarterly, on April 9, 1955. What payment must be made to clear the debt when due?
4. Using the compound interest formula to find the amount for a fractional part of a period, compare the amount, by this procedure, on \$500 for $\frac{1}{3}$ of a year, interest at 4% converted annually, with that obtained by the business practice.

123. Compound amount at changing rates

Although some investments such as notes and mortgages specify a definite rate of interest which must be paid by the borrower, other investments such as savings deposits in banks and building and loan associations do not carry a fixed interest rate. Thus many savings banks which paid 4% interest twenty years ago are now paying as low as 1% in some cases. To find the compound amount under such conditions, the whole period of the investment is broken up into intervals during which time the rate is constant. The compound amount is computed to the end of the first period at the original rate and then to the end of the next period at the new rate, and so on through each of the intervals of the whole period. The following example illustrates the proper procedure.

Example. Mr. Eberly deposits \$500 in a savings bank paying 4% converted semiannually. After 5 years, he is notified that the interest rate has been reduced to 3% converted semiannually. In another 8 years the interest is reduced to 2% converted semiannually. What amount does Mr. Eberly have on deposit after 15 years, assuming he has made no additional deposits?

Solution. The indicated time graph illustrates the proper time intervals at the various rates. Referring to the graph,

```
|     4%      |        3%         |    2%    |
 0  1  2  3  4  5  6  7  8  9  10 11 12 13 14 15
```

256   COMPOUND INTEREST AND COMPOUND DISCOUNT

it is seen that $500 amounts to $500(1.02)^{10}$ at the end of 5 years or 10 periods. This amount carried forward at interest for the next 8 years or 16 periods at the new rate of $1\frac{1}{2}\%$ per period is $500(1.02)^{10}(1.015)^{16}$, which is the new amount at the end of the 13th year. The interest rate for the next two years is 2% converted semiannually. Hence the amount at the end of 15 years is

$$S = 500(1.02)^{10}(1.015)^{16}(1.01)^4.$$

Using logarithms, $\quad S = \$804.85.$

EXERCISE 4

Find the amount of $1000 at interest for the following periods at the rates indicated:

1. 5% converted annually for 3 years, 4% converted annually for the next 5 years.

2. 4% converted semiannually for 8 years, 3% converted semiannually for the next 2 years.

3. 2% converted quarterly for 5 years, 3% converted quarterly for the next 2 years, 4% converted quarterly for the next 4 years.

4. 1% converted annually for 3 years, $1\frac{1}{2}\%$ converted semiannually for the next 8 years.

5. Find the amount of a deposit of $1500 made in a building and loan association if interest is 6% converted annually for the first two years, 4% converted semiannually for the next 5 years, and 3% converted quarterly for the last 3 years.

6. A deposit of $600 was made in a savings bank. After 8 years, what is the amount of the deposit if interest was paid at the rate of $1\frac{1}{2}\%$ converted semiannually for the first 5 years and 2% converted quarterly for the balance of the time?

7. A deposit of $4050 earned interest at the rate of 6%, converted quarterly, for 4 years. During the next two years no interest was paid at all, but interest payments were then resumed at the rate of 3%, converted semiannually, for the following 4 years. What was the amount of the deposit at the end of 10 years?

8. It is estimated that a city whose population is now 55,681 will increase in population at the rate of 8% per year for the next 5 years, 7% per year for the following 5 years, and 6% per year for the five years after that. What is the estimated population after 15 years?

9. Which is the better investment and by how much: (a) an investment of $1000 which pays 3% for 10 years, or (b) one of $1000 which pays $3\frac{1}{2}\%$ for the first 5 years followed by $2\frac{1}{2}\%$ for the next 5 years? All rates are converted annually.

10. Derive a formula for the compound amount of P if invested at an interest rate of i_1 for the first n_1 periods, i_2 for the following n_2 periods, and i_3 for the last n_3 periods. Use this formula to find the compound amount in Problem 5.

124. The time and rate problems

The compound interest formula may be solved for the time, n, in terms of S, P, and i. From the formula

$$S = P(1+i)^n,$$

we have, $$(1+i)^n = \frac{S}{P},$$

or, $$n \log (1+i) = \log S - \log P,$$

hence, $$n = \frac{\log S - \log P}{\log (1+i)}. \qquad (6)$$

Actually only the integral part of n is needed from formula (6), since interest for fractional parts of a period should be computed with simple interest. If n is an integer, formula (6) gives the desired answer; otherwise let N be the largest integer in n. In N periods P amounts to $P(1+i)^N$. Let t represent the fractional part of a period needed for $P(1+i)^N$ to accumulate to S at simple interest. We have

$$P(1+i)^N (1+ti) = S,$$

or, $$t = \frac{S - P(1+i)^N}{Pi(1+i)^N}. \qquad (7)$$

Example 1. How long will it take $500 to accumulate to $1200 if invested at 3%, converted annually?

Solution 1. The student may substitute in formula (6) but it is better to use the compound interest formula. We have

$$500(1.03)^n = 1200,$$

or, $$\log 500 + n \log 1.03 = \log 1200,$$

hence, $$n = \frac{\log 1200 - \log 500}{\log 1.03},$$

$$= 29.6184.$$

We disregard the fractional part, 0.6184, and use 29. Let t represent the part of a year that $500(1.03)^{29}$ must be carried forward at simple interest to amount to 1200. Hence,

$$500(1.03)^{29}[1 + t(0.03)] = 1200,$$

from which, $$t = 0.6145.$$

This may be expressed as $360(0.6145) = 221$ days, or 7 months, 11 days. That is, $500 will amount to $1200 in 29 years, 7 months, and 11 days if interest is computed at 3%, converted annually.

It should be noted that the fractional part of n, 0.6184, expressed in months and days, is 7 months, 13 days and hence is a good approximation to the exact answer. Such an approximation is sometimes used.

Solution 2. Another method of solving the above problem is by interpolation from the table of compound amounts, Table V. We illustrate this method:

$$(1.03)^n = \frac{1200}{500} = 2.4.$$

From Table V

$$1\left\{t\begin{cases} 29 \\ 29+t \\ 30 \end{cases} \middle| \begin{array}{c} 2.35657 \\ 2.4 \\ 2.42726 \end{array} \right\} 0.04343 \right\} 0.07069$$

$$\frac{t}{1} = \frac{0.04343}{0.07069},$$

or, $\quad t = 0.6144,$

which is 7 months, 11 days. Thus it takes 29 years, 7 months, 11 days for $500 to amount to $1200.

This is exactly what we got by the first method. Indeed it can be shown that interpolation from the table will always give the correct answer to the degree of accuracy desired.

Another problem is that of finding the interest rate when the other quantities in the compound interest formula, or relations between them, are given.

From
$$S = P(1+i)^n,$$
$$\log S = \log P + n \log (1+i),$$

from which $\quad \log (1+i) = \dfrac{\log S - \log P}{n}.\qquad$ (8)

Example 2. At what interest rate, compounded semiannually, will money double itself in 10 years?

Solution. Since the principal, P, is doubled, $S = 2P$. Hence the compound interest formula gives

$$2P = P(1+i)^{20},$$

where i is the interest rate for the half-year. We have

$$(1+i)^{20} = 2,$$

hence, $\quad \log(1+i) = \dfrac{\log 2}{20},$

$$= \frac{0.301030}{20} = 0.0150515.$$

To insure accuracy to five significant figures, the table of seven-place mantissas, Table II, must be used to find the antilogarithm. We have

$$1+i = 1.035265,$$
or, $\quad i = 0.035265.$

The nominal rate converted semiannually is 2(0.035265) or 7.0530%.

PRESENT VALUE. COMPOUND DISCOUNT

It should be noted that interpolation from the compound interest table does not give an exact answer to the rate problem but may be used as a rough approximation. Thus, in the above problem, interpolation from the table gives

$$j = 0.070507,$$

which agrees to the answer above to three significant figures. However, since rates are seldom given to closer than a hundredth of a per cent in business problems, the interpolation method may often be used.

EXERCISE 5

1. How long will it take money to double itself at 4% nominal, compounded quarterly? (Use two methods.)
2. An investment of $567.00 amounts to $1255.38 in 12 years. What rate of interest converted annually is earned on this investment? (Find the rate accurate to as many places as the 6-place table of logarithms will give, and then compare to the approximation obtained from interpolation.)
3. United States Savings Bonds increase one-third in value in 10 years. What nominal rate of interest, converted monthly, is earned on these bonds? Give the answer to the nearest hundredth of 1%.
4. Mr. Allston bought a house for $9500. He pays $789.85 for repairs and $275 for taxes immediately but receives in a single payment $800 in advance for a one-year lease on the property. At the end of the year Mr. Allston sells his house for $11,000, paying a 5% fee to the real estate broker. Assuming that other selling expenses amount to $50, what interest rate did Mr. Allston realize on his investment? Give the answer to the nearest hundredth of 1%.
5. A depositor invests $2000 in a security which will pay 4% converted semiannually for 10 years and then 3% converted annually until the original investment has doubled itself. How long will it take?
6. A city's population has been increasing at the rate of 8% per year. If the rate of increase remains constant, how long will it take the city to grow from 30,000 to 50,000 population? Give the answer to the nearest year.

125. Present value. Compound discount

The **present value** of a sum of money due at some future date is defined to be the principal needed to amount to the stated sum at the given future date. The difference between the sum of money and its present value is called the **compound discount**. Both of these quantities may be obtained from the compound interest formula.

Let S represent the sum of money, and let P represent its present value. Hence,

260   COMPOUND INTEREST AND COMPOUND DISCOUNT

$$S = P(1 + i)^n,$$

or
$$P = \frac{S}{(1 + i)^n} = S(1 + i)^{-n}. \tag{9}$$

This formula is often written in the form

$$P = Sv^n,$$

where
$$v = (1 + i)^{-1}.$$

The compound discount on S, represented by D, is given by

$$D = S - P.$$

The student should note that the compound interest on P is numerically equal to the compound discount on S.

The present value of a sum of money due at a future date is sometimes called the **discounted value**.

Example 1. What principal is needed to accumulate $5000 in 8 years at 4%, converted quarterly?

Solution. The principal needed is the present value of $5000 in 32 periods at 1% per period.

Hence, we have

$$P(1.01)^{32} = 5000,$$
$$P = \frac{5000}{(1.01)^{32}} = 5000(1.01)^{-32}.$$

The numerical work may be carried out by the use of logarithms or by the use of Table VI, Present Value of 1 at Compound Interest. Using this table,

$$P = 5000(0.7273041) = \$3636.52.$$

If the problem had been such that the use of logarithms was desirable, we would have

$$\log P = \log 5000 + \log (1.01)^{-32},$$
$$= 3.698970 + 9.861716 - 10,$$
$$= 3.560686.$$

Hence, $P = \$3636.52.$

Example 2. A note due in 8 years will be canceled by the payment of $3000 at that time. What is the note worth now if interest is computed at 4%, converted annually?

Solution. The present value of $3000 due in 8 years is

$$P = 3000(1.04)^{-8},$$
$$= \$2192.07.$$

The compound discount is

$$D = 3000 - 2192.07,$$
$$= \$807.93.$$

PRESENT VALUE. COMPOUND DISCOUNT

Example 3. A note calls for the repayment of $5000 in 7 years together with compound interest at the rate of 5%, converted semiannually. What should a person pay for this note if he wishes to earn 6%, converted annually, on his money?

Solution. The maturity value of the note is

$$5000(1.025)^{14}.$$

The present value of this maturity value at 6%, converted annually, is

$$5000(1.025)^{14}(1.06)^{-7} = \$4698.54,$$

which is the amount that can be paid for the note to earn 6%, converted annually.

Occasionally it will be necessary to find the present value of an amount due at the end of an interval of time which does not contain an integral number of interest conversion periods. The customary method of finding the present value in this case is to find the value of the amount at the conversion period just preceding the present time and then to carry this value forward at simple interest to the present time.

Example 4. Find the present value of $2000 due in 6 years, 3 months, if money is worth 5%, converted annually.

Solution. The line graph will clearly illustrate the procedure indicated above.

```
V   P
├┼┼┼┼───┼───┼───┼───┼───┼───┼───$2000
7   6   5   4   3   2   1   0
    ┆     (number of years before due date)
    Present Time
```

Let V represent the value of $2000 seven years before it is due. Thus we have

$$V = 2000\,(1.05)^{-7},$$
$$= \$1421.36.$$

This value must now be carried forward at simple interest for $\frac{3}{4}$ of a year (9 months) to bring it to the present time. Hence the present value, P, is

$$P = 1421.36[1 + \tfrac{3}{4}(0.05)],$$
$$= \$1474.66.$$

This second calculation should be carried out by the use of logarithms.

EXERCISE 6

Find the present value and the compound discount in each of the following problems:

COMPOUND INTEREST AND COMPOUND DISCOUNT

Prob. no.	Amount, S, due in time n	Interest rate	Time to due date
1.	$2000	2% converted annually	10 years
2.	$6000	3% converted semiannually	6 years
3.	$5000	4% converted quarterly	7 years
4.	$2500	5% converted monthly	12 years
5.	$3265	$4\frac{1}{2}$% converted annually	50 years
6.	$12,355	$4\frac{1}{2}$% converted annually	100 years

7. Mr. Oswald owns a note which calls for the payment of $1500 in 8 years. He sells the note using an interest rate of 5%, converted annually, for discounting purposes. Find the compound discount on the note and the amount Mr. Oswald receives for the note.

8. What sum invested now at 6% nominal, converted quarterly, will amount to $3356.80 in 27 years?

9. Mr. Whipp holds a note which calls for repayment of $2000 in 12 years, together with compound interest at 6% nominal, converted quarterly. He offers it for sale on the basis of a 4% interest rate, converted quarterly. What is the selling price of the note?

10. In exchange for a loan of $5000, Mr. Lewis accepts a note for that amount payable in 7 years, together with compound interest at the rate of 5%, converted semiannually. At the end of 3 years, needing his money, Mr. Lewis sells the note at a price to yield the buyer 6%, converted annually. What was the selling price of the note?

11. Mr. Jones borrows $700 which he must repay in 8 years together with compound interest at the rate of 5%, converted quarterly. Three years from the time the debt is contracted, Mr. Jones inherits $1000. How much of this should he invest at 3%, converted annually, so that he will have just enough from the investment to pay off his debt when it comes due?

12. Mr. Rosenfeld is offered a house for $10,000, or for a down payment of $5000 followed by a payment of $6000 at the end of 5 years. Assuming that Mr. Rosenfeld can invest his money at 4%, converted annually, which is the better offer, and by how much?

13. In Problem 12 the seller can invest his money at $3\frac{1}{2}$%, converted annually. Which is the better plan for him, and by how much?

14. A note calls for repayment of $500 in 2 years together with compound interest at the rate of 4%, converted annually. What should a buyer pay for the note if he wishes to earn 3% nominal, converted quarterly, on his money?

15. If the note in Problem 14 had called for interest at 4%, payable annually, instead of compound interest at the rate of 4%, converted annually, what should the buyer pay for the note to earn 3% nominal, converted quarterly, on his money?

EQUATION OF VALUE AND EQUATED TIME

16. Find the present value of $2500 due in $5\frac{2}{3}$ years if money is worth 6%, converted annually.

17. A note dated May 15, 1944 calls for the payment of $1000 in 10 years. The holder of the note offers it for sale on a 4% basis on July 14, 1946. Find the selling price of the note.

18. A note dated August 1, 1940 calls for the payment of $500 at the end of 15 years together with interest at 3%, converted semiannually. On August 31, 1947 the note is purchased to yield the buyer 4%, converted semiannually, on his investment. What was the purchase price?

19. An alternate method of finding the present value of an amount due at a future date, for which the time is not an integral number of interest conversion periods, is to discount the amount to the first interest conversion date after the present time and then to discount this value at simple interest for the fractional part of the period necessary to bring it to the present time. Illustrate by a line graph the relative positions of S, the amount due in $5\frac{1}{3}$ years, V, the value of S at the first interest conversion date after the present time, and P, the present value of S if money is worth 6%, converted annually.

20. Let $S = \$2500$ in Problem 19. Find the value of P.

126. Equation of value and equated time

Occasionally it becomes necessary to change one set of obligations, due at various dates, to another set, due at other dates. If these sets are equivalent at a common date of comparison, called the **focal date,** then one set is said to be commuted into the other. As in the corresponding simple interest problem, the equation expressing this equivalence of the two sets of obligations is called the **equation of value.**

The student will find a line graph very helpful in setting up problems involving an equation of value. A convenient focal date, F.D., should be marked on the graph together with the dates and amounts of the various obligations. It will also be convenient to place one set of obligations above the line and the other below. Then any sum appearing to the left of the F.D. may be brought to the F.D. by multiplying by a suitable power of the accumulation factor $(1 + i)$, while any sum to the right may be brought back to the focal date by multiplying by the proper power of the discount factor $(1 + i)^{-1}$.

Example 1. A creditor agrees to accept a single sum 5 years hence in payment of $250 due in 2 years, $400 due in 4 years, and $1000 due in 8 years. If money is worth 4%, converted annually, what does the creditor receive?

Solution. Let x represent the amount of the payment which the creditor should receive in 5 years. Let the focal date be five years hence. The proper line graph is indicated on page 60.

264 COMPOUND INTEREST AND COMPOUND DISCOUNT

```
        $250      $400 F.D.              $1000
   |  |  |  |  |  |  |  |  |
   0  1  2  3  4  5  6  7  8
                  x
```

The original obligations are indicated at the proper times above the line, and the single payment, x, into which they are commuted, is indicated below the line. Since the $250 payment is due three years before the focal date, the proper power of the accumulation factor is $(1.04)^3$. Likewise, the proper power of the accumulation factor which must be applied to the $400 payment is $(1.04)^1$ since it becomes due one year before the focal date. Since the $1000 payment is due three years after the due date, $(1.04)^{-3}$ is the proper power of the discount factor which must multiply $1000 to bring it back to the F.D. The equation of value is now

$$x = 250(1.04)^3 + 400(1.04) + 1000(1.04)^{-3}.$$

By use of the compound interest and present value tables we have:

$$x = 250(1.124864) + 400(1.04) + 1000(0.888996),$$
$$= \$1586.22.$$

It should be noted that the focal date was chosen at the time of the single substituting payment, since that time gives a simple form for the equation of value. However, as was not the case for simple interest, any other choice of the focal date would have given the same result for x.

Example 2. On January 2, 1942 Mr. Brown gives Mr. Jenkins two notes, one for $400 payable on January 2, 1952 together with compound interest at the rate of 6%, converted annually, and the other for $500 payable on January 2, 1947. Mr. Brown was unable to make the $500 payment when due, but with Mr. Jenkins' approval, he agrees to pay his whole debt in a single payment on July 2, 1950 with interest computed at 4%, converted semi-annually. What must Mr. Brown pay?

Solution. The $400 note, which calls for compound interest, is worth $400(1.06)^{10}$ on January 2, 1952. The other note is worth $500 on January 2, 1947. Let x represent the payment that Mr. Brown will make on July 2, 1950 to cancel both debts. The line graph is as follows:

```
  Jan. 2,                        July 2,   Jan. 2,
  1942                           1950      1952
                       500       F.D.      400(1.06)^10
   |  |  |  |  |  |  |  |  |  |
   0  1  2  3  4  5  6  7  8 | 9  10
                              x
```

We now proceed as in Example 1, obtaining

$$x = 500(1.02)^7 + 400(1.06)^{10}(1.02)^{-3},$$
$$= \$1249.36.$$

EQUATION OF VALUE AND EQUATED TIME

Another method of paying off a series of obligations is to pay the sum of the maturity values of the various debts at a common date determined by an equation of value. This common date is called the **equated date** and the length of time between the present date and the equated date is called the **equated time**.

Example 3. On March 1, 1947, Mr. Ballard owed Mr. Jones the following sums of money:

$500 due on Mar. 1, 1949,
$300 due on Mar. 1, 1954,
$600 due on Mar. 1, 1960.

Mr. Jones is willing to accept the sum of the maturity values, $1400 at the proper equated date figured on the basis of 4% interest, converted annually. Find this date.

Solution. It is very much better to use the present time as the focal date in all equated time problems. Let n represent the equated time and draw a line graph.

```
Mar. 1,  Mar. 1,           Mar. 1,                    Mar. 1,
 1947     1949              1954                       1960
 F.D.     $500              $300                       $600
  |   |   |   |   |   |   |   |   |   |   |   |   |   |
  0   1   2   3   4   5   6   7   8   9  10  11  12  13
```

The equation of value is

$$1400(1.04)^{-n} = 500(1.04)^{-2} + 300(1.04)^{-7} + 600(1.04)^{-13},$$
$$= 1050.60,$$

from which we have

$$(1.04)^n = \frac{1400}{1050.60} = 1.33257.$$

Interpolation from the compound interest table gives

$$n = 7 \text{ years, } 114 \text{ days,}$$

and hence the equated date is June 23, 1954.

EXERCISE 7

What single payment, made 3 years hence, is equivalent to each of the following sets of debts, if money is worth 4%, converted annually?

1. $300 due in 1 year, $500 due in 5 years.

2. $800 due in 2 years together with compound interest at 6%, converted semiannually, $400 due in 4 years, $1000 due in 10 years.

3. $100 due in 2 years together with compound interest at the rate of 3%, converted quarterly, $400 due in 6 years together with compound interest at the rate of 6%, converted monthly.

4. $1000 due in 2 years, $1000 due in 4 years.

5. In place of $500 due in 3 years and $700 due in $7\frac{1}{2}$ years, the creditor agrees to accept a single payment at the end of 5 years, which will equitably discharge the two obligations, if interest is computed at 4%, converted semiannually. Representing the single payment by x, write the equation of value for each of the focal dates: (a) 3 years from now, (b) $7\frac{1}{2}$ years from now, (c) 5 years from now. Find the value of x from each of these equations. Which focal date do you prefer to use? Why?

6. After making the down payment on a farm, Mr. Harrison agrees to pay the balance in three installments: one of $2000 in 2 years, a second of $3000 in 5 years, a third of $5000 in 10 years. In place of these payments, Mr. Harrison is given the option of making one single equivalent payment at the end of 8 years, using 5%, converted quarterly, for commuting each payment to the common focal date. Find the single payment.

7. Mr. Pettit gives Mr. Kane his note for $500 due in 8 years together with interest at 5%, compounded monthly. He also owes Mr. Kane $1000 due at the end of 6 years. Mr. Pettit is unable to pay the $1000 due at the end of 6 years but agrees to make a single payment at the end of 7 years which will cancel both debts. Mr. Kane agrees provided that interest is figured on a 6%, converted annually, basis. How much should Mr. Pettit pay?

8. Mr. Foote has the following debts: $500 due in 2 years, $300 due in 4 years, and $800 due in 10 years. His creditor is willing to accept two equal payments, one made in 8 years and the other in 9 years in place of the three debts, provided interest is computed at $5\frac{1}{2}$%, converted semiannually. How large are the equal payments?

9. Mr. Fox buys $1200 worth of furniture, paying $200 down and agreeing to pay the balance in three installments of $358 each, one in 6 months, another in a year, and the last in 18 months. If Mr. Fox can borrow money from his bank for a period of 18 months at an interest rate of 6%, converted semiannually, would he save money by borrowing from his bank and paying cash? If so, how much?

10. The debts of $200 due in $2\frac{1}{2}$ years, $400 due in 4 years, $500 due in $5\frac{1}{2}$ years are to be paid off by a single payment of $1100. When must this payment be made to discharge all the debts equitably, if money is worth 4%, converted monthly?

11. Find the equated time and equated date for the following set of obligations if the present date is September 15, 1947 and money is worth 6%, converted quarterly:

$600 due on March 15, 1949,
$1000 due on June 15, 1952,
$1500 due on December 15, 1954.

12. Show that an approximation to the equated time is given by

$$n = \frac{n_1 S_1 + n_2 S_2 + n_3 S_3 + \cdots + n_k S_k}{S_1 + S_2 + S_3 + \cdots + S_k}$$

where the amounts $S_1, S_2, S_3, \ldots S_k$ are due in $n_1, n_2, n_3, \ldots n_k$ periods respectively. (Hint: Use the binomial expansion to expand each of the powers of $(1 + i)$ in the equation of value, and then drop all terms involving i to the exponent 2 or higher.)

13. Find the equated time by the approximation given in Problem 12 for the following debts:

$1200 due in 3 years,
$800 due in 5 years,
$1000 due in 10 years.

14. Find the equated time in Problem 11 by the approximation method of Problem 12.

MISCELLANEOUS EXERCISE

1. Forty years ago Mr. Burnside bought a piece of vacant land for $5000. Assuming that the accumulated cost of taxes and expenses has been $12,000, what must Mr. Burnside receive for his property to make 4%, converted annually, on his investment?

2. Ten years ago Mr. Franklin invested $10,000 in a security paying $3\frac{1}{2}\%$ converted monthly. At the same time, Mr. Churchill invested $9850 in a security for which an interest rate of 3.7%, converted annually, was paid. By how much do the amounts of these two investments differ now? Which is larger? How do they compare five years later?

3. Mr. Rietz offers to sell Mr. Hobson a note for $1000 due in 10 years at the price of $600. Mr. Hobson can invest his money at $5\frac{1}{2}\%$, converted annually. Should he accept the offer made by Mr. Rietz? What could Mr. Hobson afford to pay for the note?

4. Wishing to endow a room at a charitable hospital for one year, Mr. Perron gives the hospital $500 with the stipulation that it invest the money at $4\frac{1}{2}\%$, converted semiannually, until $2000, the cost of the room for one year, has been accumulated. How long will it take before Mr. Perron's gift is available for use?

5. Mr. Miller invests $10,000, divided as follows: (a) $3,000 which earns interest at 2.9%, converted annually, (b) $2500 which earns interest at 4%, converted annually, and (c) $4500 at 7%, converted annually. If he intends to leave the money in these investments for 10 years, at what interest rate, converted annually, would Mr. Miller have to invest the whole $10,000 to accumulate to the same amount at the end of 10 years?

6. What effect, if any, would changing the time to 5 years have on the answer in Problem 5? What is the new interest rate?

7. Mary, now $10\frac{1}{2}$ years old, and George, now 15 years old, have just inherited $10,000 from their uncle. The will specifies that the money should be invested at 4%, compounded semiannually, and that each child should receive the same payment on his 21st birthday. Find the amount of this payment. At the time that Mary was $10\frac{1}{2}$ years old, how much more did their uncle leave George?

8. Mr. Smith owes $300 due in $1\frac{1}{2}$ years, $600 due in 2 years, and $1000 due in 4 years. A finance company agrees to meet these payments as they come due, provided that Mr. Smith will give them his note payable in 5 years for an amount equivalent to his three debts on the basis of 10%, compounded semiannually. For what amount is the note written?

9. Mr. Mathews owes three debts: (a) $400 due in $1\frac{1}{2}$ years, (b) $300 together with compound interest at the rate of 6%, converted monthly, due in $2\frac{1}{4}$ years, and (c) $500 due in $2\frac{1}{2}$ years. His creditor is willing that he settle the debts by making equal payments at the end of each year for three years. How large is each payment if money is worth 5%, compounded quarterly?

10. Find the rate of simple interest equivalent to a rate, i, compounded annually, for n years.

11. When will the amount of $100 invested at 4%, compounded annually, be equal to twice the amount of $100 invested at 4% simple interest? Give approximate answer to the nearest year.

12. Although the compound interest law was derived for integral values of n only, it is sometimes used as an approximation for the amount for fractional values of n. Show that use of the formula will give a smaller amount than that obtained by use of the business method (compound interest for the integral number of periods plus simple interest for the fractional period). Illustrate by an actual problem.

14

Introduction to Annuities

127. Preliminary concepts and definitions

Any sequence of equal or unequal payments made at regular or irregular intervals of time is called an **annuity**. If the beginning or end of the sequence of payments, or both, is dependent upon the happening of some outside event or events which cannot be foretold accurately, the sequence of payments is called a **contingent annuity**. If the beginning and end of the sequence are known, the sequence of payments is called an **annuity certain**.

Thus, payments made by an insurance company to a beneficiary of an insurance policy form a contingent annuity, since the beginning of the annuity is dependent upon the death of the insured. These payments may also be dependent upon the life of the beneficiary, in which case the end of the sequence of payments is indefinite. Examples of annuities certain are numerous. Thus, payments made into a savings account over a definite period of time, installment payments, and taxes on a given piece of property are a few of the examples we may give. Examples may also be found in the chapter on *Simple Interest and Discount*, in connection with the problem of equation of value.

In this chapter, as in common business practice, we shall use the word "annuity" to mean annuity certain. Furthermore, we shall consider only those annuities for which equal payments are made at equal intervals of time. The time between the equal payments will be called the **payment period**. The payment itself is sometimes referred to as the **rent** and the rent multiplied by the number of payment intervals in a year is called the **annual rent**. The **term** of the annuity is the time between the beginning of the first payment period and the end of the last such period. We shall usually give the term in interest conversion periods although at times it may be expressed in years.

An **ordinary annuity** is an annuity for which the payments are made at the ends of the payment intervals. An **annuity due** is an annuity for which the payments are made at the beginnings of the payment intervals. If nothing is said to the contrary, it is assumed that the annuities are ordinary annuities.

Annuities for which the payments continue forever are called **perpetuities**. If the payments are made at the ends of the periods, the perpetuity is called an **ordinary perpetuity**; if the payments are made at the beginnings of the year, it is called a **perpetuity due**.

To fix the above definitions in mind, consider a sequence of 12 payments of $50 each where the payments are made at the end of each 6 months. These payments form an ordinary annuity certain for which the payment interval is one-half year, the rent is $50, the annual rent is $100, and the term of the annuity is 12 periods or 6 years.

Again, consider a piece of property for which a tax of $200 is due now and a like amount is due each year forever. These tax payments form a perpetuity due of annual rent $200 for which the payment interval is one year.

128. Evaluation of ordinary annuities

In this book we shall follow the common business practice, in regard to annuities, of assuming that the interest conversion period is equal to the payment period unless explicitly stated otherwise. Methods of evaluating the very few exceptional cases will be considered in the next chapter.

The following numerical example will illustrate the method of finding the value of an annuity by making use of the equation of value principle.

Example 1. Mr. Dover has contracted a debt which he can settle in either of three ways: a single cash payment now, $100 at the end of each year for 5 years, or a single payment made at the end of 5 years. If money is worth 5%, converted annually, find the single payment which will cancel the debt now and also the equivalent payment which will cancel it 5 years from now.

Solution. We use a line graph to indicate the term of the annuity and the relative positions of the payments.

```
     100   100   100   100   100
  |   |     |     |     |     |
  0   1     2     3     4     5
```

Since we wish to find the sum of these payments now, we write the equation of value with the present time (time 0 on the graph) as the focal date. We have, calling the sum of the payments A_5,

EVALUATION OF ORDINARY ANNUITIES

$$A_5 = 100(1.05)^{-1} + 100(1.05)^{-2} + 100(1.05)^{-3} + 100(1.05)^{-4} + 100(1.05)^{-5},$$

which may be computed by using Table VI. Hence,

$$A_5 = 95.238 + 90.703 + 86.384 + 82.270 + 78.353,$$
$$= \$432.95.$$

Hence the single payment now of $432.95 will cancel the debt.

To find the payment needed at the end of five years, we use 5 on the graph as the focal date. Designating the payment by S_5 we have

$$S_5 = 100(1.05)^4 + 100(1.05)^3 + 100(1.05)^2 + 100(1.05) + 100.$$

Using Table V, we have

$$S_5 = 121.551 + 115.762 + 110.250 + 105.000 + 100,$$
$$= \$552.56.$$

Hence a single payment of $552.56 will cancel the debt if made 5 years from now.

In the above problem the single payment, A_5, is called the **present value** of the annuity and S_5 is called the **accumulated value** or the **amount** of the annuity. An examination of either of the equations of value shows immediately that $A_5(1.05)^5 = S_5$, a relationship which is extremely important for a proper understanding of annuities.

Let us now consider the general problem. We represent the rent by R, the term by n (also, n equals the number of rent payments), the interest rate (per interest conversion period) by i, and the amount by S_n. We consider a payment of R made at the end of each period for n payments where the interest conversion period is equal in length to the payment interval. These payments are represented on the following line graph.

```
        R   R   R   R  ...  R    R    R
    |   |   |   |   |        |    |    |
    0   1   2   3   4       n-2  n-1   n
```

The present value of the annuity may now be found by using 0 as the focal date. The equation of value is now

$$A_n = R(1+i)^{-1} + R(1+i)^{-2} + R(1+i)^{-3} + \cdots + R(1+i)^{-(n-2)}$$
$$+ R(1+i)^{-(n-1)} + R(1+i)^{-n}.$$

This may be evaluated by the method used in Example 1, but if n is very large such a method becomes impractical. It will be observed that the terms making up A_n form a geometrical progression with common ratio $(1+i)^{-1}$. But since the sum of the geometrical progression,

$$a, ar, ar^2, \ldots, ar^{n-1}$$

is $\quad a\dfrac{1-r^n}{1-r}\left(\text{or } a\dfrac{r^n-1}{r-1}\right)$ (see Article 93, C.A.), we have

$$A_n = R(1+i)^{-1}\frac{1-[(1+i)^{-1}]^n}{1-(1+i)^{-1}} = R\frac{1-(1+i)^{-n}}{(1+i)[1-(1+i)^{-1}]},$$

or $\quad A_n = R\dfrac{1-(1+i)^{-n}}{i}.$ \hfill (1)

In this form, A_n may be determined by looking up one entry from Table VI and making a simple computation. A shorter method is to look up the complete value of $\dfrac{1-(1+i)^{-n}}{i}$ from Table VIII.

The quantity $\dfrac{1-(1+i)^{-n}}{i}$, which represents the present value of an annuity of 1 per period for n periods, is represented by the symbol $a_{\overline{n}|i}$, which may be read a *sub* n at the rate i. Formula (1) may now be written

$$A_n = R a_{\overline{n}|i}. \tag{2}$$

Now take the focal date at the end of the term of the annuity and we have

$$S_n = R(1+i)^{n-1} + R(1+i)^{n-2} + R(1+i)^{n-3} + \cdots + R(1+i)^2 + R(1+i) + R.$$

Again this may be evaluated by use of Table V, but it is easier to make use of the formula for summing a geometrical progression given above and to put it in a form for which Table VII is applicable. It is easier to rewrite S_n in the form

$$S_n = R + R(1+i) + R(1+i)^2 + \cdots + R(1+i)^{n-3} + R(1+i)^{n-2} + R(1+i)^{n-1},$$

for which the common ratio is $(1+i)$, the number of terms is n and the first term is R. Using the second form of the formula for summing a geometrical progression, we have

$$S_n = R\frac{(1+i)^n - 1}{(1+i) - 1},$$

or $\quad S_n = R\dfrac{(1+i)^n - 1}{i}.$ \hfill (3)

The quantity $\dfrac{(1+i)^n - 1}{i}$ represents the accumulated value or

EVALUATION OF ORDINARY ANNUITIES

amount of an annuity of 1 for n periods at the rate i per period and is represented by $s_{\overline{n}|i}$ (read s sub n at the rate i). Values of this quantity are given in Table VII. Formula (2) may now be written,

$$S_n = R s_{\overline{n}|i}. \tag{4}$$

Example 2. In order to purchase some country property, Mr. Huntington invests $250 at the end of each 6 months in a security paying interest at the rate of 5%, converted semiannually. Just after the 20th payment has been made, how much will Mr. Huntington have saved in his investment?

Solution. Mr. Huntington's payments into his investment form an annuity of 20 payments of $250 each, for which the interest rate is $2\frac{1}{2}\%$ per period. Since we want the value of this annuity at the end of the term, we find the amount by application of formula (3). Thus

$$S_{20} = 250 \frac{(1.025)^{20} - 1}{0.025},$$
$$= 250 s_{\overline{20}|.025}.$$

Using Table VII,

$$S_{20} = 250(25.54466),$$
$$= \$6386.16.$$

This represents the amount Mr. Huntington has available for his country property just after his 20th payment.

Example 3. How much must a father deposit with a trust company paying interest at the rate of $3\frac{1}{2}\%$, converted annually, to provide an income of $1500 per year, payable at the ends of the years, for his daughter during the next 10 years?

Solution. The cost of the annuity now is its present value. From formula (1),

$$A_{10} = 1500 \frac{1 - (1.035)^{-10}}{0.035},$$

or, $\qquad A_{10} = 1500 a_{\overline{10}|.035}.$

Using Table VIII, we have

$$A_{10} = 1500(8.316605),$$
$$= \$12{,}474.91,$$

which is the sum the father must pay the trust company to provide an annuity of $1500 for his daughter during the next 10 years.

EXERCISE 1

The first five problems below may be solved without the use of logarithms. The second five should be solved with the aid of logarithms. Find the quantities P, n, i, A_n, and S_n in each of the following problems:

INTRODUCTION TO ANNUITIES

Prob. no.	Annual rent	Term (in yrs.)	Frequency of payments	Nominal int. rate	Frequency of conversions
1.	$500	12	semiannually	4%	semiannually
2.	$1200	5	monthly	6%	monthly
3.	$600	4	bimonthly	4%	bimonthly
4.	$250	18	yearly	3%	yearly
5.	$2000	20	quarterly	5%	quarterly
6.	$350	5	monthly	7%	monthly
7.	$465	9	semiannually	8%	semiannually
8.	$950	39	yearly	$7\frac{1}{2}$%	yearly
9.	$426	17	bimonthly	$3\frac{1}{2}$%	bimonthly
10.	$1752	$9\frac{1}{2}$	quarterly	6%	quarterly

11. At the end of 6 months, a man deposits $250 in a savings bank which pays interest at the rate of $1\frac{1}{2}$%, converted semiannually. How much does he have to his credit immediately after the 30th deposit?

12. A house is offered for sale on the basis of $2000 cash and $100 at the end of each month for 8 years. What is the equivalent cash price if money is worth 5%, converted monthly?

13. In order to provide for his daughter's college education, Mr. Higgins deposits in a savings bank on January 1 a sum of money just large enough so that his daughter may withdraw $600 on July 1 and every 6 months thereafter for the next four years. If the bank pays interest at the rate of $2\frac{1}{2}$%, converted semiannually, how much money did Mr. Higgins deposit?

14. In order to provide a travel fund, Mr. Gray invests $100 at the end of each 6 months in a security which pays interest at the rate of $4\frac{1}{2}$%, converted semiannually. How much does Mr. Gray have to his credit just after his 20th payment?

15. A city has a bonded indebtedness of $4,000,000 which it wishes to retire in 50 years. How much of the principal of this debt can be retired in that time if the city can make payments of $25,000 at the ends of each year into the city investment fund, which earns interest at the rate of 4%, converted annually?

16. Twenty years ago Mr. Davis bought a lot costing him $2000. One year after buying the lot, he paid $50 in taxes and a like sum each year. Just after his 20th payment Mr. Davis sold the lot for $5000. If Mr. Davis could have invested his money at 3%, converted annually, what profit or loss did he make on the transaction?

17. A house is offered for sale at $12,000. The seller agrees to accept $100 per month for 8 years, interest being computed at 6%, converted monthly, and the balance as a down payment. What is the down payment?

18. At age 21 an heir receives an inheritance in the form of 20 equal annual payments of $2400 each, the first starting at the age of 22. What is the equivalent cash value of the inheritance if money is worth $3\frac{1}{2}\%$, converted annually?

19. Mr. Wilson has been making payments of \$30 per month, including interest at 5%, converted monthly, on a small piece of property. After he has made 20 payments, there are still 40 more payments to be made. (a) What is the value of the remaining 40 payments immediately after the 20th payment is made? (b) What is the accumulated value of the 20 payments at that time? (c) Show that the sum of the answers in (a) and (b) is the equivalent cash price of the property carried forward at interest for 20 months.

20. Show that $a_{\overline{1}|i} = (1+i)^{-1}$.

21. Show that $s_{\overline{1}|i} = 1$.

22. Prove, by direct reasoning and algebraically, that
$$a_{\overline{n}|i}(1+i)^n = s_{\overline{n}|i}.$$

23. Prove that
$$a_{\overline{m+n}|i} = a_{\overline{m}|i} + v^m a_{\overline{n}|i}.$$

24. Using the formula in Problem 23 find the value of $a_{\overline{150}|.07}$.

25. Prove that
$$s_{\overline{m+n}|i} = (1+i)^n s_{\overline{m}|i} + s_{\overline{n}|i}.$$

26. Using the formula in Problem 25, find the value of $s_{\overline{260}|.005}$.

27. Show that
$$s_{\overline{k}|i} + a_{\overline{n-k}|i} = a_{\overline{n}|i}(1+i)^k = s_{\overline{n}|i}(1+i)^{-n+k}.$$

129. Determination of the rent of an annuity

In many problems involving annuities, we know the present value or the amount, the term, and the interest rate of the annuity. The rent, or periodical payment, may then be found by solving formulas (2) and (4) for R. From formula (2),

$$A_n = R a_{\overline{n}|i},$$

Hence
$$R = \frac{A_n}{a_{\overline{n}|i}} = A_n \frac{1}{a_{\overline{n}|i}}. \tag{5}$$

Example 1. A debtor is required to pay off a debt of \$5000 by annual payments made at the end of each year for 10 years. If the creditor charges interest at the rate of 6%, converted annually, find the annual payment.

Solution. Representing the required payment by R, we have
$$R a_{\overline{10}|.06} = 5000,$$
or
$$R = 5000 \, \frac{1}{a_{\overline{10}|.06}}.$$

Table IX is a table of the reciprocals of $a_{\overline{n}|i}$ and hence we may find the value of $\dfrac{1}{a_{\overline{10}|.06}}$ rather than find the value of $a_{\overline{10}|.06}$. This avoids division and hence is advantageous if logarithms are not used. We have

$$R = 5000(0.1358680),$$
$$= \$679.34.$$

Example 2. On an interest payment date Mr. Rochester decides to withdraw his savings of \$21,865.50 from the bank. Rather than withdrawing the whole sum at once he elects to withdraw it in 20 equal semiannual installments, the first to be withdrawn in 6 months. Find the semiannual installment if interest is allowed at the rate of $2\frac{1}{2}\%$, converted semiannually.

Solution. From formula (5)

$$R = \frac{21{,}865.50}{a_{\overline{20}|.01\frac{1}{4}}}$$

Since it is best to use logarithms for this computation we have,

$$\begin{array}{r|l} \log R = \log 21{,}865.50 & 4.339759 \\ -\log a_{\overline{20}|.01\frac{1}{4}} & 1.245496 \\ \hline & 3.094263 \end{array}$$

thus, $R = \$1242.40$, which is the semiannual withdrawal that exhausts Mr. Rochester's savings account in 10 years.

If the amount of the annuity is given we use formula (4), $S_n = Rs_{\overline{n}|i}$, from which

$$R = \frac{S_n}{s_{\overline{n}|i}} = S_n \cdot \frac{1}{s_{\overline{n}|i}}. \qquad (6)$$

The computation may be carried out by the use of logarithms. However, if S_n is such that logarithms are not needed, we may carry through the computation provided we can find the reciprocal of $s_{\overline{n}|i}$ in a table. Fortunately a simple relationship exists between $\dfrac{1}{s_{\overline{n}|i}}$ and $\dfrac{1}{a_{\overline{n}|i}}$, namely:

$$\frac{1}{s_{\overline{n}|i}} = \frac{1}{a_{\overline{n}|i}} - i, \qquad (7)$$

so that the value of $\dfrac{1}{s_{\overline{n}|i}}$ may be obtained from the $\dfrac{1}{a_{\overline{n}|i}}$ table (Table IX) simply by subtracting i from the tabular entry.

To prove formula (7) we note that $\dfrac{A_n}{a_{\overline{n}|i}}$ [see formula (5)] is the rent of an annuity whose present value is A_n. Hence

DETERMINATION OF THE RENT OF AN ANNUITY

$$\frac{A_n}{a_{\overline{n}|i}} s_{\overline{n}|i} = A_n (1+i)^n,$$

or,
$$\frac{1}{a_{\overline{n}|i}} = \frac{(1+i)^n}{s_{\overline{n}|i}} = \frac{i\left[\frac{(1+i)^n - 1}{i}\right] + 1}{s_{\overline{n}|i}},$$

$$= \frac{i s_{\overline{n}|i} + 1}{s_{\overline{n}|i}} = i + \frac{1}{s_{\overline{n}|i}}.$$

Hence, $\quad \dfrac{1}{s_{\overline{n}|i}} = \dfrac{1}{a_{\overline{n}|i}} - i,\quad$ which was to be proved.

Example 3. Mr. Rochdale decides to save $1500 by making payments at the end of each month for two years in a security paying interest at the rate of 4%, converted monthly. How large is each of the payments?

Solution. Let R represent the required payment. Hence

$$R s_{\overline{24}|.00\frac{1}{3}} = 1500,$$

or, $\qquad R = 1500 \dfrac{1}{s_{\overline{24}|.00\frac{1}{3}}}.$

From Table IX, $\quad \dfrac{1}{a_{\overline{24}|.00\frac{1}{3}}} = 0.0434249.\quad$ Hence

$$\frac{1}{s_{\overline{24}|.00\frac{1}{3}}} = \frac{1}{a_{\overline{24}|.00\frac{1}{3}}} - 0.00\tfrac{1}{3} = 0.0434249 - 0.0033333,$$
$$= 0.0400916.$$

Hence, $R = 1500 (0.0400916) = \$60.14,\quad$ the required monthly payment.

EXERCISE 2

Find the rent for each of the following annuities:

Prob. no.	Term (in yrs.)	Frequency of payments	Nominal interest rate *	Value given
1.	10	quarterly	4%	$A_n = \$2500$
2.	18	annually	$2\frac{1}{2}\%$	$S_n = \$10{,}000$
3.	15	semiannually	3%	$A_n = \$15{,}000$
4.	6	monthly	7%	$S_n = \$6525$
5.	8	monthly	5%	$A_n = \$13{,}235$

* It is assumed that the interest conversion period is equal to the payment period (see Article 25).

6. What payment, made at the end of each month for eight years, is necessary to pay off a debt of $4000 now if money is worth 4%, converted monthly?

7. How much must be deposited at the end of each year in a security paying $4\frac{1}{2}\%$ to amount to $8500 in 17 years?

8. What payment will be realized from an annuity for which the payments are made at the end of each quarter for 20 years and which can be purchased for $23,161.80, if money is worth 3%, converted quarterly?

9. A piece of property is advertised for sale at $25,000. The seller will take $5000 down followed by 100 equal payments, made at the ends of the months, including interest at 5%, converted monthly. How large are the payments?

10. At the end of 10 years, Mr. Harte plans to purchase a farm costing $10,000. He plans to make an equal payment into a building and loan association at the end of each 6 months until 20 payments have been made. How large must these payments be so that Mr. Harte can buy his farm, if the building and loan association allows interest at the rate of 3%, converted semiannually?

11. In order to pay off a debt of $5255 due in 5 years, Mr. Jacobs deposits a sum of money at the end of each quarter in a security paying interest at the rate of 4%, converted quarterly. How large should Mr. Jacob's deposit be in order that he will have accumulated the amount of the debt at the end of 5 years?

12. A widow receives the equivalent of $10,000 from her husband's insurance at his death. Under the provisions of the insurance she is to receive $5000 cash and the balance in 60 equal monthly payments, the payments being made at the ends of the months. What is the size of each monthly payment if the insurance company allows interest at 3%, converted monthly?

13. A debt of $6500 is to be paid off by 10 equal annual payments made at the ends of the years. Interest is to be computed at 8%, converted annually. After 6 payments have been made, the debtor asks for a reduction in the interest rate. The creditor agrees to reduce the rate to 6%, converted monthly, on the outstanding debt, provided that the debtor will make monthly payments instead of annual payments for the remaining four years. How large was the annual payment and what is the new monthly payment?

14. Mr. Parker planned to accumulate $10,000 in 20 years by making a deposit at the end of each 6 months in a savings bank paying 4%, converted semiannually. After 15 years the interest rate was reduced to 3%, converted semiannually. By how much must Mr. Parker increase his semiannual payment in order that he will still have his $10,000 when planned?

15. Prove algebraically that

$$\frac{1}{s_{\overline{n}|i}} = \frac{1}{a_{\overline{n}|i}} - i.$$

130. Determination of the time

Certain problems arise in annuities where it is necessary to determine the time, having given the rent, the amount or present value, and the interest rate. Observation of formulas (1) and (3) with R, A_n or S_n, and i given indicates that we have an exponential equation to solve for n in each case. Such equations may be solved

DETERMINATION OF THE TIME

by logarithms, but since integral values of n only have meaning for time problems in annuities, it is easier to use the tables. Problems arising from the solution of the time equations will be discussed in the solutions of the following examples.

Example 1. A debt of $600 is to be paid off by payments at the ends of the years of $75 each with interest at 5%, converted annually. How many full payments of $75 each are required and what partial payment, made one year after the last full payment, is needed to pay off the debt?

Solution. From formula (1)

$$600 = 75 a_{\overline{n}|.05}$$

or

$$a_{\overline{n}|.05} = 8.$$

From Table VIII,

$$a_{\overline{10}|.05} = 7.7217349,$$
$$a_{\overline{11}|.05} = 8.3064142.$$

Hence it appears that 10 full payments of $75 each are required followed by a partial payment. The partial payment may be easily found by making use of a line graph or an equation of value. Let x represent the partial payment. The focal date is taken at the beginning of the term.

```
     $75 $75 $75 $75 $75 $75 $75 $75 $75 $75   x
      |   |   |   |   |   |   |   |   |   |    |
      0   1   2   3   4   5   6   7   8   9   10  11
    $600
```

The equation of value is

$$75 a_{\overline{10}|.05} + x(1.05)^{-11} = 600.$$

Hence,

$$x(1.05)^{-11} = 600 - 75 a_{\overline{10}|.05},$$
$$x = (600 - 75 a_{\overline{10}|.05})(1.05)^{11},$$
$$= \$35.69.$$

Example 2. Mr. Fremont deposits $500 in a building and loan association at the end of each quarter. If interest is allowed at the rate of 3%, converted quarterly, how many full deposits of $500 each are needed to accumulate $10,000, and what partial payment, if any, is required if made one quarter after the last full deposit is made?

Solution. From Formula (2) we have

$$10{,}000 = 500 s_{\overline{n}|.00\frac{3}{4}},$$

or,

$$s_{\overline{n}|.00\frac{3}{4}} = 20.$$

Table VII gives

$$s_{\overline{18}|.00\frac{3}{4}} = 19.1947185,$$
$$s_{\overline{19}|.00\frac{3}{4}} = 20.3386789.$$

Thus we see that 18 full payments of $500 each are needed. If 19 full payments had been made the accumulated value would have been

$$500 s_{\overline{19}|.00\frac{3}{4}} = 500(20.3386789),$$
$$= \$10{,}169.34.$$

But this is too much by $169.34. Hence a partial deposit of
$$500 - 169.34 = \$330.66,$$
is required for the 19th payment instead of the full deposit of $500.

Example 3. A security pays interest at the rate of 8%, converted annually. How long will it take to accumulate $5000 by making investments of $250 at the end of each year in this security? And, if needed, how large is the last partial deposit if made one year after the last full deposit?

Solution. From formula (4)
$$5000 = 250 s_{\overline{n}|.08},$$
or,
$$s_{\overline{n}|.08} = 20.$$
Using Table VII,
$$s_{\overline{12}|.08} = 18.9771265,$$
$$s_{\overline{13}|.08} = 21.4952966.$$

Thus 12 full deposits of $250 each are required. If 13 full deposits are made, a total of $250(21.4952966) = \$5373.82$ would be accumulated, which is $373.82 too much. Since this amount is greater than the full deposit of $250, an additional deposit is not needed. Thus it appears that the amount after 12 deposits, $250(18.9771265) = \$4744.28$, is sufficient to amount to $5000 due to interest earned at some time between the 12th and 13th years. Since simple interest is used for fractional parts of a period, we have
$$4744.28(1 + 0.08t) = 5000,$$
where t represents the fractional part of a year needed for $4744.28 to accumulate to $5000. Solving for t, we have
$$t = 0.67375,$$
which, counting 30 days per month is 8 months, 3 days. Thus the total time needed to accumulate $5000, by means of deposits of $250 at the ends of the years, is 12 years, 8 months, 3 days.

EXERCISE 3

Find the number of full payments needed for the annuities in the following six problems.

Prob. no.	Value of annuity	Nominal interest rate	Frequency of conversion	Rent *
1.	$A_n = \$3000$	4%	annually	$500
2.	$S_n = \$4000$	6%	semiannually	$250
3.	$A_n = \$10,000$	8%	monthly	$200
4.	$S_n = \$5000$	7%	monthly	$800
5.	$A_n = \$1500$	5%	semiannually	$50
6.	$S_n = \$6878$	3%	quarterly	$250

* Paid at the end of each interest conversion period.

DETERMINATION OF THE TIME

7. If money is worth 6% converted bimonthly, how many full bimonthly payments of $50 each made at the ends of the periods, are necessary to pay off a debt of $2500, and how large is the last partial payment if made 2 months after the last full payment?

8. How long will it take to accumulate $7000 by means of payments of $350 each made at the end of each 6-month period if money is worth 4%, converted semiannually? If a partial payment is needed, how large must this payment be if made 6 months after the last full payment of $350?

9. Mr. Robinson can afford to save $25 at the end of each month from his salary. He plans to buy a beach lot as soon as he can accumulate $2000. How long will it take him if he can invest his money at 4%, converted monthly, and, if a partial payment is needed, how large must it be if made one month after the last full payment?

10. The cash price of a house is $12,000. The seller is willing to sell it on the basis of $4500 down and the balance in monthly payments, starting at the end of one month, of $100 each including interest at 6%, converted monthly. Find the number of full payments needed and the size of the last partial payment if made one month after the last full payment.

11. The cash price of a set of furniture is $1850, but it can be bought for $350 down, together with payments of $150 at the end of each month until the balance is less than $150. If interest is charged at the rate of 12%, converted monthly, how large is the concluding partial payment if made one month after the last $150 payment? If the present value of the last partial payment had been added to the down payment, how many months would it have taken to pay off the debt?

12. A city plans to retire $20,000 in bonded indebtedness by setting aside $2000 at the end of each year in a fund paying interest at the rate of $2\frac{1}{2}$%, converted annually. At the time of the last full payment, the city adds the balance needed to pay off the bonds. How long does it take to accumulate the $20,000 and how much must be added at the time of the last full payment, to pay off the bonds?

13. An alternate method of obtaining the last partial payment, made one period after the last full payment, is as follows: Let t represent the fractional part of a year obtained by interpolation from the $a_{\overline{n}|i}$ table. The quantity, t, multiplied by the full payment gives the partial payment. In Example 1, the interpolation gives

$$1\left\{t\begin{cases}10\\10+t\\11\end{cases}\quad\begin{array}{l}7.721735\\8\\8.306414\end{array}\left.\begin{array}{l}\\0.278265\\\end{array}\right\}0.584679\right.$$

$$\frac{t}{1} = \frac{0.278265}{0.584679},$$

or, $\qquad t = 0.475927.$

Since the full payment was $75, the last partial payment, made one year later is
$$x = (0.475927)(75),$$
$$= \$35.69.$$

Prove that this method always gives the partial payment, if made one period after the last full payment.

14. In the problem of determination of the time needed to accumulate a certain sum of money by periodical payments, let n represent the number of full payments needed. Interpolation between $s_{\overline{n}|i}$ and $s_{\overline{n+1}|i}$ for time gives $n + t$ where t is less than 1. Prove that Rt is the present value of the partial payment provided $Rt(1 + i)^{n+1}$ is less than R. Also prove that if $Rt(1 + i)^{n+1}$ is greater than or equal to R, no additional payment is needed and the problem of finding the time is similar to that in the illustrative example (Example 3).

131. Determination of the interest rate

In many respects, the problem of finding the interest rate when the present value or amount, the rent, and the time are known is one of the most important problems in annuities. Such a problem occurs in the usual installment purchases. The buyer knows the cash price, the installment payment, and the number of payments required, from which he wishes to determine the interest rate being charged.

An examination of formulas (1) and (2) shows that an attempt to solve for i results in a polynomial equation of degree $n + 1$ from formula (1) and one of degree n from formula (2). In general n is greater than 2, so that the solution of these polynomial equations usually means the finding of approximations to the roots. In view of this, it appears best to interpolate for the interest rate directly from the proper table. Such an interpolation will be in error, but for the tables in this text, it is safe to assume that the error is not over 5% of the tabular difference in the values of i between which the interpolation is made.

As an example, consider an interpolation between $i = 0.04$ and 0.045 from the $s_{\overline{n}|i}$ table. The tabular difference is 0.005 and hence the error is not greater than $(0.05)(0.005) = 0.00025$.

Closer approximations may be obtained by computing additional entries, for the table used, such that the tabular difference is smaller.

Example 1. The present value of an annuity of $70 per month, paid at the ends of the months, for 5 years is $3500. Find the nominal rate of interest, converted monthly, and state the probable error in the result.

DETERMINATION OF THE INTEREST RATE

Solution. Since $70 a_{\overline{60}|i} = 3500$, we have $a_{\overline{60}|i} = 50$.
Interpolation from Table VIII is as follows:

Interest Rate	$a_{\overline{60}|i}$
$\frac{7}{12}\%$	50.5019939
i	50.0000000
$\frac{2}{3}\%$	49.3184333

$$\frac{i - 0.005833333}{0.00083333} = \frac{0.5019939}{1.1835606},$$
$$i = 0.0062.$$

Only 4 decimal places were retained since the error in interpolation may be as large as $(0.05)(0.000833)$ or 0.000042. The nominal rate is $12(0.0062) = 0.0744$, with an error not greater than $12(0.000042)$ or 0.000504. Hence the nominal rate of interest can be given as 7.4%, accurate to the nearest tenth of 1%.

Example 2. A car costing $2000 cash is sold under the 6% plan for $500 down, followed by 18 monthly payments. Find the carrying charge, the monthly payments, and the interest rate, converted monthly, that are involved.

Solution. We solved this same example in Article 69, Example 4, using a formula which gave an approximation to the simple interest. The answer found was $i = 0.11\frac{7}{19}$. We find as before that the outstanding debt is $2000 - 500 = \$1500$, the carrying charge is $1500(0.06)(1\frac{1}{2}) = \$135$, and the monthly payment is

$$\frac{1500 + 135}{18} = \$90.83.$$

Hence, $90.83 a_{\overline{18}|i} = 1500$, where we now are to determine the compound interest, converted monthly, which is involved.

$$a_{\overline{18}|i} = \frac{1500}{90.83} = 16.51.$$

By interpolation from the table,

$$i = 0.0093,$$

or the nominal interest rate, converted monthly, is 11%, which is lower than that obtained by simple interest.

EXERCISE 4

For each of the following annuities, find the nominal rate of interest converted as often as payments are made. Retain only as many decimal places in your answer as is warranted by the interpolation.

Prob. no.	Value of annuity	Rent	Frequency of payments	Time (in years)
1.	$A_n = \$2500$	$250	annually	13
2.	$S_n = \$6000$	$150	quarterly	8
3.	$A_n = \$12,000$	$300	semiannually	$22\frac{1}{2}$
4.	$S_n = \$14,565$	$100	bimonthly	14
5.	$A_n = \$5000$	$150	quarterly	11

6. Mr. Smith owes $4500 which he may pay off by making 45 semiannual payments of $150 each, the first due in 6 months. What nominal rate of interest, converted semiannually, does Mr. Smith pay?

7. Deposits in a building and loan association of $250 at the end of each quarter for 10 years amount to $12,000. Find the average nominal rate of interest, converted quarterly, paid by this building and loan association for the 10-year period.

8. A mail order house advertises time payments on the 10% plan. Goods costing $585 require a down payment of $185, with the balance, including the carrying charge, payable in 12 monthly payments. What is the monthly payment, and what nominal interest rate, converted monthly, is involved in this transaction?

9. Find the nominal interest rate, converted monthly, involved in the transaction of Problem 8 if the balance is paid off in 18 monthly installments.

10. A savings association advertises that deposits of $50 at the end of each month for 8 years will give the depositor $5500 at the end of 8 years. What nominal rate of interest, converted monthly, does the investor earn?

11. The income of a trust fund is $500, payable at the end of each year for 10 years. This income must be immediately reinvested at a rate not less than 3.2%, converted annually. An investment is chosen for which the amount at the end of the 10 years is $5850.00. Does this investment satisfy the condition of the trust?

12. A finance company, which specializes in small unsecured loans, advertises that $300 may be borrowed provided that the borrower will repay the loan by monthly payments of $29 each at the end of each month for 12 months. What interest rate, converted monthly, does the borrower pay?

13. Mr. Eckhardt lends $5000 to Mr. Higgins on a note, due in 10 years and calling for interest at 6% payable at the end of every 6 months. As Mr. Higgins makes the interest payments, Mr. Eckhardt invests them and finds that at the end of 10 years he has $3600 to his credit from the interest payment investments. What rate of interest, converted semiannually, did he make from this reinvestment?

14. Suppose Mr. Eckhardt, in Problem 13, had invested his money originally in a note calling for repayment of $5000 at the end of 10 years together with interest, converted semiannually. What should the interest rate be so that he would earn the same that he did on the other investment?

MISCELLANEOUS EXERCISE

1. Mr. Ogden, at age 40, decides to invest $100 at the end of each quarter for the next 25 years. If the investment pays interest at the rate of 6%, converted quarterly, find how much Mr. Ogden will have from this investment at age 65.

2. After reaching the age of 65, Mr. Ogden (Problem 1) decides to withdraw his money in quarterly installments over a period of 15 years. If the withdrawals are made at the ends of the periods, find the size of each withdrawal.

3. An investor expects to receive $5000 at the end of each year for 10 years from some timber land. After 10 years it is estimated that the land will sell for $10,000. What is the present value of the investment if money is worth 5%, converted annually?

4. Three years ago Mr. Lawrence signed a note promising to pay Mr. Lasser $4500 at the end of 6 years together with interest at the rate of 4%, payable annually. Mr. Lawrence has made all the interest payments to date but requests that, in place of the original arrangement, he be allowed to pay off his debt by making equal payments including principal and interest at the end of each year for the next 6 years. Mr. Lasser grants the request on the condition that interest be computed at 5%, converted annually. What equal annual payments must Mr. Lawrence make?

5. Mr. Johnson has two debts, one for which he must pay $5000 at the end of 5 years and another which calls for the payment of $4000 at the end of $3\frac{1}{2}$ years. What payment, made at the end of each month for 6 years would be equivalent to Mr. Johnson's two payments if money is worth 6%, converted monthly?

6. The Friendly Loan Corporation advertises that it is prepared to make loans which may be repaid by equal payments at the ends of the months in accordance to the indicated rate chart. Find the nominal interest rate, converted monthly, charged for each loan indicated, first on the 12-months plan and then on the 18-months plan.

Rate chart		
Amount loaned	Monthly 12 months	Payment 18 months
$150	$14.58	$10.40
$500	$47.82	$33.91

7. Mr. Horn owes the following debts:
(a) $600 due in 18 months
(b) $1200 due in 24 months
(c) $400 due in 30 months.
The Friendly Loan Corporation offers to pay off all his debts provided he

will pay them back $39.50 at the end of each month for 5 years. What rate of interest, converted monthly, will Mr. Horn pay if he accepts this offer?

8. Mr. Dill buys a piece of property for which he agrees to pay $1000 down, $1000 at the end of 5 years, and another $1000 at the end of 7 years, together with monthly payments of $100 made at the end of each month, for 7 years. If money is worth 5%, converted monthly, what would be the equivalent cash price?

9. To encourage thrift among their employees, the Arlington Die Casting Company offers to pay 5% interest, converted monthly, on the funds of any employee who is willing to allow a 10% salary deduction for this purpose. What will an employee whose monthly salary is $325 have accumulated under this plan at the end of 5 years?

10. At age 13, a boy receives an inheritance of $5000 together with $500 at the end of each month until he reaches the age 21. The will stipulates that the child's guardian must reinvest 30% of all the money as received. What does the boy have to his account on his 21st birthday if his investments pay 4%, converted monthly?

11. To help with his son's college education, Mr. Wade deposits $2400 to his son's account in a bank paying 2%, interest converted semiannually. If the son withdraws $300 at the end of each 6 months, how many full payments of $300 each will he have? If he draws out the balance at the time of the last full payment, how much will he have, including the last full payment?

12. Mr. Reddick buys a farm costing him $15,000 for which he agrees to pay $8000 down, followed by payments of $100 at the end of each month for 5 years, followed by monthly payments of $75 until the debt is paid off. If interest is charged at the rate of 6%, converted monthly, how many full payments of $75 each are needed and how large is the last partial payment if made one month after the last $75 payment?

13. Mr. Brunk buys a new car for which he will need to borrow $1200. The Automobile Finance Co. will lend him the money on the 6% plan for which repayments will be made in 24 monthly payments, the first in one month. He may also borrow the $1200, plus a cost of $42.50 for making the loan, with his house as security, paying interest at the rate of 5%, converted monthly. This loan is also to be repaid in 24 monthly payments. Which plan is better for Mr. Brunk and by how much per month?

14. A house is offered for sale for either (1) $3000 cash followed by payments of $50 each made at the end of each month for 15 years, or (2) $6000 cash followed by payments of $23 per month for 15 years. If money is worth 6%, converted monthly, which is the better offer for the buyer? (*Hint:* Make use of the formula in Problem 23, Exercise 1 of this chapter.)

15. In order to finance his college education, John borrows $75 from his uncle at the end of each month for the four years he is in college. He promises to repay the loan by making payments at the end of each month for eight years beginning one month after he finishes college. How much must John pay each month if his uncle charges interest at the rate of 3%, converted monthly?

DETERMINATION OF THE INTEREST RATE

16. A club with 200 members plans a new clubhouse which will cost $40,000. It is agreed that building will start in 10 years and that the cost will be met by investing a part of each member's dues for the next 10 years. If the club can invest its funds at 5%, how much must be set aside at the ends of the years, from each member's dues?

17. A manufacturer needs $3000 to replace a machine in 10 years. He places equal amounts at the end of each year for 10 years in a fund which pays interest at the rate of 4% converted annually. How large is each payment? After 6 years, the manufacturer finds that he will need $4000 rather than $3000 to make the replacement. By how much must he increase his payments for the last four years to meet this increase in cost?

18. Mr. Ralston has a debt which he is repaying at the rate of $50 at the end of each month with interest at 6%, converted monthly. He may pay off the entire balance at the time of any monthly payment provided he pays a bonus of $25. Five years before his last payment, Mr. Ralston paid off the balance of his debt. If he could have invested his money at 5%, converted monthly, did he gain or lose by paying off the debt and by how much per month for 5 years?

19. How much will a man have to his credit after 25 years if he deposits $500 at the end of each year and an additional $1000 at the end of each 5 years? Money is worth 4%, converted annually.

20. Mr. Williamson has deposited in an investment company $50 at the end of each quarter for the past 15 years. During the first 10 years the investment earned 4%, converted quarterly, and during the last 5 years 3%, converted quarterly. How much does he have to his credit now?

21. How long will it take Mr. Marks to accumulate $4000 by making payments of $250 at the end of each year for 10 years, followed by annual payments of $200 each, if money is worth 5%, converted annually? Find the last partial payment, if needed, if it is paid one year after the last full payment.

22. Work Problem 21 if Mr. Marks wants $4200 rather than $4000.

15

Other Types of Annuities Certain. Perpetuities and Capitalized Cost

132. Annuities due

In the preceding chapter, we defined an **annuity due** as one for which the payments are made at the beginnings of the payment periods. The value of such an annuity at a specified date may be obtained directly by the use of the geometrical progression or better by the use of known formulas. We shall represent * the present value of an annuity due by,

$$\ddot{A}_n = R\ddot{a}_{\overline{n}|i}$$

and the accumulation by

$$\ddot{S}_n = R\ddot{s}_{\overline{n}|i}.$$

These symbols are simply the corresponding symbols used for ordinary annuities with the trema placed over the letters.

The two line graphs indicated below will show the relationship between the annuity due formulas and the ordinary annuity formulas.

```
    R   R   R   R   R   R      R    R
    |   |   |   |   |   |  ... |    |
    0   1   2   3   4   5     n-2  n-1  n
    |                                    |
  R ä_{\overline{n}|i}              R s̈_{\overline{n}|i}
    |   |   |   |   |   |      |    |
    0   1   2   3   4   5  ... n-1  n
                            6
```

The first line graph shows the payments as they are made. Under the 0 in the first line graph is $R\ddot{a}_{\overline{n}|i}$, the sum of these payments at the beginning of the term, and under the n is $R\ddot{s}_{\overline{n}|i}$, the sum of the payments at the end of the term. The second line graph indicates an n period term with its 0 time one period earlier than the zero on the

---

* The symbols $\ddot{a}_{\overline{n}|i}$ and $\ddot{s}_{\overline{n}|i}$ are the recently adopted symbols of the International Congress of Actuaries.

288

ANNUITIES DUE

first graph. Hence the time n on this scale falls just below $n-1$ on the first graph.

Consider the value of the n payments of R each at the time indicated by zero on the second scale. This is simply the present value, $Ra_{\overline{n}|i}$, of an ordinary annuity. To bring this to time zero on the first scale, we need only multiply by $(1+i)$. Hence the present value of an annuity due is

$$\ddot{A}_n = R\ddot{a}_{\overline{n}|i} = Ra_{\overline{n}|i}(1+i). \tag{1}$$

An alternate formula is obtained from the first line graph by observing that the present value of the first payment is R, and since the remaining $(n-1)$ payments may be considered as though they are paid at the ends of the periods, we have

$$\ddot{A}_n = R + Ra_{\overline{n-1}|i} = R(1 + a_{\overline{n-1}|i}). \tag{2}$$

Example 1. An annuity consists of 10 payments of $50 each made at the ends of the years. If money is worth 4%, converted annually, find the value of this annuity at the time of the first payment.

Solution 1. The line graph indicates the payments and the focal date at which the value of the annuity is to be computed:

```
       R   R   R   R   R   R   R   R   R   R
   |---|---|---|---|---|---|---|---|---|---|
   0   1   2   3   4   5   6   7   8   9   10
      F.D.
                    R = 50
```

The value of the ordinary annuity at time 0 is $Ra_{\overline{n}|i}$; hence at the time of the first payment, one period later, we have

$$Ra_{\overline{n}|i}(1+i) = 50a_{\overline{10}|.04}(1.04),$$
$$= 50(8.11090)(1.04),$$
$$= \$421.77.$$

Thus we see that finding the value of this ordinary annuity at the time of its first payment is actually the problem of finding the present value of an annuity due at the time of the first payment. Hence the above result may have been obtained by using formula (1).

Solution 2. An alternate procedure is to use formula (2). We have

$$\ddot{A}_{\overline{10}|} = 50(1 + a_{\overline{9}|.04}),$$
$$= 50(8.43533),$$
$$= \$421.77.$$

It should be noted that the second method is better than the first from a computational standpoint.

Referring again to the two line graphs near the beginning of this article, we see that the value of the annuity at time n on the second graph is $Rs_{\overline{n}|i}$, but this is one period earlier than the time n on the first graph. Hence the accumulation of an annuity due is

$$\ddot{S}_n = R\ddot{s}_{\overline{n}|i} = Rs_{\overline{n}|i}(1+i). \tag{3}$$

An alternate formula is obtained by using the first line graph only. If another payment is added at the end of the term (one period after the last payment) the accumulation is $Rs_{\overline{n+1}|i}$. This is too much by exactly this extra payment, hence

$$\ddot{S}_n = Rs_{\overline{n+1}|i} - R = R(s_{\overline{n+1}|i} - 1). \tag{4}$$

Example 2. Mr. Linhart plans to accumulate a fund by depositing $150 at the beginning of each six-month period in a savings bank paying $1\frac{1}{2}\%$, converted semiannually. How much does he have at the end of 6 years, just before he makes the next payment?

Solution. The interest rate for the six-month period is $\frac{1}{2}(0.015)$ or (0.0075). The line graph below indicates the payments that are to be summed at the end of 12 periods (6 years) and just before the next payment is made.

```
  R   R   R   R   R   R   R   R   R   R   R   R
  |   |   |   |   |   |   |   |   |   |   |   |
  0   1   2   3   4   5   6   7   8   9  10  11  12
                      R = 150
```

Obviously, this is the problem of finding the accumulation of an annuity due. Hence by direct reasoning or by formula (3),

$$\ddot{S}_{12} = 150 s_{\overline{12}|.0075}(1.0075),$$
$$= \$1890.21,$$

where the computation was carried out by the use of logarithms.

The use of formula (4) gives

$$\ddot{S}_{12} = 150(s_{\overline{13}|.0075} - 1),$$
$$= 150(13.60139 - 1),$$
$$= 150(12.60139),$$
$$= \$1890.21,$$

where this computation can easily be carried out without the use of logarithms. However, had R been such that logarithms are desirable, then the first method would have been as good as the second.

EXERCISE 1

Find the value of each of the following annuities at the time indicated.

ANNUITIES DUE

Prob. no.	Rent	Frequency of payments	Total no. of payments	Nominal int. rate *	Value of annuity
1.	$200	semiannually	15	0.04	(a) at time of 1st payment (b) 6 mos. before 1st payment
2.	$500	quarterly	20	0.06	(a) at time of last payment (b) 1 quarter after last payment
3.	$1000	annually	30	0.05	(a) 1 yr. after last payment (b) at time of last payment
4.	$200	monthly	60	0.04	(a) 1 mo. before 1st payment (b) at time of 1st payment

* Interest is converted as frequently as the payments are made.

5. Find the present value and amount of an annuity due for which the payments are $700 bimonthly, the term is 15 years, and the interest rate is 3%, converted bimonthly.

6. Find the present value and amount of an annuity due for which the payments are $150 semimonthly, the term is 4 years, and the interest rate is 6%, converted semimonthly.

7. A small building may be rented on a 5-year lease for $500 per month with payments at the beginnings of the months. The owner is willing to accept a single cash payment made now which is equivalent to the monthly payments, provided that interest is figured at 4%, converted monthly. What is the cash payment which will pay off the lease in advance?

8. Mr. Clovis buys an insurance policy, costing him $45 at the beginning of each quarter for 15 years, which will pay him $3000 at the end of 15 years provided he lives. Should he die within this 15-year period, his beneficiary will receive $3000. Assuming that Mr. Clovis will live to receive the $3000, what is the cost of the insurance feature of this policy if money is worth 3%, converted quarterly?

9. Certain types of standard merchandise such as jewelry, cameras, and like articles are sometimes sold on the installment plan with no carrying charge. Thus an article costing $60 may be paid off by 12 monthly payments of $5 each, the first due immediately. If a person can invest his money at 3%, converted monthly, how much extra does he pay for this $60 article when he pays cash?

10. To meet a debt of $10,000 due in 20 years, Mr. Ransome plans to make 20 equal annual payments, starting now, in an investment which pays 5%, converted annually. How large must the payments be?

11. A set of furniture may be bought either for $935 cash now or on the installment plan by making 10 monthly payments of $95 each, the first due now. If money is worth 5%, converted monthly, which is the better offer?

12. A lot may be bought for $3200 cash or by the installment plan in 10 equal annual payments including interest at 6%, converted annually. (a) What is the annual payment if the first is due now? (b) What is the annual payment if the first is due in one year?

13. Show that the last partial payment, x, in illustrative Example 1, Article 130, may be obtained from the equation,

$$75\ddot{s}_{\overline{11}|.05} + x = 600(1.05)^{11}.$$

In what way is this method of obtaining the last partial payment better than those previously given in Article 130?

14. A debt of $4000 will be paid off by making an annual payment of $300 at the beginning of each year, including principal and interest at 4%, converted annually. Find the number of full payments necessary and the last partial payment if it is made one year after the last full payment.

15. Show algebraically that
$$s_{\overline{n}|i}(1+i) = s_{\overline{n+1}|i} - 1.$$

16. Show algebraically that
$$a_{\overline{n}|i}(1+i) = 1 + a_{\overline{n-1}|i}.$$

17. Show that
$$\ddot{a}_{\overline{n}|i}(1+i) = \ddot{s}_{\overline{n}|i}.$$

18. Show that
$$\frac{1}{s_{\overline{n}|i}} = \frac{1}{a_{\overline{n}|i}} - iv.$$

19. Derive the formula for the present value of an annuity due, by use of the geometrical progression.

20. Derive the formula for the amount of an annuity due, by use of the geometrical progression.

133. Deferred annuities

The annuities previously considered have been such that the term began at once whether they were of the ordinary or the due type. Such annuities will be called **immediate annuities**. In contrast to these, we have the **deferred annuities** for which the term starts at some future date. If the term starts at the end of m periods, the annuity is said to be deferred m periods.

DEFERRED ANNUITIES

We first observe that the amount of a deferred annuity is the same as that of the corresponding immediate annuity.

In finding the present value of a deferred annuity, we consider first the ordinary deferred annuity. The following line graph indicates the payments for an ordinary annuity for n periods, deferred m periods.

```
|←Interval of deferment→|←--------Term of annuity------→|
                         R   R   R   R       R    R
|   |   |   |  ...  |    |   |   |   | ...   |    |
0   1   2   3       m   m+1 m+2 m+3       m+n-2 m+n-1 m+n
```

At time m, this annuity obviously has the value $Ra_{\overline{n}|i}$ and hence, representing the present value of the annuity by $_m|A_n$,

$$_m|A_n = R_m|a_{\overline{n}|i} = Ra_{\overline{n}|i}(1+i)^{-m}, \qquad (5)$$

where $_m|a_{\overline{n}|i}$ represents the present value of an ordinary annuity of 1, deferred m periods, and running for n periods.

An alternate formula may be obtained by assuming that payments of R each will be made at the end of each period in the interval of deferment. Then the present value of all the payments including these is $Ra_{\overline{m+n}|i}$. But since the first m of these payments do not belong to the deferred annuity, we must subtract their present value which is $Ra_{\overline{m}|i}$. Thus

$$_m|A_n = Ra_{\overline{m+n}|i} - Ra_{\overline{m}|i} = R(a_{\overline{m+n}|i} - a_{\overline{m}|i}). \qquad (6)$$

The advantage of this second formula is that the computational work is simpler if logarithms are not used.

It should be noted that similar formulas may be set up for the present value of a deferred annuity due. Such formulas, however, are not needed since a deferred annuity due is simply an ordinary deferred annuity with the interval of deferment one period less than that for the deferred annuity due. Let k represent the deferment interval of the deferred annuity due, then

$$R_k|\ddot{a}_{\overline{n}|i} = R_{k-1}|a_{\overline{n}|i}. \qquad (7)$$

Example 1. The payments of an ordinary deferred annuity are made semiannually for 5 years. The interval of deferment is 4 years, the rent is $250, and the interest rate is 6%, converted semiannually. Find the amount and the present value of this annuity.

Solution. Referring to the line graph

```
|←---Interval of deferment---→|←--------Term of annuity-------→|
                               R  R  R  R  R  R  R  R  R  R
|  |  |  |  |  |  |  |  |  |  |  |  |  |  |  |  |  |  |
0  1  2  3  4  5  6  7  8  9 10 11 12 13 14 15 16 17 18
```
Six-months periods, $R = \$250$, $i = 0.03$

it is obvious that the amount of the annuity is
$$250s_{\overline{10}|.03} = 250(11.46388),$$
$$= \$2865.97.$$

To obtain the present value, we first find the value at time 8; it is $250a_{\overline{10}|.03}$; hence
$$_8|A_{10} = 250a_{\overline{10}|.03}(1.03)^{-8},$$
which is the present value of the value of the annuity at time 8. Using logarithms as an aid in the calculation
$$_8|A_{10} = \$1683.45.$$

This result may have been obtained by substituting in formula (5). Using formula (6) we have
$$_8|A_{10} = 250(a_{\overline{18}|.03} - a_{\overline{8}|.03}),$$
$$= 250(13.75351 - 7.01969),$$
$$= \$1683.46.$$

Example 2. The returns from an investment are 16 annual payments of $500 each, the first due in 7 years. What is the present value of this investment if money is worth 5%?

Solution. If this annuity is to be considered as an ordinary deferred annuity, its term starts in 6 years, that is, one period before the first payment. Hence $m = 6$ and the present value of the investment [using formula (6)] is
$$_6|A_{16} = 500(a_{\overline{22}|.05} - a_{\overline{6}|.05}),$$
$$= 500(13.16300 - 5.07569),$$
$$= \$4043.66.$$

EXERCISE 2

Find the present value of each of the following ordinary deferred annuities.

Prob. no.	Rent	Term (in years)	Interval of deferment (in years)	Frequency of rent payments	Nominal interest rate*
1.	$250	4	10	quarterly	4%
2.	$500	6	3	semiannually	6%
3.	$1000	3	5	monthly	5%
4.	$25	8	2	monthly	4%
5	$137.50	7	10	annually	3%
6.	$23.57	5	8	quarterly	5%

* Interest is converted as frequently as payments are made.

7. Find the present value and amount of an ordinary annuity consisting of 15 annual payments of $200, deferred for 10 years, if money is worth $3\frac{1}{2}\%$, converted annually.

DEFERRED ANNUITIES

8. Find the present value and the amount of an annuity due consisting of 10 semiannual payments of $250 each, deferred for 8 years, if money is worth 4%, converted semiannually.

9. In addition to the down payment of $2000 on a piece of property, Mr. Bridges agrees to make annual payments, starting in 5 years, of $400 each for 10 years. If interest is to be computed at 6%, converted annually, find the equivalent cash price of the property.

10. An orchard is expected to yield 30 crops, worth $2000 each. If the first crop is harvested at the end of 6 years and if payments for the crops are received at the time they are harvested, find the present value of these crops. Assume that money is worth 3%, converted annually.

11. A 40-year lease calls for rental payments, at the beginnings of the years, of $500 each for the first 10 years, followed by 30 annual payments of $600 each. If money is worth 5%, converted annually, what single cash payment, made now, would completely pay off the lease?

12. What single payment now is equivalent to payments of $50 each, made at the end of each month for $1\frac{1}{2}$ years, followed by monthly payments of $75 each for the following $2\frac{1}{2}$ years? Money is worth 6%, converted monthly.

13. After making the down payment of $200,000 on a piece of timber land costing $500,000, the Rawlins Lumber Company agrees to make annual payments on the balance including interest at $4\frac{1}{2}$%, converted annually. How much should the annual payments be if they start in 5 years and continue for 10 years?

14. To provide for his retirement, Mr. Wood plans to save $200 at the end of each year for 10 years, followed by savings of $300 at the end of each year for the next 20 years of his employment and, finally, $500 at the end of each year for the next and last 10 years of his employment. How much does he have at the end of 40 years if he invests his money at 4%, converted annually? What is the present value of Mr. Wood's payments?

15. The terms of a 99-year lease call for rental payments of $10,000 per year, paid at the beginning of each of the years. Find the present value of the first 10 rental payments and compare it to the present value of the last 10 payments if money is worth 4%, converted annually.

16. A will calls for the division of $65,000 between two children, now 13 and 18 years old, in which the younger is to receive $15,000 immediately and the elder $10,000 immediately, and both are to receive equal payments from the balance of the estate for 10 years beginning when the child reaches the age of 21. (a) How large are these payments if the money is invested at 5%? (b) Which child receives the larger inheritance and by how much?

17. Mr. Moore owes a debt which calls for 18 yearly payments of $500 each, beginning in 5 years. If Mr. Moore wishes to start equal annual payments at the end of each year beginning now, what should the payments be, if money is worth 5%, converted annually, and if 23 payments in all are made?

18. Payments of $100 each are made at the end of each year for 15 years. If money is worth 4%, converted annually, find the value of this annuity:

(a) now; (b) one year from now; (c) 5 years from now; (d) 15 years from now; (e) 16 years from now; (f) 20 years from now; (g) 8 years ago.

19. Prove algebraically that

$$Ra_{\overline{m}|i}(1+i)^{-m} = R(a_{\overline{m+n}|i} - a_{\overline{m}|i}).$$

20. Prove algebraically that

$$Rs_{\overline{m}|i}(1+i)^k = R(s_{\overline{n+k}|i} - s_{\overline{k}|i}).$$

21. Prove that

$$R_k|\ddot{a}_{\overline{m}|i} = R\ddot{a}_{\overline{m}|i}(1+i)^{-k}.$$

22. Prove that

$$R_k|\ddot{a}_{\overline{m}|i} = R(\ddot{a}_{\overline{k+n}|i} - \ddot{a}_{\overline{k}|i}).$$

134. General case annuities

In practically all of the annuities which arise in business, the interest conversion period is equal to the payment period. Occasionally, however, problems do arise in which the interest conversion period is either shorter or longer than the payment period. An annuity for which this is true will be called a **general case annuity**. Formulas may be derived for the present value and amount of such an annuity which are general formulas in the sense that the formulas already derived are special cases. However, because of the relative unimportance of the general case annuity, it seems more desirable to reduce problems involving general case annuities to the simple case where the payment period is equal to the interest conversion period. This may be done very easily by changing the given interest rate to an equivalent rate for which the conversion period is equal to the annuity payment period (see Article 121). By the use of this procedure, no new tables are needed; in fact, only the compound interest table, present value table, and a table of values of $(1+i)^{\frac{1}{p}}$ are needed. The illustrative examples will demonstrate the methods used.

Example 1. Find the present value of an ordinary annuity consisting of 10 annual payments of \$100 each if money is worth 6%, converted semi-annually.

Solution. We wish to change the interest rate to the equivalent rate, converted annually. We have, letting i represent the equivalent annual rate,

$$1 + i = (1.03)^2,$$

or

$$i = (1.03)^2 - 1.$$

Now the required present value is

$$A_{10} = 100a_{\overline{10}|i} = 100\frac{1 - (1+i)^{-10}}{i}.$$

GENERAL CASE ANNUITIES

Substituting $(1.03)^2$ for $1+i$ and $(1.03)^2 - 1$ for i, we have

$$A_{10} = 100 \frac{1 - (1.03)^{-20}}{(1.03)^2 - 1}.$$

We now use Table VI to find $(1.03)^{-20}$ and Table V to find $(1.03)^2$ obtaining

$$A_{10} = 100 \frac{1 - 0.553676}{1.0609000 - 1} = 100 \frac{0.446324}{0.0609000},$$

$$= \$732.88.$$

Example 2. Find the present value of an ordinary annuity consisting of 24 monthly payments of $50 each if money is worth 5%, converted annually.

Solution. In this case we find the interest rate, i, for the period of one month, which is equivalent to the annual rate of 5%. We have

$$(1+i)^{12} = 1.05 \quad \text{or} \quad 1+i = (1.05)^{\frac{1}{12}}$$

and hence, $\quad i = (1.05)^{\frac{1}{12}} - 1.$

The required present value is

$$A_{24} = 50 a_{\overline{24}|i} = 50 \frac{1 - (1+i)^{-24}}{i}.$$

Substituting the values of $1+i$ and i given above, we have

$$A_{24} = 50 \frac{1 - (1.05)^{-2}}{(1.05)^{\frac{1}{12}} - 1}.$$

Using Tables VI and X, we have

$$A_{24} = 50 \frac{1 - 0.9070295}{1.0040741 - 1} = 50 \frac{0.0929705}{0.0040741},$$

$$= \$1141.00.$$

Example 3. Find the amount of an annuity due consisting of 20 semiannual payments of $200 each if money is worth 4%, converted quarterly.

Solution. The interest rate for the 6-month period, equivalent to the given nominal rate of 4%, converted quarterly, is found from

$$(1+i)^2 = (1.01)^4,$$
$$1+i = (1.01)^2,$$
$$i = (1.01)^2 - 1.$$

The required amount, using formula (3), Article 132, is

$$\ddot{S}_{20} = 200 \ddot{s}_{\overline{20}|i} = 200 s_{\overline{20}|i}(1+i) = 200 \frac{(1+i)^{20} - 1}{i}(1+i),$$

$$= 200 \frac{(1+i)^{21} - (1+i)}{i} = 200 \frac{(1.01)^{42} - (1.01)^2}{(1.01)^2 - 1}.$$

Using Table V, we have

$$\ddot{S}_{20} = 200 \frac{1.518790 - 1.020100}{1.0201000 - 1} = \frac{0.498690}{0.0201000},$$

$$= \$4962.08.$$

Example 4. Find the present value of 36 monthly payments of $300 each if the first payment is made in one year and money is worth 6%, converted semiannually.

Solution. The interest relations are

$$(1 + i)^{12} = (1.03)^2 \quad \text{or,} \quad 1 + i = (1.03)^{\frac{1}{6}},$$

from which we have

$$i = (1.03)^{\frac{1}{6}} - 1.$$

The value of the annuity eleven months from now is $300a_{\overline{36}|i}$. To find the present value we discount this value for eleven periods. Hence

$$A_{36} = 300 \frac{1 - (1 + i)^{-36}}{i} (1 + i)^{-11}$$

$$= 300 \frac{1 - (1.03)^{-6}}{(1.03)^{\frac{1}{6}} - 1} (1.03)^{-\frac{11}{6}}.$$

Since the factor $(1.03)^{-\frac{11}{6}}$ may be written $(1.03)^{-2}(1.03)^{\frac{1}{12}}(1.03)^{\frac{1}{12}}$, we have

$$A_{36} = 300 \frac{1 - (1.03)^{-6}}{(1.03)^{\frac{1}{6}} - 1} (1.03)^{-2}(1.03)^{\frac{1}{6}},$$

$$= 300 \frac{1 - 0.837484}{1.0049386 - 1} (0.942596)(1.00494),$$

$$= 300 \frac{0.162516}{0.0049386} (0.942596)(1.00494).$$

Using logarithms,

$$A_{36} = \$9351.40.$$

EXERCISE 3

Find the indicated value of each of the following annuities.

Prob. no.	Rent	Term in yrs.	Frequency of payments	Nominal int. rate	Frequency of conversion	Type of annuity	Value wanted
1.	$300	18	annually	4%	semiannually	ordinary	present value
2.	$200	5	semiannually	5%	annually	ordinary	amount
3.	$500	14	annually	4%	monthly	due	amount
4.	$50	10	quarterly	6%	semiannually	due	present value
5.	$150	7½	semiannually	4%	quarterly	ordinary	amount
6.	$60	1 5/12	monthly	5%	semiannually	ordinary	present value

INCREASING AND DECREASING ANNUITIES   299

7. Find the present value of an annuity of $75 per year for 10 years if the first payment is made in 7 years and money is worth 8%, converted monthly.

8. Mr. Bergen offers a piece of property for $2000 and payments of $50 at the end of each month for 6 years, provided that the buyer will pay interest at the rate of 8%, converted semiannually. What is the cash price of the property?

9. To redeem a bond issue of $50,000, due in 10 years, a municipal utility district wishes to make equal deposits in a sinking fund at the end of each year for 10 years. If this fund earns $3\frac{1}{2}$%, converted semiannually, how large must each payment be?

10. Mr. Friedman sells a house for $15,000 with $5000 down and the balance in payments at the end of each year for 20 years. If interest is to be charged at the rate of 6%, converted semiannually, find the payment.

11. What payment, made at the beginning of each year for 15 years, will be needed to accumulate $3000 if money is worth 4%, converted monthly?

12. Mr. Saks made 20 semiannual payments of $200 each in a savings bank which paid interest at the rate of 2%, converted semiannually, for the first 6 years. The rate was then changed to 2%, converted quarterly. (a) What was the amount at the end of 10 years? (b) What would the amount have been if there had been no change in the interest rate?

135. Increasing and decreasing annuities

An annuity for which the successive payments increase by a fixed sum is called an **increasing annuity**. Likewise, if the successive payments decrease by a fixed sum, the annuity is called a **decreasing annuity**. Thus the sequence of payments, $50, $60, $70, $80, $90, $100, made at the end of the first, second, third, fourth, fifth, sixth years, respectively, is an example of an ordinary increasing annuity. Similarly, the sequence of payments, $600, $500, $400, $300, made at the end of the first, second, third, fourth month, respectively, is an example of an ordinary decreasing annuity. If the payments are made at the beginnings of the periods, we have an increasing annuity due or a decreasing annuity due.

The following examples illustrate how increasing and decreasing annuities may be evaluated without the use of special formulas. However, if the number of payments is large, special formulas are desirable. These will be developed later.

Example 1. Find the amount and present value of an ordinary increasing annuity having annual payments of $50, $60, $70, $80, $90, $100, if money is worth 5%, converted annually.

Solution. We may break the annuity up into six annuities, one for which the rent is $50 for 6 years, another for which the rent is $10 for 5 years, a third with rent of $10 for 4 years, a fourth with rent of $10 for 3 years, a fifth with rent of $10 for 2 years, and the last an annuity consisting of one payment of $10. The student may find it helpful to draw a line graph for each of these six annuities. Hence, designating the amount of the increasing annuity by S'_6 we have:

$$S'_6 = 50s_{\overline{6}|.05} + 10s_{\overline{5}|.05} + 10s_{\overline{4}|.05} + 10s_{\overline{3}|.05} + 10s_{\overline{2}|.05} + 10s_{\overline{1}|.05}.$$

Using the $s_{\overline{n}|i}$ table we have

$$S'_6 = 50(6.8019) + 10(5.5256 + 4.3101 + 3.1525 + 2.0500 + 1),$$
$$= \$500.48.$$

To find the present value we may discount the amount for 6 years. Hence, designating the present value by A'_6, we have:

$$A'_6 = \$500.48(1.05)^{-6} = 500.48(0.746215),$$
$$= \$373.47.$$

Example 2. Find the present value and amount of a decreasing annuity consisting of four monthly payments of $600, $500, $400, $300, made at the end of the first, second, third, fourth months, respectively, if money is worth 6%, converted monthly.

Solution. In Example 1 the amount of the increasing annuity was computed first. However, for a decreasing annuity it is better to compute the present value first. We see that this annuity may be broken up into the present value of an annuity for which the payment is $300 for four months, another for which the payment is $100 for three months, a third of $100 for two months, and a fourth of $100 for one month. Hence, designating the present value of the decreasing annuity by A''_4, we have:

$$A''_4 = 300a_{\overline{4}|.005} + 100a_{\overline{3}|.005} + 100a_{\overline{2}|.005} + 100a_{\overline{1}|.005},$$
$$= 300(3.95050) + 100(2.97025 + 1.98510 + 0.99502),$$
$$= \$1780.19.$$

We may now find the amount of the decreasing annuity, S''_4, by carrying A''_4 forward at interest for 4 months, Hence

$$S''_4 = \$1780.19(1.005)^4,$$
$$= \$1816.06.$$

We now proceed to set up the formulas for these annuities. Consider first the increasing annuity. Let R represent the first payment made at the end of the first period. Let d represent the fixed sum by which each payment is increased and let n represent the number of payments. The payments are, then,

$$R, R + d, R + 2d, \cdots, R + (n-1)d.$$

Hence it is seen that the amount, S'_n, of an ordinary increasing annuity is the sum of the amount of an annuity of R for n periods, the amount of an annuity of d for $(n-1)$ periods, and so on to the amount of an annuity of d for 1 period. Hence, we have

INCREASING AND DECREASING ANNUITIES

$$S'_n = Rs_{\overline{n}|i} + ds_{\overline{n-1}|i} + ds_{\overline{n-2}|i} + \cdots + ds_{\overline{1}|i},$$

$$= Rs_{\overline{n}|i} + d\left[\frac{(1+i)^{n-1}-1}{i} + \frac{(1+i)^{n-2}-1}{i} + \cdots + \frac{(1+i)^1-1}{i}\right],$$

$$= Rs_{\overline{n}|i} + d\left[\frac{(1+i)^{n-1} + (1+i)^{n-2} + \cdots + (1+i) + 1 - n}{i}\right].$$

Hence the amount of an ordinary increasing annuity is

$$S'_n = Rs_{\overline{n}|i} + \frac{d}{i}(s_{\overline{n}|i} - n). \tag{8}$$

To obtain the present value, A'_n, of an ordinary increasing annuity, we multiply S'_n by the discount factor $(1+i)^{-n}$. Hence

$$A'_n = Ra_{\overline{n}|i} + \frac{d}{i}\left[a_{\overline{n}|i} - n(1+i)^{-n}\right]. \tag{9}$$

For an ordinary decreasing annuity, let R' represent the smallest payment, which in this case will be the last payment, rather than the first, as in the case of the increasing annuity. The n payments are, then, in the order they are made,

$$R' + (n-1)d,\ R' + (n-2)d, \cdots,\ R' + d,\ R'.$$

The present value of such an annuity is then seen to be the sum of n present values, namely, the present value of an annuity of R' for n periods, an annuity of d for $n-1$ periods, an annuity of d for $n-2$ periods, and so on. Finally, we have the present value of an annuity of d for one period. Hence, representing the present value of a decreasing annuity by A''_n, we have,

$$A''_n = R'a_{\overline{n}|i} + da_{\overline{n-1}|i} + da_{\overline{n-2}|i} + \cdots + da_{\overline{1}|i},$$

$$= R'a_{\overline{n}|i} + d\left[\frac{1-(1+i)^{-(n-1)}}{i} + \frac{1-(1+i)^{-(n-2)}}{i} + \cdots + \frac{1-(1+i)^{-1}}{i}\right],$$

$$= R'a_{\overline{n}|i} + d\left\{\frac{(n-1) - [(1+i)^{-(n-1)} + (1+i)^{-(n-2)} + \cdots + (1+i)^{-1}]}{i}\right\},$$

$$= R'a_{\overline{n}|i} + \frac{d}{i}[(n-1) - a_{\overline{n-1}|i}].$$

If R represents the first payment of a decreasing annuity, then $R = R' + (n-1)d$ or $R' = R - (n-1)d$. Hence the present value of an ordinary decreasing annuity is

$$A''_n = [R - (n-1)d]a_{\overline{n}|i} + \frac{d}{i}[(n-1) - a_{\overline{n-1}|i}]. \tag{10}$$

The amount, S_n'', of an ordinary decreasing annuity may then be found by multiplying A_n'' by the accumulation factor $(1+i)^n$. Hence

$$S_n'' = [R - (n-1)d]s_{\overline{n}|i} + \frac{d}{i}[(n-1)(1+i)^n - s_{\overline{n-1}|i}(1+i)]. \quad (11)$$

A similar set of formulas may be obtained for the corresponding annuities due, but since an annuity due is obtained by multiplying the corresponding ordinary annuity by $(1+i)$, such a set is not necessary.

Example 3. Find the amount and the present value of the increasing annuity in Example 1, making use of the formulas.

Solution. We have $R = 50$, $d = 10$, $n = 6$, $i = 0.05$. Hence, substituting in formula (8), we have the amount,

$$S_6' = 50s_{\overline{6}|.05} + \frac{10}{0.05}(s_{\overline{6}|.05} - 6),$$

$$= 50(6.8019) + \frac{10}{0.05}(6.80191 - 6),$$

$$= \$500.48.$$

Substituting in formula (9) we have the present value,

$$A_6' = 50a_{\overline{6}|.05} + \frac{10}{0.05}[a_{\overline{6}|.05} - 6(1.05)^{-6}],$$

$$= 50(5.0757) + \frac{10}{0.05}[5.07569 - 6(0.74622)],$$

$$= \$373.46.$$

Example 4. Find the present value and amount of the decreasing annuity in Example 2, making use of the formulas.

Solution. We have $R = 600$, $d = 100$, $n = 4$ and $i = 0.005$. Substituting in formula (10), we find the present value

$$A_4'' = 300a_{\overline{4}|.005} + \frac{100}{0.005}(3 - a_{\overline{3}|.005}),$$

$$= 300(3.95050) + \frac{100}{0.005}(3 - 2.970248),$$

$$= \$1780.19.$$

Substituting in formula (11) to find the amount, we have

$$S_4'' = 300s_{\overline{4}|.005} + \frac{100}{0.005}[3(1.005)^4 - s_{\overline{3}|.005}(1.005)],$$

$$= 300(4.03010) + \frac{100}{0.005}[3(1.0201505) - (3.015025)(1.005)],$$

$$= \$1816.06.$$

EXERCISE 4

1. Find the amount of an ordinary increasing annuity consisting of 10 semiannual payments, the first of which is $40, followed by payments each of which is $20 larger than the preceding payment. Money is worth 3%, converted semiannually.

2. Find the present value of an ordinary increasing annuity consisting of 60 monthly payments, the first of which is $25, followed by payments each of which is $5 more than the preceding payment. Money is worth 8%, converted monthly.

3. Find the present value of an ordinary decreasing annuity consisting of 40 annual payments, the first of which is $200 followed by payments, each of which is $2 less than the preceding payment. Money is worth 4%, converted annually.

4. Find the amount of an ordinary decreasing annuity consisting of 20 quarterly payments, the first of which is $500, followed by payments each of which is $20 less than the preceding payment. Money is worth 6%, converted quarterly.

5. Starting now with a deposit of $200 in a building and loan association which pays 3%, converted annually, Mr. George plans to make like deposits increased by $50 each year until a total of 35 have been made. What does Mr. George have to his credit at the end of 35 years?

6. A 20-year lease calls for annual rental payments starting with $5000 now, followed by payments each of which is $50 less than the preceding payment. If money is worth 5%, what single payment made now would be equivalent to the annual payments?

7. Find the equal annual payment, made at the end of each year for 20 years, which would be equivalent to the rental agreement made in Problem 6.

8. If $R = d$, show that formula (8), the amount of an ordinary increasing annuity, reduces to

$$S_n' = \frac{d}{i}[(1+i)s_{\overline{n}|i} - n].$$

9. If $R = d$ show that formula (9), the present value of an ordinary increasing annuity, reduces to

$$A_n' = \frac{d}{i}[(1+i)a_{\overline{n}|i} - n(1+i)^{-n}].$$

10. If $R = nd$ show that formula (10), the present value of an ordinary decreasing annuity, reduces to

$$A_n'' = \frac{d}{i}(n - a_{\overline{n}|i}).$$

11. If $R = nd$ show that formula (11), the amount of an ordinary decreasing annuity, reduces to

$$S_n'' = \frac{d}{i}[n(1+i)^n - s_{\overline{n}|i}].$$

12. After making the down payment of $5000 on a piece of property, Mr. Rochester agrees to make 12 additional monthly payments, the first being $25 made at the end of the first month, followed by subsequent monthly payments each of which is $25 larger than the preceding payment. If interest is charged at the rate of 6%, converted monthly, find the equivalent cash price of the property.

13. Mr. Murray owes Mr. Reynolds $5000, the principal of which he agrees to repay in installments of $1000 at the end of each year for 5 years. Mr. Murray also agrees to pay interest at the rate of 5%, payable annually, on the outstanding debt. Mr. Reynolds invests the principal and interest payments in a savings bank paying interest at the rate of 2%, converted annually. How much does Mr. Reynolds have to his credit by the time Mr. Murray has repaid his loan?

14. The present value of an ordinary decreasing annuity consisting of 10 annual payments is $2000. The smallest payment is equal to the common difference between payments. If money is worth 5%, find the first and last payments.

15. Mr. Paine wishes to accumulate $2000 by making a certain deposit in a savings bank at the end of 6 months, another twice as large at the end of one year, and another three times as large as the first at the end of $1\frac{1}{2}$ years, and so on until 20 deposits have been made. Find the first and last deposit if the bank pays interest at the rate of $1\frac{1}{2}\%$ converted semiannually.

136. Perpetuities

An annuity whose payments continue forever is called a **perpetuity**. Thus, payments of $20 at the end of each year forever would be an example of an ordinary perpetuity. If money is worth 4%, it is obvious that the present value of this perpetuity is $500, for $500 invested at 4% will provide $20 interest at the end of each year forever, the principal of $500 being left intact. We may easily find the present value, A_∞, of an ordinary perpetuity of R per period if the interest rate is i per period, since A_∞ invested at the interest rate i must provide R at the end of each period. Hence

$$A_\infty i = R,$$

or
$$A_\infty = \frac{R}{i}. \tag{12}$$

The symbol A_∞ is used since we may consider the perpetuity as an annuity with an infinite number of payments. Indeed, we may derive its formula by taking the "sum to infinity" of the infinite series,

$$R(1+i)^{-1} + R(1+i)^{-2} + R(1+i)^{-3} + \cdots.$$

From Article 95, we have that the "sum to infinity" of a geometrical series is $\dfrac{a}{1-r}$, where a is the first term and r is the common ratio. Hence, for the above series,

$$A_\infty = \frac{R(1+i)^{-1}}{1-(1+i)^{-1}} = \frac{R}{(1+i)-1} = \frac{R}{i},$$

the result previously obtained. If we represent the limit of $a_{\overline{n}|i}$, as n approaches infinity, by $a_{\overline{\infty}|i}$, it follows that

$$A_\infty = Ra_{\overline{\infty}|i} = \frac{R}{i}.$$

Example 1. An alumnus wishes to provide his university with an annual scholarship of $350 forever, the first award to be made at the end of one year. If the university can invest its funds at $3\frac{1}{2}\%$, converted annually, what donation must the alumnus make?

Solution. Representing the donation by A_∞, we have that the annual interest must equal the scholarship payment of $350. Hence

$$0.035 A_\infty = 350,$$

or
$$A_\infty = \frac{350}{0.035} = \$10{,}000.$$

This result might have been obtained by substituting in formula (12).

To find the present value of a perpetuity due, we observe that it differs from the present value of an ordinary perpetuity by one payment, the first. Hence

$$\ddot{A}_\infty = R\ddot{a}_{\overline{\infty}|i} = R\left(1 + \frac{1}{i}\right). \tag{13}$$

Example 2. What donation must the alumnus make in Example 1 if the first scholarship is to be awarded immediately?

Solution. It will take exactly $350 more than previously required if the scholarship awards are made at the ends of the years. Hence the donation is

$$\ddot{A}_\infty = \$350 + \$10{,}000 = \$10{,}350.$$

The student may verify this result by use of formula (13).

The present value of an ordinary deferred perpetuity may be obtained by the methods used for deriving formulas (5) and (6) in Article 133. Representing the present value of an ordinary deferred perpetuity by $_m|A_\infty$, we have

$$_m|A_\infty = R_m|a_{\overline{\infty}|i} = \frac{R}{i}(1+i)^{-m}, \tag{14}$$

since the value of the perpetuity m periods hence is $\dfrac{R}{i}$, and its present value is then obtained by applying the discount factor $(1+i)^{-m}$.

We may likewise consider the present value of such a perpetuity as the difference between the present value of an ordinary perpetuity and the present value of an ordinary annuity for m periods. Hence

$$_m|A_\infty = R(a_{\overline{\infty}|i} - a_{\overline{m}|i}),$$

or
$$_m|A_\infty = R\left(\frac{1}{i} - a_{\overline{m}|i}\right). \tag{15}$$

It should be noted that there is no necessity for the corresponding perpetuity-due formulas since, as for deferred annuities due [see formula (7)], we have

$$R_k|\ddot{a}_{\overline{\infty}|i} = R_{k-1}|a_{\overline{\infty}|i}. \tag{16}$$

That is, the present value of an annuity due deferred k periods is equal to the present value of an ordinary annuity deferred for one less period.

Example 3. A church receives a donation of $10,000 which it is required to invest at 3%, converted annually. After 50 years, the church may start withdrawing equal annual payments of such a size that they will continue forever. How large are these payments if the first is withdrawn at the end of 50 years?

Solution. The payments form an ordinary perpetuity deferred 49 years. Hence, substituting in either formula (14) or (15), we may find R, the payment required. Using formula (14),

$$10,000 = \frac{R}{0.03}(1.03)^{-49},$$

or
$$R = 300(1.03)^{49},$$
$$= \$1276.87.$$

If the payment interval of a perpetuity is not the same as the interest conversion period, we may treat the problem as we did a general case annuity. That is, we may change the interest conversion period so that it corresponds to the payment period. An alternate procedure is to change the payment period so that it is equal to the interest conversion period. This second method will be used for perpetuities.

Consider a perpetuity consisting of payments of R each made at the end of $k, 2k, 3k, \cdots$ interest conversion periods forever. We change the single payment R made at the end of k periods to k payments of R' each made at the end of each period. It follows that R is the amount of an annuity of R' consisting of k payments with interest at the rate of i per period. Hence

$$R's_{\overline{k}|i} = R,$$

or
$$R' = R\frac{1}{s_{\overline{k}|i}}.$$

PERPETUITIES

Hence the present value, A'_∞, of a perpetuity for which the payments are made at the end of each k periods forever is

$$A'_\infty = \frac{R'}{i} = \frac{R}{i} \frac{1}{s_{\overline{k}|i}}. \qquad (17)$$

Example 4. Find the present value of a perpetuity of $500 paid at the end of each 10 years forever, if money is worth 4%, converted annually.

Solution. From the above formula we have

$$A'_\infty = \frac{500}{0.04} \frac{1}{s_{\overline{10}|.04}} = \frac{500}{0.04}(0.0832909) = 500(2.08227),$$

$$= \$1041.14.$$

It is instructive to note that $1041.14 carried forward at compound interest for 10 years is $(1041.14)(1.04)^{10} = \$1541.14$. From this is deducted the $500 payment, leaving $1041.14 to accumulate to exactly $1541.14 in another 10 years, and so on forever.

EXERCISE 5

Find the present value of each of the following ordinary perpetuities.

Prob. no.	Perpetuity payment	Frequency of payments	Nominal interest rate	Frequency of conversion
1.	$150	annually	4%	annually
2.	$100	monthly	5%	monthly
3.	$250	quarterly	6%	quarterly
4.	$5000	semiannually	3%	semiannually
5.	$500	every 5 years	2%	semiannually
6.	$750	every 8 years	$3\frac{1}{2}$%	annually

7. It is estimated that the taxes on a piece of property will average $100, payable at the end of each year forever. If money is worth 3%, converted annually, find the sum of money needed now to pay the taxes forever.

8. How much can a city afford to spend on a permanent underpass at a school crossing if it costs the city $2400 per year for a school guard? Assume that money is worth 3%, converted annually, and that the annual salary payments must be available at the beginning of each year.

9. The first payment of a perpetuity of $100 per year is due in 5 years. Find the present value of this perpetuity if money is worth 4%, converted annually.

10. Find the present value of an ordinary annuity of $10 per year for 200 years, if money is worth 5%, converted annually. Compare this value to the present value of an ordinary perpetuity of $10 per year at the same interest rate.

11. A group of 100 parishioners agree to contribute equally to an endowment fund for their church. If the endowment fund is to be invested at 4%, converted annually, and $10,000 per year is to be used beginning in 50 years, how much must each parishioner contribute?

12. A hospital will need a replacement on its ambulance in 5 years and each 5 years thereafter. It is estimated that the cost for replacements will be $4000. If the hospital can invest its money at 3%, converted semiannually, how much is needed now to provide for the ambulance forever?

13. A philanthropist plans to establish a university scholarship which pays $600 at the beginning of each year for 3 years, followed by a payment of $1000 at the beginning of the fourth year. This scholarship is to be awarded to a worthy student when he enters the university and is to continue to him for the entire four years. If the award of the scholarship is to be made each four years and if the university can invest its money at 3%, converted annually, what must the philanthropist donate?

14. Derive the formula for the present value of an ordinary perpetuity, by use of the geometrical progression.

137. Capitalized cost

The **capitalized cost** of an article is defined as its original cost plus the present value of its replacements forever. The replacement cost may or may not be the same as the original cost.

Let the various quantities, involved in the problem of finding the capitalized cost, be represented as follows:

C = the original cost of the article,

k = time (in interest conversion periods) elapsed, between replacements,

S = **salvage value** of the article,

W = difference between the original cost and the salvage value of the article, that is, the **wearing value** of the article,

K = the capitalized cost of the article.

We note that $W = C - S$ and that this sum is needed at the end of each K periods forever for replacements. By formula (17), in Article 136, the present value of the replacements is $\dfrac{W}{i}\dfrac{1}{s_{\overline{k}|i}}$. Hence by definition,

$$K = C + \frac{W}{i}\frac{1}{s_{\overline{k}|i}}. \qquad (18)$$

An important special case of this formula is obtained if the salvage value is zero. The quantity W becomes C (since $W = C - S$). Hence, we have

$$K = C + \frac{C}{i}\frac{1}{s_{\overline{k}|i}} = \frac{C}{i}\left(i + \frac{1}{s_{\overline{k}|i}}\right).$$

CAPITALIZED COST

From formula (7), Article 129, we have that $i + \dfrac{1}{s_{\overline{k}|i}} = \dfrac{1}{a_{\overline{k}|i}}$, hence when $S = 0$ the capitalized cost is

$$K = \frac{C}{i}\frac{1}{a_{\overline{k}|i}}. \tag{19}$$

One important use of the capitalized cost formula is to determine the sum of money needed now to buy an article and to make its replacements indefinitely. Thus donations for specific purposes are often determined by the use of the principle of capitalized cost.

Another and perhaps a more important use is that of comparing the relative costs of two articles whose original costs, salvage values, and replacement times are known. It follows that the article with the lower capitalized cost is the more economical. Both of these uses are illustrated in the following examples.

Example 1. Find the capitalized cost of an article whose original cost is $500 and whose salvage value after 4 years is $150. Money is worth 3%, converted annually.

Solution. The wearing value is $500 - 150$ or $350. Hence, using formula (18) we have

$$K = 500 + \frac{350}{0.03}\frac{1}{s_{\overline{4}|.03}} = 500 + \frac{350}{0.03}(0.2390270),$$

$$= \$3288.65.$$

The student should note that $3288.65 provides $500 now to buy the article, leaving a balance of $2788.65. But this balance carried forward at compound interest for 4 years is $2788.65(1.03)^4$ or $3138.65. From this, we take $350 to use (together with this salvage value) to buy a new article, leaving $2788.65 to accumulate again to $3138.65 in another 4 years. Hence it is seen that the article may be replaced indefinitely.

Example 2. Which is more economical: a water heater costing $60 which must be replaced in five years, or one costing $90 which lasts for eight years? Assume that there is no salvage value for either heater and that money is worth 3%, converted annually.

Solution. The capitalized cost of the $60 heater by the use of formula (19) is

$$K = \frac{60}{0.03}\frac{1}{a_{\overline{5}|.03}} = \frac{60}{0.03}(0.218355),$$

$$= \$436.71.$$

By the use of the same formula, the capitalized cost of the other article is

$$K = \frac{90}{0.03}\frac{1}{a_{\overline{8}|.03}} = \frac{90}{0.03}(0.142456),$$

$$= \$427.37.$$

Hence the article whose original cost is $90 is the more economical.

310   ANNUITIES CERTAIN. PERPETUITIES

Example 3. How much could a telephone company afford to pay for creosoting a pole whose cost (installed) is $20, if by doing so its life is extended from 10 years to 15 years? Assume that money is worth 4%, converted annually, and that the salvage value in either case is $2.

Solution. Let X represent the cost of the creosoted pole, installed. To be equally economical, the capitalized costs of the untreated and treated poles must be equal. Hence

$$X + \frac{(X-2)}{0.04}\frac{1}{s_{\overline{15}|.04}} = 20 + \frac{18}{0.04}\frac{1}{s_{\overline{10}|.04}},$$

or

$$X + \frac{X}{0.04}\frac{1}{s_{\overline{15}|.04}} = 20 + \frac{18}{0.04}\frac{1}{s_{\overline{10}|.04}} + \frac{2}{0.04}\frac{1}{s_{\overline{15}|.04}}.$$

Since the left member of this equation is equal to $\dfrac{X}{0.04}\dfrac{1}{a_{\overline{15}|.04}}$, we have

$$X = 0.04 a_{\overline{15}|.04}\left\{20 + \frac{18}{0.04}\frac{1}{s_{\overline{10}|.04}} + \frac{2}{0.04}\frac{1}{s_{\overline{15}|.04}}\right\},$$

$$= a_{\overline{15}|.04}\left\{(20)(0.04) + 18\frac{1}{s_{\overline{10}|.04}} + 2\frac{1}{s_{\overline{15}|.04}}\right\},$$

$$= 11.1184\{0.8 + 18(0.0832909) + 2(0.0499411)\},$$

$$= (11.1184)(2.39912),$$

$$= \$26.68.$$

Thus the telephone company could afford to spend $6.68 in creosoting the pole.

Example 4. A college alumni association votes to donate enough money to its college to provide a $100,000 clubhouse, which it is estimated will need renovation every 25 years at a cost of $25,000. Furthermore, they agree to contribute $3000 per year for upkeep and maintenance. If the upkeep and maintenance money is to be made available at the beginnings of the years, and if the college can invest its funds at 3%, how much money must the alumni association donate?

Solution. Although this is not strictly a question of capitalized cost, we may find the sum of money needed to purchase the building and to provide for its continuous renovation by considering that the original building has a scrap value of $75,000 after 25 years. However, the building is not sold but merely renovated, so that it is put into condition for another 25 years, and so on. We may then use the capitalized cost formula. The upkeep and maintenance cost is the present value of a perpetuity due. Hence the sum of money which must be donated by the alumni association is equal to

$$100,000 + \frac{25,000}{0.03}\frac{1}{s_{\overline{25}|.03}} + 3000\left(1 + \frac{1}{0.03}\right),$$

or $225,857.

Example 5. A stove costs $150, lasts 25 years, and has a salvage value of $25. If money is worth 5%, converted annually, what sum of money, now, would buy this stove and would provide for infinite replacements? What payment made at the end of each year forever would be equivalent to this sum?

Solution. The capitalized cost is the sum now which will buy the stove and provide for infinite replacements. Hence, we have

$$K = 150 + \frac{125}{0.05} \frac{1}{s_{\overline{25}|.05}},$$
$$= \$202.38.$$

Let R represent the annual cost, paid at the ends of the years, of this stove and its replacements forever. These payments form an ordinary perpetuity whose present value is the capitalized cost of the stove. Hence

$$R a_{\overline{\infty}|.05} = 202.38,$$

or

$$R = \frac{202.38}{a_{\overline{\infty}|.05}} = \frac{202.38}{\dfrac{1}{0.05}} = (202.38)(0.05),$$
$$= \$10.12.$$

Since the annual cost is, obviously, the interest on the capitalized cost, this result might have been obtained by one step, that is $0.05(202.38) = \$10.12$.

EXERCISE 6

Find the capitalized cost for each article in the following problems.

Prob. no.	Original cost	Salvage value	Replacement time (in yrs.)	Nominal interest rate	Frequency of conversion
1.	$500	$100	6	$3\frac{1}{2}$%	annually
2.	$1000	$250	10	4%	semiannually
3.	$700	0	4	5%	monthly
4.	$850	$50	12	6%	quarterly
5.	$900	$400	2	4%	quarterly
6.	$1500	0	30	3%	semiannually

7. A roof, which must be replaced every 8 years, costs $237.50 installed. Assuming that there is no salvage value and that money is worth 5%, converted annually, find the capitalized cost of this roof.

8. A truck costing $2250 must be replaced every 5 years at a cost of $1750. Find the capitalized cost of the truck if money is worth 3%, converted annually.

9. A bridge costing $50,000 must be replaced every 50 years at a cost of $55,000. Find the capitalized cost of the bridge if money is worth 4%, converted semiannually.

10. A shingle roof costs Mr. Bates $500 and he estimates that it will last 10 years. If money is worth 3%, converted quarterly, how much could Mr. Bates afford to spend on an aluminum roof which is guaranteed to last 25 years?

11. A section of pavement on a city street costs $10,000, must be resurfaced every 5 years at a cost of $1000, and requires an annual upkeep cost of $50, which must be available at the beginnings of the years. If money is worth $4\frac{1}{2}\%$, converted semiannually, how much could be spent on an equivalent section of pavement which will last 30 years and for which the upkeep cost will be $100 at the end of every 5 years?

12. How much could a city afford to spend to install a signal at a busy intersection, it being estimated that the signal must be replaced at the same cost every 25 years and that the operating cost is $200 per year (to be available at the beginnings of the years), if the signal is to replace one full-time policeman whose salary is $3600 per year? (Assume that this money must be available at the beginnings of the years.) Money is worth 4%, converted annually.

13. Show that the rent, R, of an ordinary perpetuity, which is equivalent to the capitalized cost of an article, is

$$R = Ci + W\frac{1}{s_{\overline{k}|i}}.$$

14. Show that the rent, R, of a perpetuity due, which is equivalent to the capitalized cost of an article, is

$$R = Civ + Wv\frac{1}{s_{\overline{k}|i}}.$$

15. A bridge whose original cost is $50,000 must be replaced by the county at the end of each 30 years at a cost of $60,000. If money is worth $3\frac{1}{2}\%$, converted annually, find the equivalent annual cost at the end of each year forever to provide this bridge.

16. What would be the annual cost in Problem 15 if it is figured at the beginning of each year?

17. A tennis court costs $2500 and it is estimated that repairs will amount to $50 at the end of each 3-year period. Miscellaneous expenses, including taxes, amount to $120 a year, a sum which must be available at the beginning of each year. One hundred members of a club plan to endow the court by making 5 equal annual payments to the club. If the club can invest its money at 4%, converted annually, what must each member contribute if payments are to be made at the ends of the years?

MISCELLANEOUS EXERCISE

1. An annuity consists of 18 semiannual payments of $50 each. If money is worth 4%, converted semiannually, find the value of this annuity at the following times:

CAPITALIZED COST

(a) 4 years before the first payment,
(b) $\frac{1}{2}$ year before the first payment,
(c) at the time of the first payment,
(d) at the time of the eighth payment,
(e) at the time of the last payment,
(f) $\frac{1}{2}$ year after the last payment,
(g) 3 years after the last payment.

2. In place of a $10,000 cash payment from an insurance policy, the beneficiary may receive 100 equal monthly payments together with interest at 3%, converted monthly. If the first payment is to be made immediately, how large are the monthly payments?

3. During the past 8 years, Mr. Thorne has been paying $80 at the beginning of each month for rent. If these payments had been invested in a security paying 4%, converted monthly, what amount would Mr. Thorne have now?

4. The Alston family has saved $100 at the beginning of each 6-month period for the past 15 years. This money was deposited in a bank paying 2%, converted semiannually. How much do they have on their account now, just after making a $100 deposit?

5. What sum invested at 4%, converted semiannually, is needed now to provide a series of 20 semiannual scholarships of $400 each, if the first award is to be made at the end of 30 years?

6. Mr. Sparks plans to deposit $500 at the end of each year for 14 years in a building and loan association which pays interest at the rate of 3%, converted annually. (a) How much will Mr. Sparks have on deposit at the end of 14 years? (b) Assume that because of unforeseen difficulties, Mr. Sparks was delayed in starting his deposits and made the first deposit at the end of 5 years. How much does he have on deposit at the time of the last payment under the original plan? How much does he have at the time of the 28th and last payment under the new plan?

7. Mr. Tate receives $1000 at the end of each year from one of his investments. This income is deposited, as it is received, in a bank paying interest at the rate of 2%, converted semiannually. How much will he have on deposit immediately after his 25th deposit?

8. Mr. Clemson can invest his money at 6%, converted quarterly. He agrees to lend $5000 to a friend, provided the friend will repay it in 10 annual installments made at the ends of the years with interest at exactly the rate earned by Mr. Clemson. How large are the payments?

9. Mr. Day sells a house for which the buyer agrees to pay the balance due of $10,000 in 10 equal installments of $1000 each together with interest at 6%, payable yearly, on the outstanding principal. The installment and interest payments are deposited in an investment paying 4%, converted annually. What does Mr. Day have on deposit just after he makes the last deposit from his house payments?

10. Mr. Hall plans to deposit $100 at the end of one year and $25 more at the end of each year, thereafter, in an annuity fund which pays interest at the rate of $3\frac{1}{2}\%$, converted annually. He is to retire at the end of 30 years. What does he have on deposit at the time of his retirement?

11. Mr. Keep offers to sell a piece of land for $5000 down, with the balance to be paid in installments of $500 at the end of the first year, $600 at the end of the second year, and so on for 10 installments. What is the equivalent cash price of the house if interest is charged at the rate of 8%, converted annually?

12. Mrs. Sanders pays $50 down for a set of furniture and agrees to make 9 additional monthly payments, each $5 less than the preceding payment. If interest is charged at the rate of 7%, converted monthly, find the equivalent cash price of the furniture.

13. To provide a perpetual income of $2000 payable at the end of each year, what sum must be invested now if the investment earns 4%, converted annually?

14. In order to endow a professorship of mathematics at its university, an alumni association with 10,000 active members votes to pay an assessment immediately, sufficiently large to provide $6000 at the beginning of each year indefinitely. If the university can invest its money at 4%, what must each member pay?

15. To provide for the perpetual salary, estimated at $3000, of a curate at their church, 100 parishioners agree to pay an equal sum into the treasury of the church at the end of each year for the next 10 years. If the church can invest its funds at $3\frac{1}{2}\%$, converted annually, what is the annual payment of each parishioner, it being assumed that the first $3000 salary payment for the curate must be available at the beginning of the 11th year?

16. Find the present value of an ordinary perpetuity of $500 deferred 8 years, payments made semiannually, if money is worth 4%, converted semiannually.

17. The quantity $a_{\overline{\infty}|.04}$ may be used as an approximation to $a_{\overline{500}|.04}$. To how many significant places is this approximation correct?

18. A philanthropist donates a sum of money now which will provide an ordinary annuity of $100, paid semiannually, running for 50 years but deferred for 50 years. What additional sum would the philanthropist have to donate if he wanted the payments to be perpetual? Money is worth $2\frac{1}{2}\%$, converted semiannually.

19. A machine costing $3500 can be sold at the end of 25 years for $1000. What is the capitalized cost of this machine if money is worth 4%, converted quarterly?

20. One machine costing $5000 has a life of 8 years and a salvage value of $1000. A second machine, performing the same work, may be bought for $10,000 but has a salvage value of $2000 at the end of 20 years. Which is the more economical purchase and what is the annual saving, calculated at the ends of the years, in using the better buy? Money is worth 3%, converted annually.

21. A paint company can make a house paint, which lasts 3 years, for $3.00 per gallon. What should the company charge for an improved paint which will last 5 years if the cost of painting with either paint is $10 per gallon? Money is worth $4\tfrac{1}{2}\%$, converted annually.

22. Untreated gas pipe in a certain city lasts 10 years and costs 25 cents per foot installed. If money is worth 5%, converted semiannually, what can the gas company afford to pay per foot to treat the pipe so it will last 30 years?

23. What sum of money is needed to endow a boys' clubhouse if the original cost is $25,000, if the annual upkeep charge is $3000, to be available at the beginning of each year, and if the clubhouse must be repaired at a cost of $5000 at the end of each 10 years? Money is worth 3%, converted annually.

24. Prove that $\quad s_{\overline{n+1}|i} = s_{\overline{n}|i} + (1+i)^{n+1}$.
25. Prove that $\quad \ddot{a}_{\overline{n-1}|i} = \ddot{a}_{\overline{n}|i} - (1+i)^{-n+1}$.

16

Retirement of Debts by Installment Payments

138. Methods and definitions

A debt is said to be **amortized** if it is paid off, principal and interest, by a sequence of payments which may be equal or unequal in size.

A fund set up for the purpose of providing a given sum of money at some future date is called a **sinking fund**.

If a debt is amortized by a sequence of payments, principal and interest, the debt is said to be paid off by the **amortization method**. Usually, but not always, the payments are equal in size and are made at equal intervals of time.

If the interest only is paid on the debt as it comes due and if a sinking fund is set up to pay off the principal when it comes due, the debt is said to be amortized by the **sinking fund method**. The usual procedure is to make equal payments, at equal intervals of time, to the sinking fund.

139. The amortization method of retiring a debt using equal payments at equal intervals of time

Representing the debt by P, the payment by R, and the interest rate by i, we have

$$P = R a_{\overline{n}|i}$$

where it is assumed that the debt is to be paid off in n equal payments made at equal intervals of time. Solving for R,

$$R = P \frac{1}{a_{\overline{n}|i}}. \tag{1}$$

Hence our problem is not a new one. Since the debt P is the present value of the payments which will amortize it, this is simply the problem of finding the rent when n, i, and A_n are given. Thus formula (1) is formula (5) of the Chapter on *Introduction to Annuities*, rewritten with P substituted for A_n.

AMORTIZATION METHOD

In any repayment of debts it is important, especially for income-tax purposes, that both debtor and creditor know just what portion of each payment consists of interest and what part is principal. For this purpose an **amortization schedule** is made, as illustrated in the following example.

Example 1. A debt of $500 is to be amortized by 6 semiannual payments made at the ends of the periods. If interest is charged at the rate of 5%, converted semiannually, find the semiannual payment and make a schedule showing how the payment is divided between interest and principal and what the outstanding principal is at the end of each year.

Solution. We have at once that
$$R = 500 \frac{1}{a_{\overline{6}|.025}},$$
$$= \$90.775.*$$

The amortization schedule may now be set up:

AMORTIZATION SCHEDULE

(a) Period	(b) Semiannual installment	(c) Interest on outstanding principal at $2\frac{1}{2}\%$	(d) For amortization of principal of the debt	(e) Outstanding principal of the debt
0				$500.000
1	$90.775	$12.500	$78.275	421.725
2	90.775	10.543	80.232	341.493
3	90.775	8.537	82.238	259.255
4	90.775	6.481	84.294	174.961
5	90.775	4.374	86.401	88.560
6	90.775	2.214	88.561	− 0.001

The following items should be noted from the table.

First: In the first row, the only two entries are 0 under (a) to indicate the present time, and $500, the debt at this time, under (e).

Second: In the second row, opposite (1), and under (b), we enter $90.775, the payment at the end of the first period. Under (c) we have the interest at $2\frac{1}{2}\%$ on $500 for 1 period. Under (d) we have $78.275, the difference between $90.775 and the interest $12.500. This difference then is used to reduce the outstanding principal of the debt, $500, to obtain the new entry, $421.725, in column (e). The next row is obtained in like manner — thus under (c) we have $10.543, the interest on $421.725 for one period at $2\frac{1}{2}\%$. Hence $90.775 − $10.543 gives $80.232, the entry under (d), and finally $421.725 − $80.232 gives $341.493, the new entry under (e).

* This figure is carried to mills accuracy to assure cents accuracy in the amortization schedule.

Third: The final entry under (e) should be zero, but because of the process of rounding off, this may differ from zero by a few mills. In ordinary business problems, the table is taken to the nearest cent and any discrepancy in cents is taken care of by a slight change in the last payment.

As an exercise the student should recalculate this amortization schedule carrying all entries to cents accuracy only. Round off the payment to $90.78. What is the discrepancy in the last entry of (e)?

The outstanding principal immediately after a payment has been made may easily be computed without the use of the amortization schedule. If h payments have been made, the principal of the outstanding debt, X, will be the value of the remaining $n - h$ payments at the time of the hth payment. Hence

$$X = Ra_{\overline{n-h}|i}. \tag{2}$$

Example 2. Find the outstanding principal of the debt in Example 1 immediately after the fourth payment has been made, and find what portion of the next payment is used for interest and what portion for amortization.

Solution. Since 4 payments have been made the value of the remaining 2 payments at the time of the fourth payment is

$$X = 90.775 a_{\overline{2}|.025}$$
$$= \$174.96,$$

which is the value given in the amortization schedule, rounded off to the nearest cent. The interest on this for the next period is $(174.96)(0.025) = \$4.37$, and hence the portion of the payment for amortization is $90.77 - 4.37 = \$86.40$, which agrees with the schedule.

EXERCISE 1

Find the payment needed to amortize each of the following debts, principal and interest, and the balance due immediately after the kth payment has been made.

Prob. no.	Debt	Time in years to due date	Frequency of payments	Interest rate *	k
1.	$5,000	15	annually	4%	10
2.	$2,000	25	semiannually	5%	12
3.	$6,000	25	quarterly	6%	96
4.	$10,000	40	semiannually	2%	66
5.	$3,000	8	monthly	3%	80
6.	$1,000	8	monthly	7%	32
7.	$7,000	20	quarterly	2%	17
8.	$8,000	15	quarterly	4%	23
9.	$1,915	6	monthly	3%	10
10.	$3,786	23	annually	8%	20

* Interest is converted as often as payments are made.

AMORTIZATION METHOD

11. Mr. Morris plans to amortize a debt of $1200 by making equal payments at the end of each year for five years. What payment must Mr. Morris make if he pays interest at the rate of 4%, converted annually? Construct an amortization schedule.

12. What semiannual payment for 4 years must be made at the end of each half-year to amortize a debt of $6000 if interest is charged at the rate of 5%, converted semiannually? Construct an amortization schedule.

13. A debt of $12,000 is to be amortized by equal payments made at the end of each quarter for 10 years. If interest is charged at the rate of 6%, converted quarterly, find: (a) the quarterly payment, (b) the outstanding principal of the debt just after 25 payments have been made, and (c) the portion of the payment which is used for interest at the end of the 26th period.

14. Mr. Jones is amortizing a debt of $3500 by making equal payments at the end of each month for 5 years. If interest is charged at the rate of 4%, converted monthly, find: (a) the monthly payment, (b) the outstanding principal of the debt just after the 30th payment has been made, and (c) the portion of the 30th payment which is used for amortization of the principal.

15. A debt of $500 is to be paid off, principal and interest, in 8 equal annual payments made at the beginnings of the years. If interest is charged at the rate of $4\frac{1}{2}$%, converted annually, find the annual payment. Construct an amortization schedule.

16. A debt of $2000 is to be paid off by equal monthly payments made at the beginning of each month for 3 years. If interest is charged at the rate of 3%, converted monthly, find: (a) the monthly payment, (b) the outstanding principal of the debt just after the 4th payment, and (c) the outstanding principal of the debt just before the 4th payment is made.

17. Mr. Reimers has been amortizing a debt of $4000 by making equal semiannual payments at the end of each 6-month period for 5 years, interest being charged at the rate of 4%, converted semiannually. After making 6 payments, Mr. Reimers, with the consent of his creditors, pays off the balance of his debt. How much does he pay?

18. Mr. Allen owes $6000 which he agrees to amortize, principal and interest, in 12 years by equal payments made at the end of each year. If interest is charged at the rate of $5\frac{1}{2}$%, converted annually, find the yearly payment. With the consent of his creditor, Mr. Allen, after making 4 payments, plans to pay off the balance of his debt in exactly 4 additional payments. How large should the new payments be?

19. A debt of $10,000 is to be completely amortized by making equal semiannual payments, the first in 5 years and the last at the end of 25 years. If interest is charged at the rate of 7%, converted semiannually, find the size of each payment.

20. Mr. Riegels agrees to pay off a debt of $800 by making equal payments at the end of each year for 20 years. After making 5 payments, Mr. Riegels fails to make the following 3 payments. However, he arranges with his creditor to increase the following 12 payments by an amount sufficient to compensate for the defaulted payments. How large are the new payments if interest is charged at the rate of 6%, converted annually?

21. A debt of $8000 is to be amortized in 10 years by equal payments made at the end of each of the first 6 years, followed by 4 equal annual payments, each twice the size of the preceding payments. If interest is charged at the rate of $4\frac{1}{2}\%$, converted annually, find the size of each payment.

22. A state borrows $500,000 which it plans to amortize in 50 years by making equal payments at the end of each 2-year period. If interest is charged at the rate of 4%, converted annually, how large is the payment? How much of the principal of the debt is outstanding immediately after the 10th payment has been made?

23. A debt of $500 is to be amortized by three equal payments made at the end of the 3rd, 6th, and 9th years. If interest is charged at the rate of 6%, converted annually, find the payment. Construct an amortization schedule.

24. Mr. Stone contracts a debt of $5000 which he agrees to pay off in 20 equal payments at the ends of the years. He also agrees to pay interest at the rate of 5% for the first 10 years and 4% for the following 10 years, both rates being converted annually. How large is the annual payment?

25. Show that formula (2) may be replaced by, $X = P(1 + i)^h - Rs_{\overline{h}|i}$, where P is the original debt and R is the periodical payment.

140. Amortization of a bonded debt and other methods of amortization

A **bond** is a written agreement to pay: (1) a certain sum of money at some future date, and (2) at the end of each interest period the interest due at that time. Thus a $1000 bond due in 10 years with interest payable semiannually at the rate of 4% means that $1000 must be paid at the end of 10 years and that $20 must be paid at the end of each 6 months for 10 years. Bonds are usually issued by various governmental units and corporations and are so written that the whole amount must be paid off as a unit when they come due. Hence it would not be possible to amortize a bond issue by exactly equal payments but only by approximately equal payments. The following example will illustrate the method.

Example 1. A city plans to issue $50,000 worth of $1000 bonds with interest at 5%, payable annually. The issue is to be completely amortized in 8 years by payments, including principal and interest, which are as nearly equal as possible. Make an amortization schedule from which the city may determine how many bonds would come due at the end of each year.

Solution. If the debt could be retired by equal payments, the payment would be $R = 50,000 \dfrac{1}{a_{\overline{8}|.05}} = \$7736.09$. The number of bonds retired each year will be such that the annual payment will be as near to $7736.09 as possible.

AMORTIZATION OF A BONDED DEBT

Amortization Schedule

(a) Year	(b) Interest on outstanding debt at 5%	(c) Number of bonds retired	(d) Value of bonds retired	(e) Total payment	(f) Value of outstanding bonds
0	—	—	—	—	$50,000
1	$2500	5	$5000	$7500	45,000
2	2250	6	6000	8250	39,000
3	1950	6	6000	7950	33,000
4	1650	6	6000	7650	27,000
5	1350	6	6000	7350	21,000
6	1050	7	7000	8050	14,000
7	700	7	7000	7700	7,000
8	350	7	7000	7350	0

As in the previous schedule, the beginning of the first year is indicated, in the column marked (a), by 0; the end of the first year, or the beginning of the second, is indicated by 1; and so on. We also note that the entry in (b) for any row, is 5% of the entry in (f) for the preceding row. The entry under (c) is determined in such a way that the sum of (b) and (d), entered in (e), approximately equals R and at the same time is such that the difference between the largest and smallest values under (e) is as small as possible. The first entry in (f) is, of course, the value of the total bond issue and each succeeding entry is obtained by subtracting the value in (d) from the value in (f) occurring in the preceding row. The student is very likely to find it necessary to try several schedules before he can determine the best one.

Another method of amortizing debts by unequal payments is to pay off equal portions of the principal of the debt at equal intervals of time, together with interest on the outstanding principal for the preceding period.

As before, we represent the debt by P, the principal of which will be amortized by n payments of $\dfrac{P}{n}$ each. The interest payment will decrease each time so that the periodical payments are unequal. The interest payments are readily seen to be $Pi, \left(P - \dfrac{P}{n}\right)i, \left(P - \dfrac{2P}{n}\right)i,$ ... and so on. It should be noted that each interest payment is $\dfrac{P}{n}i$ less than the preceding payment.

Example 2. A debt of $5000 is to be repaid in 5 installments, payments at the end of each year, together with interest payable at the rate of 4% annually on the outstanding principal of the debt. Construct a schedule showing the amortization of this debt.

Solution. The reduction in the principal of the debt each year is $\frac{5000}{5}$ or $1000. Hence the amortization schedule is as follows:

AMORTIZATION SCHEDULE

Period	Interest on outstanding debt at 4%	Payment on principal of debt	Total installment payment	Outstanding principal of debt
0	—	—	—	$5000
1	$200	$1000	$1200	4000
2	160	1000	1160	3000
3	120	1000	1120	2000
4	80	1000	1080	1000
5	40	1000	1040	0

Occasionally loans are amortized in a more or less haphazard fashion in that only a term and an interest rate are fixed. Payments of interest may be regular or irregular and payments on the principal of the debt may be made at any time during the term of the loan as long as the debt is completely paid off in the stated time. The only problem connected with such an amortization plan is a schedule which obviously cannot be constructed before the payments are made. Its construction is usually made during the term of the loan and serves as a record of payments.

EXERCISE 2

1. A state is planning to issue $100,000 worth of $1000 bonds, with interest payable at the rate of 3% annually. The issue is to be completely amortized in 10 years in such a way that the payments, including interest and principal, will be as nearly equal as possible. Make an amortization schedule from which the state may determine the number of bonds which should come due at the end of each of the years.

2. A city plans to issue $40,000 worth of $500 bonds with interest at the rate of 4%, payable semiannually. Interest payments only are to be made during the first 10 years, but during the following 5 years the issue is to be completely amortized in such a way that payments on principal and interest will be as nearly equal as possible. Make a schedule from which the city may determine the number of bonds to be retired at semiannual periods for 5 years beginning in $10\frac{1}{2}$ years.

3. A bank grants a farmer a loan of $1000, provided that he will amortize the principal of the debt in 10 equal payments made at the ends of the years and will at the same time pay interest on the outstanding principal of the debt at the end of each year at the rate of 5%. Construct an amortization schedule which includes a column that gives the total annual payments.

4. A debt of $2400 is to be amortized over a period of 10 years by equal payments made on the principal at the ends of the months. In addition, interest is payable monthly at the rate of 6% on the outstanding principal of the debt. What is the equal monthly payment on the principal, and what is the total payment, principal and interest, which must be made at the end of 5 years?

5. Mr. Brink lends Mr. Thompson $500, charging interest at the rate of 7%, payable annually, on the outstanding principal of the debt. Mr. Brink sets a time limit of 5 years for the repayment of the debt, but he allows Mr. Thompson to make payments at times convenient to him. Mr. Thompson made the following payments:

$150 at the end of 2 years,
$300 at the end of 4 years,
the balance at the end of 5 years,

and, in addition, he made the required interest payments annually. Construct an amortization schedule showing the total payment made by Mr. Thompson at the end of each year.

6. Mr. Ryder borrows $1000 from a friend on a "pay-as-you-like" basis, it being understood, however, that the entire loan is to be paid within a period of 10 years and that interest at the rate of 4% is payable annually on the outstanding principal. If any interest payments are missed, these must be paid at some future interest payment date, with compound interest at the rate of 4%, converted annually. The following table indicates the actual payments made at the ends of the years indicated:

Year	Payment on principal	Interest payment
1	$100	required interest
2	none	none
3	none	none
4	none	none
5	$400	all back interest paid up
6	none	required interest
7	none	required interest
8	$300	required interest
9	none	none
10	balance due	balance due

Make a schedule showing the amortization of this debt.

141. The sinking fund method of retiring a debt

Many loans are made on the **mortgage plan,** that is, the borrower gives his note for the amount of the debt, offering his property

324 RETIREMENT OF DEBTS BY INSTALLMENT PAYMENTS

as security with the understanding that interest is payable periodically and that the principal of the debt is to be repaid in one sum at the due date.

For such loans, it is very desirable for the borrower to set up a sinking fund into which he makes payments sufficiently large to accumulate to the principal of the debt when it comes due. Usually, though not always, the interest payable on the debt is larger than that earned on the sinking fund. The following symbols will be used in the formulas which follow.

P = principal of the debt,
i = interest rate, per period, on the debt,
r = interest rate, per period, earned on the sinking fund,
R' = interest payment made to the creditor,
R'' = equal periodical payment made to the sinking fund,
R = total periodical payment needed to amortize the debt,
S_k = amount in the sinking fund at the end of k periods,
B_k = book value of the debt at the end of k periods.

The periodical interest is obviously

$$R' = Pi. \qquad (3)$$

From Article 129, formula (6), we have that the sinking fund payment is

$$R'' = P \frac{1}{s_{\overline{n}|r}}. \qquad (4)$$

Hence the total payment is

$$R = R' + R''. \qquad (5)$$

It should be noted that the interest payment part of this total payment goes to the creditor, while the other part goes to the sinking fund. The amount in the sinking fund after k periods is obviously given by

$$S_k = R'' s_{\overline{k}|r}. \qquad (6)$$

The book value, B_k, of the debt after k periods is defined as the original debt less the amount in the sinking fund at that time. Hence

$$B_k = P - R'' s_{\overline{k}|r}. \qquad (7)$$

Example 1. A mortgage of $8000 is due in 3 years and calls for interest at the rate of 4%, payable quarterly. What quarterly interest must be paid? What payment, made at the end of each quarter for 3 years, must be paid to a sinking fund earning 3%, converted quarterly, in order that the amount of

THE SINKING FUND METHOD OF RETIRING A DEBT 325

the debt will be accumulated at the end of 3 years? Make a schedule showing how the sinking fund is accumulated and how the book value is decreased.

Solution. Since the interest rate on the debt is $\frac{1}{4}(0.04)$ or 0.01 per quarter, we have

$$R' = 8000\ (0.01),$$
$$= \$80,$$

the interest payment which must be made to the creditor at the end of each quarter. The sinking fund payment is

$$R'' = 8000\ \frac{1}{s_{\overline{12}|.00\frac{3}{4}}} = 8000(0.0799515),$$
$$= \$639.612.$$

The total payment is

$$R = 80 + 639.612,$$
$$= \$719.61.$$

The sinking fund schedule follows:

SINKING FUND SCHEDULE

(a) Time in quarters	(b) Interest at $\frac{3}{4}\%$	(c) Sinking fund payment	(d) Increase in sinking fund	(e) Amount in sinking fund	(f) Book value of debt
0	—	—	—	—	$8000.000
1	0	$639.612	$639.612	$ 639.612	7360.388
2	$ 4.797	639.612	644.409	1284.021	6715.979
3	9.630	639.612	649.242	1933.263	6066.737
4	14.499	639.612	654.111	2587.374	5412.626
5	19.405	639.612	659.017	3246.391	4753.609
6	24.348	639.612	663.960	3910.351	4089.649
7	29.328	639.612	668.940	4579.291	3420.709
8	34.345	639.612	673.957	5253.248	2746.752
9	39.399	639.612	679.011	5932.259	2067.741
10	44.492	639.612	684.104	6616.363	1383.637
11	49.623	639.612	689.235	7305.598	694.402
12	54.792	639.612	694.404	8000.002	− 0.002

We note the following in regard to the construction of the schedule, indicating, by the letters at the head of each column, the values in any row:

(d) = (b) + (c)
(e) = (d) + [preceding entry in (e)]
(b) = 0.00$\frac{3}{4}$ + [preceding entry in (e)]
(f) = 8000 − (e)

We should also note that each of the entries in (e), the amount in the sinking fund, might have been obtained by the use of formula (6). Thus the entry under (e) in the row marked 8 is S_8, where

$$S_8 = 639.612 s_{\overline{8}|.00\frac{3}{4}},$$
$$= \$5253.25,$$

which agrees with the value given in the schedule.

Likewise the entries in (f), the book values, may be obtained by the use of formula (7). Thus we have

$$B_8 = 8000 - 639.612 s_{\overline{8}|.00\frac{3}{4}},$$
$$= 8000 - 5253.25,$$
$$= \$2746.75,$$

which agrees with the schedule.

A borrower is sometimes confronted with a choice between two methods of borrowing money. Thus, he may have to make a choice between the amortization and sinking fund methods or between these and other plans. From a strictly mathematical standpoint, the best plan is the one for which the total periodical payment, needed to cancel a given debt, is the smallest. However, other considerations may enter. Under the amortization plan, a part of each payment is used to reduce the principal of the debt and it is paid directly to the creditor. Under the sinking fund method, the interest only is paid to the creditor and the balance of the periodical payment is placed in a sinking fund which accumulates to the principal of the debt when it comes due. Actually the principal of the debt under this plan remains constant throughout the life of the loan and will be paid off if a sufficient amount of money is collected by the time of the due date. If the security in which the debtor is investing proves to be bad, a part or all of the money which he is saving to pay off the principal of his debt may be lost. In such a case he would have been far better off if he had chosen the amortization method even though it may have cost more.

Since we cannot foresee just what may happen for any particular loan, our comparisons between various plans will be strictly mathematical and we will say that the plan best for the borrower is the plan which has the set of smallest payments for a given debt.

Example 2. Mr. Reynolds buys a house for $12,000, paying $3000 down. The balance is payable in 40 equal installments made at the ends of the semiannual periods including interest at 5%, converted semiannually. Mr. Reynolds' creditor is willing to accept a note for $9000, due in 20 years, with interest payable semiannually at 4%, in place of the above arrangement. Mr. Reynolds can accumulate the face of the note by making equal payments

THE SINKING FUND METHOD OF RETIRING A DEBT

at the ends of the 6-month periods for 20 years in a sinking fund earning interest at the rate of 3%, converted semiannually. Which is the better plan for Mr. Reynolds and what is the semiannual difference in the payments?

Solution. Under the amortization plan, the semiannual payment is

$$R = 9000 \frac{1}{a_{\overline{40}|.025}}$$
$$= \$358.53.$$

Under the sinking fund method, the semiannual interest on the note is

$$R' = 9000(0.02),$$
$$= \$180.$$

The semiannual payment to the sinking fund needed to accumulate $9000 is

$$R'' = 9000 \frac{1}{s_{\overline{40}|.015}} = 9000(0.0184271),$$
$$= \$165.84.$$

The total payment needed each 6 months under the sinking fund method is

$$180 + 165.84 = \$345.84.$$

The sinking fund method is better in this case and the semiannual difference in payments is

$$358.53 - 345.84 = \$12.69.$$

EXERCISE 3

In each of the following sinking fund problems, find the payment needed to accumulate to the amount indicated and find the amount in the sinking fund immediately after the kth payment has been made.

Prob. no.	Amount to be accumulated	Number of years fund accumulates	Frequency of payments	Interest rate *	k
1.	$2000	7	monthly	4%	80
2.	$7000	15	semiannually	2%	24
3.	$5000	20	quarterly	1%	37
4.	$8000	25	quarterly	$1\frac{1}{3}$%	70
5.	$9000	30	semiannually	$3\frac{1}{2}$%	39
6.	$3000	22	annually	$6\frac{1}{2}$%	20
7.	$4000	18	annually	$7\frac{1}{2}$%	7
8.	$1000	8	monthly	4%	87
9.	$2135	13	bimonthly	$4\frac{1}{2}$%	50
10.	$1567	4	semimonthly	6%	60

* Converted as often as payments are made.

11. A sinking fund is created to pay off a debt of $1500 due in 5 years, with an equal payment to be made at the end of each year to a building and loan association which figures interest at the rate of 3%, converted annually. Find the size of each payment, and construct a sinking fund schedule to show how the fund is accumulated and how the book value of the debt is decreased.

12. A mortgage on Mr. Morton's property required the repayment of $5000 at the end of 3 years and the payment of interest quarterly at the rate of 5%. Mr. Morton accumulates the principal of the debt by making equal quarterly payments, at the time of his interest payments, to a sinking fund earning 4%, converted quarterly. Find: (a) the quarterly interest payment, (b) the quarterly payment to the sinking fund, (c) the total quarterly payment needed. Set up a sinking fund schedule including a column for book values.

13. A debt of $6000, bearing interest at the rate of 4%, payable annually, is due in 6 years. A sinking fund is formed by making an equal payment at the end of each year for 6 years. If the sinking fund earns 3%, converted annually, find: (a) the total annual payment needed on this debt, (b) the amount in the sinking fund immediately after the 4th payment, without the use of a sinking fund schedule, and (c) the book value immediately after the 4th payment.

14. Mr. Ray owes $2000 which he may amortize by 10 equal payments, made at the ends of the years, including interest at 6%, converted annually. He is given the alternative of using the sinking fund method provided he pays interest on the debt annually at the rate of 5%. If he can earn $2\frac{1}{2}$%, converted annually, on a sinking fund to which he makes payments at the end of each year for 10 years, which method is cheaper for Mr. Ray and by how much per year?

15. What interest rate (Problem 14) would Mr. Ray have to earn on his sinking fund to make the costs of the two plans equal?

16. If the interest on the sinking fund is left unchanged, to what must the interest on the debt under the amortization plan be changed in order to make the costs of the two methods the same in Problem 14?

17. A town builds a library which is financed by a $400,000 bond issue bearing interest at 5%, payable annually. The bonds are due in 40 years and are to be paid off by making payments at the ends of the years to a sinking fund earning interest at the rate of $3\frac{1}{2}$%, converted annually. What total annual increase in taxes must be made for the next 40 years to finance the library?

18. In order to make the principal payment on a $10,000 debt due in 20 years, Mr. Reagan makes equal payments to a sinking fund, at the end of each year, which earns interest at the rate of 4%, converted annually. After 12 years the earnings on the sinking fund drop to 3%. By how much must Mr. Reagan increase his payments to meet the $10,000 obligation when due?

19. Mr. Jones makes equal payments at the end of each year to a sinking fund earning $3\frac{1}{2}$%, converted annually, for the purpose of paying off a debt of $3500 in 10 years. After making 6 payments, Mr. Jones finds that he must reduce his payments to the sinking fund to $200 per year. How much of his debt must he refinance when it comes due?

AMORTIZING DEBTS BY FIXED PAYMENTS

20. Mr. Lamb owes $6000, the principal of which is to be paid off in 6 years. Interest is payable semiannually at 5%. A provision in the contract allows Mr. Lamb to pay off any part of the debt at the end of three years. He may then pay the balance, principal and interest, at the rate of 6%, converted semiannually, under the amortization plan by 6 equal payments made at the ends of the half-years. Mr. Lamb accumulates a sinking fund earning 2% interest, converted semiannually, by making payments sufficiently large at the ends of the half-years to meet the principal payment when due. However, Mr. Lamb avails himself of the privilege of changing the method of paying his debt at the end of three years. He pays all he has accumulated in his sinking fund on the loan and then amortizes the balance by equal semi-annual payments at the ends of the half-years for 3 years. Find: (a) the amount accumulated in the sinking fund at the end of 3 years, and (b) the equal semiannual payment, made at the end of each period, needed to amortize the debt during the following three years.

21. Mr. Rees owes $5000 secured by a mortgage on his property. The note calls for repayment of the loan in 6 years with interest payable quarterly at 6%. A provision in the note allows Mr. Rees to pay off the debt at any interest payment date provided that he pays an additional quarter of a year's interest in advance. Mr. Rees makes equal payments to a sinking fund at the ends of the months, sufficiently large to accumulate the $5000 in 6 years if interest is allowed at 3%, converted monthly. However, immediately after the 16th payment is made, Mr. Rees decides to pay off the balance of his debt. What amount is needed in addition to what has been accumulated in the sinking fund?

22. A debt of $12,000, bearing interest at 7%, payable yearly, is due in 16 years. A sinking fund is set up to pay off the debt in 16 years by equal monthly payments made at the ends of the months to a sinking fund paying interest at the rate of 4%, converted monthly. Find the book value of the debt at the end of 12 years. (*Hint:* Make use of the formula in Problem 25, Exercise 1, in the chapter on *Introduction to Annuities*.)

142. Amortizing debts by fixed payments — unknown time methods

Debts are oftentimes paid off, principal and interest, by means of fixed payments made at the ends of convenient periods for as long as is necessary to amortize the debt. In general, the last payment is only a partial payment. The problem of finding the total number of full payments needed and the partial payment is identical to that discussed in Article 130. We restate the problem here in symbols. Let P represent the debt and R, the fixed payment, where R is greater than Pi. We have

$$Ra_{\overline{n}|i} = P,$$

or,
$$a_{\overline{n}|i} = \frac{P}{R}. \tag{8}$$

The total number of full payments needed may now be found by the use of the table for $a_{\overline{n}|i}$. The last partial payment may be found by one of the methods given in Example 1, Article 130; Problem 13, Article 130; or by Problem 13, Article 132.

Example 1. A house may be bought for $12,000 cash or for $5000 down and the balance in monthly payments of $100, including principal and interest at the rate of 5%, converted monthly. Determine the total number of full payments needed and the last partial payment if made one month after the last full payment.

Solution. From formula (8), we have

$$a_{\overline{n}|.00\frac{5}{12}} = \frac{7000}{100} = 70.$$

From Table VIII, we have $n = 82$ — that is, 82 full payments of $100 each are needed. Let Y represent the partial payment, made one month later, required to amortize the debt completely. Using the method of Problem 13, Article 132, we have

$$Y + 100 s_{\overline{82}|.00\frac{5}{12}} = 7000(1.00\tfrac{5}{12})^{83},$$
$$Y = 7000(1.00\tfrac{5}{12})^{83} - 100(s_{\overline{83}|.00\frac{5}{12}} - 1),$$
or $\qquad Y = \$93.41.$

The balance due on any debt after h payments have been made is the present value of the remaining payments needed to amortize the debt. Thus formula (2) gives the balance due on a debt if there are exactly $n - h$ payments yet to be made. Considering our present problem immediately after h payments have been made, we have $n - h$ full payments remaining and the partial payment Y made one period after the last full payment. Hence, representing the outstanding debt by X, we have

$$X = R a_{\overline{n-h}|i} + Y(1 + i)^{-(n-h+1)}. \tag{9}$$

This method of finding the outstanding debt at a given time is called the **prospective method** since we are looking ahead to the payments still due.

Another method of determining what the outstanding debt is at a given time is called the **retrospective method** since we look back at what has already been paid. The outstanding debt, immediately after h payments have been made, is

$$X = P(1 + i)^h - R s_{\overline{h}|i}. \tag{10}$$

This second method, of course, gives the same result as the first and is usually easier to use from the standpoint of computation.

Example 2. Find the value of the outstanding debt in Example 1 immediately after the 60th monthly payment has been made.

Solution. Using the prospective method we have, from formula (9),

$$X = 100a_{\overline{22}|.00\frac{5}{12}} + 93.41(1.00\frac{5}{12})^{-23},$$
$$= \$2182.90.$$

Using the retrospective method, formula (10) gives

$$X = 7000(1.00\tfrac{5}{12})^{60} - 100s_{\overline{60}|.00\frac{5}{12}},$$
$$= \$2182.90,$$

which checks with the previous value.

The following problem illustrates how a method involving fixed payment and unknown time may be used in conjunction with the sinking fund method.

Example 3. The interest on a debt of \$500 is computed at the rate of 4%, payable annually. The debt may be paid off in full at any one of its interest payment dates. The debtor accumulates a sinking fund by making a payment of \$50 at the end of each year in a security which earns interest at the rate of 3%, converted annually. Find: (a) the total annual payment the debtor must make, (b) the earliest time possible for which there is enough money in the sinking fund to pay off the debt, (c) the amount left in the sinking fund immediately after the debt is paid.

Solution. (a) The interest on the debt is

$$R' = 500(0.04) = \$20.$$

The payment to the sinking fund is \$50, hence the total payment is

$$R = 20 + 50 = \$70.$$

(b) To find the earliest time that it will be possible to pay off the debt from the sinking fund we solve the equation,

$$50s_{\overline{n}|.03} = 500,$$

for n. Using Table VII, we find $n = 9$. Hence the debt may be paid off at the time of the 9th interest payment.

(c) For $n = 9$, $s_{\overline{9}|.03} = 10.15911$. Hence $50(10.15911) = \$507.96$ is the amount in the sinking fund immediately after the 9th payment to the sinking fund. Since \$500 of this is used to retire the debt, we have \$7.96 remaining in the sinking fund.

EXERCISE 4

1. A debt of \$600, bearing interest at the rate of 6%, converted semiannually, is amortized by semiannual payments of \$100 each, including principal and interest. Make an amortization schedule from which the number of full payments and the last partial payment may be determined. Check your answers by the methods used in illustrative Example 1.

2. A debt of \$7500, bearing interest at the rate of 5%, converted monthly, is amortized by making a payment of \$100 at the end of each month for as long as is necessary. Find: (a) the number of full payments needed and the last partial payment if it is made one month after the last full payment, (b) the outstanding debt immediately after the 15th payment is made.

3. Mr. Lucas contracts to pay off a debt of $5000 by making a payment of $100 at the end of each quarter until principal and interest at 4%, converted quarterly, are paid off. However, Mr. Lucas has the privilege of paying off all the outstanding debt at any payment date provided he will pay a bonus equal to the interest payment for the following quarter. At the time of his 32nd payment, Mr. Lucas decides to pay off his outstanding debt. How much must he pay?

4. Mr. Lane owes $4100 which calls for interest at the rate of 6%, payable quarterly, and which may be paid off completely at the date of any interest payment. Mr. Lane sets up a sinking fund, which earns interest at the rate of $2\frac{1}{3}\%$, converted quarterly, to pay off the debt. If his payment to the sinking fund is $100 at the end of each quarter, how long will it be before Mr. Lane can pay off his debt, and how much will he have left in his sinking fund immediately after paying off the debt?

5. If Mr. Lane, of Problem 4, was required to pay a bonus of one full quarter's interest for the privilege of paying off his debt any time before 10 years had passed, how long would it be before he could pay off his debt and what would he have left in his sinking fund immediately after paying off the debt?

6. A debt of $575 carries interest at the rate of 8%, payable annually. It may be paid off in full at the time of any interest payment. The debtor accumulates a sinking fund by making a payment of $50 at the end of each year in a security which earns interest at the rate of 3%, converted annually. Find: (a) the total annual payment the debtor must make, (b) the earliest possible time for which there is enough money in the sinking fund to pay off the debt, (c) the amount left in the sinking fund after the debt is paid.

7. If a bonus of a half-year's interest is required for paying off the debt in Problem 6 any time before 15 years, find the earliest time that the debt can be paid and find the amount in the sinking fund immediately after the debt is paid off.

8. Prove algebraically that the value obtained for the outstanding debt by the prospective method (formula 9) is equal to that obtained by the retrospective method (formula 10). That is, prove that

$$Ra_{\overline{n-h}|i} + Y(1+i)^{-(n-h+1)} = P(1+i)^h - Rs_{\overline{h}|i}.$$

MISCELLANEOUS EXERCISE

1. A debt of $600 is to be paid off by 4 equal semiannual payments, including principal and interest, at the rate of 6%, converted semiannually. Find the semiannual payment if it is made at the ends of the periods, and construct an amortization schedule.

2. A small business borrows $10,000, giving a mortgage on its property

as security. The debt is due in 10 years and bears interest at 5%, payable annually. A sinking fund is accumulated to pay off the debt when it is due. The sinking fund earns 3%, converted annually, and 10 annual payments are made at the ends of the years. Determine: (a) the annual payment that must be made to the sinking fund to have just enough to pay off the debt when it is due, (b) the annual interest payment, (c) the amount in the sinking fund immediately after the 6th payment has been made, and (d) the book value of the debt at that time. Check your answers to (a) and (c) by making a sinking fund schedule.

3. A government wishes to retire a bond issue consisting of 100 bonds of $500 each. The interest on the bonds is 4%, payable annually. If the bonds are retired over a period of 6 years, what is the best retirement plan so that the total yearly payment on principal and interest will be as nearly equal as possible? Make a schedule showing your retirement plan.

4. A city wishes to retire a bonded indebtedness of $50,000, which consists of 25 bonds of $1000 denomination and 50 bonds of $500 denomination. All the bonds bear interest at the rate of 6%, payable semiannually. Make a schedule for the retirement of this debt over a period of 5 years such that the total semiannual payments will be as nearly equal as possible.

5. Mr. Elson is amortizing a debt of $6500, principal and interest, at 4% converted quarterly, by equal payments made at the end of each quarter for 10 years. Mr. Elson defaults on the 9th, 10th, and 11th payments but agrees to pay the equivalent of these payments at the time of the 12th payment. What total payment is needed at that time?

6. Mr. Randolph buys a house costing $9000 for which he pays $3000 cash and the balance by equal payments made at the end of each month for 10 years. The agreed interest rate is 6%, converted monthly for the first 6 years, and then a reduction to 5%, converted monthly, will be made, provided Mr. Randolph makes all of his payments on time during the first 6 years. Assuming that Mr. Randolph makes all his payments on time during the first 6 years, find the size of the monthly payments.

7. A debt of $87,000, with interest at the rate of $4\frac{1}{2}\%$, converted annually, may be amortized by 15 equal annual payments, made at the ends of the years. However the debt of $87,000 may also be amortized under the sinking fund method where interest at the rate of 4%, payable annually, is charged on the debt, and where a sinking fund, earning interest at the rate of $3\frac{1}{2}\%$, converted annually, is accumulated. Which total annual payment is the smaller, and by how much?

8. In order to pay off a debt of $7500 due in 10 years, a payment of $650 is made to a sinking fund at the end of each year for 6 years. What equal annual payment is needed for the next 4 years to accumulate an amount just large enough to pay off the debt if interest is earned at the rate of 4%, converted annually?

9. Mr. Ruggles is accumulating a sinking fund paying interest at the rate of $3\frac{1}{2}\%$, converted semiannually, by making equal semiannual payments at the end of each six-month period for 8 years, at which time he wishes to have

$7850 available to pay off a debt. Mr. Ruggles experiences a temporary financial reverse at the time of the 10th payment and hence misses this payment as well as the next three. By what equal amount must each of the following payments be increased to make up for the payments missed?

10. Mr. White may pay off a debt of $3675 either by (a) the amortization method, making 10 equal annual payments, including interest at 5%, converted annually, or by (b) the sinking fund method, with interest payable annually at the rate of $4\frac{1}{2}\%$ on the debt. What interest rate must be earned on the sinking fund to make the two plans equal in cost to Mr. White?

11. Mr. Jenkins has a mortgage of $7500, due in 6 years, on his property. He must pay interest at the rate of 4%, payable quarterly. He plans to accumulate a sinking fund by making at the end of each quarter for 6 years, equal payments, on which interest is earned at the rate of $2\frac{1}{3}\%$, converted quarterly. What interest rate, converted quarterly, could Mr. Jenkins afford to pay if he paid off the debt by the amortization method with quarterly payments equal to the total quarterly payment under the sinking fund plan?

12. A debt of $3000 bearing interest at 4%, converted monthly, is amortized, principal and interest, by payments of $50 each made at the ends of the months until the debt is fully paid. Find: (a) the total number of full payments, (b) the last partial payment if made one month after the last full payment, (c) the total payment necessary to pay off the debt at the time the last full payment is made, and (d) the value of the unpaid debt immediately after the 14th payment is made.

13. A sinking fund earning interest at the rate of 3%, converted annually, is started by making payments of $300 at the end of each year. A mortgage of $4000 with interest at $4\frac{1}{2}\%$, payable annually, may be paid off at the time of any interest payment. (a) Find the earliest time at which the sinking fund is just large enough to pay off the mortgage. (b) Find the amount remaining in the sinking fund right after the mortgage is paid. (c) What additional amount would be needed right after the 8th payment into the sinking fund to pay off the mortgage?

14. A bond issue of $50,000 in $500 bonds with interest at 5%, payable semiannually, is callable over a period of 6 years beginning at the end of 8 years. A sinking fund earning interest at the rate of 4%, converted semiannually, is formed by making payments of $2000 at the end of each six-month period for 8 years. From this sinking fund, 12 equal withdrawals will be made at the end of each six-month period, beginning in $8\frac{1}{2}$ years, for the retirement of the bonds. Make a schedule for the retirement of the bonds during the 6-year period such that the total additional payments needed will be as nearly equal as possible.

15. In Problem 14, choose a sinking fund payment for the first 8 years such that it will be approximately equal to the extra payments needed during the last 6 years of the bond retirement period.

16. From formula (5), Article 141, we have

AMORTIZING DEBTS BY FIXED PAYMENTS

$$R = R' + R''$$

or, $$R = Pi + P\frac{1}{s_{\overline{n}|r}}.$$

Show that $$R = P(i - r) + P\frac{1}{a_{\overline{n}|r}}.$$

If $r = i$, find the value of R. How is this related to formula (1), Article 139?

17. Mr. Burns has a mortgage of $10,000, due in 8 years, for which interest is payable annually at the rate of 5%. He plans to accumulate a sinking fund to pay off the mortgage when due by making equal payments at the ends of the years for 8 years. The sinking fund earns interest at the rate of 4%, converted annually. Using the formula in Problem 16, find the annual payment, R, that Mr. Burns must make to retire his debt.

17

Depreciation: Valuation of Income Property

143. Definitions

Most equipment, such as buildings, machinery, and other physical property, undergoes a decrease in value even though such equipment is kept in good repair. This loss in value, which cannot be replaced by current repairs, is called **depreciation**. To offset this depreciation, a fund is set up called the **depreciation fund** or **replacement reserve**. The periodical payment, R, (usually annual) made to the depreciation fund is called the **periodical contribution** to the depreciation fund.

Sometimes the periodical payments to the depreciation fund are actually set aside, but very often they are reinvested in the business and the fund is in a sense fictitious, being used for bookkeeping purposes only.

Let F_h represent the amount in the depreciation fund at the end of h periods, C the **original cost** of the equipment, and S its **salvage value** at the end of n periods, the useful life of the equipment. Notice that h is less than or equal to n.

The **book value**, B_h, of the equipment at the end of h periods is defined as the original cost of the equipment minus the amount in the depreciation fund at the end of h periods. Hence

$$B_h = C - F_h. \tag{1}$$

The **wearing value**, W_h, of the equipment at the end of h periods is defined as the difference between the book value at that time and the salvage value. Hence

$$W_h = B_h - S. \tag{2}$$

The wearing value, W_0, of the equipment at the beginning of its life is called its replacement cost. Hence

$$W_0 = C - S, \tag{3}$$

THE STRAIGHT LINE METHOD

since the book value of the equipment when first purchased is equal to its cost.

The **depreciation charge**, D_h, at the end of h periods is the decrease in the book value for that period. Thus

$$D_h = B_{h-1} - B_h. \tag{4}$$

For a given piece of equipment the reader should note the following carefully:

(1) During its useful life of n periods, the cost C and salvage value S remain constant.

(2) The amount in the depreciation fund, F_h, varies from zero at the beginning of the equipment's useful life to the replacement cost, W_0, at the end of its useful life.

(3) The book value, B_h, varies from the cost of the equipment at the beginning of its useful life to the salvage value, S, at the end of the useful life of the equipment.

(4) The wearing value, W_h, varies from the replacement value, W_0, to zero at the end of the useful life of the equipment.

The following sections will describe the most commonly used methods for estimating depreciation.

144. The straight line method

By this method, no interest is figured on the depreciation fund, and furthermore it is assumed that equal periodical contributions are made to the depreciation fund. The periodical contribution to the depreciation fund is

$$R = \frac{W_0}{n} = \frac{C - S}{n}. \tag{5}$$

The amount in the depreciation fund after h periods is

$$F_h = hR. \tag{6}$$

The book value after h periods is

$$B_h = C - hR. \tag{7}$$

From formula (7) it will be noted that the periodical decrease in the book value is equal to the periodical contribution R, and hence the depreciation charge D_h is equal to R.

Example. It is estimated that a truck costing $2000 depreciates to a salvage value of $500 in 5 years. Using the straight line method find:

(a) the annual contribution to the depreciation fund,
(b) the amount in the depreciation fund at the end of 3 years,

(c) the book value at the end of 3 years,
(d) the depreciation charge for the third year,
(e) the wearing value at the end of 3 years.

Make a depreciation schedule showing the annual contribution, R, the amount in the depreciation fund, F_h, the book value, B_h, and the depreciation charge, D_h.

Solution. (a) From formula (5) we have that the annual contribution to the depreciation fund is

$$R = \frac{2000 - 500}{5} = \$300.$$

(b) The amount in the fund at the end of 3 years is

$$F_3 = 3(300) = \$900,$$

from formula (6).

(c) The book value at the end of 3 years is

$$B_3 = 2000 - 3(300) = \$1100,$$

from formula (7).

(d) The depreciation charge for the third year is equal to the annual contribution to the depreciation fund, which is $300.

(e) The wearing value at the end of the third year is the book value at the end of the third year minus the salvage value. Hence

$$W_3 = 1100 - 500 = \$600.$$

DEPRECIATION SCHEDULE — STRAIGHT LINE METHOD

Time h	Annual contribution R	Amount in depreciation fund F_h	Book value B_h	Depreciation charge D_h
0	0	0	$2000	0
1	$300	$ 300	1700	$300
2	300	600	1400	300
3	300	900	1100	300
4	300	1200	800	300
5	300	1500	500	300

If the book value is plotted against time, the result is a straight line, as indicated in the following graph. This graph also shows a straight line relationship between the amount in the depreciation fund and time. It is because of these relationships that this method of estimating depreciation is called the straight line method.

THE STRAIGHT LINE METHOD

[Graph showing Book Value decreasing from $2000 to 0 and Amount in the Depreciation Fund increasing from 0 to $2000 over Time 0 to 5]

EXERCISE 1

Using the straight line method, find the quantities indicated for each of the following problems.

Prob. no.	Cost of equipment	Salvage value	Useful life of equipment in years	
1.	$1000	$ 100	6	Find D_4, B_5.
2.	$1500	$ 200	13	Find R, F_{10}.
3.	$4000	$1000	15	Find R, B_8.
4.	$ 250	$ 50	8	Find D_5, F_6.
5.	$ 700	$ 150	4	Find W_2, D_3.

6. A machine costing $6000 may be sold for $400 at the end of 8 years. Find: (a) the annual contribution to a depreciation fund for replacing the machine under the straight line method, (b) the amount in the depreciation fund at the end of 5 years, (c) the book value at the end of 5 years, (d) the depreciation charge for the fifth year, (e) the wearing value at the end of 5 years. Check your answers for (b), (c), (d), and (e) by making a depreciation schedule.

7. A stove costing $150 lasts 15 years and has a salvage value of $30. Using the straight line method of estimating depreciation, find the book value of the stove at the end of 10 years.

8. It is estimated that a car costing $1500 will have a second-hand value of $500 in 6 years. Using the straight line method, find the amount in the depreciation fund at the end of 4 years.

9. A gas furnace costing $200 lasts 25 years, at the end of which time it is valueless. (a) What is the annual contribution to the depreciation fund under the straight line method? (b) What is the wearing value after 10 years? (c) What is the replacement cost?

10. Under the straight line method, prove that the wearing value after h periods, is given by the formula

$$W_h = W_0 - hR.$$

145. The constant per cent method

Under this method, no interest is figured on the depreciation fund and the periodical contribution to the depreciation fund is based upon a constant per cent of the book value. Hence this means that the contribution to the depreciation fund decreases since the book value of the equipment considered will decrease. This method may give a truer picture of the depreciation of certain assets (such as office furniture) which depreciate more during the early years of its life than during the later years. Let r represent the constant per cent expressed in hundredths. The contribution to the depreciation fund at the end of the first period is

$$R_1 = rC,$$

and the book value is

$$B_1 = C - rC = C(1 - r).$$

The contribution to the depreciation fund at the end of the second period is

$$R_2 = rB_1 = rC(1 - r),$$

and the book value is

$$B_2 = C(1 - r) - rC(1 - r) = C(1 - r)^2.$$

In like manner the book value at the end of h periods is

$$B_h = C(1 - r)^h, \tag{8}$$

and the contribution to the depreciation fund for the period just ended is

$$R_h = rB_{h-1}. \tag{9}$$

Since the book value after n periods is the salvage value, we have using formula (8)

$$C(1 - r)^n = S. \tag{10}$$

Solving this equation for r gives the constant per cent r which is needed for computing the contribution to the depreciation fund. We have

$$R_{h+1} = rB_h. \tag{11}$$

We should note that formula (10) cannot be used if $S = 0$. Furthermore, if S is small, the value of r is very large, necessitating very large depreciation charges in the early life of the equipment.

Example. It is estimated that a truck costing $2000 depreciates to a salvage value of $500 in 5 years. Using the constant per cent method, find: (a) the constant per cent, (b) the book value at the end of 2 years, (c) the book value at the end of 3 years, (d) the contribution to the depreciation fund for

THE CONSTANT PER CENT METHOD

the third year, (e) the depreciation charge for the third year, (f) the amount in the depreciation fund at the end of 3 years, (g) the wearing value at the end of the 3rd year.

Solution. (a) We find r from the equation

$$2000(1 - r)^5 = 500.$$

Using logarithms.

$$\log 2000 + 5 \log (1 - r) = \log 500,$$

$$\log (1 - r) = \frac{\log 500 - \log 2000}{5},$$

$$= \frac{2.698970 - 3.301030}{5},$$

$$= 9.879588 - 10.$$

Hence
$$1 - r = 0.757858,$$
$$r = 0.242142.$$

Thus the constant per cent is 24.2142%.

(b) The book value at the end of 2 years is by formula (1),

$$B_2 = 2000 (1 - r)^2.$$

Using logarithms we have

$$\log B_2 = \log 2000 \qquad\qquad 3.301030$$
$$+ 2 \log (1 - r) \qquad 9.759176 - 10$$
$$\qquad\qquad\qquad\qquad\qquad\qquad 3.060206$$

Hence $\qquad B_2 = \$1148.70.$

It should be noted that no additional logarithms had to be read from the table, since the logarithm of 2000 was previously used, and since, furthermore, the logarithm of $1 - r$ had been previously computed in finding r.

(c) In like manner, the book value at the end of 3 years is

$$B_3 = 2000(1 - r)^3 = \$870.55.$$

(d) The contribution to the depreciation fund for the third year is

$$R_3 = rB_2 = 0.242142(1148.70) = \$278.15.$$

(e) The depreciation charge for the third year is the decrease in the book value for that year. Hence

$$D_3 = B_2 - B_3 = 1148.70 - 870.55 = \$278.15.$$

Since there is no interest figured on the depreciation fund, the depreciation charge for any year should equal the annual contribution for that year. Comparing the answers to (d) and (e), we see that this is certainly true for the third year.

(f) The amount in the depreciation fund at the end of the third year will be equal to the total decrease in the book value to that time. [See formula (1).] Hence

$$F_3 = C - B_3,$$
$$= 2000 - 870.55 = \$1129.45.$$

(g) From formula (2), we see that the wearing value after 3 years is
$$W_3 = B_3 - S,$$
$$= 870.55 - 500 = \$370.55.$$

DEPRECIATION SCHEDULE — CONSTANT PER CENT METHOD

Time h	Annual contribution R_h	Amount in depreciation fund F_h	Book value B_h	Depreciation charge D_h
0	0	0	$2000.00	0
1	$484.28	$ 484.28	1515.72	$484.28
2	367.02	851.30	1148.70	367.02
3	278.15	1129.45	870.55	278.15
4	210.80	1340.25	659.75	210.80
5	159.75	1500.00	500.00	159.75

EXERCISE 2

Using the constant per cent method find the quantities indicated for each of the following problems.

Prob. no.	Cost of equipment	Salvage value	Useful life of equipment	
1.	$1000	$100	6	Find r, B_5.
2.	$1500	$200	13	Find r, F_{10}.
3.	$4000	$1000	15	Find r, D_3.
4.	$250	$50	8	Find r, F_6.
5.	$700	$150	4	Find r, W_3.

6. An automobile costing $1400 depreciates to $500 in 6 years. Using the constant per cent method, make a depreciation schedule showing the annual depreciation, amount in the depreciation fund, book value, and the depreciation charge for each year.

7. A house costing $8000 depreciates to $1000 in 25 years. Find the constant per cent of depreciation.

8. Using the constant per cent method, find the book value of an asset after 6 years if the original cost of the asset is $15,000, if its life is 50 years, and if it has a salvage value of $2000.

9. Find the wearing value at the end of 7 years, under the constant per cent method, of a machine costing $1800 and lasting 12 years, if its salvage value is $350.

THE SINKING FUND METHOD 343

10. Under the constant per cent method of estimating depreciation, show that the periodical contribution made at the end of h periods is given by the formula
$$R_h = rC(1-r)^{h-1}.$$

146. The sinking fund method

Using this method, interest is figured on the depreciation fund and the periodical contributions are equal. The periodical contributions constitute an annuity whose amount is the wearing value $C - S$. Therefore

$$Rs_{\overline{n}|i} = W_0 = C - S,$$

or
$$R = (C - S)\frac{1}{s_{\overline{n}|i}}. \tag{12}$$

The amount in the depreciation fund after h periods is

$$F_h = Rs_{\overline{h}|i}, \tag{13}$$

and hence the book value at the end of h periods is

$$B_h = C - Rs_{\overline{h}|i}. \tag{14}$$

The depreciation charge for the hth period is

$$D_h = B_{h-1} - B_h = C - Rs_{\overline{h-1}|i} - (C - Rs_{\overline{h}|i}),$$
or
$$= R(s_{\overline{h}|i} - s_{\overline{h-1}|i}),$$
thus
$$D_h = R(1+i)^{h-1}. \tag{15}$$

Thus we see that the depreciation charge increases from period to period.

Example. It is estimated that a truck costing $2000 depreciates to a salvage value of $500 in 5 years. Using the sinking fund method where the depreciation fund earns 3%, find: (a) the annual contribution to the depreciation fund, (b) the amount in the depreciation fund at the end of 2 years, (c) the amount in the depreciation fund at the end of 3 years, (d) the book value at the end of 2 years, (e) the book value at the end of 3 years, (f) the depreciation charge for the third year, (g) the wearing value at the end of the third year.
Make a depreciation schedule.

Solution. (a) The constant annual contribution to the sinking fund is, from formula (12):

$$R = (2000 - 500)\frac{1}{s_{\overline{5}|.03}} = \$282.53.$$

(b) The amount in the sinking fund at the end of the second year from, formula (13) is

$$F_2 = 282.53 s_{\overline{2}|.03} = \$573.54.$$

(c) Likewise, the amount in the depreciation fund at the end of three years is
$$F_3 = 282.53 s_{\overline{3}|.03} = \$873.27.$$

(d) The book value at the end of two years is
$$B_2 = C - F_2 = 2000 - 573.54,$$
$$= \$1426.46.$$

(e) Likewise
$$B_3 = C - F_3 = 2000 - 873.27,$$
$$= \$1126.73.$$

(f) Hence the depreciation charge for the third year is
$$D_3 = B_2 - B_3 = 1426.46 - 1126.73,$$
$$= \$299.73.$$

This value may have been obtained by the use of formula (15). Thus
$$D_3 = 282.53(1.03)^2,$$
$$= \$299.73,$$
which agrees with the previous result.

(g) The wearing value at the end of the third year is
$$W_3 = B_3 - S = 1126.73 - 500$$
$$= \$626.73.$$

DEPRECIATION SCHEDULE — SINKING FUND METHOD

Time h	Annual contribution R	Interest at 3% on amount in fund	Amount in depreciation fund F_h	Book value B_h	Depreciation charge D_h
0	0	0	0	$2000.00	0
1	$282.53	0	$ 282.53	1717.47	$282.53
2	282.53	8.48	573.54	1426.46	291.01
3	282.53	17.21	873.28	1126.72	299.74
4	282.53	26.20	1182.01	817.99	308.73
5	282.53	35.46	1500.00	500.00	317.99

It should be noted in the above schedule that D_h is increased at the end of each year by the annual contribution plus the interest earned on the depreciation fund for that year. The balance of the entries in the schedule are self-explanatory.

If the periodical payments are reinvested in the business, the interest rate used for the sinking fund may be the rate earned by the business.

EXERCISE 3

Using the sinking fund method in estimating depreciation, find the values of the quantities indicated for the equipment in each of the following problems:

Prob. no.	Cost of equipment	Salvage value	Useful life in years	Interest rate *	
1.	$300	$50	5	4%	Find R, D_3
2.	$1200	$230	8	6%	Find R, B_7
3.	$750	$50	10	5%	Find R, W_5
4.	$2000	$500	12	3%	Find R, B_{10}
5.	$1250	$250	7	$4\frac{1}{2}$%	Find R, D_6

* Interest converted annually.

6. A refrigerator costing $250 has a salvage value of $35 after 8 years of use. Construct a depreciation schedule using the sinking fund method of estimating depreciation. The depreciation fund earns 4%.

7. A truck costing $1600 has a second-hand value of $500 after 6 years of use. If a depreciation fund earns $3\frac{1}{2}$% interest, find the annual contribution under the sinking fund method and the depreciation charge for the third year.

8. A building costing $30,000 has an estimated life of 40 years and a salvage value of $4000. Using the sinking fund method, find the book value of the house at the end of 30 years. The depreciation fund earns interest at the rate of 4%, converted annually. What is the wearing value of the house at the end of 30 years?

9. A bus costing $10,000 depreciates to $1000 in 5 years. Under the sinking fund plan with interest at 4%, find the amount that interest contributes to the depreciation charge for the third year.

10. Prove algebraically that

$$iF_{h-1} = D_h - R.$$

147. Unit cost method of evaluating a machine

Each of the foregoing methods is used extensively by companies and individuals for estimating depreciation, the choice of method usually being made to fit best the particular depreciation problem in question. None of the above methods, however, take into consideration the question of the effect of newer and better equipment that may make the old equipment obsolete or nearly so. This question becomes particularly pertinent if we are evaluating a machine which is used in a plant to produce a certain amount of work. In the proper evaluation of such a machine, we should assume that the cost of putting out a unit of work, called the **unit cost**, should be the same as that for a new machine. We shall use the following symbols.

V = value of machine,
n = number of periods of remaining life,
E = operating expense per period, including upkeep,
S = salvage value,
i = interest rate per period earned on the depreciation fund and charged on the investment,
y = number of units of work produced by machine in one period,
u = unit cost.

Consider now a new machine for which all the items listed above are known. We shall assume that a sinking fund is set up to replace the machine after n periods. The total cost of y units of work produced in one period will include interest on the investment, Vi, periodical contribution to the depreciation fund, $(V - S)\dfrac{1}{s_{\overline{n}|i}}$, and the operating and upkeep expense, E. Hence

$$yu = Vi + (V - S)\frac{1}{s_{\overline{n}|i}} + E$$

or the unit cost is

$$u = \frac{Vi + (V - S)\dfrac{1}{s_{\overline{n}|i}} + E}{y}. \qquad (16)$$

Consider next an old machine, now in use producing y_o units of work, for which the periodical operating and upkeep cost is E_o, whose estimate remaining life is n_o, and whose salvage value is S_o. The value, V_o, of the old machine must be such that the cost per unit of work will be the same as that for the new machine. We have

$$\frac{V_o i + (V_o - S_o)\dfrac{1}{s_{\overline{n}|i}} + E_o}{y_o} = u$$

or
$$V_o\left(i + \frac{1}{s_{\overline{n}|i}}\right) - S_o\frac{1}{s_{\overline{n}|i}} + E_o = y_o u.$$

But
$$i + \frac{1}{s_{\overline{n}|i}} = \frac{1}{a_{\overline{n}|i}},$$

hence,
$$V_o \frac{1}{a_{\overline{n}|i}} = y_o u + S_o \frac{1}{s_{\overline{n}|i}} - E_o,$$

or
$$V_o = \left(y_o u + S_o \frac{1}{s_{\overline{n}|i}} - E_o\right)a_{\overline{n}|i}. \qquad (17)$$

Actually the value, V_o, just obtained may be used as the book value of the machine at the time considered and at the end of each

UNIT COST METHOD OF EVALUATING A MACHINE 347

period a like computation may be made. However, the chief use of this method is not for estimating depreciation but for estimating the value of an old machine in comparison to a new machine.

We may also use this method to compare the relative values of two new machines producing different amounts of work and for which the other charges may differ.

Example 1. A new machine that costs $5000 produces 10,000 units of work per year. It is estimated that its salvage value at the end of 10 years is $500. Operating and upkeep cost amounts to $3000 per year. On a 5% basis, find the cost of one unit of work.

Solution. The reader should recall that the total annual cost of producing 10,000 units of work consists of three items: the interest on the investment, the annual contribution to the depreciation fund, and the annual operating and upkeep charge. Hence the total cost for 10,000 units of work is

$$10{,}000u = 5000(0.05) + (5000 - 500)\frac{1}{s_{\overline{10}|.05}} + 3000,$$

$$= 250 + 4500\frac{1}{s_{\overline{10}|.05}} + 3000,$$

$$= \$3607.77,$$

or the unit cost is

$$u = \$0.360777.$$

Example 2. Compared to the machine in Example 1, what is the value of a machine that puts out 9000 units of work per year and will last 6 years, at the end of which time it has a scrap value of $400? Assume that the annual upkeep and operating cost is $3200 and that money is worth 5%.

Solution. We may use formula (17) but it would be far more instructive to work the problem out directly. The cost of producing 9000 units of work is the sum of the interest on the investment V_o, the amount that must be put in the sinking fund for depreciation, and the annual upkeep and operation cost. We have that this sum is

$$V_o(0.05) + (V_o - 400)\frac{1}{s_{\overline{6}|.05}} + 3200,$$

which should be equal to the cost of producing 9000 units of work at the cost per unit given in Example 1, that is, 0.360777. Hence

$$V_o(0.05) + V_o\frac{1}{s_{\overline{6}|.05}} - 400\frac{1}{s_{\overline{6}|.05}} + 3200 = 9000(0.360777)$$

$$V_o\left(0.05 + \frac{1}{s_{\overline{6}|.05}}\right) = 400\frac{1}{s_{\overline{6}|.05}} - 3200 + 3246.99,$$

$$V_o\frac{1}{a_{\overline{6}|.05}} = 58.81 - 3200 + 3246.99,$$

$$= 105.80,$$

or

$$V_o = 105.80\, a_{\overline{6}|.05} = \$537.01,$$

which is the value of the machine compared to the machine in Example 1.

348 DEPRECIATION: VALUE OF INCOME PROPERTY

Example 3. Make a schedule showing the value (book value) of the machine in Example 2 for each year of its life and the depreciation charge for each year, using the unit cost method. The interest rate is to be figured at 5% and the comparison machine is the one in Example 1.

Solution. Using formula (17) successively, we may fill in the following schedule.

Time	Book value	Depreciation charge
0	$537.01	—
1	516.85	$20.16
2	495.69	21.16
3	473.49	22.20
4	450.18	23.31
5	425.63	24.55
6	400.00	25.63

It should be noted that the last entry under the column headed "Book value" is not obtained by the use of formula (17) since this formula is not valid for $n = 0$. Thus its book value is simply the salvage value. We should also remark, as emphasized before, that this method of estimating the depreciation charge, even though it may have merit, is seldom used.

Example 4. A machine which produces 400 units of work per year has an estimated life of 8 years and a salvage value of $350. Its operating and upkeep cost is $2300 per year. A new machine designed to do the same kind of work can produce 500 units of work per year, for which the annual upkeep and operating cost is $2000. On a 4% basis, what is the value of the old machine if the new machine may be bought for $10,000 and has a salvage value of $1000 after 15 years? Should the old machine be replaced immediately?

Solution. The unit cost as determined by the new machine may be obtained by use of formula (16).

$$u = \frac{10{,}000(0.04) + (10{,}000 - 1000)\dfrac{1}{s_{\overline{15}|.04}} + 2000}{500}$$

or

$$u = \$5.69894.$$

By use of formula (17) we have

$$V_o = \left[400(5.69894) + 350 \frac{1}{s_{\overline{8}|.04}} - 2300 \right] a_{\overline{8}|.04}.$$
$$= \$118.23.$$

Thus we see that the old machine, compared to the new, has a value of only $118.23, which is lower than its scrap value. Hence the machine is obsolete and should immediately be replaced by the new machine.

UNIT COST METHOD OF EVALUATING A MACHINE 349

EXERCISE 4

Find the cost of producing a unit of work for each of the following machines.

Prob. no.	V	S	E	n	i	y
1.	$2000	$100	$200	6	2%	100
2.	$6300	$300	$500	10	3%	250
3.	$10,000	$1000	$750	20	4%	300
4.	$15,000	$2000	$1000	25	$3\frac{1}{2}$%	1000
5.	$12,500	$2500	$1200	15	$2\frac{1}{2}$%	680

6. A new machine, producing 1000 units of work per year, costs $3000 and has a salvage value of $500 at the end of its estimated life of 10 years. Find the unit cost if the annual operating and upkeep cost is $800 and if money is worth 5%, converted annually.

7. The unit cost of a new machine is $1.26784. Under the unit cost method, find the value of an old machine which does the same kind of work if its remaining life is estimated at 6 years, its scrap value at $200, its upkeep and operating expense at $450, and if it produces 400 units of work. Money is worth 4%, converted annually.

8. Find the value one year later of the machine in Problem 2. What is the depreciation charge for this intervening year under the unit cost method?

9. The upkeep and operating expense of a machine producing 250 units of work per year is $1450, and its estimated remaining life is 10 years. A salesman of a new machine which costs $3000 and does the same work guarantees that his machine will produce 300 units of work per year, will last 15 years, but will cost $1500 for upkeep and operating expense. If money is worth 5%, find the value of the old machine, it being assumed that neither machine would have any salvage value.

10. Wishing to make a sale, the salesman in Problem 9 reduces the price of his machine to a point which makes the old machine valueless. What is the reduced price of the new machine?

11. The upkeep and operating expense of a machine producing 900 units of work per year is $4000, its salvage value is $500, and its probable life is 10 years. It is estimated that a new machine doing the same kind of work will produce 1000 units of work per year at an annual upkeep and operating cost of $4200. On a 3% basis, find the value of the old machine if the new machine costs $6000 and has a salvage value of $1000 at the end of its useful life of 15 years.

12. What cost of the new machine in Problem 11 would make the old machine worth its salvage value only?

13. What unit output of the new machine in Problem 11 would make the value of the old machine equal to its salvage value, assuming that the other costs remain the same?

148. Evaluation of exhaustible income properties

Certain properties (such as mines) diminish in value due to the using up of the product produced. Such a decrease in the value of a property is called **depletion**. To take care of such a depletion, the investor is concerned with the restoration of his original investment as well as with an adequate return on his investment. This restoration of the investment may be accomplished by setting aside a certain portion of the periodical income for building up a sinking fund sufficiently large to restore the investment less any salvage value that the depleted property may have.

We first need an estimate of the net periodical (usually annual) income from the property which is to be depleted and also an estimate of the number of years that such a property will last. These two estimates may often be in error, so that an investor must figure a large investment rate to take care of this uncertainty. From the estimated data, a mathematically correct value of the property can be found. We use the following symbols:

V = value of the property (to be determined),
S = salvage value,
n = estimated life in periods,
R = estimated periodical income, that is, net income after operating and other charges have been paid,
r = interest rate per period earned on the sinking fund,
i = the investment rate of interest.

From the net income R, we first subtract the amount that must be earned on the investment, that is, Vi. The balance $R - Vi$ will then be put into a sinking fund at the end of each period for n periods. The accumulation of these payments should be equal to the value of the property less its salvage value. We have

$$(R - Vi)s_{\overline{n}|r} = V - S.$$

Hence, solving for V, we have

$$V = \frac{S + Rs_{\overline{n}|r}}{1 + is_{\overline{n}|r}}. \tag{18}$$

An important special case is when $S = 0$ which may often be assumed to help compensate for any errors in estimation. We set $S = 0$ in formula (18) and obtain

$$V = \frac{Rs_{\overline{n}|r}}{1 + is_{\overline{n}|r}},$$

EVALUATION OF EXHAUSTIBLE INCOME PROPERTIES

or after dividing by $s_{\overline{n}|r}$, we have

$$V = \frac{R}{\dfrac{1}{s_{\overline{n}|r}} + i}. \tag{19}$$

Example 1. It is estimated that a mine will yield a net annual income of $50,000 for 10 years, at the end of which time the salvage value of the property will be $5000. If a sinking fund can be accumulated at 4%, what is the value of the property to earn (a) 6% on the investment, (b) 8% on the investment?

Solution. (a) Let V represent the purchase price of the mine. The interest earned on the investment is then equal to $V(0.06)$. It follows that the amount $50,000 - V(0.06)$ may be used for the sinking fund at the end of each year. Since the accumulated value of this amount must be equal to the original investment less the salvage value, we now have the equation

$$[50,000 - V(0.06)]s_{\overline{10}|.04} = V - 5000.$$

Solving for V we have

$$5000 + 50,000 s_{\overline{10}|.04} = V + V(0.06)s_{\overline{10}|.04},$$
$$= V(1 + 0.06 s_{\overline{10}|.04}).$$

Hence
$$V = \frac{5000 + 50,000 s_{\overline{10}|.04}}{1 + 0.06 s_{\overline{10}|.04}},$$
$$= \$351{,}846.$$

(b) If the investment rate is 8% we have by formula (18)

$$V = \frac{5000 + 50,000 s_{\overline{10}|.04}}{1 + 0.08 s_{\overline{10}|.04}}$$
$$= \$308{,}752.$$

Example 2. What is the value of the mine in Example 1, if the salvage value is assumed to be zero?

Solution. (a) Using formula (19) with an investment rate of 6%, we have

$$V = \frac{50{,}000}{\dfrac{1}{s_{\overline{10}|.04}} + 0.06},$$
$$= \$348{,}940.$$

(b) Using an investment rate of 8%, we have from formula (19),

$$V = \frac{50{,}000}{\dfrac{1}{s_{\overline{10}|.04}} + 0.08},$$
$$= \$306{,}202.$$

EXERCISE 5

1. Find the value of a mine for which the estimated net income is $30,000 per year for 15 years, if the salvage value of the property is $10,000, if the investment rate is 7%, and if 3% can be earned on the sinking fund.

2. It is estimated that a given oil property will produce a net annual income of $40,000 for the next 30 years, at the end of which time the property has a value of $5000. What should a buyer pay for this property if he wishes to earn 8% on his investment and if he can earn 4% on a sinking fund for restoration of the original investment?

3. Find the value of a quarry which yields a net income of $10,000 per year for 15 years if the property is valueless at the end of that time. The buyer plans to make 6% on his investment and can earn 3% on a sinking fund set up to restore the original investment.

4. The rocks from a piece of land yield a net income of $25 per month. It is estimated that the rocks will last for 5 years, at the end of which time the property will be worth $10,000. Find the value of the property if the investment rate of interest is 12%, converted monthly, and if a sinking fund can earn 5%, converted monthly.

5. A timber tract will produce a net semiannual income of $15,000 for 20 years. How much should an investor pay for this property if he expects to earn 6%, converted semiannually, on his investment and can earn 5%, converted semiannually, on a sinking fund? The salvage value of the property is $25,000.

6. An investor pays $200,000 for a piece of mining property which is estimated will produce a semiannual net income of $10,000 for 20 years, at the end of which time the property is worthless. Semiannual payments are made to a sinking fund which earns 3%, converted semiannually. What interest rate, converted semiannually, does the investor earn on his money?

7. It is estimated that a patent will yield $5000 at the beginning of each year for the next 10 years. Assuming that deposits are made into a sinking fund paying 3% at the beginnings of the years, how much should an investor pay for the patent to yield $7\frac{1}{2}$%?

8. How much of the annual income from the investment in Problem 7 is used for interest on the investment at the beginnings of the years? How much is put annually into the sinking fund?

9. A timber tract is offered for sale at $50,000. The timber is to be cut during the next 10 years, at the end of which time the tract is worth $10,000. A sinking fund earning 4% can be established for restoration of the investment. Find the net annual income payable at the ends of the years for 10 years which will earn 8% on the investment.

10. A mine costing $100,000 produces a net income of $16,000 at the end of each year. A sinking fund can be accumulated at 4%. For how many years must the mine produce, to earn 7% on the investment, it being assumed that the mine is worthless at the end of that time?

11. If $r = i$ in formula (18) prove that

$$V = S(1 + i)^{-n} + Ra_{\overline{n}|i}.$$

12. If $r = i$ in formula (19) prove that

$$V = Ra_{\overline{n}|i}.$$

EVALUATION OF EXHAUSTIBLE INCOME PROPERTIES

MISCELLANEOUS EXERCISE

1. A truck costing $2200 has an estimated second-hand value of $500 after 5 years of use. (a) Find the annual contribution to the depreciation fund, using the straight line method. (b) What is the book value of the machine at the end of 3 years?

2. A house and lot costing $10,000 depreciate to $2000 in 40 years. (a) Find the annual contribution to the depreciation fund, using the straight line method. (b) Find the amount in the depreciation fund at the end of 31 years.

3. A farm pumping unit costing $450 has a probable life of 20 years and a salvage value of $50. (a) Using the sinking fund method, find the annual contribution to a depreciation fund which earns 4%, converted annually. (b) What is the depreciation charge for the 8th year?

4. A saw assembly selling for $40 has a probable life of 20 years and a salvage value of $5. (a) Under the sinking fund method, find the annual contribution to the depreciation fund if it earns 3%. (b) Find the wearing value after 15 years.

5. A tractor costing $1200 has a useful life of 10 years, after which it has a salvage value of $200. (a) Using the sinking fund method, what is the annual contribution to a sinking fund earning 3%? (b) How much is in the sinking fund after 8 years?

6. The problem of finding a weighted average of the lives of the several parts and machines in a plant may be solved by using the idea of **composite life,** where the composite life of a plant is defined as the time it takes the sum of the contributions of the separate parts of the plant to accumulate to the sum of the replacement costs. Consider a small plant containing the following machines:

Equipment	Cost	Salvage value	Probable life in years
A	$4000	$ 500	20
B	2500	1500	5
C	3000	300	30

Using the straight line method, we see that the wearing values of plants A, B, C, and the corresponding contributions to the depreciation fund are respectively, $3500, $1000, $2700, and $175, $200, $90. Hence the composite life is the time for (175 + 200 + 90) to accumulate to (3500 + 1000 + 2700). Find this composite life to the nearest year.

7. Using the sinking fund method, find the composite life to the nearest year of the plant in Problem 6, if the depreciation fund earns 4% interest.

8. The composite life of a plant is sometimes used by investors as a maximum period of time for which they will make a loan on the plant. A group of investors decide to make a loan on a plant consisting of the following parts.

354 DEPRECIATION: VALUE OF INCOME PROPERTY

Find this time, using the straight line method and the composite life as a maximum period of time for the loan.

Part	Cost	Salvage value	Probable life in years
Buildings	$250,000	$50,000	50
Machine A	20,000	2000	20
Machine B	55,000	5000	30
Machine C	12,000	500	25
Machine D	18,000	0	10

9. A concrete pipe line costing $150,000 has a probable life of 50 years. If it costs $10,000 extra for each replacement to remove the old line, find the contribution to the depreciation fund (a) under the straight line method, (b) under the sinking fund method if the depreciation fund earns 5%.

10. For a machine costing $5000, it is estimated that its life is 25 years and that its salvage value after 25 years will be $500. After 15 years has passed, it becomes evident that the machine will last only 5 years longer and that its scrap value will be only $100. By how much must the contributions to the depreciation fund be increased for the next 5 years to take care of the changed conditions if the sinking fund method is used and if the depreciation fund earns 3% interest?

11. A stove costing $150 has a salvage value of $25 after 10 years. (a) Using the constant per cent method, find the constant per cent which is written off each year. (b) What is the book value after 6 years?

12. A small lathe costing $250 will be used for 20 years, after which it will be sold for $50. (a) Using the constant per cent method, find the depreciation charge for the 13th year. (b) Find the wearing value at the end of 13 years.

13. A home power plant costing $540 has a probable life of 20 years, after which the salvage value is $50. (a) Using the constant per cent method, find the depreciation charge for the 9th year. (b) Find the amount in the depreciation fund after the 13th payment is made.

14. The constant per cent method is used to estimate the depreciation on a hot water heater costing $70 and lasting 8 years. (a) If the constant per cent is 40%, find the salvage value. (b) Find the book value after 4 years.

15. For Problem 14, find the depreciation charge for the 4th year and the amount in the depreciation fund at the end of the 4th year.

16. Is it possible to use the constant per cent method on a problem for which the salvage value is zero? Why?

17. If the depreciation fund is invested in the business rather than in outside securities, we have what is sometimes called the **compound interest method** of estimating depreciation. The contribution to the depreciation fund, the book value, and depreciation charges are the same as the corresponding quantities under the sinking fund method. The combined allowance which a concern would want to meet at the end of each period is the depreciation charge for that period plus interest on the book value of the machine for the preceding period at the rate of interest earned by the business. Thus the combined allowance after h periods, A_h, is

$$A_h = D_h + B_{h-1}i',$$

where the symbols D and B are used in the same sense as in the article on the sinking fund method and i' is the rate of interest earned by the business. Show that

$$A_h = R(1+i)^{h-1} + (C - Rs_{\overline{h-1}|i})i'.$$

18. Under the compound interest method of Problem 17, find the combined allowance at the end of 8 years for a machine costing $800, with probable life of 12 years and a salvage value of $200. The interest on the depreciation fund is to be figured at 4%, and the rate of interest earned in the business is 10%.

19. The cost of operation and upkeep on an old machine is $1200, its probable life is 7 years, and it turns out 225 units of work per year. A new machine can be bought to replace the old machine at a cost of $4000. Its cost of operation and upkeep is $1100, its life is 25 years, and it can turn out 250 units of work. Find the value on a 5% basis of the old machine by use of the unit cost method, assuming no salvage value for either machine.

20. How many units of work would the new machine in Problem 19 have to turn out to make the old machine valueless?

21. A machine costing $1500 has an estimated life of 20 years, a scrap value of $200, and an upkeep and operation cost of $625 per year. It is able to produce 75 units of work per year. After the machine has been in use for 13 years, there appears on the market a new machine which costs $1600, and has a salvage value of $300 and a probable life of 25 years. Its operation and upkeep cost is $550 but it can produce 90 units of work per year. Would it be advantageous to purchase the new machine if money is worth $4\frac{1}{2}\%$?

22. A purchaser bought a mine for $400,000 which will be exhausted in 40 years. A sinking fund can be accumulated at 4%. What annual net income must be earned to make 8% on the investment and to provide for the annual payment to the sinking fund?

23. A copper mine produces a net annual income of $45,000, which it is estimated will last for 45 years. The salvage value of the property after the mine is exhausted is $10,000. A sinking fund can be accumulated at 3% for the restoration of the investment. What should an investor pay if the mine is to yield 8%?

24. A temporary business which is expected to last 6 years yields a net annual income of $6000. A sinking fund is set up earning 4% to restore the original investment. If an annual return of $7\frac{1}{2}\%$ is expected on the investment, find the amount invested in the business if the salvage value is $300.

25. A tract of timber land is offered for sale at $80,000. It is expected to yield a net income of $10,000 per year for 10 years, after which it will be worth $15,000. If a sinking fund can be set up earning 4%, what yield rate of interest will an investor make if he buys the timber land?

18

Bonds and Reinvestments

149. Introduction and definitions

A **bond** is a written promise to pay on or before a specified date a stated amount of money together with interest at stated times. We have already seen that such a promise given by one individual to another is called a promissory note. In fact a bond differs very little from such a note. A bond is usually issued by a corporation or by some governmental agency and for periods of time much greater than for an ordinary note.

We shall first consider what may be called the conventional type of bond, which consists of a promise to pay a **redemption price** at a future date, called the **redemption date,** together with a promise to pay interest at a fixed rate on the **face** or **par value** of the bond. The par value of a bond is called the **denomination** of the bond and is usually $1000 but it may be $100, $500, or higher than $1000.

Other types of bonds and variations of the conventional type will be considered later in this chapter.

The **purchase price** of a bond is the amount an investor pays for a bond. This price may vary considerably from the redemption price due to variations in the current rate of interest from the rate stated on the bond. Changes in the stability of the issuing corporation or government may also cause marked changes in the purchase price of a bond.

The actual interest rate earned on an investment in a bond is called the **investment** or **yield rate of interest** in contrast to the **bond rate of interest.**

If a bond sells for more than the redemption price at any interest payment date, it is said to be sold at a **premium on the redemption price.** If it is sold at a price less than the redemption price on such a date, it is said to be sold at a **discount on the redemption price.**

We may also speak of a **premium on the par value** of a bond when the bond sells at a price greater than its par value. Likewise, if it

INTRODUCTION AND DEFINITIONS 357

sells at a price less than par, it is said to be sold at a **discount on the par value of the bond.**

The **bond interest** (sometimes called the dividend) is usually paid semiannually, although a few bonds pay interest quarterly and some annually. The bond rate of interest is always quoted as a yearly rate, and likewise, the yield rate of interest is quoted as a nominal rate of interest converted as often as interest payments on the bond are made. Any variation from this procedure must be specifically stated in the particular situation under consideration.

A bond may be **registered,** in which case it bears the owner's name. Transfer of the bond can be made only by proper endorsement of the owner. Interest payments on such bonds may be mailed directly to the owner. Other bonds are said to be **unregistered,** in which case the usual method of paying the interest is by means of **coupons.** These coupons are printed on the bond, with the amount of the interest and the due date indicated. The holder may then cut off the coupons as they mature and present them to his bank for payment.

The following symbols will be used in deriving the bond formulas.

F = face or par value of the bond,
r = interest rate per period on the bond,
C = redemption price of the bond,
n = number of periods before redemption,
i = investment or yield rate of interest per period,
V_n = purchase price of the bond n periods before redemption to yield an interest rate of i per period,
I = bond interest or the amount of the coupon,
P_n = premium on the redemption price of the bond n periods before redemption. If this quantity is negative, it is a discount on the redemption price of the bond.

The following examples and exercise are designed to acquaint the student with the above symbols and to familiarize him with the business terminology associated with bonds.

Example 1. A $1000 coupon bond is described in a bond book as follows:

Payne Pipe Co. Ser. B, 5s, '66, Ao.

Give the meaning of each of the abbreviations and find the amount of the coupon on this bond.

Solution. The Payne Pipe Co. probably issued several series of bonds. This particular bond belonged to the B series. The notation "5s" indicates that the annual bond rate of interest is 5%. The next notation indicates that the bond is redeemable in 1966, and Ao indicates that the bond interest is paid on April 1 and October 1 each year. The capital A indicates that the date of issue was April 1 not October 1. When no numerals follow these letters, the date is assumed to be the first day of the month. We can state definitely that the redemption date is April 1, 1966.

Since interest is payable twice yearly, $r = 0.025$, and we then have

$$I = 0.025(1000),$$
$$= \$25,$$

the amount of the coupon.

Example 2. On October 1, 1948, the bond in Example 1 was bought for $1107.44 to yield 6%. What is the premium and what is the investment rate per period?

Solution. Since nothing is said to the contrary, the bond is assumed to be redeemed at par. The bond pays interest semiannually and is redeemable on April 1, 1966. Hence there are 35 periods (half-years) before redemption. Thus the premium would be represented by P_{35} and is equal to $1107.44 - 1000 = \$107.44$. The investment rate, i, for the period (half-year) is $\frac{1}{2}(0.06) = 0.03$.

Example 3. In the description of a $500 bond, we find the following: $5\frac{1}{2}$s, '69, mS15, redeemable at 105. This bond was bought on September 15, 1947 at $101\frac{1}{4}$. When are the coupons payable and on what date was the bond issued? Find r, I, n, C, V_n, P_n.

Solution. The bond interest payments, or coupons, are payable on March 15 and September 15 of each year. The bond was issued on September 15. Since there are two interest payments per year, the bond rate of interest per period is $r = \frac{1}{2}(0.055) = 0.0275$. The bond interest is $I = (0.0275)(500) = \$13.75$. Since the difference in time between the due date, September 15, 1969, and September 15, 1947 is 22 years, we have $n = 44$.

Bonds are quoted with 100 as the base. Thus the statement redeemable at 105 means that the redemption price is, $C = 500(1.05) = \$525$. In like manner the purchase price is $V_{44} = 500(1.0125) = \$506.25$.

The premium on the redemption price is $P_{44} = 506.25 - 525 = -\$18.75$, which, being negative, should be called a discount.

It is interesting to note in this case that the premium on the par value of the bond is $506.25 - 500 = \$6.25$, which is not negative and is therefore an actual premium. This premium, however, is of no importance in connection with the evaluation of bonds, and hereafter when we use the word "premium," it will refer to premium on the redemption price of the bond (see page 356) unless specifically stated otherwise.

EXERCISE 1

From the bond description given, fill in the spaces indicated. Assume that $500 is par value for each bond.

Prob. no.	Bond description	F	r	C	n	i	V_n	I	P_n
1.	6s, '70, Jj, redeemable at par, bought for $555.25 on July 1, 1947 to yield 7%.								
2.	3s, '80, mS, redeemable at 101, bought for $410.89 on Mar. 1, 1948 to yield 4%.								
3.	2s, '50, Jan. 15, redeemable at par, bought for $539.18 on Jan. 15, 1942 to yield 1½%.								
4.	6s, '54, Mjsd, redeemable at par, bought for $464.25 on Mar. 1, 1944 to yield 7%.								
5.	5s, '65, Fa15, redeemable at par, bought on Feb. 15, 1945 for $516.05 to yield 4½%.								

150. Purchase price of a bond to yield a given investment rate

The price of a bond on an interest payment date to yield a given investment rate is simply the sum of two values: the present value of the redemption price plus the present value of the coupons.

Since the redemption price is C, the quantity Cv^n represents the present value of C, discounted at compound interest for n periods at rate i, as shown in the following line diagram:

$$C(1+i)^{-n} \quad \begin{array}{cccccc} 0 & 1 & 2 & 3 & & n \\ | & | & | & | & \cdots & | \\ & & & & & C \end{array}$$

Investment rate $= i$

Also, the quantity $rFa_{\overline{n}|i}$ is the present value of an ordinary annuity. That is, the coupons constitute an ordinary annuity of n equal payments of rF each. The line diagram follows:

$$
\begin{array}{ccccc}
rF & rF & rF & & rF \\
| & | & | & \cdots & | \\
0 & 1 & 2 & 3 & n
\end{array}
$$

$rFa_{\overline{n}|i}$

Investment rate $= i$

The purchase price is therefore the sum of the present value of a single amount of money C plus the present value of an ordinary annuity of n payments of rF each, or

$$V_n = Cv^n + rFa_{\overline{n}|i}. \tag{1}$$

Example 1. Find the purchase price of a $1000, $3\frac{1}{2}\%$ bond, Jj15, bought on Jan. 15, to yield 4%, 10 years before redemption.

Solution. Since this bond has semiannual interest payments, we have $r = 0.0175$, $i = 0.02$, and $n = 20$. Hence the purchase price is given by

$$\begin{aligned}
V_{20} &= 1000v^{20} + 17.50a_{\overline{20}|.02}, \\
&= 672.971 + 286.150, \\
&= \$959.12.
\end{aligned}$$

Example 2. Find the purchase price of a $1000, 3% bond, mS, redeemable at 110, bought on Sept. 1 to yield $3\frac{1}{2}\%$, 50 years before redemption.

Solution. The redemption price is $1100, $r = 0.015$, $i = 0.0175$, $n = 100$. Hence the purchase price is given by

$$\begin{aligned}
V_{100} &= 1100v^{100} + 15a_{\overline{100}|.0175}, \\
&= 194.067 + 705.922, \\
&= \$899.99.
\end{aligned}$$

Example 3. Find the purchase price of a $500, 6% bond, jAjo15, bought on April 15 to yield 4%, 25 years before redemption.

Solution. Since this is a quarterly bond, $r = 0.015$, $i = 0.01$, and $n = 100$. Hence the purchase price is

$$\begin{aligned}
V_{100} &= 500v^{100} + 7.50a_{\overline{100}|.01}, \\
&= 184.856 + 472.717, \\
&= \$657.57.
\end{aligned}$$

It should be noted that an error of one cent would have been made in this last problem if the rounding off to cents accuracy had been done before the addition.

PURCHASE PRICE

The student should note the increasing importance of the coupons as the period to maturity increases. Thus in Example 2, out of a total payment of $899.99 the larger portion, $705.92, is the present value of the coupons while the smaller portion, $194.07, is the present value of the redemption price, even though the redemption price is more than face. The student should observe the corresponding quantities in Examples 1 and 2.

EXERCISE 2

Find the purchase price of each of the following bonds to yield the indicated investment rate of interest i. Each bond is redeemable at par.

Prob. no.	F Denomination	Bond rate of interest per year	Interest payment dates	r Bond rate of interest per period	Number of years before redemption	n Periods	Bought to yield	i Interest rate per period
1.	$1000	5%	Ms	0.025	24	48	4%	0.02
2.	$500	6%	jajO	0.015	$13\frac{1}{4}$	53	5%	0.0125
3.	$1000	3%	jJ	0.015	$15\frac{1}{2}$	31	4%	0.02
4.	$1000	$3\frac{1}{2}$%	May 15	0.035	30	30	$4\frac{1}{2}$%	0.045
5.	$100	$2\frac{1}{2}$%	Fa	0.0125	$45\frac{1}{2}$	91	$3\frac{1}{2}$%	0.0175

Find the purchase price of each of the following bonds to yield the indicated investment rate of interest. (Note: Both the bond rate and the investment rate of interest are nominal, with the conversion interval of the investment rate of interest equal in length to the payment interval for the bond rate of interest.)

Prob. no.	Denomination	Bond rate of interest	Interest dates	Redemption date	Purchase date	Redemption price	Investment rate of interest
6.	$1000	4%	Jj	Jan. 1, '72	Jan. 1, '42	$1000	$3\frac{1}{2}$%
7.	$1000	3%	Ms15	Mar. 15, '67	Mar. 15, '47	$1080	$3\frac{1}{2}$%
8.	$500	5%	aO	Oct. 1, '87	Oct. 1, '43	$500	4%
9.	$1000	$4\frac{1}{2}$%	Fa	Feb. 1, '98	Aug. 1, '48	$1000	4%
10.	$100	$3\frac{1}{2}$%	mN15	Nov. 15, '65	May 15, '48	$110	$4\frac{1}{2}$%

11. The Southwestern Pacific Co. $4\frac{1}{2}$s, '79, fA, are redeemable at 110. Find the purchase price on Aug. 1, 1946 of a $1000 bond of this series to yield 5%.

362 BONDS AND REINVESTMENTS

12. The Small Lakes Tent Co. 3s, '57, jAjo are redeemable at par. Find the purchase price on July 1, 1947 of a $1000 bond of this issue to yield 4%.

13. A $500, 3% bond, interest payable annually on July 1, is redeemable at par on July 1, 1982. Find the purchase price on July 1, 1950 to yield 5%.

14. Another bond formula for determining the purchase price of a bond to yield a given investment rate of interest is

$$V_n = \frac{rF}{i} + \left(C - \frac{rF}{i}\right)(1 + i)^{-n}.$$

Derive this formula. It should be noted that this formula requires no annuity table.

15. Using the formula of Problem 14, find the value of a $100, 5% bond, Jj, redeemable at par, bought $13\frac{1}{2}$ years before redemption to yield 6%.

16. Mr. Abernathy wishes to invest his funds for at least 6% converted quarterly. Would 5% bonds with interest payable semiannually, redeemable at par in 25 years, now selling at $86\frac{1}{4}$, make a suitable investment? (Hint: Change the desired investment rate of interest to a rate converted semiannually and then figure the purchase price to make this exact rate.)

151. Premium and discount

We previously defined the premium on the redemption price of a bond as its purchase price less its redemption price. If this premium is negative, its numerical value is commonly called the discount on the redemption price of the bond. A premium,* either positive or negative, decreases in absolute value to zero as the redemption date is reached. We shall consider a positive premium, commonly called the premium, first in regard to its decrease in amount to zero as the redemption date is reached. This reduction in value is called the **amortization** of the premium.

From each coupon or interest payment on the bond we must set aside a certain portion for amortization. Since the bond interest is rF and the interest on the redemption price at the yield rate is iC, we have the amount $(rF - iC)$ at the end of each interest payment date for the amortization of the premium. Since the present value of the premium is P_n we have

$$P_n = (rF - iC)a_{\overline{n}|i}. \tag{2}$$

From this premium formula, we may easily write another formula for the purchase price of a bond to yield an investment rate of i per period. Since $V_n = C + P_n$ we have

$$V_n = C + (rF - iC)a_{\overline{n}|i}. \tag{3}$$

---
* According to the agreement in Article 149, the word premium or discount will be taken to mean premium or discount on the redemption price of the bond unless otherwise specifically stated.

PREMIUM AND DISCOUNT

This formula has an advantage over formula (1), Article 150 since it requires the use of only one table. Its disadvantage is that it is not so easily remembered as the first bond formula.

If the premium is negative, it is called a **discount** which means that the coupon or interest payment is not sufficient to take care of the interest on C at the yield rate. We need the amount $(iC - rF)$ each interest payment date to accumulate to the discount; hence

$$\text{Discount} = (iC - rF)a_{\overline{n}|i}. \qquad (4)$$

The purchase price is the redemption price less the discount; hence

$$V_n = C - (iC - rF)a_{\overline{n}|i},$$
or
$$V_n = C + (rF - iC)a_{\overline{n}|i},$$

which is the same as formula (3) of this article.

Example 1. Find the premium (or discount) and purchase price on a $100, 3% bond, Jj, redeemable at par, bought on January 1, 10 years before redemption, to yield 4%.

Solution. The interest on the redemption price, $1000, at the yield rate, 0.02, is $20 at the end of each half year. The bond interest is only $15, which is not sufficient to pay the $20. The balance of $5 must be taken from what is obviously a discount. Hence

$$\text{Discount} = 5a_{\overline{20}|.02},$$
$$= \$81.76.$$

The negative of this value would have been obtained by use of formula (2), thus

$$P_{20} = (15 - 20)a_{\overline{20}|.02},$$
$$= -\$81.76.$$

This negative premium therefore indicates a discount of $81.76. The purchase price is now simply

$$V_{20} = 1000 - 81.76,$$
$$= \$918.24.$$

Example 2. Find the premium (or discount) and the purchase price of a $500, 5% bond, mS, redeemable at par, bought on March 1, 3½ years before redemption, to yield 4%.

Solution. By use of formula (2) we have

$$P_7 = (12.50 - 10)a_{\overline{7}|.02},$$
$$= \$16.18,$$

which is an actual premium since it is positive. Hence the purchase price is

$$V_7 = 500 + 16.18 = \$516.18.$$

EXERCISE 3

Find the premium (or discount) and the purchase price of the following bonds to yield the indicated investment rate of interest.

Prob. no.	Denomination	Bond rate of interest	Interest dates	Redemption date	Purchase date	Redemption price	Investment rate
1.	$100	6%	jD31	Dec. 31, '69	Dec. 31, '45	$100	5%
2.	$1000	5%	Ms	Mar. 1, '64	Mar. 1, '46	$1030	6%
3.	$500	$2\tfrac{1}{2}$%	jD	Dec. 1, '50	June 1, '40	$507.50	4%
4.	$1000	5%	Mn	May 1, '54	Nov. 1, '48	$1000	$4\tfrac{1}{2}$%
5.	$1000	5%	April	Apr. 1, '57	Apr. 1, '47	$1000	$3\tfrac{1}{2}$%

6. The Hydro Electric Railroad Co. 3s, '78, fA, redeemable at par, are bought to yield an investor 4%. What is the premium (or discount) on a $1000 bond of this series if bought on August 1, 1948?

7. The Bestgrade Food Co. $5\tfrac{1}{2}$s, '65, jajO15, redeemable at 102 are bought to yield an investor 5%. What is the premium (or discount) on a $1000 bond of this series if bought on July 15, 1945?

8. The Inland Electric Corp. 6s, '80, Mn, redeemable at 105, are bought to yield an investor 5%. (a) What is the premium (or discount) on a $100 bond of this issue if bought on May 1, 1945? (b) What is the corresponding premium (or discount) on the par value of this bond?

9. The Montana-Wyoming Coal Co. 3s, '65, jD, redeemable at $101\tfrac{1}{2}$, are bought to yield an investor 4%. (a) What is the premium (or discount) on a $500 bond of this issue if bought on December 1, 1945? (b) What is the corresponding premium (or discount) on the par value of this bond?

10. The Peoples Sugar Co. $3\tfrac{1}{2}$s, '70, Jan. 15, redeemable at 115, are bought to yield an investor 3%. (a) What is the premium (or discount) on a $1000 bond of this issue if bought on January 15, 1948? (b) What is the corresponding premium (or discount) on the par value of this bond?

11. Another formula for the purchase price of a bond is credited to Makeham, a famous English actuary. This formula is

$$V_n = K + \frac{g}{i}(C - K), \qquad (5)$$

where $K = C(1 + i)^{-n}$, $g = \dfrac{rF}{C}$. Prove this formula and show that the following premium formula may be deduced from it.

$$P_n = (C - K)\left(\frac{g - i}{i}\right). \qquad (6)$$

Notice that formulas (5) and (6) require only one table, namely $(1 + i)^{-n}$.

12. (a) Use Makeham's formula [see formula (5) above] to compute the purchase price of a $1000, 4% bond, Jj, redeemable at 105, bought on

January 1, 10 years before redemption to yield 3%. (b) As a check, compute the purchase price of this bond by use of the premium formula given by (6) above.

152. Amortization of premium and accumulation of discount

When a bond is bought at a premium, the investor receives, at the time of the maturity of the bond, an amount which is less than he invested. This decrease in his investment is obviously the premium paid for the bond. Sound investment practice requires that in addition to the interest received on the investment, the principal invested must be restored. Hence a part of each bond interest payment must be used for the restoration of this premium. We saw in Article 151 that the amount $(rF - iC)$ would be sufficient to amortize the premium; in fact, the present value of these amounts due at the end of each period is the premium. It is desirable, for bookkeeping purposes, to establish an amortization schedule for each bond bought, showing the decrease in the value of the bond from one interest payment date to the next, the periodical interest from the bond, the amount used as investment interest, and the amount used for amortization.

An illustrative example will be used to show how such a schedule is made. In the illustrative example the **book value** is the value or purchase price at an interest payment date.

Example 1. The Consolidated Lumber and Gravel Co. 6s, '50, Ms, redeemable at 101, are bought by an investor to yield 5%. Make a schedule showing the book value, the bond interest, the investment interest, and the amount for amortization at the end of each period for a $1000 bond of this issue bought on September 1, 1947.

Solution. The price of the bond by formula (3) is

$$V_5 = 1010 + [0.03(1000) - (0.025)1010]a_{\overline{5}|.025},$$
$$= 1010 + 4.75 a_{\overline{5}|.025},$$
$$= \$1032.068.$$

Hence the premium is $1032.068 - 1010.00 = \$22.068$, which must be amortized in 5 periods.

It should be noted that column (c) is obtained by taking $2\frac{1}{2}\%$ of the book value in (a), one row above. Column (d) is obtained by subtracting the entry in (c) from the entry in (b). The book value for any row is obtained by subtracting the entry in (d) from the book value in the row just preceding. Furthermore, no interest is figured on the amounts available for amortization. Thus the last column, (e), is the sum of all the entries in (d), preceding and including the entry in the same row.

Schedule for Amortization of Premium on Bond

Date	(a) Book value	(b) Bond interest at 3%	(c) Investment interest at $2\frac{1}{2}\%$	(d) Available for amortization of premium	(e) Amortization fund
Sept. 1, 1947	$1032.068	—	—	—	—
Mar. 1, 1948	1027.870	$30	$25.802	$4.198	$ 4.198
Sept. 1, 1948	1023.567	30	25.697	4.303	8.501
Mar. 1, 1949	1019.156	30	25.589	4.411	12.912
Sept. 1, 1949	1014.635	30	25.479	4.521	17.433
Mar. 1, 1950	1010.001	30	25.366	4.634	22.067

Example 2. The Clinton Transportation Co. 2s, '55, Apr., redeemable at 105, are bought to yield the investor 3%. Make a schedule showing the book values, the bond interest, the investment interest, and the amount for the accumulation of the discount at the end of each year for a $1000 bond of this issue bought on April 1, 1949.

Solution. The price of the bond is

$$V_6 = 1050 + [(1000)(0.02) - (1050)(0.03)]a_{\overline{6}|.03},$$
$$= \$987.702,$$

which means that the discount is

$$1050 - 987.702 = \$62.298.$$

Schedule for Accumulation of Discount on Bond

Date	(a) Book value of bond	(b) Bond interest at 2%	(c) Investment interest at 3%	(d) For accumulation of discount	(e) Accumulation fund
Apr. 1, 1949	$987.702	—	—	—	—
Apr. 1, 1950	997.333	$20	$29.631	$9.631	$9.631
Apr. 1, 1951	1007.253	20	29.920	9.920	19.551
Apr. 1, 1952	1017.471	20	30.218	10.218	29.769
Apr. 1, 1953	1027.995	20	30.524	10.524	40.293
Apr. 1, 1954	1038.835	20	30.840	10.840	51.133
Apr. 1, 1955	1050.000	20	31.165	11.165	62.298

It should be noted that the amounts needed for accumulation of the discount in column (d) are not available until the bond is redeemed. Only $20 of the amount needed for investment interest is available to the investor at the end of each year.

EXERCISE 4

Make a schedule showing the book values, the bond interest, the investment interest, and the amount for the amortization of the premium or for the accumulation of the discount, at the end of each period, for the following bonds.

Prob. no.	Denomination	Bond rate of interest	Interest dates	Redemption date	Purchase date	Redemption price	Investment rate of interest
1.	$1000	5%	Ms	Mar. 1, '51	Sept. 1, '48	$1000	4%
2.	$500	3%	Jj	Jan. 1, '52	Jan. 1, '49	$500	4%
3.	$1000	4%	aO	Oct. 1, '52	Apr. 1, '49	$1010	$3\frac{1}{2}$%
4.	$1000	3%	jD	Dec. 1, '51	Dec. 1, '48	$1050	$4\frac{1}{2}$%
5.	$100	$4\frac{1}{2}$%	Feb. 15	Feb. 15, '55	Feb. 15, '49	$110	5%

153. Bonds bought between interest payment dates

When an investor decides to buy a bond, he usually does not wait for an interest payment date to make his purchase. This means that some adjustment must be made to the seller, for he clearly is entitled to part of the interest payment.

Using the value of the bond at the interest payment date just preceding the purchase, we may determine the correct price to be paid by merely carrying this value forward at the investment rate of interest to the purchase date. Since the time is less than one period, the conventional business practice is to use simple interest. If V_n represents the value of the bond at the interest payment date just preceding the purchase, and if t represents the fractional part of the period from the preceding interest payment date to the time of purchase, we have that the correct purchase price, V'_n, is

$$V'_n = V_n(1 + ti). \qquad (7)$$

This purchase price (that is, the actual price paid for the bond) is sometimes called the "flat" price. However, there are serious objections to the use of this terminology, because in the market a bond that is selling flat means one that is sold at the quoted price without the addition of a proportional part of the interest. Some bonds specify that they should be traded on this basis while others sell flat due to default in interest payments. We shall not use the term "flat" price to mean the purchase price of a bond between interest payment dates in this book.

The usual method of computing t, in figuring bond interest, is to use approximate time, that is, 360 days to the year and 30 days to the month. Thus, in general, for bonds, ordinary simple interest, with approximate time (see Article 57), is used in computing interest for partial periods.

One exception to the above practice is to use exact simple interest with exact time for certain United States government bonds — that is, to count 365 days to the year and to count the exact number of days between dates.

We shall use the standard bond method first mentioned, unless exact simple interest is stated.

Example 1. The Great Creek Electric Co. 5s, '69, Ms, redeemable at par, are bought to yield an investor 4% on Apr. 16, 1949. What is the purchase price of a $1000 bond of this issue?

Solution. The interest payment date preceding the purchase is Mar. 1, 1949. Hence the time from this date to the redemption date, Mar. 1, 1969, is 20 years or 40 half-year periods. We compute V_{40}, obtaining,

$$V_{40} = 1000 + (25 - 20)a_{\overline{40}|.02},$$
$$= \$1136.78,$$

the purchase price of the bond 40 periods before redemption. Now the number of days from this interest payment date to Apr. 16 is

$$\begin{array}{ll} \text{March} & \text{29 days (30 days} - 1 \text{ day)} \\ \text{April} & \underline{\text{16 days}} \\ & \text{45 days.} \end{array}$$

Hence $t = \frac{45}{180} = \frac{1}{4}$ period. In this computation, we did not count the day on which the interest is payable, but we did count the purchase date. The same result would obviously be obtained if we counted the first day and excluded the day of purchase. In fact, this second method is quite commonly used in the sale of bonds. We now have

$$V'_{40} = 1136.78[1 + \tfrac{1}{4}(0.02)],$$
$$= \$1142.46,$$

which is the required purchase price of the bond to yield 4%, converted semiannually.

Example 2. The Dryden Chemical Co. 3s, '75, Jj15, redeemable at 101, are bought to yield the investor $4\tfrac{1}{2}$% on Nov. 9, 1948. What is the purchase price of a $500 bond of this issue?

Solution. The time from July 15, 1948 to the redemption date is $26\tfrac{1}{2}$ years or 53 periods. Hence

$$V_{53} = 505 + (7.50 - 11.3625)a_{\overline{53}|.0225},$$
$$= \$386.12,$$

BONDS BOUGHT BETWEEN INTEREST PAYMENT DATES 369

the purchase price of the bond 53 periods before redemption. The value of t may be determined as follows:

$$
\begin{array}{ll}
\text{July} & \text{15 days} \quad (30 \text{ days} - 15 \text{ days}) \\
\text{Aug.} & \text{30 days} \\
\text{Sept.} & \text{30 days} \\
\text{Oct.} & \text{30 days} \\
\text{Nov.} & \text{9 days} \\
\hline
& \text{114 days.}
\end{array}
$$

Hence $t = \frac{114}{180} = \frac{19}{30}$ and we have

$$V' = 386.12[1 + \tfrac{19}{30}(0.0225)],$$
$$= \$391.62,$$

the purchase price of the bond to yield $4\tfrac{1}{2}\%$, converted semiannually.

We should now examine the business practice of quoting bond prices between interest payment dates. If we wish to buy a $1000, 6% bond, Jj, 60 days after an interest payment date, the bond salesman would tell us that we must pay the **quoted price and interest**. He finds from the newspaper or other sources that the quoted price on the given date is $95\tfrac{1}{4}$, that is, $952.50 for the $1000 bond. The bond interest is $30, hence he adds $\tfrac{60}{180}(30) = \$10$ to the quoted price making a purchase price of $952.50 + \$10 = \$962.50$. In general, if the quoted price, sometimes called the "and interest" price, is represented by Q, and if, as before, V'_n represents the purchase price, t the fractional part of a period measured from the latest interest payment date, and i the bond interest, we have

$$V'_n = Q + tI. \tag{8}$$

The quantity, tI, is commonly called the **accrued interest**.

Formula (8) may be stated in words as follows: *purchase price equals the quoted price plus the accrued interest.* From this we may write the following statement: *the quoted price equals the purchase price less the accrued interest.*

It should be noted that this formula enables us to compute the quoted price if V'_n is known. Actually, the quoted price is obtained in practice by a simple interpolation between V_n and V_{n-1}, where these values may be obtained from a bond table (a sample of which is shown on page 372). Since simple interest is used for partial periods, the student may easily verify that the quoted price is given by

$$Q = V_n + t(V_{n-1} - V_n). \tag{9}$$

Example 3. The Little River Flour Co. 4s, Jj, redeemable at par, were quoted at $102\frac{1}{2}$ on May 16, 1947. What was the purchase price of a $1000 bond of this issue at that date?

Solution. The number of days from the latest interest payment date to May 10 is 135. Hence the fractional part of the period is $\frac{135}{180} = \frac{3}{4}$. Hence to the quoted price we add $\frac{3}{4}$ of the interest, that is $\frac{3}{4}(20)$ or $15. Hence the purchase price is,

$$V'_n = 1025 + 15,$$
$$= \$1040.$$

The student should note that the yield rate of interest is not needed in this problem nor is the redemption date necessary.

Example 4. The Big Rock Quarry Co., 3s, '68, Ms, redeemable at 100, are bought to yield the investor $3\frac{1}{2}\%$ on June 16, 1948. (a) Find the purchase price of a $100 bond of this issue at that date. (b) Find the quoted or "and interest" price of this bond on the same date by means of formula (8) and by direct interpolation from the extract of a bond table given on page 372.

Solution. (a) We determine the purchase price of the bond on March 1, 1948 which is 40 periods before redemption. Hence

$$V_{40} = 100 + (1.50 - 1.75)a_{\overline{40}|.0175},$$
$$= \$92.85.$$

The bond is bought 105 days after the interest payment date; hence

$$V'_{40} = 92.85[1 + \tfrac{105}{180}(0.0175)],$$
$$= \$93.80.$$

(b) By use of formula (8) we find that the quoted price on June 16, 1948 is

$$93.80 = Q + \tfrac{105}{180}(1.50),$$
or
$$Q = 93.80 - 0.87,$$
$$= \$92.93.$$

Using the bond table, an interpolation gives

$$Q = 92.85 + \tfrac{105}{180}(92.98 - 92.85)$$
$$= \$92.93,$$

which corresponds with the foregoing result.

EXERCISE 5

Find the purchase price of each of the following bonds bought between interest payment dates as indicated. Secondly, find the quoted or "and interest" price in each case.

BONDS BOUGHT BETWEEN INTEREST PAYMENT DATES

Prob. no.	Denomination	Bond rate of interest	Interest dates	Redemption date	Purchase date	Redemption price	Investment rate
1.	$1000	4%	Ms	Mar. 1, '80	June 16, '48	$1000	5%
2.	$100	3%	Jj	Jan. 1, '85	Mar. 16, '48	$100	4%
3.	$500	5%	Mn15	May 15, '70	July 15, '50	$550	4%
4.	$1000	$3\frac{1}{2}$%	jD	Dec. 1, '65	Feb. 16, '49	$1100	3%
5.	$1000	$4\frac{1}{2}$%	Jd15	June 15, '75	Aug. 15, '51	$1050	4%
6.	$1000	2%	fA	Aug. 1, '60	Apr. 3, '49	$1000	3%
7.	$100	$2\frac{1}{2}$%	aO	Oct. 1, '80	Aug. 16, '50	$100	3%
8.	$1000	3%	Apr. 15	Apr. 15, '60	July 5, '48	$1200	$3\frac{1}{2}$%
9.	$1000	6%	Ms15	Mar. 15, '65	Oct. 15, '49	$1010	5%
10.	$500	4%	Jj23	Jan. 23, '75	Mar. 5, '50	$500	3%

Find the purchase price of each of the following bonds whose quoted price is given:

Prob. no.	Denomination	Bond rate of interest	Interest dates	Quoted price on date given in last column	Date of purchase
11.	$100	4%	Jj	$102.50	Mar. 16, '48
12.	$1000	5%	mS	$998.75	Oct. 1, '49
13.	$1000	3%	jJ	$998.75	Feb. 16, '50
14.	$500	6%	Ao15	$521.88	Jan. 15, '50
15.	$1000	$4\frac{1}{2}$%	May 15	$1050.00	July 17, '48

Using the extract from the bond table given on page 372, find, by interpolation, the quoted price of each of the following bonds. Secondly, find the purchase price in each case.

Prob. no.	Denomination	Bond rate of interest	Interest dates	Redemption date	Purchase date	Redemption price	Investment rate
16.	$1000	3%	Jj	Jan. 1, '68	Mar. 16, '48	par	$2\frac{1}{2}$%
17.	$1000	3%	Ms	Mar. 1, '70	Aug. 16, '49	par	$2\frac{3}{4}$%
18.	$1000	3%	Mn	May 1, '71	July 1, '50	par	$3\frac{3}{4}$%
19.	$100	3%	jJ	July 1, '73	July 16, '51	par	4%
20.	$500	3%	fA	Aug. 1, '71	Apr. 13, '50	par	$4\frac{1}{2}$%

21. Prove that the quoted, or "and interest" price of a bond, as given by formula (9), is algebraically equivalent to that given by formula (8).

22. Prove that the purchase price of a bond bought between interest payment dates may be obtained by interpolation between V_n and $(V_{n-1} + I)$.

23. Find the purchase price of the bond in Problem 16 by the method indicated in Problem 22.

24. Find the quoted price and the purchase price of a $1000, 5% bond, Jj, bought on Mar. 15 to yield 5%.

Extract from a Bond Table

| Value of a $1000 Bond with Interest Payable Semiannually at 3% ||||||||
Yield rate of interest	19½ years	20 years	20½ years	21 years	21½ years	22 years
2.50	1076.80	1078.32	1079.82	1081.30	1082.77	1084.22
2.55	1068.80	1070.16	1071.50	1072.82	1074.12	1075.41
2.60	1060.88	1062.07	1063.25	1064.41	1065.56	1066.70
2.65	1053.03	1054.06	1055.08	1056.09	1057.08	1058.07
2.70	1045.25	1046.13	1046.99	1047.85	1048.69	1049.52
2.75	1037.54	1038.26	1038.98	1039.68	1040.38	1041.06
2.80	1029.90	1030.47	1031.03	1031.59	1032.14	1032.68
2.85	1022.32	1022.75	1023.17	1023.58	1023.99	1024.39
2.90	1014.81	1015.10	1015.37	1015.65	1015.91	1016.18
2.95	1007.37	1007.51	1007.65	1007.79	1007.92	1008.05
3.00	1000.00	1000.00	1000.00	1000.00	1000.00	1000.00
3.05	992.69	992.56	992.42	992.29	992.16	992.03
3.10	985.45	985.18	984.91	984.65	984.39	984.14
3.15	978.27	977.87	977.47	977.08	976.70	976.32
3.20	971.15	970.62	970.10	969.59	969.08	968.59
3.25	964.10	963.44	962.80	962.16	961.54	960.92
3.30	957.11	956.33	955.56	954.81	954.07	953.34
3.35	950.18	949.28	948.40	947.53	946.67	945.83
3.40	943.32	942.30	941.29	940.31	939.34	938.39
3.45	936.51	935.37	934.26	933.16	932.08	931.02
3.50	929.76	928.51	927.29	926.08	924.89	923.73
3.55	923.08	921.72	920.38	919.07	917.78	916.51
3.60	916.45	914.98	913.54	912.12	910.73	909.36
3.65	909.88	908.80	906.76	905.24	903.74	902.28
3.70	903.37	901.69	900.04	898.42	896.83	895.26
3.75	896.92	895.13	893.38	891.66	889.98	888.32
3.80	890.52	888.63	886.79	884.97	883.19	881.44
3.85	884.18	882.20	880.25	878.34	876.47	874.63
3.90	877.89	875.81	873.78	871.78	869.81	867.89
3.95	871.66	869.49	867.36	865.27	863.22	861.21
4.00	865.49	863.22	861.00	858.83	856.69	854.60
4.05	859.37	857.01	854.70	852.44	850.22	848.05
4.10	853.30	850.86	848.46	846.12	843.82	841.57
4.15	847.28	844.76	842.28	839.85	837.47	835.14
4.20	841.32	838.71	836.15	833.64	831.19	828.78
4.25	835.41	832.72	830.08	827.49	824.96	822.49
4.30	829.55	826.78	824.06	821.40	818.80	816.25
4.35	823.75	820.89	818.10	815.37	812.69	810.07
4.40	817.99	815.06	812.19	809.39	806.64	803.95
4.45	812.28	809.28	806.34	803.46	800.65	797.89
4.50	806.63	803.55	800.54	797.59	794.71	791.89
4.55	801.02	797.87	794.79	791.78	788.83	785.95
4.60	795.46	792.24	789.09	786.01	783.00	780.06
4.65	789.95	786.66	783.45	780.31	777.23	774.23
4.70	784.49	781.13	777.85	774.65	771.52	768.46
4.75	779.08	775.65	772.31	769.05	765.86	762.74
4.80	773.71	770.22	766.82	763.49	760.25	757.08
4.85	768.39	764.84	761.38	757.99	754.69	751.47
4.90	763.11	759.50	755.98	752.54	749.19	745.91
4.95	757.88	754.21	750.64	747.14	743.74	740.41
5.00	752.70	748.97	745.34	741.79	738.34	734.96

154. Yield rate of interest of a bond bought at a given price

Perhaps the most important problem for the investor in bonds is that of finding the yield rate of interest when a bond is purchased at a given price. We have calculated the prices of bonds to yield the investor certain interest rates, but actually when he buys a bond he must pay for it the asked price. His question, then, is simply what interest rate he will realize if he pays the asked price. By computing the yield rate on the various bonds offered, he may choose the bond which most nearly gives him the interest rate desired.

An examination of any of the bond formulas, such as formula (1) or formula (3), shows that even for relatively small values of n, the solution of the equation for i, when all the other quantities are given, involves the solution of a high-degree equation in i. For this reason, approximation methods have been developed for finding the yield rate. The first two to be given are based upon assumptions which are approximations while the third method is an approximation to the actual rate.

FIRST METHOD. Assuming that the bond interest is the amount earned on the investment (that is, the purchase price), then the ratio of this interest to the purchase price of the bond (at an interest payment date) is called the **current yield rate** of the bond. That is

$$\text{Current yield rate} = \frac{I}{V_n}, \tag{10}$$

which, of course, may be expressed as a nominal rate when the bond interest is payable more than once per year. This current yield rate may be used as an approximation to the actual yield rate. It is obvious that this may give a very poor approximation if the bond sells at either a premium or a discount for the cases when the time to the redemption date is short. On the other hand, the current yield rate gives a very good approximation to the actual yield for long-term bonds.

Example 1. The purchase price of a $1000, 4% bond, Jj, '80, redeemable at par, on Jan. 1, 1950 is $950. Find the current yield rate.

Solution. The bond interest, I, is $20; hence the current yield for the semi-annual period is

$$\tfrac{20}{950} = 0.0211,$$

or a nominal rate of 4.22%.

SECOND METHOD. Taking into consideration the premium or discount involved, another approximate yield rate may be obtained.

Thus, in the case of a discount bond, the total discount will be repaid at the redemption date to the owner of the bond. We assume that this amount is evenly divided over the period that the bond is held, and hence the average income is the bond interest per period added to the result of dividing the discount by the number of periods before redemption. If the bond is bought at a premium, the average income is found by subtracting (a) the quotient obtained by dividing the premium by the number of periods before redemption, from (b) the bond interest per period. If we consider, as was done previously, that the discount is a negative premium, we may express this approximate yield by means of a single formula as follows:

$$\text{Approximate yield rate} = \frac{I - \frac{P_n}{n}}{\frac{V_n + C}{2}}, \qquad (11)$$

where $\frac{V_n + C}{2}$ is defined as the average investment. In the future, we shall refer to this yield rate as the **approximate yield rate.**

Example 2. Find the approximate yield rate in Example 1.

Solution. The discount is $50. Hence, in the formula, $P_n = -50$, and since $n = 60$, we have

$$\text{Approximate yield rate} = \frac{20 - \frac{-50}{60}}{\frac{950 + 1000}{2}},$$

$$= 0.0213,$$

or expressed as a nominal rate, we have 4.26%, which is relatively close to the current yield rate previously obtained.

THIRD METHOD. The third method of finding the yield rate is by use of interpolation either from a bond table or, if one is not available, from a portion of such a table which can be easily constructed by use of an annuity table. This method differs from the two previous methods in that it uses the formula from which the actual yield rate may be obtained. By continued interpolation, we may obtain any desired degree of accuracy to this actual rate. We shall distinguish the yield rate so obtained by calling it simply the **yield rate by interpolation.**

Example 3. Find by interpolation the yield rate in Example 1.

YIELD RATE OF INTEREST

Solution. Since the two previous approximations give a rate between 2% and $2\frac{1}{4}$%, we calculate V_{60}, using first $2\frac{1}{4}$%. We have,
$$V^{60} = 1000 + (20 - 22.50)a_{\overline{60}|.0225},$$
$$= \$918.13,$$
which means that the yield rate of interest is a little less than 0.0225, since the purchase price was $950. The next lower interest rate in the table is 2% from which we obtain, necessarily, $V_{60} = \$1000$. A table may now be made:

Interest Rate	V_{60}
0.02	1000
i	950
0.0225	918.13

Interpolation gives
$$\frac{i - 0.02}{0.0225 - 0.02} = \frac{950 - 1000}{918.13 - 1000},$$
from which $i = 0.0215$, or the corresponding nominal rate is 4.30%.

As stated before, the yield rate may be obtained to any desired degree of accuracy by repetition of this method. Thus, by the use of logarithms, V_{60}, in Example 3, may be computed for $i = 0.0215$. If this gives a value of V_{60} less than $950, we would then compute the value of V_{60} for $i = 0.0214$. If this new value is greater than $950, we can then interpolate between these two values of V_{60} for a new and better approximation to the yield rate of interest. However, one interpolation will give a sufficiently accurate result for practical purposes.

In all the cases discussed above, it was assumed that the bond was bought at an interest payment date. If the bond is bought between such dates, we may use the first method, substituting the quoted price for the actual price in the formula. The second method may also be used where the quoted price on the date of purchase is used in place of V_n at that interest payment date nearer to the purchase date. The third method may be applied again, using quoted prices rather than actual prices. It is readily seen that the same result will be obtained if actual prices are used.

Example 4. The Riverdale Creamery 3s, '70, Jj, redeemable at par, are quoted at $105\frac{1}{2}$ on September 1, 1949. Find the current yield rate, the approximate yield rate and the yield rate by interpolation.

Solution. Since the yield rate is independent of the denomination of the bond used, we may use a $1000 bond of the issue in question. The current yield rate is
$$\frac{15}{1055} = 0.0142,$$
or the equivalent nominal rate is 2.84%.

376 BONDS AND REINVESTMENTS

To find the approximate yield rate, we note that $n = 41$, since September 1 is nearer to July than to the following January. Hence the approximate rate is given by

$$\frac{15 - \dfrac{55}{41}}{\dfrac{1055 + 1000}{2}} = 0.0133,$$

or a nominal rate of 2.66%.

To find the yield rate by interpolation, we may compute the quoted price by interpolation between periods from the extract of the bond table given on page 372. We interpolate between $n = 41$ and $n = 40$, or between $20\frac{1}{2}$ years and 20 years, at the yield rate (nominal) of 2.65%. We have:

$$Q = 1055.08 + \tfrac{1}{3}(1054.06 - 1055.08),$$
$$= \$1054.74.$$

At the nominal rate of 2.60%, we have

$$Q = 1063.25 + \tfrac{1}{3}(1062.07 - 1063.25),$$
$$= \$1062.86.$$

Now interpolation from the following table will give the required result where $2i$ represents the nominal yield rate of interest.

Nominal Yield Rate	Q
2.60	1062.86
$2i$	1055.00
2.65	1054.74

and we have $2i = 2.65\%$.

EXERCISE 6

Find the current yield rate, the approximate yield rate, and the yield rate by one interpolation for each of the following bonds, giving the results in each case as nominal rates.

Prob. no.	Denomi- nation	Interest payment dates	Bond rate of interest	Purchase price n periods before redemption	n	Redemp- tion price
1.	$1000	Jj	3%	$985.00	42	par
2.	$500	Fa	4%	$506.25	80	par
3.	$100	Ms	5%	$110.75	30	$105.50
4.	$1000	Apr.	$1\frac{1}{2}\%$	$958.75	44	par
5.	$1000	Mn	2%	$955.00	100	$1020

CALLABLE BONDS

Find the current yield rate, the approximate yield rate, and the yield rate by one interpolation for each of the following bonds, giving the results in each case as nominal rates.

Prob. no.	Denomination	Bond rate of interest	Interest payment dates	Redemption date	Redemption price	Quoted price at date given in next column	Purchase date
6.	$1000	3%	Ms	Mar. 1, 1970	par	$1015.00	June 16, '48
7.	$1000	4%	Ao	Apr. 1, 1999	$1010	$987.50	May 1, '49
8.	$1000	1½%	May	May 1, 1990	par	$1072.50	Aug. 16, '50
9.	$100	2%	Jd	June 1, 2000	par	$102.50	Aug. 13, '52
10.	$500	3%	jJ	July 1, 1969	$510	$500.00	Oct. 31, '48

11. Using the interpolation method which of the following bonds gives the better yield rate of interest:

$1000, 3½%, jD, '68, redeemable at par, bought Dec. 1, 1945 for $1075.00.
$1000, 3½%, aO, '70, redeemable at par, bought Oct. 1, 1945 for $1082.00.

12. Prove that the same result is obtained for the yield rate of interest for a bond bought between interest payment dates if the interpolation is made using actual purchase prices rather than quoted prices.

13. Find the yield rate of interest by interpolation for the illustrative Example 4, making use of the method of Problem 12.

14. Show that the current yield rate is always less than the actual yield rate if a bond is sold at a discount.

15. Show that the current yield rate is always greater than the actual yield rate if a bond is sold at a premium.

155. Callable bonds

A **callable bond** is one for which the issuing corporation or government reserves the right to retire the bond at some date prior to the redemption date. In such a case, the exact provisions for such a prior redemption are written on the face of the bond. Often a provision is made for a redemption price greater than par if the issuing corporation exercises the callable feature of the bond. Less often, but in many U.S. Government bonds, the callable provision is applicable only after a certain date.

In buying callable bonds, the investor must assume that the debtor corporation will or will not exercise the callable feature of their bonds depending upon whether it will be favorable or unfavorable to their interests. Thus, a bond selling below the call price is not likely to be called by the issuing corporation, and the investor should then assume that it will run to its due date in figuring his yield rate of interest. A bond selling at a price greater than the call price, however, is quite likely to be called at the earliest call date possible, and the investor should assume that this will be done. In other words, the investor should assume on such bonds that the least favorable yield rate to him is the one he most likely will earn on his investment.

Example 1. The Worthington Electric 4s, '81, Apr., callable at par, were quoted at $93\frac{1}{4}$ on April 1, 1945. What was the most likely yield rate of interest that an investor would make if he bought a $100 bond of this issue at that date?

Solution. The current yield rate is $\frac{4}{93.25}$ or 0.0429. The actual yield rate will be greater than this (See Problem 14, Exercise 6) so we may use $i = 0.045$ as our first trial rate. We have

$$V_{36} = 100 + (4 - 4.5)a_{\overline{36}|.045},$$
$$= \$91.167.$$

This is less than the actual purchase price, so the yield interest rate is lower than 0.045. The next entry in the table is 0.04; hence $V_{36} = 100$, for this yield rate of interest. Interpolating between these values, we have $i = 0.0438$ or 4.38%.

Example 2. The U.S. Treasury $2\frac{1}{2}$s, Ms15, callable at par at any interest payment date between 1967 and 1972, were quoted at 103.12 on March 15, 1947. What is the most likely interest rate that an investor would make on his money if he bought a bond of this issue at that date?

Solution. Since the bond was bought at a premium we assume that it will be called at the earliest possible date, namely, March 15, 1967. U.S. Government bonds are quoted in 32nds. The number 103.12 means $103 and $\frac{12}{32}$ of a dollar or $103.375 for a $100 bond. The current yield rate is $\frac{1.25}{103.375} = 0.0121$. But the actual yield rate will be less than this (see Problem 15, Exercise 6) since the bond is sold at a premium. The first value given in the tables which is less than 0.0121 is $1\frac{1}{8}\%$ or 0.01125. We find that the purchase price on March 15, 1947 at this rate, assuming that the bond will be redeemed at its earliest call date, is $V_{40} = \$104.009$, which is more than was paid for the bond. We try the next higher rate in the table, $1\frac{1}{4}\%$, and find $V_{40} = \$100$. Interpolation between these values gives $i = 0.01144$, or a nominal rate of 2.29%.

Example 3. The Elderwood Mining Co. $3\frac{3}{4}$s, '70, Ao, redeemable at par on the due date but callable at 103 beginning on April 1, 1950 and at any interest date thereafter, were quoted at 103.50 on April 1, 1946. What is the most likely rate of interest that an investor would make if he bought a $1000 bond of this issue on that date?

Solution. If the bond is redeemed at par on its due date, the nominal yield rate of interest is 3.53%, as may be determined by interpolation. However, if the bond is called at the first opportunity possible, the yield rate would be 3.51%. Hence the most likely yield rate would be 3.51%.

EXERCISE 7

1. The Larsen Refrigerator Co. 5s, '65, Ms, callable at par, were quoted at 98 on March 1, 1948. What would be the most likely yield rate of interest that an investor would make if he bought a $100 bond of this issue on that date?
2. The U.S. Government $2\frac{1}{2}$s, '69, Jd15, callable at par on June 15, 1964 or at any interest date thereafter, were quoted at 101.21 on June 15, 1945. What was the most likely yield rate of interest that an investor would make if he bought a $1000 bond of this issue?
3. The Pleasant Valley Telephone Co. 6s, '61, Ao, callable on or after October 1, 1951 at 105, but redeemable at par on the due date, were quoted at $108\frac{1}{8}$ on Apr. 1, 1947. What is the most likely yield rate of interest that an investor would make if he bought a $1000 bond of this issue at that date?
4. A $1000 bond, 5%, '81, Mn, callable on or after March 1, 1961 at 103, was bought for $1025 on March 1, 1948. Between what limits does the buyer's yield rate of interest fall? (Note: This bond is redeemable at 103 even as late as the due date.)
5. A $1000 bond, 3%, '81, Apr., callable at 101, but redeemable at par on the due date, was bought for $1008.25 on April 1, 1941. Between what limits does the buyer's yield rate of interest fall?

156. Other types of bonds

Perhaps the simplest of the various other types of bonds not yet considered is the United States Government Savings Bond for which the investor pays a certain amount now and receives at the maturity date the principal invested, together with all the interest earned, in one single sum which is called the maturity value of the bond. The most popular of these issues, previously mentioned (Problem 3, Exercise 5, Article 124), increase one third in value over a period of 10 years. These bonds are sold in small denominations, being designated by their maturity values. Thus a $25 bond sells for $18.75, a $50 bond for $37.50 and so on.

These bonds cannot be resold and hence the only problem involved is the problem of finding the interest rate earned if such a bond is held to maturity. This problem has already been considered in the above-mentioned reference. The government also provides that the bond may be cashed prior to the maturity date, but in such cases the investor suffers a decrease in the interest rate earned in accordance with the terms printed on the bond.

Another type of bond, or to be more exact a type of bond issue, is the **serial bond**. Such a bond belongs to an issue which is retired in installments over a period of years. These bonds are of the conventional type; hence no new problem is involved in treating the individual bonds of such serial bond issues.

Example 1. The Hillard Corporation serial 4s, Ms, are to be redeemed at par beginning March 1, 1965 and continuing each 5 years, the last redemption date being on March 1, 1985. Find the total purchase price of 5 of these bonds on March 1, 1950 to yield 5%, if the denomination of each bond is $1000 and if one is due on March 1, 1965, another on March 1, 1970, and so on.

Solution. The problem is that of finding the values of five bonds due at different dates. We have

$$V_{30} = 1000 + (20 - 25)a_{\overline{30}|.025} = 895.35$$
$$V_{40} = 1000 + (20 - 25)a_{\overline{40}|.025} = 874.49$$
$$V_{50} = 1000 + (20 - 25)a_{\overline{50}|.025} = 858.19$$
$$V_{60} = 1000 + (20 - 25)a_{\overline{60}|.025} = 845.46$$
$$V_{70} = 1000 + (20 - 25)a_{\overline{70}|.025} = 835.51$$
$$\text{Total price of the bonds to yield } 5\% = \$4309.00$$

A third type of bond may be designated as an **annuity bond** in which a given obligation is to be paid off in equal periodical payments. Such obligations were considered in Article 139 in reference to the amortization of debts. Letting C represent the value of the debt to be retired, and R the amount of the equal payment needed to retire the debt in k periods, we have

$$R = C \frac{1}{a_{\overline{k}|r}}, \qquad (12)$$

where r represents the bond or obligation rate of interest. This is, of course, equivalent to formula (1) of Article 139. The purchase price of this obligation, to earn an investment rate of interest of i, n periods before it is completely paid off, is simply,

$$V_n = Ra_{\overline{n}|i},$$
$$V_n = \frac{Ca_{\overline{n}|i}}{a_{\overline{k}|r}}, \qquad (13)$$

where n is equal to or less than k.

Example 2. On June 1, 1945 the Friendly Valley Creamery borrowed $50,000 under a contract which called for the repayment of principal and interest at 4% in 25 equal payments made at the ends of each year. What would be the purchase price of this contract (annuity bond) on June 1, 1950 if the holder of the bond offered it for sale to yield the investor 5%?

OTHER TYPES OF BONDS

Solution. The annual payment is

$$R = 50{,}000 \,\frac{1}{a_{\overline{25}|.04}},$$
$$= \$3200.60.$$

On June 1, 1950 the bond has 20 years to run so we have

$$V_{20} = 3200.60 a_{\overline{20}|.05},$$
$$= \$39{,}886.50,$$

the purchase price to yield 5%. This result may be obtained by direct substitution in formula (13) if the amount of the payment is not needed.

It is evident that no new problem is involved in buying such an annuity bond between payment intervals. Thus we simply find the value of the bond at the latest payment date and then proceed as in the case of the conventional bond. The problem of finding the yield rate of interest for such a bond offered for sale at a given price may readily be determined by interpolation between two values of V_n obtained from formula (13).

Still another type of bond to be considered is the **perpetual bond,** which is a contract that promises to pay at the end of each period a fixed amount which we may call the coupon or bond interest. Examples of such bonds are the British "consols," the French "rentes," and certain Canadian railroad bonds. Since such obligations carry no promise to repay a principal sum, the interest payments are the only benefits from the purchase of the bond. It is obvious that these payments form a perpetuity, and hence the purchase price of a perpetual bond bought to yield an interest rate of i per period is

$$V = \frac{I}{i}, \tag{14}$$

where I represents the amount of the coupon.

Example 3. The Canadian Pacific Debenture 4s, Jj, are perpetual bonds. What was the purchase price on March 15, 1945 of a bond of this issue if it yielded $3\frac{3}{4}\%$?

Solution. The purchase price on January 1, 1945 would be $V = \frac{2}{0.01875}$ = \$106.67. On March 16, 75 days later, the price would be

$$106.67 \left[1 + \tfrac{75}{180}\,(0.01875)\right] = \$107.50.$$

Example 4. A perpetual bond which pays \$5 per year, sold for \$110 on an interest payment date. What was the yield rate of interest?

Solution. Since \$110 is invested for a \$5 return, the yield rate is

$$\tfrac{5}{110} = 0.0455,$$

which could also have been obtained by substitution in formula (14).

EXERCISE 8

1. Mr. Jones buys a U.S. Savings bond for $75, which at maturity, 10 years later, is redeemed at $100. What yield rate of interest, converted annually, will Mr. Jones make on his investment if he holds the bond to maturity?

2. After 5 years Mr. Jones, in Problem 1, finds he needs his money from his bond. He receives $82.00 when he cashes the bond. What yield rate of interest, converted annually, did he make?

3. A $30,000 bond issue of the Windsor Electric Co. consisting of thirty $1000 bonds, 3%, Mn, is redeemable in six equal installments beginning May 1, 1970 and continuing yearly for six years. What offer should an investment company make on May 1, 1950 for this entire issue to yield 4%?

4. The Wayside Hotel borrows $50,000 on a mortgage which calls for semiannual interest payments at the rate of 6% and for the repayment of the principal in 5 equal installments made at intervals of four years, the first due at the end of 4 years. The creditor decides to sell the mortgage to yield 5% immediately after he receives his second payment on principal. What is the selling price?

5. Find the purchase price of a perpetual bond with $5 coupons on an interest payment date to yield $4\frac{1}{2}\%$.

6. A perpetual bond paying $2 on January 1 and July 1 was bought on April 16 to yield 3%. What was the purchase price?

7. A perpetual bond, paying interest coupons of $30 semiannually, was bought on an interest payment date for $1200. What yield rate of interest was made by the buyer?

8. A perpetual bond, paying interest coupons of $10 semiannually, is bought on an interest payment date for $920. What yield rate of interest is earned?

9. Show that the purchase price of a serial bond issue retired in s equal payments of C each, the first at the end of n periods, the next at the end of $n + k$ periods, and so on with the last payment in $n + (s - 1)k$ periods, is given by

$$V = \frac{rFs}{i} - \frac{rF - iC}{i}(1 + i)^{-n} \frac{a_{\overline{sk}|i}}{a_{\overline{k}|i}},$$

where F is the face value corresponding to a redemption price of C, r is the bond rate of interest per period, and i is the yield rate per period.

10. Use the formula in Problem 9 to work Problem 3.

11. Use the formula in Problem 9 to work Problem 4.

12. If the serial issue of Problem 9 is redeemed in installments beginning at the end of the first period and then at the end of each period until a total of s installments have been paid, show that the purchase price is

$$V = Ca_{\overline{s}|i} + \frac{rF}{i}(s - a_{\overline{s}|i}).$$

157. The reinvestment problem

Money invested at 4%, converted semiannually, can actually be said to earn 4%, since each six months' interest earned is added to the principal and begins to earn interest at the same rate that applies to the original principal. However, quite another state of affairs exists if a person lends his money on the mortgage plan at the rate of 4%, payable semiannually. The lender must now consider what to do with his interest payments as they come to him at the ends of the six-month periods. If he can reinvest these payments at 4%, converted semiannually, as they are received, he will still be making 4% on his money. However, the usual case is either a delay in reinvestment or reinvestment at a different rate, which means that this investment does not earn 4%.

Let us consider first the amount of an investment of V which bears interest at the rate of i payable at the end of each period. Suppose that we can reinvest the interest payments at the rate of r per period. The amount, S, at the end of n periods is

$$S = V + Vis_{\overline{n}|r},$$
or
$$S = V(1 + is_{\overline{n}|r}). \tag{15}$$

Formula (15) is sometimes called the generalized compound interest law.

Example 1. Which is better from the standpoint of the investor: (a) an opportunity to invest $1000 of his money at 4%, converted semiannually, for 10 years, or (b) to invest it at 5% interest, payable semiannually, where he can reinvest his interest payments at 3%, converted semiannually?

Solution. (a) At 4%, converted semiannually, the compound amount of $1000 in ten years is

$$1000(1.02)^{20} = \$1485.95.$$

(b) By the other plan of earning 5%, payable semiannually, and reinvesting the interest payments at the rate of 3%, converted semiannually, we have that the generalized compound amount is

$$S = 1000(1 + 0.02s_{\overline{20}|.015}),$$
$$= \$1462.47.$$

Hence the first plan is better by $23.48 for the investor.

The preceding example suggests the desirability of setting up a formula from which the value V' can be obtained, which if invested at a given yield rate of interest i', will amount to as much as investing V at the rate i and for which the interest payments are reinvested at the rate r. We have

$$V'(1+i')^n = V(1+is_{\overline{n}|r}),$$
$$V' = V(1+is_{\overline{n}|r})(1+i')^{-n}. \tag{16}$$

Example 2. Mr. Elfenbein can invest his money at compound interest for an interest rate of 4%, converted semiannually. What can he afford to pay for a $1000 note, due in 10 years, with interest at the rate of 5%, payable semiannually, provided that the interest payments can be reinvested, when payable, at the rate of 2%, converted semiannually?

Solution. Letting V' represent the amount that Mr. Elfenbein can afford to pay, we have

$$V'(1.02)^{20} = 1000(1 + 0.025s_{\overline{20}|.01}),$$
from which
$$V' = 1000(1 + 0.025s_{\overline{20}|.01})(1.02)^{-20},$$
$$= \$1043.43.$$

This amount represents the amount Mr. Elfenbein can afford to pay for the $1000 note. To repeat, if he invests this much at compound interest at the rate of 4%, converted semiannually, he will have just as much on deposit at the end of 10 years as he would have from the note which pays $1000 at the end of 10 years and in addition interest payments of $25, at the end of each quarter, which are immediately reinvested at 2%, converted semiannually.

Obviously a very slight change can be made in formula (16) to make it applicable to a bond investment or any dividend-paying venture. Let C and I represent the same quantities for which they were used in Article 149 in case the investment is a bond; otherwise let C represent the value of the investment after a given number of years and let I represent the dividend per period. We then have

$$V' = (C + Is_{\overline{n}|r})(1+i')^{-n}. \tag{17}$$

Again, if instead of comparing with an investment made at compound interest, we compare with one for which interest is payable periodically at the rate of i' and for which the reinvestment rate is the same as for the reinvestment of I, we would have

$$V'(1 + i's_{\overline{n}|r}) = C + Is_{\overline{n}|r},$$
$$V' = \frac{C + Is_{\overline{n}|r}}{1 + i's_{\overline{n}|r}}. \tag{18}$$

It is interesting to note that this formula is identical with formula (18), Article 148, for determining the value of a mining property when the salvage value is different from zero. In fact, a little thought on the part of the student will convince him that the two problems are also similar. We also note that if $r = i'$ (that is, if the reinvestment rate is the same as the yield rate), we have

$$V' = \frac{C + Is_{\overline{n}|i}}{1 + i'\frac{(1+i')^n - 1}{i'}} = \frac{C + Is_{\overline{n}|i}}{(1+i')^n},$$

$$= C(1+i')^{-n} + Ia_{\overline{n}|i},$$

which is the first bond formula given in Article 150.

Example 3. Mr. Thomas can invest his money in a building and loan association which computes interest at the rate of 3%, converted semiannually. What can he afford to pay on an interest payment date for a $1000 bond, redeemable in 10 years, at $1100, which pays interest semiannually at the rate of 4%, it being assumed that he can reinvest his money from the interest payments at the rate of $1\tfrac{1}{2}$%, converted semiannually?

Solution. This is clearly a case where formula (17) applies. Hence V', the amount Mr. Thomas can afford to pay for the bond is,

$$V' = (1100 + 20s_{\overline{20}|.0075})(1.015)^{-20},$$
$$= \$1135.85.$$

Example 4. Assume that Mr. Thomas, in Example 3, can invest his money in a ten-year mortgage for which the interest rate is 5%, payable semiannually. What could he afford to pay for the bond in Example 3?

Solution. We apply formula (18) obtaining

$$V' = \frac{1100 + 20s_{\overline{20}|.0075}}{1 + 0.015 s_{\overline{20}|.0075}},$$
$$= \$1156.88.$$

Example 5. A $1000, 5% bond, Jj, redeemable at par in 20 years, was bought on January 1 for $988.50. Interest payments can be reinvested immediately, when paid, at 2%, converted semiannually. At what rate of interest, converted semiannually, could the purchase price have been invested to earn the same as earned by the purchase of the bond?

Solution. We immediately see that the purchase price, carried forward at compound interest at the rate to be determined, will be equal to the redemption price of the bond plus the accumulation of the interest payments at the reinvestment rate of interest. Hence,

$$988.50(1 + i')^{40} = 1000 + 25 s_{\overline{40}|.01}.$$

It should be observed that this result could have been obtained by use of formula (17). A logarithmic solution may be obtained giving

$$i' = 0.02046,$$

which, expressed as a nominal rate, is 4.092%, converted semiannually.

EXERCISE 9

1. Mr. Kern lends $10,000 on a note due in 8 years with interest at the rate of 6%, payable annually. He reinvests his interest payments, as they are

made, at the rate of 3%, converted annually. How much will this investment amount to at the end of 8 years?

2. A church can invest $20,000 of its endowment fund at the rate of 3%, converted semiannually. However, it is considering a plan to lend this money, secured by 6-year mortgages, to members of its congregation who desire such loans, at the rate of 4%, payable semiannually. If the church can reinvest the interest payments on these mortgages at 1%, converted semiannually, which plan will give the church the greater income? Using the better plan how much more will it have at the end of 6 years?

3. Which is better for the investor and by how much at the end of 7 years: (a) $5000 invested at 6%, interest payable quarterly, or (b) this amount invested at 4% interest, converted quarterly, if the interest payments on the first plan can be reinvested at 2%, converted quarterly?

4. A college can, in general, invest its funds at 3%, converted annually. What can it afford to pay for a note of $6000 due in 15 years with interest at the rate of 5%, payable annually, if the interest payments can be reinvested at 2%, converted annually?

5. An investment company wishes to earn $4\frac{1}{2}$%, converted semiannually, on its investments. What can they pay for a $500 bond on an interest payment date if the bond pays 6% interest, payable semiannually, is redeemable in 40 years at par, and if the bond interest can be reinvested at 3%, converted semiannually?

6. Mr. Kirkpatrick, who wishes to earn 3%, converted semiannually, on his investments, is considering the purchase of a $1000 bond, interest payable semiannually at 4%, redeemable in 20 years at $1050. If he can reinvest his interest payments at $2\frac{1}{2}$%, converted semiannually, what should he pay for the bond on the interest payment date 20 years before redemption?

7. The Yerkes Automobile Corp. 3%, Ms, '69, redeemable at 105, are bought to yield the investor the equivalent of 4%, converted semiannually. If his reinvestment rate is 2%, converted semiannually, what should he pay for a $1000 bond of this issue on March 1, 1949?

8. If an insurance company can invest its funds in mortgages at the rate of 4% payable semiannually, what can it afford to pay on an interest payment date for a $10,000, 5%, Jj, bond due in 35 years, if the reinvestment rate that the company can earn is $2\frac{1}{2}$%, converted semiannually?

9. Mr. Burnside buys 100 shares of preferred stock at $75\frac{1}{2}$. He sells the stock in 12 years at the same price. In the meantime, the stock has paid $4 per year per share in dividends. If Mr. Burnside reinvested his dividends at 2%, at what rate, converted annually, could he have invested his money so that it would amount to the same as it did on the stock investment?

10. Mr. Lamb can invest his money in mortgages due in 10 years with interest payable semiannually at the rate of 5%. He can reinvest the interest payments at 2%, converted semiannually. He buys, however, 50 shares of common stock at 80 which pay a $3 dividend per share payable in two installments of $1.50 each. At what price must he sell his stock 10 years later so that

he will make just as much on this investment as he would have made on the mortgages?

11. The Willow Creek Power Co. 4s, Ms, '70, redeemable at 108, sold at 104 on March 1, 1948. If an investor can reinvest the interest payments at 2%, converted semiannually, what rate of interest, payable semiannually, would he have to make on an investment due in 22 years, if he can reinvest these interest payments also at 2%, converted semiannually, in order that one investment be equivalent to the other?

12. An investor can earn 5%, converted quarterly, on $10,000. He can buy a note for $10,000, due in 20 years, which pays interest at the rate of 4%, payable quarterly. What reinvestment rate, converted quarterly, must he earn on the interest payments to make the total earnings equivalent to the first plan?

13. Prove that the compound interest law is obtained by substituting $r = i$ in formula (15).

14. Solve for i' in formula (16) by the use of logarithms.

15. Solve for i' in formula (17) by the use of logarithms.

16. A debt, K, is to be paid off in n equal installments of R each made at the ends of the periods with compound interest computed at the rate of i per period. The creditor can reinvest the payments from this debt at compound interest at the rate of r per period. Show that he will have

$$S = K \frac{s_{\overline{n}|r}}{a_{\overline{n}|i}},$$

accumulated at the end of n periods.

17. Show that the investment rate of interest, i', compounded periodically for n periods, earned by the creditor in Problem 16, is given by the equation

$$(1 + i')^n = \frac{s_{\overline{n}|r}}{a_{\overline{n}|i}}.$$

18. Mr. Kline lends $5000 at 5%, converted annually, under the provision that the loan is to be repaid, principal and interest, in 20 equal annual payments, the first due at the end of the first year. If Mr. Kline can reinvest the repayments of this loan at 3%, converted annually, what does his total reinvestment amount to by the time the debt is repaid?

19. What interest rate, converted annually, will earn just as much for Mr. Kline in Problem 18, if the entire loan, principal and interest, is to be repaid at the end of 20 years?

20. Mr. Stuart has the choice of two ways for investing $9987.50. The first is a mortgage loan for which he will be repaid, principal and interest, at 4%, converted semiannually, in 20 semiannual payments the first at the end of six months. Mr. Stuart can reinvest these repayments at 2%, converted semiannually. The second investment is in ten $1000 bonds redeemable in 10 years at 110, interest at $3\frac{1}{2}$%, payable semiannually. These bonds can be bought on the interest payment date 10 years before redemption at $99\frac{7}{8}$, and the interest payments can be reinvested at 2%, converted semiannually. Which investment gives the best return and by how much?

MISCELLANEOUS EXERCISE

1. Fifty $1000 bonds of the Sandy Creek Rayon Co. 5s, Ms, '85, redeemable at par, were purchased on March 1, 1948 to yield the investor 4%, converted semiannually. What was the total purchase price?

2. The Blue Lakes Fish Co. 3s, Jj, '65, are redeemable at 105. Find the purchase price of a $500 bond of this issue on July 1, 1950, to yield the investor $3\frac{1}{2}\%$ converted semiannually.

3. The trustees of a college wish to invest their endowment fund at $3\frac{1}{2}\%$, converted semiannually. What is the maximum they can pay for a $1000, 4% bond, Ms, on March 1, 25 years before its redemption at 105?

4. A $1000 bond of the Riverdale Creamery Co. 3s, Fa, '51, redeemable at 110, was purchased on August 1, 1948 to yield $3\frac{1}{2}\%$. Find the purchase price and make a schedule showing the book values, the bond interest, the investment interest, and the amount for the amortization of the premium or the accumulation of the discount.

5. A $500 bond of the Clovis Smelting Co. 5s, Mn, '52, redeemable at 105, was purchased to yield 4% on November 1, 1948. Find the purchase price and make a table showing book values, the bond interest, the investment interest, and the amortization of the premium.

6. The U.S. Treasury $2\frac{1}{2}$s, Jd15, are redeemable at par at any interest payment date beginning June 15, 1962 to December 15, 1967. An investor bought a $1000 bond of this issue on June 15, 1948 to yield 2%. (a) Assuming that the bond will be retired at the earliest redeemable date possible, what did he pay? (b) If the bond is not retired until the latest possible redemption date, what interest rate will the investor make, assuming he bought the bond at the price computed in (a). (Use the interpolation method for solving this problem).

7. A $1000, 5% bond, Ms, '63, redeemable at par, was bought on May 13, 1947 to yield 4%. (a) What was the purchase price of the bond? (b) What was the quoted price of the bond on that date?

8. A $500, 3% bond, Mar. 15, '75, redeemable at 105 was bought on July 23, 1948 to yield 4%. (a) What was the purchase price of the bond? (b) What was the quoted price of the bond on that date?

9. The Stony Valley Petroleum Co. 4s, Jj, '84, redeemable at par, were quoted at 101 on March 15, 1948. (a) What was the purchase price of a $1000 bond of this issue on that date? (b) Find the yield rate of interest by interpolation, expressed as a nominal rate.

10. Find the current yield rate of interest on a $1000, 5% bond, Mar. 15, bought on April 15 for $989.17.

11. The quoted price on a $500, 3% bond, Jj, on Feb. 28 is $101\frac{1}{2}$. What is the current yield rate of interest expressed as a nominal rate?

12. Find the approximate yield rate, expressed as a nominal rate of interest, on a $1000 bond of the Stone Mountain Corp. 4s, '65, Fa, redeemable at 101, bought for $1045.25 on May 1, 1948.

13. Find the approximate yield rate expressed as a nominal rate of interest on a $1000 bond of the Regent Tobacco Co. 4s, '89, fA, redeemable at 110, if this issue was quoted at $102\frac{1}{2}$ on June 20, 1947.

14. The Samson Canning Corp. 2s, '58, jD, callable and redeemable at 101, were quoted at $98\frac{5}{8}$ on June 1, 1947. What would be the most likely yield rate of interest that an investor would make if he bought a $1000 bond of this issue on that date?

15. A $1000, 3% bond, '91, Jj, callable at 105, but redeemable at par on the due date, was bought for $1061.50 on June 1, 1948. Between what limits does the buyer's yield rate of interest lie?

16. Mr. Miller bought a $100 U.S. Government Savings bond on January 1, 1945 for $75. (a) After holding the bond for $1\frac{1}{2}$ years he turns it in and receives $76.00. What nominal rate of interest, converted semiannually, does he earn on his money? (b) If he had held the bond for 3 years, he would have received $78.00. What nominal interest rate would he have made on his money? (c) If he holds the bond to maturity, 10 years later, what nominal rate of interest, converted semiannually, will he make?

17. The Franklin and Churchill Corp. serial 3s, Ao, are to be redeemed at 101 beginning on April 1, 1965 and on April 1 every year thereafter for 10 years. These bonds are offered for sale in blocks of ten $1000 bonds each with a different redemption date. What is the cost, on April 1, 1949, of a block of these bonds to yield the investor $3\frac{1}{2}\%$?

18. A note for $10,000 calls for repayment of principal and interest at 6%, converted monthly, in equal monthly payments made at the ends of the months for 8 years. Immediately after 17 payments have been made, the owner of the note sells it to yield 5%, converted monthly, for the buyer. What was the sale price of the note?

19. A perpetual bond pays $25 semiannually. What is the purchase price of the bond on an interest payment date to yield 4%, payable semiannually?

20. What is the purchase price of the bond in Problem 19 forty-five days after an interest payment date to yield 4%, payable semiannually?

21. Mr. Mace can invest $10,000 of his money in a note with interest payable quarterly at the rate of 6%. To what does this investment amount in 10 years, if he can reinvest the interest payments at the rate of 3%, converted quarterly?

22. Mr. Moray can invest his money in 10-year notes with interest at the rate of 5%, payable semiannually, and he can reinvest his interest payments at the rate of 3%, converted semiannually. At what rate, converted semiannually, could he invest his money to make the same on his money as he would on the note investment?

23. Mr. Snyder can invest $6000 of his funds at 4% converted quarterly. He is offered 4.4%, payable quarterly, for the $6000 on a 10-year note. At what rate must Mr. Snyder be able to reinvest the interest payments so that the note offer is equivalent to the first method of investing his money?

24. Mr. Fox may invest his money either at $4\frac{1}{2}\%$, converted annually, or in 6-year trust deed notes with interest payable annually. If he can reinvest the interest payments from the notes at 3%, converted annually, what interest rate must Mr. Fox obtain from the trust deed notes to be equivalent to the first method of investing his money?

25. Mr. Steiner can invest his money in a $1000, 5%, Jj, 20-year bond, redeemable at 110. If the interest payments can be reinvested at 3%, converted semiannually, what can he afford to pay for the bond on January 1 if he could invest his money at 4%, converted semiannually?

26. A $1000 bond of the Ocean Refining Co. 5s, '85, Fa, redeemable at 102 was sold on February 1, 1948 at $102\frac{1}{2}$. If the interest payments can be reinvested at 3%, converted semiannually, at what interest rate, converted semiannually, could the purchase price have been invested to earn the same amount as obtained by the bond investment?

27. A man has the chance to invest his money in a mortgage note payable in 6 years with interest at the rate of 4% payable semiannually. Assume that the interest payments on the note can be reinvested at 2%, converted semiannually. What could this man afford to pay for a $1000, 5% bond, Jj, on an interest payment date 6 years before its redemption at par if the interest payments from the bond can be reinvested at 2%, converted semiannually?

28. A $1000, 5% bond, Jj, redeemable at 105 in 10 years was bought for $997.50. Assume that the interest payments on the bond can be reinvested at 3%, converted semiannually. At what rate could the $997.50 have been invested in a 10-year mortgage note with interest payable semiannually, if the interest payments on the note can be reinvested at 3%, converted semiannually.

19

Life Annuities

158. Introduction and definitions

A contingent annuity (see Article 127), for which the continuation of the payments is dependent upon the life of an individual, is called a **life annuity**. The individual concerned is called the **annuitant**.

A life annuity is called an **immediate life annuity** if its payments start either now or not later than the end of the first year. If the payments of a life annuity start after one year, the life annuity is said to be deferred or is called a **deferred life annuity**.

A life annuity whose payments cease only at the time of the death of the annuitant is called a **whole life annuity**. Contrasted to the whole life annuity is the **temporary life annuity**, an annuity for which the payments cease at the time of the death of the annuitant or at the end of a specified time if the annuitant is still alive.

If the payments of a life annuity are made at the ends of the years, the life annuity is called an **ordinary life annuity**; if the payments are made at the beginnings of the years, it is called a **life annuity due**.

Thus if Mr. Busman receives $500 at the end of each year for as long as he lives, he is receiving an immediate, ordinary, whole life annuity. If the payments are received at the beginning of each year, the annuity becomes an immediate, whole life, annuity due. If a further stipulation is made that Mr. Busman will cease to receive payments after reaching the age of 60, the annuity becomes an immediate, temporary, life annuity due.

In life annuities we consider a series of payments. If, instead of such a series of payments, a person is to receive only one payment of R at the end of n years, we have what is called an **n-year pure endowment** of R.

Life annuities and endowments may be purchased from most of the life insurance companies. The contract between the individual and the company is called the **policy**. The mathematically correct payment which should be made for the policy is called the **net premium**, which often is paid in several installments. To each net premium is added a small amount to cover agent fees and other expenses. The amount added is called the **loading** and the resultant premium is called the **gross premium**, which is the sum that the annuitant actually pays.

Since the amount of loading varies somewhat from company to company, we will not attempt to compute gross premiums in this text but will determine the net premiums. Hereafter we shall use the word premium to mean net premium unless otherwise explicitly stated.

EXERCISE 1

Classify the following life annuities in accordance with the definitions given in the above article:

Prob. no.	Annuity starts	Payments start	Payments cease at
1.	Now	Now	Death of annuitant
2.	Now	In 1 year	Death of annuitant
3.	In 5 years	In 6 years	Death of annuitant
4.	In 5 years	In 5 years	Death of annuitant
5.	Now	Now	Death of annuitant or at end of 20 years depending upon which occurs first
6.	Now	In 1 year	Death of annuitant or after 20 years depending upon which occurs first.
7.	In 10 years	In 10 years	Death of annuitant or at the end of 30 years depending upon which occurs first.
8.	In 10 years	In 11 years	Death of the annuitant.

9. A man now 40 is to receive $2000 if he reaches the age of 60. What is this payment called?

159. Present value of a pure endowment

It will be recalled (see Article 109) that the mathematical expectation E, of winning a prize M, is $E = pM$, where p is the probability of winning the prize. This formula assumes that the prize money is to be paid immediately.

Assume that the prize money is to be paid n years after the prize

PRESENT VALUE OF A PURE ENDOWMENT

is won. Then in place of M we must put its present value, $M(1+i)^{-n}$ or Mv^n. Hence,

$$E = pMv^n. \qquad (1)$$

In finding the present value of an n-year pure endowment of 1, we must determine from the mortality table the probability that a person now aged x will live for n years. This probability is equal to $\dfrac{l_{x+n}}{l_x}$ (see Article 108). Hence, letting $_nE_x$ represent the required present value, we have by substituting in (1)

$$_nE_x = \frac{l_{x+n}}{l_x} \cdot 1 \cdot (1+i)^{-n},$$

or

$$_nE_x = \frac{l_{x+n}}{l_x} v^n. \qquad (2)$$

If the n-year pure endowment is for R instead of 1, the present value is obviously $R\,_nE_x = R\,\dfrac{l_{x+n}v^n}{l_x}$.

Example 1. Jane Jessup, aged 10, is to receive an inheritance of $5000 provided that she reaches the age of 21. What is the present value of her inheritance if money is worth 2%?

Solution. This is an 11-year pure endowment of $5000; hence

$$5000\,_{11}E_{10} = 5000\,\frac{l_{21}v^{11}}{l_{10}}.$$

Using the mortality table (Table XII) we have,

$$5000\,_{11}E_{10} = 5000\,\frac{(949171)(0.8042630)}{971804},$$
$$= \$3927.66.$$

This means that Jane Jessup's inheritance is worth only $3927.66 when she is 10. However, if she lives to be 21, she will receive the entire $5000. If she should die before reaching the age of 21, neither she nor her heirs receive any of the inheritance.

Table XII is the Commissioner's Standard Ordinary (1941) Mortality Table, a table which is now in general use by almost all the insurance companies in the United States for figuring premiums on insurance policies. Although life insurance companies usually use special mortality tables, such as the 1937 Standard Annuity Table, for figuring premiums on life annuities, we shall use the CSO table for life annuities as well as life insurance in all the problems in this text.

Formula (2) may be rewritten in the form

$$_nE_x = \frac{l_{x+n}v^{x+n}}{l_x v^x},$$

by multiplying numerator and denominator in (2) by v^x. Designating $l_x v^x$ by D_x, we have $l_{x+n}v^{x+n} = D_{x+n}$ and formula (2) becomes

$$_nE_x = \frac{D_{x+n}}{D_x}, \tag{3}$$

a form very easily remembered. Furthermore, it has a great advantage over formula (2), in that Table XIII gives the values of D_x (and hence D_{x+n}) directly for a $2\frac{1}{2}\%$ interest rate. The calculation can then be accomplished by a single division. If the rate is not $2\frac{1}{2}\%$, either formula (2) must be used or else another table for D_x must be computed for the given rate.

Example 2. Mr. Chisholm, now 30 years old, is to receive $1000 provided he reaches the age of 50. Using both formulas (2) and (3), find the present value of Mr. Chisholm's expectancy on a $2\frac{1}{2}\%$ basis.

Solution. By formula (2),

$$1000\,_{20}E_{30} = 1000\,\frac{l_{50}v^{20}}{l_{30}} = 1000\,\frac{(810900)(0.610271)}{924609},$$

$$= \$535.22.$$

By formula (3)

$$1000\,_{20}E_{30} = 1000\,\frac{D_{50}}{D_{30}} = 1000\,\frac{235925}{440801},$$

$$= \$535.22.$$

Unless otherwise stated, it will be assumed hereafter that the interest rate is $2\frac{1}{2}\%$ for all problems.

Example 3. Mr. E. R. Strong is 30 years old. What 35-year pure endowment can he purchase for $2000?

Solution. Let X represent the endowment. We have

$$X\,_{35}E_{30} = 2000,$$

or

$$X = \frac{2000}{_{35}E_{30}} = \frac{2000 D_{30}}{D_{65}},$$

$$= \frac{2000(440801)}{116088}$$

$$= \$7594.26,$$

the endowment Mr. Strong will receive if he lives to the age of 65.

EXERCISE 2

Find the present value of each of the following n-year pure endowments.

Prob. no.	Amount of endowment	Age of person to whom endowment is payable	n
1.	$2000	20	40
2.	$2000	50	40
3.	$4000	30	20
4.	$8000	30	20
5.	$7000	25	30
6.	$7000	25	60

7. Find the premium of a 10-year pure endowment of $500 for a person aged 25: (a) if money is worth 2%, (b) if money is worth $2\frac{1}{2}$%.

8. Find the premium on a 25-year pure endowment of $1500 for a person aged 30: (a) if money is worth $3\frac{1}{2}$%, (b) if money is worth $2\frac{1}{2}$%.

9. Determine the cost of a 25-year pure endowment of $5000, if money is worth $2\frac{1}{2}$%, for a man aged 35. How much would this man have to deposit in a security paying $2\frac{1}{2}$% so that he or his heirs will receive $5000 in 25 years? Explain why these two answers differ.

10. David Jones, at age 15, becomes heir to $10,000 payable when he reaches 25, provided that he is then alive. What is the present value of his inheritance if money is worth $2\frac{1}{2}$%?

11. Mrs. Selma David, at age 40, is given the choice of an inheritance of $20,000 payable in 10 years, provided that she is then alive, or an inheritance of $19,000 payable to her or her heirs in 10 years. Which is the better of the two choices if money is worth $2\frac{1}{2}$%?

12. As defined in the text, $D_x = l_x v^x$. Verify the entries for D_{26}, D_{50}, D_{90} in Table XIII, for which the interest rate is $2\frac{1}{2}$%.

13. What 20-year pure endowment can a man aged 40 buy with $1500?

14. Mr. Elmer Miles, aged 21, receives a $10,000 inheritance with the stipulation that one-half must be used for the purchase of a 30-year pure endowment. What is the size of such an endowment?

160. Immediate whole life annuities

We shall represent the present value of an **immediate ordinary whole life annuity** of 1 per year for a person aged x, by the symbol a_x. Since the payments are to be received at the end of the first year, at the end of the second year, at the end of the third year, and so on as long as the annuitant lives, these payments constitute a series of pure endowments of 1 to a person aged x. We have

$$a_x = {}_1E_x + {}_2E_x + {}_3E_x + \cdots \text{ to the end of the table,}$$
$$= \frac{D_{x+1}}{D_x} + \frac{D_{x+2}}{D_x} + \frac{D_{x+3}}{D_x} + \cdots \text{ to the end of the table,}$$
$$= \frac{D_{x+1} + D_{x+2} + D_{x+3} + \cdots \text{ to the end of the table}}{D_x}.$$

Obviously the computation by direct use of the above formula is laborious unless the annuitant is very old. For this reason the commutation column, headed N_x in Table XIII, is used. We note that $N_x{}^* = D_x + D_{x+1} + D_{x+2} + \cdots + D_{x+n} + \cdots$ to the end of the table. Hence

$$a_x = \frac{N_{x+1}}{D_x}. \tag{4}$$

If the payment is R instead of 1 we have

$$Ra_x = R\frac{N_{x+1}}{D_x}.$$

A second method of deriving this formula is to assume that l_x people, all of age x, desire to share equally in the cost of providing a fund which will pay to each member of the group \$1 at the end of each year as long as they live. At the end of the first year, l_{x+1} members of the group are still alive and hence l_{x+1} dollars are needed at the end of one year. The present value of this amount is vl_{x+1}. Likewise l_{x+2} dollars are needed at the end of two years and its present value is $v^2 l_{x+2}$ and so on. Hence the present value of all the money needed is

$$vl_{x+1} + v^2 l_{x+2} + v^3 l_{x+3} + \cdots \text{ to the end of table.}$$

Since each person is to share equally, the cost to each of the l_x persons in the group is

$$a_x = \frac{vl_{x+1} + v^2 l_{x+2} + v^3 l_{x+3} + \cdots \text{ to the end of table}}{l_x}.$$

Multiplying numerator and denominator by v^x, we have

$$a_x = \frac{v^{x+1} l_{x+1} + v^{x+2} l_{x+2} + v^{x+3} l_{x+3} + \cdots \text{ to the end of table}}{v^x l_x},$$
$$= \frac{D_{x+1} + D_{x+2} + D_{x+3} + \cdots \text{ to the end of the table}}{D_x},$$
$$= \frac{N_{x+1}}{D_x},$$

which agrees with formula (4). This method of deriving the formula for a_x is sometimes called the **mutual fund method.**

* The symbol N_x replaces $\overline{N}_x$ in accordance with the recent agreement of the International Congress of Actuaries.

IMMEDIATE WHOLE LIFE ANNUITIES

Example 1. What is the premium on a whole life annuity for a person aged 30 if the payments of $1000 each are to be received at the ends of the years?

Solution. By the use of formula (4) we have that

$$1000 a_{30} = 1000 \frac{N_{31}}{D_{30}},$$
$$= 1000 \frac{10153479.81}{440800.58},$$
$$= \$23{,}034.20,$$

where this result is correct only to the nearest 10 cents since 6-place logarithms were used for the division.

Consider now the problem of finding the present value, or premium, of an immediate whole life annuity due of 1. We shall represent such a present value by $\ddot{a}_x$, using the trema over the symbol for the ordinary annuity. Since the first payment is certain, we have

$$\ddot{a}_x = 1 + a_x,$$
$$= 1 + \frac{N_{x+1}}{D_x},$$
$$= \frac{D_x + N_{x+1}}{D_x}.$$

From the definition of N_{x+1} we have

$$D_x + N_{x+1} = D_x + D_{x+1} + D_{x+2} + \cdots \text{ to end of table}$$
$$= N_x.$$

Hence,

$$\ddot{a}_x = \frac{N_x}{D_x}. \tag{5}$$

As before, if the payment is R instead of 1, we have

$$R\ddot{a}_x = R\frac{N_x}{D_x}.$$

Example 2. Miss Verna Gates, 35 years old, receives an inheritance of $500 per year for life, the first payment to be made to her at once. What is the present value of her inheritance?

Solution. This is an immediate whole life annuity due; hence the present value of Miss Gates's inheritance is

$$500\ddot{a}_{35} = 500 \frac{N_{35}}{D_{35}},$$
$$= 500 \frac{8510443.06}{381995.63},$$
$$= \$11{,}139.50.$$

Example 3. At the age of 65, Mr. Niels has $20,000 with which to buy a life annuity which will give him annual payments for life. How large is the annual payment if paid at the ends of the years?

Solution. Let R represent the annual payment. Since the payments form an immediate ordinary whole life annuity we have

$$20,000 = R \frac{N_{66}}{D_{65}},$$

or
$$R = 20,000 \frac{D_{65}}{N_{66}},$$

$$= \frac{(20,000)(116088.15)}{1056041.64},$$

$$= \$2198.55,$$

the annual payment which Mr. Niels will receive as long as he lives.

EXERCISE 3

(*Note:* In accordance with our previous agreement, all interest rates are assumed to be $2\frac{1}{2}\%$ unless otherwise stated.)

Determine the present value of each of the following immediate whole life annuities.

Prob. no.	Annual payment	Time payable	Annuitant's age
1.	$2000	At ends of years	30
2.	$2000	At ends of years	50
3.	$2000	At ends of years	70
4.	$2000	At beginnings of years	70
5.	$ 500	At beginnings of years	10
6.	$1000	At beginnings of years	20
7.	$5000	At ends of years	65
8.	$5000	At ends of years	75

9. Mrs. Elliot, aged 67, is to receive, at the death of her husband, $3000 at the end of each year for life, from his insurance policy. What is the equivalent cash value of these payments?

10. Life membership in an alumni association costs $100. The annual membership dues are $4 payable at the beginnings of the years. (a) Which is cheaper for a man 25 years old? (b) For a man 35 years old?

11. Find the premium on a whole life annuity for a person aged 95 if the annual payment of $6000 is received at the beginnings of the years. How much smaller is this premium if interest is computed at $3\frac{1}{2}\%$ instead of $2\frac{1}{2}\%$?

12. A college professor has $25,000 with which to buy an annuity policy when he retires at age 67. What yearly payment will this annuity provide for life if payments are made at the ends of the years?

13. When reaching age 67, the professor in Problem 12 decides he would like to teach until he is 70, at which time he purchases an annuity with his $25,000. What yearly payment will he receive for life if the payments are made at the ends of the years?

14. Mr. Schuster has $30,000 at age 65 with which to buy a whole life annuity, payments at the ends of the years. (a) If Mr. Schuster had invested his money in an annuity certain which paid him back in payments equal to that obtained from the life annuity, how long would he have to live to receive back his entire investment with interest? (b) Suppose Mr. Schuster dies at age 70. What do his heirs receive under each plan? (c) If he is alive at age 80 what would he receive under each plan?

161. Deferred whole life annuities

As defined in Article 158, a deferred whole life annuity is one for which the payments start at some time after the first year and continue for life. Let n represent the number of years the annuity is deferred and let the present value of such an annuity of 1 for a person aged x be represented by $_n|a_x$, if the first payment is made at the end of $n+1$ years. If the first payment is made at the end of n years, represent the present value of the annuity by $_n|\ddot{a}_x$. In the first case, we have the present value of a deferred ordinary whole life annuity of 1, and in the second case the present value of a deferred whole life annuity due of 1.

Considering the present value of the deferred ordinary whole life annuity as the sum of a series of n-year pure endowments we have,

$$_n|a_x = {}_{n+1}E_x + {}_{n+2}E_x + {}_{n+3}E_x + \cdots \text{ to end of table,}$$

$$= \frac{D_{x+n+1} + D_{x+n+2} + D_{x+n+3} + \cdots \text{ to end of table}}{D_x},$$

or, $$_n|a_x = \frac{N_{x+n+1}}{D_x}. \qquad (6)$$

In like manner,

$$_n|\ddot{a}_x = {}_nE_x + {}_{n+1}E_x + {}_{n+2}E_x + \cdots \text{ to end of table,}$$

$$= \frac{D_{x+n} + D_{x+n+1} + D_{x+n+2} + \cdots \text{ to end of table}}{D_x},$$

or, $$_n|\ddot{a}_x = \frac{N_{x+n}}{D_x}. \qquad (7)$$

Example 1. Find the premium on a deferred ordinary whole life annuity of $1000 per year for a person aged 30, if the period of deferment is 35 years.

Solution. From formula (6) we have that the present value or premium, is

$$1000_{35|}a_{30} = 1000\frac{N_{66}}{D_{30}},$$

$$= \frac{(1000)(1056041.64)}{440800.58},$$

$$= \$2395.72.$$

Example 2. Find the premium on a deferred whole life annuity due of $1000 per year for a person aged 30, if the period of deferment is 35 years.

Solution. From formula (7) we have that the present value or premium is

$$1000_{35|}\ddot{a}_{30} = 1000\frac{N_{65}}{D_{30}},$$

$$= \frac{(1000)(1172129.79)}{440800.58},$$

$$= \$2659.09.$$

Example 3. A person aged 30 has $2000 available for the purchase of a deferred ordinary whole life annuity. What annual payment will he receive if the interval of deferment is 10 years?

Solution. Let R represent the annual payment. We have

$$R_{10|}a_{30} = 2000,$$

or

$$R = \frac{2000}{_{10|}a_{30}} = \frac{2000 D_{30}}{N_{41}},$$

$$= \frac{2000(440801)}{6379590},$$

$$= \$138.19.$$

The student should note that the answer to Example 2 may be obtained by considering the annuity as a deferred ordinary whole life annuity for a person aged 30, with a period of deferment of 34 years.

EXERCISE 4

Find the premium for each of the following deferred whole life annuities.

Prob. no.	Annuity payment	Annuitant's age	Interval of deferment	Type of annuity
1.	$500	20	40	Ordinary
2.	$500	20	60	Ordinary
3.	$1000	20	40	Ordinary
4.	$500	20	40	Due
5.	$2000	40	40	Due
6.	$1000	10	60	Due
7.	$1000	60	10	Due
8.	$1500	50	5	Ordinary

TEMPORARY LIFE ANNUITIES

9. Find the premium on a deferred ordinary whole life annuity of $400 per year for a person aged 38, if the period of deferment is 10 years.

10. Find the premium on a deferred whole life annuity due of $650 per year for a person aged 50, if the period of deferment is 20 years.

11. A company offers all its employees with 30 years or more of service an annuity of $2400 per year, starting when the employee reaches the age of 60 years. Find the present value of an employee's expected pension if he starts working for the company at the age of 30.

12. From the proceeds of an insurance policy of $10,000, Mrs. White, aged 55, buys a whole life annuity from which she wishes to receive annual payments starting at age 65. How large are her payments?

13. Suppose that Mrs. White, in Problem 12, had invested her $10,000 in a security paying 3% interest compounded annually, and after 10 years had purchased an immediate whole life annuity due. How large would her payments be? Explain why these payments are smaller than those received in Problem 12.

14. Mr. Grunner, aged 35, is offered either (a) an annuity certain of $2000 per year for 10 years, starting at age 60, or (b) a deferred whole life annuity of $3584 per year starting at age 60. Which is the better offer on a $2\frac{1}{2}\%$ basis?

15. Show that $a_x = {}_1|\ddot{a}_x$.

16. Show that ${}_n|\ddot{a}_x = {}_nE_x + {}_n|a_x$.

17. Derive the formula for the present value of an ordinary whole life annuity of 1 deferred for n years, for a person aged x, by the mutual fund method.

162. Temporary life annuities

As defined in Article 158, a temporary life annuity pays periodical payments to the annuitant over a definite term of n years, provided he lives throughout the entire term. If he dies any time during the term of the annuity, his payments cease. Otherwise the payments cease after n years. We may consider the present value of such an annuity as the difference between an immediate whole life annuity and a deferred whole life annuity.

If the payments are at the ends of the years, we have an ordinary temporary life annuity for n years. Representing the present value of such an annuity of 1 for a person aged x by $a_{x:\overline{n}|}$, where n indicates the term of the annuity, we have

$$a_{x:\overline{n}|} = a_x - {}_n|a_x,$$

$$= \frac{N_{x+1}}{D_x} - \frac{N_{x+n+1}}{D_x},$$

or

$$a_{x:\overline{n}|} = \frac{N_{x+1} - N_{x+n+1}}{D_x}. \tag{8}$$

If the payments are made at the beginnings of the years, we have a temporary life annuity due. Representing the present value of such an annuity of 1 by $\ddot{a}_{x:\overline{n}|}$, where n indicates the term of the annuity we have

$$\ddot{a}_{x:\overline{n}|} = \ddot{a}_x - {}_n|\ddot{a}_x,$$

$$= \frac{N_x}{D_x} - \frac{N_{x+n}}{D_x},$$

or
$$\ddot{a}_{x:\overline{n}|} = \frac{N_x - N_{x+n}}{D_x}. \tag{9}$$

Example 1. Find the premium on an ordinary temporary life annuity of $2000 for 20 years for a person aged 50.

Solution. By use of formula (8) we have

$$2000 a_{50:\overline{20}|} = 2000\,\frac{N_{51} - N_{71}}{D_{50}},$$

$$= 2000\,\frac{3613562.55 - 583035.431}{235925.04},$$

$$= \$25690.70.$$

Example 2. A wife receives from her husband's estate $3000 now and a like amount at the beginning of each year until 20 payments have been made, it being further stipulated that payments will cease should she die before the 20 payments have been made. Find the present value of her inheritance if she is 53 when she receives the first payment.

Solution. The payments form a temporary life annuity due of $3000 for a person aged 53. Hence from formula (9)

$$3000 \ddot{a}_{53:\overline{20}|} = 3000\,\frac{N_{53} - N_{73}}{D_{53}},$$

$$= 3000\,\frac{3167380.15 - 441348.341}{210456.33},$$

$$= \$38{,}858.90.$$

Example 3. Starting at age 25, Mr. Hill pays $180 at the beginning of each year to an insurance company, the last payment being made at age 64 or in the year prior to his death should he die before 64. In return, he is to receive a whole life annuity starting at 65. How large is the payment he expects?

Solution. The payments Mr. Hill makes form a temporary life annuity due of $180 running for 40 years. The present value of the payments of, say, R each that he receives forms a deferred whole life annuity due. Since the present value of one must be equal to the present value of the other, we have

$$180\ddot{a}_{25:\overline{40}|} = R\,_{40|}\ddot{a}_{25}$$

or
$$R = \frac{180\ddot{a}_{25:\overline{40}|}}{_{40|}\ddot{a}_{25}} = \frac{180\,\dfrac{N_{25} - N_{65}}{D_{25}}}{\dfrac{N_{65}}{D_{25}}},$$

$$= 180\,\frac{N_{25} - N_{65}}{N_{65}} = 180\,\frac{12992619.10 - 1172129.79}{1172129.79},$$

$$= \$1815.23.$$

EXERCISE 5

Find the present value of each of the following temporary life annuities whose term is indicated.

Prob. no.	Annuity payment	Annuitant's age	Term of the annuity	Type of annuity
1.	$1000	27	20	Ordinary
2.	$1000	27	40	Ordinary
3.	$1000	54	20	Ordinary
4.	$3000	65	20	Due
5.	$3000	70	20	Due
6.	$3000	75	20	Due

7. Find the premium on a temporary ordinary life annuity of $1500 for 20 years if the annuitant is 43 years old.

8. A person aged 50 buys a temporary life annuity due of $2500 running for 25 years. What premium must he pay?

9. Compare the costs of the following on a $2\tfrac{1}{2}\%$ basis:

(a) A temporary ordinary life annuity of $2000 running for 20 years for a person aged 10.

(b) A temporary ordinary life annuity of $2000 running for 20 years for a person aged 65.

(c) An ordinary annuity certain of $2000 running for 20 years.

10. By making payments of $300 per year, payable at the beginnings of the years, for 35 years provided he lives, Mr. Smith, aged 30, expects a pension starting at age 65. What payments will he receive?

11. With $18,000 Mr. Wayne, aged 47, buys a temporary ordinary life annuity for 25 years. What annual payment will Mr. Wayne receive?

12. If Mr. Wayne, in Problem 11, had bought a temporary life annuity due, what would be the annual payment he receives?

13. At age 27, Mr. Sehnert estimates that he will need a pension of $2400 per year starting at age 70. How much must he pay for this pension to an insurance company at the beginning of each year until he is 70, provided that he lives?

14. Suppose Mr. Sehnert, in Problem 13, had wanted to pay for his pension in 30 years. How large would each payment be? (Note: the pension still starts at age 70.)

15. A pension plan used by some companies and institutions is to have the employee set aside a certain percentage of his salary to be matched by the employer. The employer invests these funds, and at the time the employee retires an immediate whole life annuity is purchased for him.

Under this plan, find the pension, starting at 66, of an employee who at age 33 set aside $250 and a like amount at the end of each year until he reached 65, at which time he retired. The employer matched equally all payments made by the employee and earned 3% on his pension fund.

16. How large would the pension payment be in Problem 15 if the annual payments contributed by the employee and employer are used immediately to purchase a deferred life annuity?

163. Other types of life annuities

Assume that a person aged x is to receive an n-year, temporary life annuity due. The annuitant elects to leave the money in the insurance company, during the period of n years, allowing it to accumulate to a pure endowment at age $x + n$. In other words, he forbears to draw the annuity, and hence such an annuity is called a **forborne temporary life annuity due.**

Let $_nu_x$ represent the accumulated value of a forborne temporary life annuity due of 1 for a person aged x when he reaches age $x + n$. Assume that l_x persons of the same age contribute to such a fund by the payments due them from n-year temporary life annuities due of 1. We see that the sum of the total contributions is

$$l_x(1+i)^n + l_{x+1}(1+i)^{n-1} + \cdots + l_{x+n-1}(1+i).$$

Since each of the surviving persons at age $x + n$ share in this accumulated sum, we have

$$_nu_x = \frac{l_x(1+i)^n + l_{x+1}(1+i)^{n-1} + \cdots + l_{x+n-1}(1+i)}{l_{x+n}}.$$

Multiplying numerator and denominator by v^{x+n}, we have

$$_nu_x = \frac{v^{x+n}l_x(1+i)^n + v^{x+n}l_{x+1}(1+i)^{n-1} + \cdots + v^{x+n}l_{x+n-1}(1+i)}{v^{x+n}l_{x+n}},$$

$$= \frac{v^n l_x + v^{x+1}l_{x+1} + \cdots + v^{x+n-1}l_{x+n-1}}{v^{x+n}l_{x+n}},$$

$$= \frac{D_x + D_{x+1} + \cdots + D_{x+n-1}}{D_{x+n}},$$

or $\quad _nu_x = \dfrac{N_x - N_{x+n}}{D_{x+n}}.$ \hfill (10)

OTHER TYPES OF LIFE ANNUITIES

Example 1. From her husband's insurance policy, Mrs. Ames, aged 45, is entitled to receive annual payments, the first paid now, of $1000 each to run for 20 years provided she survives. She may also allow these payments to accumulate with the insurance company for 20 years, at the end of which time she withdraws the accumulated sum in one payment. How much will she receive at age 65 if she elects the second plan?

Solution. Mrs. Ames' $1000 payments left with the insurance form a forborne temporary life annuity due of $1000 for 20 years. Hence by formula (10), we have

$$1000 \,_{20}u_{45} = 1000 \frac{N_{45} - N_{65}}{D_{65}},$$

$$= 1000 \frac{5161996.00 - 1172129.79}{116088.15},$$

$$= \$34{,}369.40.$$

From another standpoint, a forborne temporary life annuity due may be considered as the n-year pure endowment that a person, aged x, can purchase with n payments of 1 each at the beginning of each year for n years provided that the person lives to age $x + n$. Since the payments form a temporary life annuity due, we have

$$\frac{N_x - N_{x+n}}{D_x} = (_nu_x)(_nE_x),$$

or

$$_nu_x = \frac{\dfrac{N_x - N_{x+n}}{D_x}}{\dfrac{D_{x+n}}{D_x}},$$

$$= \frac{N_x - N_{x+n}}{D_{x+n}}, \text{ which is formula (10)}.$$

Example 2. A person, aged 20, makes payments of $100 at the beginning of each year for 30 years, to an insurance company. What pure endowment will he receive at age 50, provided that he lives to receive it?

Solution. The accumulated value of this set of payments is the same as that of a forborne temporary life annuity due. Hence, by formula (10)

$$100 \,_{30}u_{20} = 100 \frac{N_{20} - N_{50}}{D_{50}} = 100 \frac{15744200 - 3849490}{235925},$$

$$= \$5041.73.$$

Example 3. Suppose that the person in Example 2 wishes to purchase a life annuity due with his payments, instead of a pure endowment. What annual payment will he receive from the insurance company?

Solution 1. Since 1 at age 50 will buy a life annuity due of $\dfrac{D_{50}}{N_{50}}$ per year, as can be seen from formula (5), it follows that $5041.74 will buy a life annuity due of $5041.73\dfrac{D_{50}}{N_{50}}$, or $5041.73\left(\dfrac{235925}{3849490}\right)$, or $309.00 per year.

Solution 2. An alternate solution is obtained by setting up the equation which states that the present value of the annual premiums is equal to the present value of the benefits. Thus we have

$$100\frac{N_{20} - N_{50}}{D_{20}} = R\frac{N_{50}}{D_{20}},$$

where R is the desired payment. Solving,

$$R = 100\frac{N_{20} - N_{50}}{N_{50}} = \frac{100(15744200 - 3849490)}{3849490},$$

$$= \$309.00.$$

A life annuity in which a certain number of payments are guaranteed or certain may be considered as a combination of an annuity certain and a deferred life annuity. If the sum of the payments certain, interest not considered, is equal to the cost of the annuity, the annuity is called a **refund annuity**.

Example 4. Find the present value of an annuity, to a person aged 40, which pays 10 payments certain of $500 each at the end of each year, followed by payments of an equal amount for as long as he lives.

Solution. The present value of this annuity is the sum of the present values of an ordinary annuity certain of $500 for 10 years and an ordinary life annuity of $500 deferred for 10 years. Hence

$$\text{Present value} = 500a_{\overline{10}|.025} + 500_{10}|a_{40},$$

$$= 500(8.75206) + 500\frac{N_{51}}{D_{40}},$$

$$= 4376.03 + 500\left(\frac{3613560}{328984}\right),$$

$$= \$9868.02.$$

Example 5. Find the present value and the number of payments certain of a refund annuity for a person, aged 50, which pays $500 at the end of each year.

Solution. Let n represent the number of payments certain. Then

$$500n = 500a_{\overline{n}|.025} + 500_n|a_{50},$$

or

$$n = a_{\overline{n}|.025} + \frac{N_{n+51}}{D_{50}}.$$

OTHER TYPES OF LIFE ANNUITIES

We can find an approximate solution of this equation by substitution of values of n until one side of the equation is as nearly equal to the other side as possible. We make the following table.

n	$a_{\overline{n}|.025}$	$\dfrac{N_{n+51}}{D_{50}}$	$a_{\overline{n}|.025} + \dfrac{N_{n+51}}{D_{50}}$
16	13.05500	4.01515	17.07015
17	13.71220	3.58469	17.29689
18	14.35336	3.18429	17.53765

Thus, if 18 payments of $500 each are guaranteed, followed by like payments for life, the present value or cost should be $500(17.53765) = \$8768.82$. It should be noted that the equation from which n is obtained does not, in general, have an integral solution.

EXERCISE 6

Find the accumulated value of each of the following forborne temporary life annuities due.

Prob. no.	Payment	Age of annuitant at beginning of forborne period	Number of years in forborne period
1.	$1000	50	20
2.	$2500	60	10
3.	$500	55	10
4.	$800	65	15
5.	$675.55	40	25
6.	$738.90	48	30
7.	$250	70	10

8. At age 60, Mr. Morton is to receive $1500, payable at the beginning of each year for 20 years, or for as long as he lives if he dies before he reaches the age of 80. If he leaves the payments with the insurance company, what single payment will he receive from the company if he reaches age 80?

9. In Problem 8, assume that Mr. Morton reaches the age 80. How much would he have had on deposit if he had taken the payments of $1500 each as they came due and deposited them in a security which earns interest at the rate of $2\frac{1}{2}\%$, converted annually? How do you explain the difference between this answer and that obtained in Problem 8?

10. Mr. Ingalls, aged 27, pays $300 at the beginning of each year for 40 years, in exchange for a life annuity due beginning at age 67. What annual payment will he receive, beginning at age 67, until his death?

11. If the payments of a forborne annuity are made at the ends of the years, show that the accumulated value of such an annuity of R per year is

$$R \frac{N_{x+1} - N_{x+n+1}}{D_{x+n}}.$$

12. In exchange for payments of $600 made at the end of each year for 20 years, provided that he lives, an insurance company will pay a person, now aged 30, the accumulated value of a forborne annuity if he reaches the age 50. How much will he receive if he is alive at age 50?

13. At age 60, Mr. Luke buys an annuity which will pay him or his heirs $2500 at the end of each year for 10 years and then like payments to him as long as he lives. What must he pay for this annuity?

14. What would be the cost of the annuity in Problem 12 if the $2500 payment is to be made only as long as Mr. Luke is alive?

15. Mr. Luke of Problem 13 decides that he can wait until he is 71 before he needs the first payment of $2500. What is the cost of the annuity under this new arrangement?

16. Work Problem 15 assuming that no payments are certain.

17. Find the cost of a refund annuity of $250 per year, payments at the ends of the years, for a person aged 43.

18. Find the annual income to a person aged 60 from a refund annuity, payable at the ends of the years, whose cost is $10,000.

19. Under the terms of her husband's $10,000 life insurance policy, Mrs. Burdette is to receive 10 annual payments certain and then like payments for life. Mr. Burdette dies when his wife is 63 years old. What payments does Mrs. Burdette receive if the payments are made at the beginnings of the years?

20. If Mrs. Burdette, in Problem 19, had the privilege of choosing a life annuity due, with no payments certain, how large would her payments have been?

21. If Mrs. Burdette, in Problem 19, had the privilege of choosing a refund annuity, how large would her payments have been?

164. Life annuities with payments m times a year

Often life annuity payments are made more frequently than once a year, usually for the convenience of the annuitant. If the mortality table were made to show the number of persons dying at monthly intervals, then the present formulas would be sufficient to solve all problems involving the usual annuity payment periods: namely, the month, the quarter, the half-year, and the year. Without such a table it is possible to set up approximate formulas which serve for most practical purposes. The following is one of the most commonly used approximations.

Consider the present value of a whole life annuity due $\ddot{a}_x$ and the present value of an ordinary whole life annuity a_x, where $a_x = \ddot{a}_x - 1$;

LIFE ANNUITIES WITH PAYMENTS m TIMES A YEAR

that is, the value of an annuity of 1, with the first payment due in one year, is 1 less than the value of an annuity with its first payment due now. Therefore we assume that the value of an annuity of 1, first payment $\frac{1}{m}$th of a year later, is $\ddot{a}_x - \frac{1}{m}$; $\frac{2}{m}$th of a year later it is $\ddot{a}_x - \frac{2}{m}$, and so on. Representing the present value of an annuity of 1 paid in m installments of $\frac{1}{m}$ each at the ends of the periods by $a_x^{(m)}$, we have

$$m a_x^{(m)} = \ddot{a}_x - \frac{1}{m} + \ddot{a}_x - \frac{2}{m} + \ddot{a}_x - \frac{3}{m} + \cdots + \ddot{a}_x - \frac{m}{m}.$$

$$= m\ddot{a}_x - \frac{1}{m}(1 + 2 + 3 + \cdots + m).$$

But since $\ddot{a}_x = a_x + 1$ and $1 + 2 + 3 + \cdots + m$ is an arithmetical progression whose sum is $\frac{m}{2}(m+1)$, we have

$$m a_x^{(m)} = m(a_x + 1) - \frac{1}{m} \cdot \frac{m}{2}(m+1),$$

$$= m a_x + \frac{m-1}{2},$$

or $\qquad a_x^{(m)} = a_x + \frac{m-1}{2m}.$ \hfill (11)

Example 1. Find the present value of an ordinary whole life annuity of $1200 per year, paid in monthly installments of $100 each, for a person aged 30. Compare this present value or cost with that for a whole life annuity of $1200 paid once a year.

Solution. Since the payments are monthly, $m = 12$, hence

$$1200 a_{30}^{(12)} = 1200\left(a_{30} + \frac{11}{24}\right) = 1200\left(\frac{N_{31}}{D_{30}} + \frac{11}{24}\right),$$

$$= 1200\left(\frac{10153480}{440801} + \frac{11}{24}\right),$$

$$= \$28{,}191.00.$$

The cost of an ordinary life annuity of $1200 per year in one installment is

$$1200 a_{30} = 1200\left(\frac{10153480}{440801}\right),$$

$$= \$27{,}641.00,$$

which is less than the corresponding cost when the annuity is paid in 12 installments.

We next consider the present value of an ordinary deferred life annuity of 1 paid in m installments of $\dfrac{1}{m}$ each. Since the value of such an annuity at the *end of the deferment interval* is $a_{x+n}^{(m)}$, the annuitant, now aged x, will receive this sum of money if he survives n years. This is equivalent to the present value of an n-year pure endowment of $a_{x+n}^{(m)}$. Hence,

$$_n|a_x^{(m)} = {_nE_x}(a_{x+n}^{(m)}),$$

or,
$$_n|a_x^{(m)} = {_nE_x}\left(a_{x+n} + \frac{m-1}{2m}\right). \tag{12}$$

Since the present value of a temporary life annuity is equal to the difference between a whole life annuity and a deferred annuity, we have

$$a_{x:\overline{n}|}^{(m)} = a_x^{(m)} - {_n|a_x^{(m)}},$$

$$= a_x + \frac{m-1}{2m} - {_nE_x}(a_{x+n}^{(m)}),$$

$$= a_x + \frac{m-1}{2m} - {_nE_x}\left(a_{x+n} + \frac{m-1}{2m}\right),$$

$$= a_x - {_nE_x}(a_{x+n}) + \frac{m-1}{2m}(1 - {_nE_x}).$$

But $a_x - {_nE_x}(a_{x+n})$ is exactly $a_{x:\overline{n}|}$, hence

$$a_{x:\overline{n}|}^{(m)} = a_{x:\overline{n}|} + \frac{m-1}{2m}(1 - {_nE_x}). \tag{13}$$

We readily see that the present value of a whole life annuity due of 1 paid in installments of $\dfrac{1}{m}$ each is

$$\ddot{a}_x^{(m)} = \frac{1}{m} + a_x^{(m)}$$

$$= \frac{1}{m} + a_x + \frac{m-1}{2m}.$$

Hence
$$\ddot{a}_x^{(m)} = a_x + \frac{m+1}{2m}. \tag{14}$$

The student may easily verify the following. The present value of a deferred life annuity due of 1 paid in m installments of $\dfrac{1}{m}$ each is

LIFE ANNUITIES WITH PAYMENTS m TIMES A YEAR

$$_n|\ddot{a}_x^{(m)} = {_nE_x}(a_{x+n}^{(m)})$$

or

$$_n|\ddot{a}_x^{(m)} = {_nE_x}\left(a_{x+n} + \frac{m+1}{2m}\right). \qquad (15)$$

The present value of a temporary life annuity due of 1 paid in m installments of $\frac{1}{m}$ each is

$$\ddot{a}_{x:\overline{n}|}^{(m)} = \ddot{a}_{x:\overline{n}|} - \frac{m-1}{2m}(1 - {_nE_x}). \qquad (16)$$

EXERCISE 7

Find the present value or cost of each of the following life annuities paid in installments as indicated:

Prob. no.	Annual payment	Number of payments per year	Age of the annuitant	Ordinary or due	Value wanted
1.	$1200	12	50	Ordinary	Whole life
2.	$600	4	60	Due	Whole life
3.	$500	2	40	Ordinary	Deferred 20 years
4.	$750	2	45	Due	Deferred 10 years
5.	$675	4	30	Ordinary	Temporary for 20 years
6.	$1800	12	37	Due	Temporary for 10 years
7.	$800	4	30	Ordinary	Deferred for 50 years
8.	$1500	2	80	Ordinary	Whole life
9.	$2400	12	60	Ordinary	Whole life
10.	$1200	4	60	Ordinary	Temporary for 35 years

The present value of an ordinary whole life annuity is $12,000 for a person aged 40. Find the indicated payment for each of the cases following:

11. Monthly payment   12. Quarterly payment
13. Semiannual payment 14. Annual payment

The present value of a whole life annuity due is $15,000 for a person aged 60. Find the indicated payment for each of the cases following:

15. Monthly payment   16. Quarterly payment
17. Semiannual payment 18. Annual payment

19. The beneficiary, aged 50, of an insurance policy may elect to take either (a) a cash payment of $20,000 or (b) a temporary life annuity due paid in two installments per year for 20 years. What would be the semiannual payment if the latter plan is elected?

20. Mr. Slater, aged 25, plans to save $200 at the beginning of each year for 40 years. If he uses this to buy a deferred whole life annuity, which pays

quarterly payments beginning at age 65, how large will each quarterly payment be?

165. Summary of important formulas

The student will find the following collection of formulas helpful, especially in regard to the relationship between the various types of annuities.

Annuity or endowment	Formula	Represents
n-year pure endowment	$_nE_x = \dfrac{D_{x+n}}{D_x}$	Present value
Ordinary whole life annuity of 1	$a_x = \dfrac{N_{x+1}}{D_x}$	Present value
Whole life annuity due of 1	$\ddot{a}_x = \dfrac{N_x}{D_x}$	Present value
Ordinary whole life annuity of 1, deferred n years	$_n|a_x = \dfrac{N_{x+n+1}}{D_x}$	Present value
Whole life annuity due of 1, deferred n years	$_n|\ddot{a}_x = \dfrac{N_{x+n}}{D_x}$	Present value
Ordinary temporary life annuity of 1	$a_{x:\overline{n}|} = \dfrac{N_{x+1} - N_{x+n+1}}{D_x}$	Present value
Temporary life annuity due of 1	$\ddot{a}_{x:\overline{n}|} = \dfrac{N_x - N_{x+n}}{D_x}$	Present value
Forborne annuity purchased by payments of 1 at the beginning of each year for n years	$_nu_x = \dfrac{N_x - N_{x+n}}{D_{x+n}}$	Value at age $x+n$ (accumulated value)

It should be noted that:

1. The value of the quantity indicated is at the age given by the subscript of the D in each denominator.

2. In each formula which contains N's in the numerators, the subscript of the N indicates the age at which the first payment is received or made.

3. If only one N appears in the numerator, the payments continue for life.

4. If a second N appears, the payments terminate and the subscript of the second N indicates the earliest age for which there is no payment.

MISCELLANEOUS EXERCISE

1. At age 5, James inherits $20,000, payable at age 21 provided that he is alive at that time. What is the present value of the inheritance?

2. A father wishes to provide his son William, aged 2, with a certain

SUMMARY

amount of money for college expenses when William reaches the age of 18. If his father can afford to set aside $1000, what pure endowment will it buy for William?

3. If William's father, in Problem 2, had invested his $1000 by depositing it in a building and loan association which allows interest at the rate of $2\frac{1}{2}\%$, converted annually, what would be available for William when he reaches 18? Explain the difference in the amounts received by the two plans.

4. What 40-year endowment will $200, paid at the beginning of each year for 40 years, buy if a person is 25 years old?

5. Suppose that the person in Problem 4 wishes a whole life annuity starting at age 65 in place of the endowment purchased by the $200 payments. What are the annual payments that he will receive?

6. Find the cost of a whole life annuity due of $2500 for a person aged 38.

7. Find the cost of an ordinary whole life annuity of $2500 for a person aged 38.

8. Mr. Reagan, aged 25, buys a whole life annuity due of $3000, deferred 40 years. What is the premium?

9. What annual premium for 40 years, provided that he lives, would Mr. Reagan have to pay for the annuity in Problem 8, if the payments are made at the beginnings of the years?

10. Mr. Baker, aged 65, has $20,000. From the mortality table, his complete expectancy of life is 11.55 years. Which provides the greater annual payment: (a) an ordinary annuity certain, for 11 years, purchased with the $20,000, or (b) an ordinary whole life annuity purchased with the $20,000? Use an interest rate of $2\frac{1}{2}\%$, converted annually, for the annuity certain as well as for the life annuity.

11. Find the premium for an ordinary whole life annuity of $1200 for a person aged 27, if the first 10 payments are certain.

12. Find the cost of the annuity in Problem 11 if the first 20 payments are certain.

13. A man, aged 55, offers a university $100,000, provided that the university will pay him interest at the rate of 3%, payable annually, for as long as he lives. If the university accepts the gift, what will it cost to provide an ordinary whole life annuity for an amount equal to the required interest?

14. It is estimated that $4200 is the average annual earnings of a certain person, aged 35, for 30 years. What is the present value of these earnings?

15. To make up for the loss of his support when he moves away, Mr. Love, aged 24, arranges that his church shall receive from him a whole life annuity of $200 per year starting in one year. What is the present value of his gift?

16. What is the premium and how many payments are certain on an ordinary refund life annuity of $500 for a person aged 23?

17. Find the amount of a forborne life annuity due for a person, aged 51, if the payments are $300 per year for 25 years.

18. Show that $\ddot{a}_{x:\overline{n}|} = {}_nu_x({}_nE_x)$.
19. Show that $\ddot{a}_{x+1} = {}_1u_x(\ddot{a}_x - 1)$.
20. Show that $\ddot{a}_x = \ddot{a}_{x:\overline{n}|} + {}_n|\ddot{a}_x$.

20

Life Insurance

166. Introduction and definitions

A person is said to have his life insured if at his death (or at his death during a specified interval) a company, called the **insurance company,** pays to a specified person, called the **beneficiary,** the benefit from the insurance. The written contract between the insured and the company is called the **policy** and the **face** of the policy is the **benefit.** In exchange for the benefit, the insured or policyholder pays a **gross premium** or **premiums.** The policyholder's age at issue of the policy is that age on his birthday nearest to the policy date. The **policy year** starts at the age of issue and runs for a full year, the second policy year runs for the next year, and so on.

In calculating premiums on life insurance policies, we assume, as we did for life annuities, that we are dealing with a large number of individuals and hence that the laws of probability will hold. The assumption of a rate of interest and the use of a mortality table, which now is the CSO Table, leads to the proper payment or payments which the insured should pay for his policy. These payments are called **net premiums.** To these premiums is added an extra charge to take care of expenses connected with the securing of policyholders. This process is called **loading.** The result is the **gross** or **office premium.** Since the methods of loading a premium vary from company to company, no attempt will be made in this text to figure gross premiums.

From the formulas of a relatively few standard policies, we can compute the premium on all types of complicated insurance policies. The standard types to be considered are as follows:

1. **Whole life policy.** An insurance for which the benefit is payable at death only.

2. **Deferred life policy.** An insurance policy for which the benefit is payable at death provided that it does not occur before a specified number of years, called the deferment period. This type of policy

INTRODUCTION AND DEFINITIONS

actually is not sold separately but may occur as a part of many of the present-day, complicated policies.

3. **Term policy.** A temporary insurance for which the benefit is payable at death provided that it occurs within a given interval of time.

4. **Endowment policy.** This policy is actually not a pure insurance policy, since it provides for the payment of the death benefit if death occurs within a given interval of time and provides for the payment of the benefit to the insured if he survives this given time. Thus it is a term insurance combined with an n-year pure endowment.

If the entire insurance is paid off in one payment, then the payment is called a **single premium** in contrast to annual or other methods of paying the cost of the insurance. Thus the **net single premium** on a life insurance is the present value of the face of the policy. The **net annual premium** is such that the present value of all the premiums is equal to the net single premium.

EXERCISE 1

Name the following policies, and answer the question in the last column:

Prob. no.	Face of policy	Age of issue	Provisions of the policy	What does beneficiary or insured receive at
1.	$5000	20	Benefit paid at death of insured.	Death of insured?
2.	$2000	30	Benefit paid to the beneficiary at death of insured if it occurs within 10 years, or to the insured provided he survives 10 years.	Death of insured if it occurs at age 35?
3.	$2000	30	Same as Problem 2.	Age 40 of insured?
4.	$1000	40	Benefit paid to beneficiary at death of insured provided it occurs within 20 years.	Death of insured if it occurs at age 50?
5.	$1000	40	Same as Problem 4.	Death of insured if it occurs at age 60?
6.	$3000	20	Benefit paid to beneficiary at death of insured provided it occurs 30 or more years from now.	Death of insured if it occurs at age 40?
7.	$3000	20	Same as Problem 6.	Death of insured if it occurs at age 60?

167. Whole life policy

The present value or net single premium on a **whole life policy** of 1 is represented by A_x for a person aged x. Although insurance benefits are payable immediately after proof of death is given to the company, we shall assume for the purpose of deriving formulas that all such payments are made at the end of the policy year in which death occurs. Hence for this policy we see that A_x is the sum of the mathematical expectations that the beneficiary will receive the face of the policy, 1, at the end of the first policy year, at the end of the second policy year and so on to the end of the table. Thus,

$$A_x = v\frac{d_x}{l_x} + v^2\frac{d_{x+1}}{l_x} + v^3\frac{d_{x+2}}{l_x} + \cdots \text{ to end of table,}$$

where $\frac{d_x}{l_x}$, $\frac{d_{x+1}}{l_x}$, $\frac{d_{x+2}}{l_x}$, $\cdots$ represent, respectively, the probabilities that the insured will die during the first, second, third, $\cdots$ policy years. Likewise, v, v^2, v^3, $\cdots$ represent the corresponding present values of the benefit. Multiplying numerator and denominator by v^x and using a common denominator, we have

$$A_x = \frac{v^{x+1}d_x + v^{x+2}d_{x+1} + v^{x+3}d_{x+2} + \cdots \text{ to end of table}}{v^x l_x}.$$

We represent $v^{x+k+1}d_{x+k}$ by C_{x+k}, hence

$$A_x = \frac{C_x + C_{x+1} + C_{x+2} + \cdots \text{ to end of table}}{D_x}.$$

The commutation columns (Table XIII) give the value of M_x, where

$$M_x = C_x + C_{x+1} + C_{x+2} + \cdots \text{ to end of table,}$$

hence
$$A_x = \frac{M_x}{D_x}, \tag{1}$$

where the interest rate involved is that of Table XIII, namely $2\frac{1}{2}\%$.

Example 1. Find the net single premium on a whole life policy for $5000 for a person aged 25.

Solution. The net single premium for a $1 policy is A_{25}; hence for a $5000 policy we have

$$5000 A_{25} = 5000\,\frac{M_{25}}{D_{25}} = 5000\left(\frac{189{,}701}{506{,}594}\right),$$
$$= \$1872.31.$$

The student should note that this may be called the present value of the insurance or the **cost** of the insurance.

Since most insurance policies are taken out by people who need

WHOLE LIFE POLICY

protection for their dependents, it is not likely that the insured can pay up the insurance in one single payment. The most likely arrangement will be by annual premiums* which cease at the death of the insured. Thus such payments actually form a whole life annuity. Furthermore, it is true that such annual payments are made at the beginning of each policy year. Let P_x represent the annual premium on a whole life policy of 1. We have

$$P_x \ddot{a}_x = A_x,$$

or,
$$P_x \frac{N_x}{D_x} = \frac{M_x}{D_x}.$$

Solving for P_x,
$$P_x = \frac{M_x}{N_x}. \tag{2}$$

Example 2. Find the annual premium for the insurance in Example 1.

Solution. We have
$$5000 P_{25} = 5000 \frac{M_{25}}{N_{25}} = 5000 \left(\frac{189701}{12992600} \right),$$
$$= \$73.00.$$

Often a whole life policy is bought with annual payments not for life but for a specified period of years, provided that the insured lives. Let m represent the number of years over which the insurance will be paid. These payments form a temporary life annuity due, and their present value is the present value of the insurance. Hence

$$_m P_x \ddot{a}_{x:\overline{m}|} = A_x,$$

or
$$_m P_x = \frac{A_x}{\ddot{a}_{x:\overline{m}|}} = \frac{\dfrac{M_x}{D_x}}{\dfrac{N_x - N_{x+m}}{D_x}}.$$

Simplifying,
$$_m P_x = \frac{M_x}{N_x - N_{x+m}}. \tag{3}$$

An insurance which is paid off in m payments is called a **m-payment insurance** and in particular formula (3) gives the net premium on an m-payment whole life insurance policy.

Example 3. Find the net premium on a 20-payment whole life policy of $5000 for a person aged 40.

Solution. We have
$$5000\,_{20}P_{40} = 5000 \frac{M_{40}}{N_{40} - N_{60}} = 5000 \left(\frac{165360}{6708573 - 1865614} \right)$$
$$= 5000 \left(\frac{165360}{4842959} \right) = \$170.72.$$

---

* Hereafter when the word premium is used it will mean net premium unless otherwise stated.

Example 4. In place of a $1000 settlement from an insurance company, Mrs. Raymond, aged 50, accepts a paid-up, whole life insurance. For what amount is the policy written?

Solution. If X represents the amount of the insurance, we have
$$XA_{50} = 1000,$$
$$X = \frac{1000}{A_{50}} = \frac{1000}{\dfrac{M_{50}}{D_{50}}} = 1000\,\frac{D_{50}}{M_{50}},$$
$$= 1000\left(\frac{235925}{142035}\right),$$
$$= \$1661.03.$$

Example 5. In settlement of an insurance policy, Mrs. Whitman receives $5000 and a life annuity of $500 paid at the end of each year for life. She may elect to leave the annuity payments with the company in exchange for a whole life paid-up insurance policy. For what amount would the policy be written if Mrs. Whitman is 55 years old?

Solution. Let X represent the amount of the policy. Then,
$$XA_{55} = 500 a_{55},$$
or
$$X = 500\,\frac{a_{55}}{A_{55}} = 500\,\frac{\dfrac{N_{56}}{D_{55}}}{\dfrac{M_{55}}{D_{55}}} = 500\,\frac{N_{56}}{M_{55}},$$
$$= 500\left(\frac{2560830}{126751}\right),$$
$$= \$10{,}101.80.$$

EXERCISE 2

Find the single premium, the annual premium for life, and the annual premium for m payments as indicated.

Prob. no.	Face of policy	Age of insured	Annual premium for m payments
1.	$1000	40	$m = 10$
2.	$5000	60	$m = 20$
3.	$10000	20	$m = 30$
4.	$2500	25	$m = 40$
5.	$3000	30	$m = 10$
6.	$1000	20	$m = 40$
7.	$1000	25	$m = 40$
8.	$1000	30	$m = 40$
9.	$1000	35	$m = 40$
10.	$1000	40	$m = 40$

WHOLE LIFE POLICY

11. What will a whole life insurance policy for $10,000 cost Mr. Rains when he is 35 years old, if he pays the whole cost of the insurance in one payment?

12. Mr. Rains, in Problem 11, can invest his money at 3%, converted annually. If he uses the money he plans to pay for the $10,000 policy, how long would he have to live so that he would have $10,000?

13. What net annual premium should Mr. Rains pay for his insurance in Problem 11?

14. Assume that Mr. Rains, in Problem 13, had invested the annual premiums in an investment paying 3%, converted annually, instead of buying the insurance. How long would it take for these payments to accumulate to the face of the policy and what last partial payment is needed, if any?

15. Suppose Mr. Rains, in Problems 11, 12, 13, 14, died when he was 40 years old. Which of the four methods of saving his money provides the most to his beneficiary or heirs for the least cost? What interest rate would have been earned for this best plan?

16. Suppose Mr. Rains, in Problems 11, 12, 13, 14, died when he was 70 years old. Which of the four methods of saving his money would provide the most to his beneficiary or heirs? What interest rate would have been earned for this best plan?

17. Without the use of the commutation columns, compute the value of the net single premium of a whole life policy of $5000 for a person aged 96 if the interest rate is $2\frac{1}{2}\%$, converted annually.

18. Find the net single premium in Problem 17 if the interest rate is $3\frac{1}{2}\%$, converted annually.

19. Find the net annual premium for the policy in Problem 17 without the use of the commutation columns.

20. Find the net annual premium for the policy in Problem 17 if the interest rate is $3\frac{1}{2}\%$, converted annually.

21. For a person aged 20, how much larger is the net annual premium on a 20-payment whole life policy of $1000 than that for a 30-payment life?

22. The settlement plan for an insurance policy of $10,000 for a widow, aged 60, provides for $8000 cash and provides that the balance may be used to buy a paid-up, whole life insurance policy. For what amount should the policy be written?

23. In a mutual life insurance company, the policyholder may share in the profits on his type of insurance in the form of dividends. Mr. Lacey, aged 30, has a whole life policy for $10,000 for which it is reasonably certain that the dividends will be $50 at the end of each year for life. He has the privilege of leaving these dividends with the company and thus increasing the amount of his insurance. If he guarantees to make up any difference between $50 and the dividend, by how much will his insurance be increased, it being assumed that the increase is effective immediately?

24. Mrs. Moore, aged 65 at the time of the death of her husband, is to receive $10,000 from his insurance policy and also $100 at the end of each year as long as she lives. She may leave the annuity with the insurance company and in its place receive a whole life paid-up insurance policy. For what amount would the policy be written?

25. Derive the formula for A_x by the mutual fund method used in Article 160.

168. Deferred life policy

As defined in Article 166, a **deferred life policy** pays the amount of the policy to the beneficiary, provided the insured dies after the deferment interval. Let n represent the number of years the insurance is deferred, and let $_n|A_x$ represent the net single premium for a policy of 1. We have

$$_n|A_x = \frac{v^{n+1}d_{x+n}}{l_x} + \frac{v^{n+2}d_{x+n+1}}{l_x} + \frac{v^{n+3}d_{x+n+2}}{l_x} + \cdots \text{ to end of table,}$$

$$= \frac{v^{n+1}d_{x+n} + v^{n+2}d_{x+n+1} + v^{n+3}d_{x+n+2} + \cdots \text{ to end of table}}{l_x}.$$

Multiplying numerator and denominator by v^x, we have

$$_n|A_x = \frac{v^{x+n+1}d_{x+n} + v^{x+n+2}d_{x+n+1} + v^{x+n+3}d_{x+n+2} + \cdots \text{ to end of table}}{vl_x},$$

or,

$$_n|A_x = \frac{C_{x+n} + C_{x+n+1} + C_{x+n+2} + \cdots \text{ to end of table}}{D_x}.$$

Since $M_k = C_k + C_{k+1} + \cdots$ to end of table,

$$_n|A_x = \frac{M_{x+n}}{D_x}. \tag{4}$$

Example 1. Find the net single premium on a deferred life policy of $3000 for a person aged 32 if the period of deferment is 10 years.

Solution. We have from formula (4) that

$$5000_{10}|A_{32} = 5000\frac{M_{42}}{D_{32}} = 5000\left(\frac{161326}{416507}\right),$$

$$= \$1936.65.$$

If such a policy is bought by annual premiums for life or for a specified period, we have, letting $_n|P_x$ represent the annual premium for life, paid at the beginning of each year,

$$_n|P_x \ddot{a}_x = {}_n|A_x,$$

or,

$$_n|P_x = \frac{_n|A_x}{\ddot{a}_x} = \frac{\dfrac{M_{x+n}}{D_x}}{\dfrac{N_x}{D_x}}.$$

Hence,

$$_n|P_x = \frac{M_{x+n}}{N_x}. \tag{5}$$

DEFERRED LIFE POLICY

If these payments are to be made over a specified number of years, m, provided that the insured lives, the annual payment $_mP(_n|A_x)$ may be obtained from the equation

$$_mP(_n|A_x)\ddot{a}_{x:\overline{m}|} = {_n|A_x},$$

$$_mP(_n|A_x) = \frac{_n|A_x}{\ddot{a}_{x:\overline{m}|}} = \frac{\frac{M_{x+n}}{D_x}}{\frac{N_x - N_{x+m}}{D_x}}.$$

Hence, $$_mP(_n|A_x) = \frac{M_{x+n}}{N_x - N_{x+m}}. \tag{6}$$

Example 2. Find the net annual premium for the policy in Example 1.

Solution. From formula (5) we have

$$5000_{10}|P_{32} = 5000\frac{M_{42}}{N_{32}} = 5000\left(\frac{161326}{9724960}\right),$$
$$= \$82.94.$$

Example 3. What annual premium for 5 years will pay up the insurance in Example 1?

Solution. The insurance is deferred 10 years and the payments are temporary for 5 years provided that the insured lives during this period. In formula (6) we have $m = 5$, $n = 10$ and $x = 32$; hence

$$5000_5P(_{10}|A_{32}) = 5000\frac{M_{42}}{N_{32} - N_{37}} = 5000\left(\frac{161326}{9724960 - 7757480}\right),$$
$$= 5000\left(\frac{161326}{1967480}\right),$$
$$= \$409.98.$$

It should be noted again that the deferred insurance is not usually sold as such but mainly in combination with the various new types of insurance policies offered at the present time.

EXERCISE 3

Find the premium indicated for the following deferred insurance policies:

Prob. no.	Age of insured	Amount of insurance	Interval of deferment	Premium wanted
1.	25	$1000	20	Net single premium
2.	25	$1000	40	Net single premium
3.	30	$5000	35	Net annual premium for life
4.	30	$5000	35	Net annual premium for 35 years
5.	40	$2500	25	Net annual premium for 20 years
6.	40	$2500	25	Net annual premium for 40 years
7.	40	$2500	25	Net annual premium for life
8.	50	$1000	15	Net single premium

9. An insurance policy pays $5000 provided that the insured dies during the first ten years of the life of the policy and $10,000 if death occurs at the end of 10 years or later. Find the net single premium for this policy for a person aged 25.

10. Find the annual premium for the policy described in Problem 9.

11. If the policy in Problem 9 is bought with the agreement that it be paid up in 20 annual payments, how large is each payment?

12. Mr. Sachs, now 27 years old, deposits $100, at the beginning of each year for 10 years, in a security paying $2\frac{1}{2}\%$, converted annually. At the end of 10 years he uses the money he has accumulated to buy a whole life insurance policy. How large a policy can he buy?

13. If Mr. Sachs could have deposited his $100 a year in an insurance company as payment for a whole life insurance policy deferred for 10 years how large would the policy have been? Explain the difference between this answer and the answer obtained in Problem 12.

169. Term policy

As previously defined, a **term insurance policy** pays to the beneficiary the amount of the policy, provided that the insured dies within a specified period of time, called the term of the policy. If this term is short, compared to the life expectancy of the insured, the cost of this type of insurance is low compared to others. For example, if a man wanted the maximum protection for his dependents for a specified period of time, it would be better for him to buy term insurance. However, it has one disadvantage — that is, if a person had not correctly estimated the period during which he would need protection for his dependents, he might find at the end of the term of the insurance that he could not pass the required physical examination for new insurance.

Representing by $A^1_{x:\overline{n}|}$ the net single premium for an n-year term life insurance policy of 1, we observe that the present value of such a policy of 1 is equivalent to the difference in the costs of a whole life insurance of 1 and that of a whole life insurance deferred for n years.

Hence,
$$A^1_{x:\overline{n}|} = A_x - {}_n|A_x,$$

$$= \frac{M_x}{D_x} - \frac{M_{x+n}}{D_x},$$

or
$$A^1_{x:\overline{n}|} = \frac{M_x - M_{x+n}}{D_x}. \tag{7}$$

Example 1. Find the net single premium for a 10-year term policy of $5000 for a person aged 30.

TERM POLICY

Solution. Since the insurance is for $5000 rather than $1 we have,

$$5000 A^1_{30:\overline{10|}} = 5000 \frac{M_{30} - M_{40}}{D_{30}},$$

$$= 5000 \frac{182403.5 - 165359.9}{440801},$$

$$= \frac{(5000)(17043.6)}{440801},$$

$$= \$193.32.$$

Term insurance is generally paid in annual installments over a period which cannot exceed the term of the insurance. If it is paid up in k years we have, representing the payment by ${}_kP^1_{x:\overline{n|}}$,

$${}_kP^1_{x:\overline{n|}} \ddot{a}_{x:\overline{k|}} = A^1_{x\ \overline{n|}},$$

since the payments form a temporary life annuity.

Hence
$${}_kP^1_{x:\overline{n|}} = \frac{A^1_{x:\overline{n|}}}{\ddot{a}_{x:\overline{k|}}},$$

$$= \frac{\dfrac{M_x - M_{x+n}}{D_x}}{\dfrac{N_x - N_{x+k}}{D_x}},$$

or
$${}_kP^1_{x:\overline{n|}} = \frac{M_x - M_{x+n}}{N_x - N_{x+k}}. \qquad (8)$$

An important special case is when $k = n$; in fact this is the usual case.

$$P^1_{x:\overline{n|}} = \frac{M_x - M_{x+n}}{N_x - N_{x+n}}. \qquad (9)$$

Example 2. Find the annual premium for the insurance in Example 1, if it is paid up in 10 years.

Solution. Since the payments are made throughout the term of the policy, we have

$$5000 P^1_{30:\overline{10|}} = 5000 \frac{M_{30} - M_{40}}{N_{30} - N_{40}},$$

$$= 5000 \frac{182403.5 - 165359.9}{10594280 - 6708573},$$

$$= \$21.93.$$

Example 3. Find the annual premium for a 10-payment term insurance of $5000 for a person aged 30, if the term of the insurance is 20 years.

Solution. The payments form a 10-year temporary life annuity due, and hence we may use formula (8) where the term of the insurance is 20 years.

Hence

$$5000\,_{10}P^1_{30:\overline{20}|} = 5000\,\frac{M_{30} - M_{50}}{N_{30} - N_{40}},$$

$$= 5000\,\frac{182403.5 - 142035.1}{10594280 - 6708573},$$

$$= \frac{(5000)(40368.4)}{3885707},$$

$$= \$51.94.$$

Example 4. Mr. Nellis, now 26, estimates that he can use $120 of his yearly income for insurance. He also estimates that a 30-year period will be ample for the protection of his dependents. How much whole life insurance can he buy with a $120 annual payment for 30 years? Compare this to the amount of 30-year term insurance he could buy with the same payments.

Solution. Let X represent the amount of whole life insurance he can buy by making payments of $120 at the beginning of each year for 30 years. We have

$$120\ddot{a}_{26:\overline{30}|} = XA_{26},$$

or

$$X = \frac{120(N_{26} - N_{56})}{M_{26}},$$

$$= \frac{120(12486025 - 2560828)}{188277},$$

$$= \frac{120(9925197)}{188277},$$

$$= \$6325.91,$$

the amount of whole life insurance which could be bought with payments of $120 per year for 30 years.

Let Y represent the amount of 30-year term insurance which can be bought with premiums of $120 per year. We have

$$120\ddot{a}_{26:\overline{30}|} = YA^1_{26:\overline{30}|}.$$

Solving for Y,

$$Y = \frac{120(N_{26} - N_{56})}{M_{26} - M_{56}},$$

$$= \frac{120(9925197)}{64928.2},$$

$$= \$18,343.80.$$

It should be noted that this is almost three times the amount of insurance that Mr. Nellis would have had if he had bought the whole life insurance, and hence if he needs protection for his dependents for only 30 years this arrangement would be much the best.

An interesting special case of a term insurance is the one-year term for which a person pays a single premium and for which his beneficiary is to receive the amount of the policy provided that the insured dies within one year. The premium paid is sometimes called the **natural premium**. Substituting $n = 1$ in formula (7) we have

$$A^1_{x:\overline{1}|} = \frac{M_x - M_{x+1}}{D_x}. \tag{10}$$

It should be noted that this formula can be written in the form

$$A^1_{x:\overline{1}|} = \frac{C_x}{D_x}.$$

Example 5. Find the natural premium on a $5000 term policy for one year for a person aged 30.

Solution. We have

$$5000 A^1_{30:\overline{1}|} = 5000 \frac{M_{30} - M_{31}}{D_{30}},$$

$$= 5000 \frac{182403.50 - 180872.34}{440801},$$

$$= \frac{(5000)(1531.16)}{440801},$$

$$= \$17.37.$$

Comparing this premium with the annual premium for a 10-year term policy as computed in Example 2, we note that this premium is $4.56 lower.

EXERCISE 4

Find the premium indicated for each of the following term insurance policies:

Prob. no.	Age of insured	Amount of insurance	Term of insurance in years	Premium wanted
1.	20	$2000	10	Net single premium
2.	20	$2000	20	Net single premium
3.	20	$2000	30	Net single premium
4.	20	$2000	30	Net annual premium for 10 years
5.	20	$2000	30	Net annual premium for 20 years
6.	20	$2000	30	Net annual premium for 30 years
7.	40	$2000	30	Net annual premium for 30 years
8.	40	$5000	10	Net single premium
9.	50	$5000	10	Net single premium
10.	37	$10,000	15	Net single premium

11. Find the annual premium on a 30-payment, 30-year term insurance of $1000 for a person aged 23.
12. Find the natural premium on a $1000 policy for a man aged 23.
13. Find the natural premium on a $1000 policy for a man aged 52.
14. At what age will the natural premium for a $1000 insurance be ap-

proximately equal to the annual premium for a 30-payment, 30-year term insurance for $1000 for a person aged 23? (See Problem 11.)

15. Mr. Larson, aged 32, buys an insurance policy which will pay his beneficiary $10,000 if he dies within 20 years, and $5000 if he dies at any time after this period. What annual premium for 25 years should he pay for this insurance?

16. How much 20-year term insurance can be bought with 10 annual payments of $50 each for a person aged 34? Compare this with the amount of whole life insurance that can be bought with the same payments.

17. If the person insured in Problem 16 died at age 64, what would his beneficiary receive (a) if he had bought the term insurance? (b) if he had bought the whole life insurance?

170. Endowment policy

As previously mentioned, an **endowment insurance** consists of two parts, a term insurance and a pure endowment. In a sense then, it is not a pure insurance. If the term of the endowment is n years, then it is certainly an insurance for this period. However, if the insured should survive this period, the insurance part of the policy ceases and he receives the amount of the policy as a pure endowment. Representing the net single premium by $A_{x:\overline{n}|}$ for a policy of 1 we have

$$A_{x:\overline{n}|} = A^1_{x:\overline{n}|} + {}_nE_x$$
$$= \frac{M_x - M_{x+n}}{D_x} + \frac{D_{x+n}}{D_x}.$$

Hence:
$$A_{x:\overline{n}|} = \frac{M_x - M_{x+n} + D_{x+n}}{D_x}. \tag{11}$$

Example 1. Find the net single premium for a $2000, 20-year endowment policy for a person whose age is 33.

Solution. Since formula (11) gives the required premium for $1, we have

$$2000 A_{33:\overline{20}|} = 2000 \frac{M_{33} - M_{53} + D_{53}}{D_{33}},$$
$$= 2000 \frac{177719.9 - 133203.2 + 210456.3}{404755},$$
$$= \frac{2000(254973)}{404755},$$
$$= \$1259.89.$$

Let ${}_kP_{x:\overline{n}|}$ represent the annual premium for k years which will buy the endowment insurance whose present value is $A_{x:\overline{n}|}$. We have

$${}_kP_{x:\overline{n}|} \ddot{a}_{x:\overline{k}|} = A_{x:\overline{n}|},$$
$${}_kP_{x:\overline{n}|} = \frac{M_x - M_{x+n} + D_{x+n}}{N_x - N_{x+k}}. \tag{12}$$

ENDOWMENT POLICY

It is obvious that k cannot exceed n. If $k = n$ we have,
$$P_{x:\overline{n}|} = \frac{M_x - M_{x+n} + D_{x+n}}{N_x - N_{x+n}}. \tag{13}$$

Example 2. If the policy of Example 1 is to be bought with 20 annual premiums, find the amount of each.

Solution. The annual premium is
$$2000 P_{33:\overline{20}|} = 2000 \frac{M_{33} - M_{53} + D_{53}}{N_{33} - N_{53}},$$
$$= 2000 \frac{254973}{9308450 - 3167380},$$
$$= \frac{2000(254973)}{6141070},$$
$$= \$83.04.$$

Example 3. Find the annual payment for the insurance of Example 1 if it is a 10-payment endowment.

Solution. We have
$$2000 \,_{10}P_{33:\overline{20}|} = 2000 \frac{M_{33} - M_{53} + D_{53}}{N_{33} - N_{43}},$$
$$= \frac{(2000)(254973)}{9308450 - 5751470},$$
$$= \frac{(2000)(254973)}{3556980},$$
$$= \$143.36.$$

EXERCISE 5

Find the premium indicated for each of the following endowment insurance policies.

Prob. no.	Age of insured	Amount of insurance	Term of the endowment (in years)	Premium wanted
1.	29	$2500	15	Net single premium
2.	29	$2500	15	Annual premium for 15 payments
3.	29	$2500	15	Annual premium for 10 payments
4.	59	$2500	15	Net single premium
5.	43	$10,000	20	Annual premium for 20 payments
6.	35	$5000	10	Net single premium
7.	35	$5000	20	Net single premium
8.	35	$5000	40	Net single premium
9.	32	$8000	30	Annual premium for 10 years
10.	32	$8000	30	Annual premium for 20 years

11. Mr. Jarvis, at age 31, buys a 20-payment, 20-year, $10,000 endowment insurance policy. (a) What does he receive from the company at the end of 20 years? (b) If he had bought a 20-year, $10,000 term insurance and had deposited the difference in the payments between the two policies in a security paying $2\frac{1}{2}\%$, converted annually, how much would he have on deposit at the end of 20 years?

12. If Mr. Jarvis in Problem 11 had died at age 41, what would his beneficiary or heir receive provided that (a) Mr. Jarvis had taken out the endowment policy, (b) he had taken out the term policy and accumulated the difference in costs in a security paying $2\frac{1}{2}\%$?

13. Find the net single premium for a 50-year, $3000 endowment insurance for a person aged 40. Compare this with the cost of a whole life insurance for a person of the same age.

14. Compare the single premium of a 50-year, $5000 endowment insurance for a person, aged 49, with the single premium of a $5000 whole life policy for the same person.

15. Mr. Latham, aged 30, can afford to spend $150 at the beginning of each year for 20 years for an insurance policy. (a) If he buys a 20-year endowment policy, how large a policy can he buy? (b) If the company from which he purchases the policy will sell such a policy in multiples of $500 only, how much can he buy if he does not spend more than $150 per year? (c) What is the cost, per year, of the policy he buys?

171. Combination policies

By making use of the formulas derived in this chapter and the previous chapter, it is possible to compute the cost of any type of combination insurance, annuity, or endowment policy. In fact the endowment insurance is, for example, just such a combination policy. Many other such policies are offered by insurance companies, and many new ones may be offered in the future. Illustrations of evaluating such policies will be given in the following examples.

Example 1. A double endowment insurance taken by a person, aged 45, pays $5000 to the beneficiary should the insured die within 15 years, and pays $10,000 to the insured provided that he reaches the age of 60. Find the annual premium if this insurance is paid for in 15 payments.

Solution. The payments form a temporary life annuity due for 15 years for a person aged 45; the benefits are a 15-year term insurance for $5000 and a 15-year pure endowment of $10,000. The present value of the payments is equal to the present value of the benefits, hence

$$R\ddot{a}_{45:\overline{15|}} = 5000 A^1_{45:\overline{15|}} + 10{,}000\,_{15}E_{45},$$

where R is used to designate the annual premium. Note: We do not use P in any of its forms here, since P represents the premium for a policy of face 1.

We rewrite the above equation in the form

$$R \frac{N_{45} - N_{60}}{D_{45}} = 5000\left(\frac{M_{45} - M_{60}}{D_{45}}\right) + 10000 \frac{D_{60}}{D_{45}},$$

or,
$$R = \frac{5000(M_{45} - M_{60}) + 10000 D_{60}}{N_{45} - N_{60}},$$

$$= \frac{5000(154736.6 - 108543.5) + 10000(154046)}{5161996 - 1865614},$$

$$= \frac{1771425500}{3296382},$$

$$= \$537.39.$$

Example 2. In order to allow a young man a chance to buy a larger amount of whole life insurance than he could otherwise afford, a company offers a policy for which the annual payments for the first 5 years are those of a term insurance for that period, followed by the payments for a whole life insurance for a person 5 years older. What is the cost for the first 5 years and for the balance of the time for a $6000 policy for a person aged 27?

Solution. The payments for the first 5 years are those of a term insurance for that period. Hence

$$6000 P_{27:\overline{5}|} = 6000 \frac{M_{27} - M_{32}}{N_{27} - N_{32}},$$

$$= \frac{6000 (186839.89 - 179312.73)}{11993210 - 9724960},$$

$$= \frac{(6000)(7527.16)}{2268250},$$

$$= \$19.91,$$

annual payment for the first 5 years.

The payments for life beginning at age 32 will be those for a whole life at 32, or

$$6000 P_{32} = 6000 \frac{M_{32}}{N_{32}},$$

$$= 6000\left(\frac{179313}{9724960}\right),$$

$$= \$110.63,$$

the premium to be paid starting at age 32.

Example 3. Mr. Wren, aged 26, estimates that he will need insurance coverage of $5000 for 10 years, $10,000 for the next 20 years, $5000 for the following 10 years, and $1000 for the balance of his life. What is the annual premium if he wishes to pay up his insurance in 40 payments?

Solution. Making use of the fundamental principle that the present value of the payments is equal to the present value of the benefits, we have,

$$R\ddot{a}_{26:\overline{40}|} = 5000\frac{M_{26} - M_{36}}{D_{26}} + 10000\frac{M_{36} - M_{56}}{D_{26}}$$
$$+ 5000\frac{M_{56} - M_{66}}{D_{26}} + 1000\frac{M_{66}}{D_{26}}.$$

We consider that the benefits are made up of (a) a $5000, 10-year term insurance for 10 years, (b) a $10,000, 20-year term insurance deferred 10 years, (c) a $5000, 10-year term deferred 30 years, and finally, (d) a whole life insurance deferred 40 years. It is obvious that this policy may be broken up into other types. Thus it might have been considered as a $1000 whole life, a $4000, 40-year term, and a $5000, 20-year term, deferred 10 years.

Solving for R we have

$$R = \frac{5000(M_{26} + M_{36} - M_{56}) - 4000M_{66}}{N_{26} - N_{66}},$$

$$= \frac{5000(188277.4 + 172713.3 - 123349.2) - 4000(83010.2)}{12486025 - 1056042},$$

$$= \frac{5000(237642) - 4000(83010.2)}{11430000},$$

$$= \frac{856169000}{11430000},$$

$$= \$74.91.$$

Example 4. Mr. Dorian, aged 30, buys a combination insurance and retirement policy which will give his beneficiary $8000, provided that he dies before 65, and will provide him with an annuity of $3000 for life, starting at age 65. What annual premium must he pay for this policy if he wants it paid up in 35 years?

Solution. Making use of the fact that the present value of the payments is equal to the present value of the benefits, we have

$$R\ddot{a}_{30:\overline{35}|} = 8000 A^1_{30:\overline{35}|} + 3000_{35|}\ddot{a}_{30},$$

$$R = \frac{8000\dfrac{M_{30} - M_{65}}{D_{30}} + 3000\dfrac{N_{65}}{D_{30}}}{\dfrac{N_{30} - N_{65}}{D_{30}}},$$

$$= \frac{8000(M_{30} - M_{65}) + 3000 N_{65}}{N_{30} - N_{65}},$$

$$= \frac{8000(182403.5 - 87499.6) + 3000(1172130)}{10594300 - 1172130},$$

$$= \frac{8000(94903.9) + 3000(1172130)}{9422170},$$

$$= \frac{4275621200}{9422170},$$

$$= \$453.78.$$

EXERCISE 6

1. Mr. Hadsell, at age 35, buys a double-endowment life insurance policy which pays his beneficiary $9000 provided that he dies within 30 years and pays him personally $18,000 if he reaches age 65. What annual premium for 30 years must he pay for this policy?

2. At age 65, Mr. Hadsell of Problem 1 decides to use the $18,000 to buy a paid-up whole life insurance for $1000 and a whole life annuity due. What are the annual payments of the annuity?

3. Find the net single premium for an insurance which pays $10,000 to the beneficiary provided that the insured, aged 20, dies within 20 years and $1000 to the insured provided that he lives to age 40.

4. Mr. Alt, aged 23, buys a whole life policy for $10,000 for which he has the privilege of paying the annual premium of a 10-year term for the first 10 years, followed by the annual premium, for the balance of his life, on a whole life insurance for age 33. What are the premiums?

5. The premiums on a $5000 whole life policy for a person aged 29 are R each for the first 10 years, followed by premiums of $\frac{3}{2}R$ for the balance of the person's life. What are the premiums?

6. Mr. Kime, aged 25, estimates that his insurance needs are as follows:
$5000 for 5 years,
$10,000 for the next 25 years,
$5000 for the following 10 years,
$1000 for the balance of his life.
Find the annual premium for 40 years on this policy.

7. Mr. Daniels, aged 30, wishes insurance protection of $7000 for 35 years, followed by protection of $1000 for the balance of his life, and also, starting at age 65, he wants an annuity of $3000 per year. What annual premium for 35 years will be needed for this policy?

8. Mr. Stanton, aged 30, and his wife, aged 25, buy a policy giving the following benefits:
$10,000 insurance for 35 years for Mr. Stanton,
$1000 insurance for Mr. Stanton beginning at age 65,
$1000 whole life insurance for Mrs. Stanton,
$1500 annuity starting at age 65 for both Mr. and Mrs. Stanton.
Find the annual premium for 35 years which will pay for this policy.

172. Premium payable *m* times a year

In practice, many insurance policies call for quarterly or semiannual payments rather than annual payments. Let $P^{(m)}$ represent the total premium paid in one year in m installments of $\dfrac{P^{(m)}}{m}$ each. If P represents an annual premium paid at the beginning of the year, it is clear that $P^{(m)}$ must be greater than P since part of the annual premium will be lost to the insurance company if the insured dies before all the installments are paid. Furthermore, the company has to wait longer each year for the complete premium $P^{(m)}$ and hence the delay in investing the premium results in decreased interest. Still another factor contributing to the increased premium $P^{(m)}$ is the increased cost in collecting premiums paid more than once a year.

One method of obtaining the premium $P^{(m)}$ paid in m installments of $\dfrac{P^{(m)}}{m}$ each is to increase the annual premium P by a certain per cent and then to divide the result by m. Letting r represent the per cent in hundredths, we have that the installment paid each $\dfrac{1}{m}$th of a year is

$$\frac{P^{(m)}}{m} = \frac{P(1+r)}{m}. \tag{14}$$

Example 1. An insurance company figures the quarterly premium on a given policy by increasing the annual premium paid at the beginning of each year by 6% and then dividing by 4. What is the quarterly premium if the annual premium is $216.80?

Solution. We increase $216.80 by 6% obtaining $229.81. The quarterly premium is then $\dfrac{\$229.81}{4} = \$57.45$, which may have been obtained by direct substitution in formula (14). Thus

$$\text{Quarterly payment} = \frac{216.80(1.06)}{4} = \$57.45.$$

Actually, if it were not more costly for an insurance company to collect premiums paid more often than once a year, we should use the material of Article 164 to derive formulas for installment payments. Thus the annual premium for a whole life insurance policy, $P_x^{(m)}$, paid in m installments of $\dfrac{P_x^{(m)}}{m}$ each, constitutes a whole life annuity due and we have

$$P_x^{(m)} \ddot{a}_x^{(m)} = A_x.$$

From formula (14) Chapter 19

$$\ddot{a}_x^{(m)} = a_x + \frac{m+1}{2m},$$

hence,

$$P_x^{(m)} = \frac{A_x}{a_x + \dfrac{m+1}{2m}}. \tag{15}$$

In like manner, formulas for other premiums, paid in m installments, may be derived by making use of the formulas of Article

PREMIUMS PAYABLE m TIMES A YEAR

164, Chapter 19. However, since such formulas are seldom used in practice, we leave further exploration in this field to the student.

Example 2. Using formula (15), find the quarterly premium on a whole life insurance policy of $5000 for a person aged 30. Compare this result to that obtained by using the method of Example 1.

Solution. We have from formula (15) that

hence,
$$5000 P_{30}^{(4)} = 5000 \frac{\frac{M_{30}}{D_{30}}}{\frac{N_{31}}{D_{30}} + \frac{5}{8}} = 5000 \frac{M_{30}}{N_{31} + 0.625 D_{30}},$$

$$= \frac{5000(182403)}{10153500 + 0.625(440801)},$$

$$= \$87.45.$$

Hence the quarterly premium is $\dfrac{\$87.45}{4}$ or $21.86.

Using the method of Example 1, we first compute the annual premium payable once a year. We have

$$P_x = \frac{M_x}{N_x}.$$

$$5000 P_{30} = 5000 \frac{M_{30}}{N_{30}} = \frac{(5000)(182403)}{10594300},$$

$$= \$86.09.$$

According to the plan in Example 1, we find the quarterly payment by increasing this by 6% and then we divide by 4. Hence

$$\text{Quarterly payment} = \frac{86.09(1.06)}{4},$$

$$= \$22.81.$$

We note that this is $22.81 - 21.86 = \$0.95$ larger than that obtained by the theoretical method.

EXERCISE 7

Using 4% and 6% for the per cent increase for the semiannual and quarterly payments, respectively, find the quarterly and semiannual payments for each of the following policies. Also find the corresponding premiums by use of formula (15).

Prob. no.	Policy	Amount	Age of insured
1.	Whole life	$2000	25
2.	Whole life	$10,000	29
3.	Whole life	$6000	32
4.	Whole life	$8000	35
5.	Whole life	$5000	42

6. Making use of the formulas in Article 164, show that the annual premium paid in m installments of $\dfrac{P^{(m)}_{x:\overline{n}|}^{\,1}}{m}$ each for an n-year term insurance policy is

$$P^{(m)}_{x:\overline{n}|}{}^{1} = \frac{A_{x:\overline{n}|}^{1}}{\ddot{a}_{x:\overline{n}|} - \dfrac{m-1}{m}(1 - {}_nE_x)}.$$

7. Find the quarterly payment for 10 years, using the formula in Problem 6, for a 10-year term insurance of $4000 for a man aged 33.

173. Summary of formulas for simple insurance policies

The student will find it helpful to study the following collection of formulas, especially in regard to relationships among the various policies.

INSURANCE FORMULAS

Policy	Net single premium	Net annual premium for life	Net annual premium for k years
Whole life	$A_x = \dfrac{M_x}{D_x}$	$P_x = \dfrac{M_x}{N_x}$	${}_kP_x = \dfrac{M_x}{N_x - N_{x+k}}$
Deferred life	${}_n|A_x = \dfrac{M_{x+n}}{D_x}$	${}_n|P_x = \dfrac{M_{x+n}}{N_x}$	${}_kP({}_n|A_x) = \dfrac{M_{x+n}}{N_x - N_{x+k}}$
Term	$A^{1}_{x:\overline{n}|} = \dfrac{M_x - M_{x+n}}{D_x}$	✗	${}_kP^{1}_{x:\overline{n}|} = \dfrac{M_x - M_{x+n}}{N_x - N_{x+k}},\ k \leqq n$
Endowment	$A_{x:\overline{n}|} = \dfrac{M_x - M_{x+n} + D_{x+n}}{D_x}$	✗	${}_kP_{x:\overline{n}|} = \dfrac{M_x - M_{x+n} + D_{x+n}}{N_x - N_{x+k}},\ k \leqq n$

Note that the net single premiums are always given as quotients with M's in the numerator and D's in the denominator, with the exception of the endowment insurance, which has a D in the numerator as well as M's. Since an endowment insurance is not a pure insurance, this exception was to be expected.

Also, we note that the net annual premiums are given as quotients with M's in the numerators and N's in the denominators, with the exception of the endowment insurance, which also has a D in the numerator.

From the setup of the insurance formulas in terms of the M's, N's, and D's, it is easy to read off the benefits and the method of payment. Thus, from the table of formulas, we have the expression $\dfrac{M_x - M_{x+n} + D_{x+n}}{N_x - N_{x+k}}$, which is immediately recognized as an annual

SUMMARY

premium for k years. Furthermore, the benefits are $1 to the beneficiary provided that the insured dies before age $x + n$ and $1 to the insured provided that he reaches the age $x + n$.

Example 1. State the benefits of the policy whose premium is

$$2000 \frac{M_{30} - M_{40}}{N_{30} - N_{40}}$$

and also state how the premiums are paid.

Solution. The $M_{30} - M_{40}$ expression in the numerator indicates insurance protection of $2000 to the beneficiary for a period of 10 years, starting when the insured is 30. Since the denominator contains N's, the insurance is paid for in annual installments starting at age 30 and continuing until the insured reaches 40 or dies provided that death occurs before 40. The expression given is this annual premium.

Example 2. State the benefits and the method of payment for the policy whose premium is given by the following expression.

$$\frac{5000(M_{20} - M_{65}) + 2000N_{65}}{N_{20} - N_{65}}.$$

Solution. The benefits of this policy are a 45-year term insurance for $5000 from age 20 to age 65, followed by a whole life annuity to the insured provided that he reaches the age 65, the first payment being at age 65. The expression given represents the annual payment that the insured must make, starting at age 20 and continuing for a period of 45 years, provided that he survives that period.

EXERCISE 8

State the benefits and the method of payment for each of the policies whose premiums are given by the following expressions:

1. $1000 \dfrac{M_{40}}{D_{40}}$
2. $5000 \dfrac{M_{26} - M_{46}}{D_{26}}$
3. $5000 \dfrac{M_{40}}{N_{40} - N_{65}}$
4. $1000 \dfrac{M_{35} - M_{65}}{N_{35} - N_{65}}$
5. $3000 \dfrac{M_{30} - M_{50} + D_{50}}{N_{30} - N_{50}}$
6. $2500 \dfrac{M_{27} - M_{42}}{D_{27}}$
7. $\dfrac{4000(M_{20} - M_{50}) + 10000D_{50}}{N_{20} - N_{50}}$
8. $\dfrac{4000M_{25} + 2000N_{65}}{N_{25} - N_{65}}$
9. $\dfrac{5000(M_{25} - M_{70}) + 2500N_{70}}{D_{25}}$
10. $\dfrac{500(M_5 - M_{20}) + 400D_{15} + 1000D_{20}}{D_5}$

MISCELLANEOUS EXERCISE

1. Find the single premium on a $5000 whole life policy for a person aged 21.
2. What is the annual premium for the policy in Problem 1?
3. What is the annual premium of a 20-payment, $5000 whole life policy for a person aged 21?

4. Mr. King, aged 21, buys a 20-payment, $5000, 20-year term insurance. What is the premium?

5. Mr. Reynolds, aged 21, buys a 20-payment, $5000, 20-year endowment policy. What premium does he pay?

6. What would Mr. Reynolds have on deposit at the end of 20 years if he had deposited, in a security paying $2\frac{1}{2}\%$, converted annually, the difference between the premiums for the 20-year endowment and a 20-year term policy?

7. Mr. Krieger, aged 28, buys an insurance policy which pays his wife $10,000 at the time of his death and 20 payments certain of $2000 each at the end of each year after his death. What annual premium for 40 years must Mr. Krieger pay?

8. Mr. Klein, aged 30, takes out a policy which pays his wife $10,000, provided that he dies before age 65, and pays him $2000 at the beginning of each year, starting at 65, for life. What annual premium for 20 years must he pay for this policy?

9. Mr. Kisselman, aged 25, buys a policy which pays the following benefits:
(a) $5000 to his beneficiary if he dies within 10 years,
(b) $10,000 to his beneficiary if he dies during the following 20 years, and
(c) $1000 to his beneficiary when he dies at any time thereafter.
What premium must he pay if he pays it in 30 annual installments?

10. Richard, at age 18, borrows $2000 from his uncle for college expenses. The money is to be repaid at the end of 10 years without interest. Since Richard has no security, he offers to buy a 10-year term insurance naming his uncle as beneficiary. What annual payment for 10 years must he make for this policy? What is the equivalent interest rate, payable annually, that he pays for the loan?

11. Mr. Glocke, at age 37, buys a $3000, 15-year endowment policy for which the gross annual premium was $166.89. Mr. Glocke reaches the age of 50 and receives the $3000. What interest rate, converted annually, did he make on his investment? Would it have been just as good to have made payments of $166.89 in a security paying this same interest rate? Why?

12. In Problem 11, suppose Mr. Glocke had received dividends of $15 each at the end of each year for the first 10 years of the life of the policy. What equivalent interest rate, converted annually, would he have made?

Prove each of the following identities:

13. $_nE_x = _n|\ddot{a}_{x:\overline{1}|}$.

14. $A_{x:\overline{n}|} = v\ddot{a}_{x:\overline{n}|} - a_{x:\overline{n-1}|}$.

15. $A_{x:\overline{n}|} = 1 - d\ddot{a}_{x:\overline{n}|}$, where $d = 1 - v$.

16. $P_{x:\overline{n}|} = \dfrac{1}{\ddot{a}_{x:\overline{n}|}} - d$, where $d = 1 - v$.

17. $A^1_{x:\overline{n}|} = v\ddot{a}_{x:\overline{n}|} - a_{x:\overline{n}|}$.

18. $D_x = M_x + dN_x$, where $d = 1 - v$.

19. $d = \dfrac{P_x(1 - A_x)}{A_x}$, where $d = 1 - v$.

20. $A_x = \dfrac{P_x}{P_x + d}$, where $d = 1 - v$.

21

Policy Reserves

174. The reserve fund. Definitions

In the previous chapter it was seen that annual premiums were usually constant throughout the payment interval. Such a constant annual premium is called a **level premium.**

An examination of the CSO mortality table shows that after age 10, the death rate increases with increasing age. Hence an insurance extending over a sufficiently long period of time will be such that the level premium is greater than the natural premium (see Article 169) for the early years of the life of the policy and less than the natural premium during the later years of the policy.

The excess of the level premiums over the natural premiums, during the early years of the policy, is set aside to take care of the policy years in which the level premium is not sufficient to cover the cost of the insurance. The accumulated amount of the fund set aside is called the **reserve.** If the insurance is bought by a single premium, the accumulated value of this premium less the accumulated cost of the insurance, at a given time, gives the reserve.

The reserve at the end of any policy year for a given policy is called the **terminal reserve** on that policy. This terminal reserve represents the maximum amount that a policyholder can expect from the insurance company should he discontinue his policy at the end of any policy year. Furthermore, it represents the maximum amount he could borrow from his insurance company if he offers his policy as security for a loan.

The graph on page 438 illustrates the net level premium line and the natural premium curve for a $5000 whole life insurance policy for a person aged 30. In order to demonstrate more clearly the relationship between the net level premium and the natural premium during the early years of the policy, it was necessary to choose a vertical scale that shows only a part of the natural premium curve.

POLICY RESERVES

TABLE OF VALUES FOR NATURAL PREMIUM CURVE

Age	30	40	50	54	55	60	70	80	90	99
Premium	$17.37	$30.15	$60.10	$81.22	$87.70	$129.71	$289.27	$643.18	$1370.70	$4878.10

Values of the natural premium not plotted are given in the table of values. The natural premiums for 80, 90, and 99 show how rapidly the natural premium increases for ages greater than 70.

Note also that the natural premium curve crosses the level premium line between ages 54 and 55.

EXERCISE 1

1. Plot the curves for the natural premium and the level premium for a whole life insurance of $1000 for a person aged 60. Compute values of the natural premium for ages 60, 65, 70, 75, 80, 85, 90, 95, 99.

2. Plot the curves for the natural premium and the level premium for a 10-year, 10-payment term insurance of $1000 for a person aged 40. Compute values of the natural premium for ages 40, 42, 44, 46, 48.

175. Numerical computation of the reserve

It is possible to calculate the tth terminal reserve on any policy by constructing a table which shows the total received from premiums, the interest earned, and the death claims paid. For this method we start with a group of l_x persons all of the same age. The method is illustrated by the following example.

NUMERICAL COMPUTATION OF THE RESERVE

Example. Find the terminal reserves on a 5-payment, 5-year term insurance of $1000 for a person aged 50.

Solution. The annual premium on the policy is

$$1000 P^1_{50:\overline{5}|} = 1000 \frac{M_{50} - M_{55}}{N_{50} - N_{55}},$$

$$= \frac{1000(142035.1 - 126751.1)}{3849488 - 2754769},$$

$$= \frac{1000(15284.0)}{1094720},$$

$$= \$13.9616.$$

Consider now a group of l_{50} persons each paying this premium for a 5-year term insurance. The company receives

$$l_{50}(13.9616) = (810,900)(13.9616) = \$11,321,500$$

in premiums at the beginning of the first policy year. Interest at the rate of $2\frac{1}{2}\%$ increases this to 11,321,500(1.025) or $11,604,500 by the end of the first year. But the death claims for the first year amount to

$$1000 d_{50} = 1000(9990) \quad \text{or} \quad \$9,990,000,$$

hence the reserve fund contains $11,604,500 - 9,990,000 = \$1,614,500$ at the end of the year after all death claims have been paid. This reserve should be equally divided among the l_{51} survivors, giving a first-terminal reserve of $\dfrac{1,614,500}{800,910} = \$2.01583$ for each policy in the group. In like manner we calculate the other entries for the following table. It should be noted that the 5th terminal reserve must be 0 since a term in insurance becomes void at the end of its term.

Terminal Reserves of a 5-Payment, 5-Year Term Insurance of $1000

Policy year	Premiums collected at beginning of year	Total fund at beginning of year	Value of fund at end of year before death claims paid interest at $2\frac{1}{2}\%$	Death claims	Value of fund at end of year after death claims paid	Number of survivors	Reserve per policy
0	$11,321,500	$11,321,500	—	—	—	—	—
1	$11,182,000	$12,796,500	$11,604,500	$9,990,000	$1,614,500	800,910	$2.01583
2	$11,033,600	$13,522,000	$13,116,400	$10,628,000	$2,488,400	790,282	$3.14875
3	$10,875,800	$13,434,800	$13,860,000	$11,301,000	$2,559,000	778,981	$3.28506
4	$10,708,000	$12,458,700	$13,770,700	$12,020,000	$1,750,700	766,961	$2.28265
5	—	—	$12,770,200	$12,770,000	$200	754,191	$0.000265

If, instead of a term insurance, this policy had been a 5-year endowment insurance, the final terminal reserve would have been $1000. For a whole life policy, the reserve would gradually build up to the face of the policy as the person's age approached the last entry in the mortality table.

EXERCISE 2

1. Find the terminal reserves on a 5-payment, 5-year endowment insurance of $1000 for a person aged 65, using the method of this article.

2. Find the terminal reserves on a whole life insurance of $5000 for a person aged 95 if annual payments for life are made.

176. Fackler's formula

Let $_tV$ represent the tth terminal reserve on any one of the various types of insurance policies of 1 for a person aged x. When the terminal reserve is wanted on a particular type of policy, a subscript is affixed to the $_tV$ symbol which corresponds to the subscript used for the A symbol of the policy in question.

Thus $_{10}V$ represents the 10th terminal reserve for any one of the various types of insurance policies of 1 for a person aged x. However, the symbol $_{10}V_x$ represents the 10th terminal reserve on a whole life policy for a person aged x. In like manner, $_3V^1_{50:\overline{5}|}$ represents the 3rd terminal reserve on a 5-year term insurance of 1 for a person aged 50.

It should be noted that the value of the terminal reserves represented by these symbols will vary with the method of premium payment. No confusion should result, however, in any particular problem.

The symbol P will be used for the annual premium of any type of insurance of 1 for a person aged x. Subscripts will be affixed when it is necessary to distinguish the particular type of insurance in question.

Using the general symbols $_tV$ and P we may write a very important formula known as **Fackler's accumulation formula,** which gives the terminal reserve in terms of the terminal reserve for the preceding year.

Consider l_x persons, all of the same age, each of whom has a certain life insurance policy of 1. Using exactly the method of setting up the table in Article 175, we see that

$$l_{x+t}(P + {}_tV)(1 + i) - d_{x+t} = {}_{t+1}V l_{x+t+1}.$$

Solving for $_{t+1}V$, we have

$$_{t+1}V = \frac{l_{x+t}}{l_{x+t+1}}(P + {}_tV)(1 + i) - \frac{d_{x+t}}{l_{x+t+1}},$$

or

$$_{t+1}V = \frac{D_{x+t}}{D_{x+t+1}}(P + {}_tV) - \frac{C_{x+t}}{D_{x+t+1}}. \tag{1}$$

FACKLER'S FORMULA

The quantities $\dfrac{D_x}{D_{x+1}}$ and $\dfrac{C_x}{D_{x+1}}$ are represented by u_x and k_x, respectively, in extended tables of the commutation columns. With such a table, the above formula may be written,

$$_{t+1}V = u_{x+t}(P + {}_tV) - k_{x+t}, \qquad (2)$$

the form in which Fackler's accumulation formula is generally written.

Neither formula (1) nor formula (2) can be used directly with the commutation symbols given in this text. We observe that

$$C_{x+t} = M_{x+t} - M_{x+t+1}.$$

Hence we may rewrite (1) in the form,

$$_{t+1}V = \frac{D_{x+t}(P + {}_tV) - (M_{x+t} - M_{x+t+1})}{D_{x+t+1}}, \qquad (3)$$

which now can be used with our tables.

Example. Using formula (3), calculate the first and second terminal reserves for a 5-payment, 5-year term insurance of $1000 for a person aged 50.

Solution. Since the A symbol for this policy is $A^1_{50:\overline{5}|}$, the proper V symbol is ${}_tV^1_{50:\overline{5}|}$. The first terminal reserve is

$$1000 {}_1V^1_{50:\overline{5}|}$$

$$= 1000 \, \frac{D_{50}(P^1_{50:\overline{5}|} + 0) - (M_{50} - M_{51})}{D_{51}},$$

$$= 1000 \, \frac{D_{50}\left(\dfrac{M_{50} - M_{55}}{N_{50} - N_{55}}\right) - (M_{50} - M_{51})}{D_{51}},$$

$$= 1000 \, \frac{(235925)\left(\dfrac{142035.1 - 126751.1}{3849488 - 2754769}\right) - (142035.0956 - 139199.4735)}{227335},$$

$$= \$2.01583.$$

This agrees with the value found in the table in Article 175.

Using the value just found, we may calculate the second terminal reserve. We have

$$1000 {}_2V^1_{50:\overline{5}|} = 1000 \, \frac{D_{51}(P^1_{51:\overline{5}|} + {}_1V^1_{50:\overline{5}|}) - (M_{51} - M_{52})}{D_{52}},$$

$$= 1000 \, \frac{227335(0.0139616 + 0.00201583) - 2943.1374}{218847},$$

$$= \$3.1487.$$

A serious disadvantage of this method is that we must start with the 1st terminal reserve and obtain each succeeding reserve from the one just computed. The work will necessarily become very laborious if we want a reserve much beyond the first few. The next article will give methods which are much easier to apply.

EXERCISE 3

Using Fackler's formula in the form (3), find the first and second terminal reserves for each of the following policies.

Prob. no.	Type of policy	Age of policyholder	Face of policy
1.	10-payment whole life	30	$1000
2.	20-payment, 30-year term	40	$5000
3.	30-payment, 30-year endowment	35	$2000

177. Retrospective and prospective methods of computing the reserve

A method of calculating the reserve by looking back at what has happened is called a **retrospective method**. One for which we look ahead is called a **prospective method**. The two methods given in Articles 175 and 176 are actually retrospective methods, but the first method to be given in this article usually is called **the retrospective method** of determining the tth terminal reserve.

The value of the tth terminal reserve at the end of the tth policy year should be equal to the accumulated value at age $x + t$ of all the premiums paid less the accumulated value at age $x + t$ of the insurance benefits received.

We examine first the accumulated value of the premiums paid. Suppose that m such premiums of P each have been paid, where m cannot be greater than t. The accumulated value of these premiums to the end of n years is simply a forborne life annuity due of P, whose value is $P\dfrac{N_x - N_{x+m}}{D_{x+m}}$ (see Article 163). If m is less than t, let S represent the desired accumulated value $t - m$ years later. We have

$$S(_{t-m}E_{x+m}) = P\,\frac{N_x - N_{x+m}}{D_{x+m}},$$

or
$$S = P\,\frac{N_x - N_{x+m}}{D_{x+m}} \cdot \frac{D_{x+m}}{D_{x+m+t-m}},$$

or
$$S = P\,\frac{N_x - N_{x+m}}{D_{x+t}}.$$

RETROSPECTIVE METHOD

Next we consider the value of the insurance benefits received. Clearly the value at age x is that of a t-year term policy, which is $\dfrac{M_x - M_{x+t}}{D_x}$. Let X represent its value at age $x + t$. We have

$$X(_tE_x) = \frac{M_x - M_{x+t}}{D_x},$$

$$X = \frac{M_x - M_{x+t}}{D_x} \cdot \frac{D_x}{D_{x+t}},$$

$$= \frac{M_x - M_{x+t}}{D_{x+t}}.$$

We now may write $\quad _tV = S - X$

or
$$_tV = \frac{P(N_x - N_{x+m}) - (M_x - M_{x+t})}{D_{x+t}}, \tag{4}$$

where m is less than or equal to t. This formula holds even if P is a single premium, for in such a case, $m = 1$ and $N_x - N_{x+1}$ becomes D_x.

Example 1. Find the third terminal reserve on a 5-payment, 5-year term insurance policy of $1000 for a person aged 50.

Solution. We have

$$1000\,_3V^1_{50:\overline{5}|} = 1000\,\frac{P^1_{50:\overline{5}|}(N_{50} - N_{53}) - (M_{50} - M_{53})}{D_{53}},$$

$$= 1000\,\frac{\dfrac{M_{50} - M_{55}}{N_{50} - N_{55}}(N_{50} - N_{53}) - (M_{50} - M_{53})}{D_{53}},$$

$$= 1000\,\frac{\dfrac{15284.0}{1094720}(682107) - 8831.94}{210456},$$

$$= \$3.29.$$

Example 2. Find the 30th terminal reserve on a 20-payment whole life insurance of $1000 for a person aged 25.

Solution. We may write

$$1000\,_{30}V_{25} = 1000\,\frac{_{20}P_{25}(N_{25} - N_{45}) - (M_{25} - M_{55})}{D_{55}},$$

$$= 1000\,\frac{\dfrac{M_{25}}{N_{25} - N_{45}} \cdot (N_{25} - N_{45}) - (M_{25} - M_{55})}{D_{55}},$$

$$= 1000\,\frac{M_{25} - (M_{25} - M_{55})}{D_{55}},$$

$$= 1000\,\frac{M_{55}}{D_{55}} = 1000\left(\frac{126751}{193941}\right),$$

$$= \$653.55.$$

Example 3. Find the 10th terminal reserve on a $2000, 30-year endowment insurance for a person aged 20, if a single premium was paid for the insurance.

Solution. Substituting in formula (4), we have

$$2000\,_{10}V_{20:\overline{30}|} = 2000\,\frac{\frac{M_{20}-M_{50}+D_{50}}{D_{20}}(N_{20}-N_{21})-(M_{20}-M_{30})}{D_{30}},$$

$$= 2000\,\frac{\frac{M_{20}-M_{50}+D_{50}}{D_{20}}D_{20}-M_{20}+M_{30}}{D_{30}},$$

$$= 2000\,\frac{M_{30}-M_{50}+D_{50}}{D_{30}},$$

$$= 2000\,\frac{182403.5-142035.1+235925}{440801},$$

$$= \frac{(2000)(276293)}{440801},$$

$$= \$1253.59.$$

The second method of calculating the reserve given in this article is called **the prospective method.** We look ahead to see the future benefits and the future liabilities of the policy in question. Using this method we see that:

The value of the tth terminal reserve at the end of the tth policy year is equal to the value, at age x + t, *of the future benefits less the value, at age* x + t, *of the future premiums.*

This statement may be put into equation form by representing the tth terminal reserve and the level premium, as before, by $_tV$ and P, respectively. Also represent by A the value of the insurance at age $x + t$, and represent by $\ddot{a}$ the value, at age $x + t$, of an annuity due of 1, of the type used for the payments. We may then write

$$_tV = A - P\ddot{a}, \tag{5}$$

it being understood that if there are no future payments, the second term of the right member of this equation is equal to zero, since there are no future liabilities connected with the policy.

Example 4. Using the prospective method, find the third terminal reserve on a 5-payment, 5-year term insurance policy of $1000 for a person aged 50.

Solution. We write first the general formula for a tth terminal reserve on an n-payment, n-year term insurance policy of 1 for a person, aged x.

$$_tV^1_{x:\overline{n}|} = A^1_{x+t:\overline{n-t}|} - P^1_{x:\overline{n}|}\ddot{a}_{x+t:\overline{n-t}|}.$$

PROSPECTIVE METHOD

For the particular case in question

$$1000{}_3V^1_{50:\overline{5}|} = 1000(A^1_{53:\overline{2}|} - P^1_{50:\overline{5}|}\ddot{a}_{53:\overline{2}|}),$$

$$= 1000\,\frac{M_{53} - M_{55} - \dfrac{M_{50} - M_{55}}{N_{50} - N_{55}}(N_{53} - N_{55})}{D_{53}},$$

$$= 1000\,\frac{6452.04 - \dfrac{15284.0}{1094720}(412611)}{210456},$$

$$= \$3.29.$$

This result agrees with that obtained by the retrospective method used for the same problem in Example 1.

Example 5. Using the prospective method, find the 30th terminal reserve on a 20-payment whole life insurance policy of $1000 for a person aged 25.

Solution. Since we have no future liabilities connected with this policy at the time of the 30th terminal reserve, the second term of the right member of formula (5) is zero. Hence

$$1000{}_{30}V_{25} = 1000A_{55},$$
$$= 1000\,\frac{M_{55}}{D_{55}} = 1000\left(\frac{126751}{193941}\right),$$
$$= \$653.55.$$

It is interesting to note that the result obtained here is exactly that for the same reserve in Example 2 and furthermore, that for this problem, the prospective method is much shorter.

Example 6. Find the 10th terminal reserve on a $2000, 30-year endowment insurance for a person, aged 20, if a single premium is paid for the policy.

Solution. Since there are no future liabilities connected with this policy, we have

$$2000{}_{10}V_{20:\overline{30}|} = 2000A_{30:\overline{20}|},$$
$$= 2000\,\frac{M_{30} - M_{50} + D_{50}}{D_{30}},$$
$$= 2000\,\frac{182403.5 - 142035.1 + 235925}{440801},$$
$$= \$1253.59.$$

The student should compare this result with that for Example 3.

Example 7. Find the 20th terminal reserve on a 30-payment whole life policy of $2500 for a person aged 32.

Solution. We have

$$2500\,_{20}V_{32} = 2500(A_{52} - {}_{30}P_{32} \cdot \ddot{a}_{52:\overline{10}|}),$$

$$= 2500\,\frac{M_{52} - \dfrac{M_{32}}{N_{32} - N_{62}}(N_{52} - N_{62})}{D_{52}},$$

$$= 2500\,\frac{136256.3 - \dfrac{179313}{8159690}(1820950)}{218847},$$

$$= \$1099.41.$$

We make no attempt to describe the various types of modified reserve systems which are in use by many insurance companies, since such topics belong to a more extensive treatment of insurance than can be given here. The interested student of insurance may wish to continue his studies by consulting books on insurance.*

EXERCISE 4

Find the tth terminal reserve for each of the following policies, using both the retrospective and the prospective method:

Prob. no.	Insurance policy	Face of policy	Method of paying premiums	t	Age of insured
1.	Whole life	$1000	Single premium	20	35
2.	Whole life	$1000	Annual premiums for life	20	35
3.	Whole life	$1000	10 payments	20	35
4.	Whole life	$1000	10 payments	5	35
5.	10-year term	$5000	10 payments	5	25
6.	10-year term	$5000	10 payments	10	25
7.	10-year term	$5000	5 payments	5	25
8.	25-year endowment	$2500	20 payments	15	30
9.	25-year endowment	$2500	20 payments	22	30
10.	25-year endowment	$2500	20 payments	25	30
11.	Whole life, deferred 10 years	$1000	10 payments	10	28
12.	Whole life, deferred 10 years	$1000	10 payments	5	28

Show algebraically that the left members of formulas (4) and (5) are equal for each of the following insurance policies.

* See Menge and Glover, *An Introduction to the Mathematics of Life Insurance*, The Macmillan Company, New York, 1935.

SURRENDER VALUE OF A POLICY

13. Whole life, annual premiums for life
14. n-payment, n-year term
15. Whole life, single premium

178. Surrender value of a policy

For various reasons, a policyholder may find it necessary to discontinue his policy after a certain number of years. Insurance companies usually give the policyholder three options for the settlement of his claim with the company:

1. To receive a cash settlement upon the surrender of the policy.
2. To receive extended insurance in the form of a fully paid-up policy of the same face value for a temporary period. If the original insurance was an endowment policy, this temporary period may include the entire term of the endowment policy, in which case any balance due would be paid in the form of an endowment of a lesser amount than named in the policy.
3. To receive a fully paid-up policy of the type originally bought, but for a portion of the original face.

Theoretically, the value of a policy at the time of surrender should be the terminal reserve, but the laws of most states allow the insurance company to charge a fee for the privilege of surrendering a policy. The charge made is called the **surrender charge.** The **cash surrender value** is the terminal reserve less the surrender charge. This cash surrender value is used as a basis for figuring the settlements in options (2) and (3) listed above.

Example 1. Find the cash surrender value on a 20-payment whole life insurance of $1000 for a person aged 25, at the end of 30 years. The company charges $8 per $1000 face as a surrender charge.

Solution. The terminal reserve on this policy is

$$1000_{30}V_{25} = 1000 \frac{M_{55}}{D_{55}},$$

$$= \frac{(1000)(126751)}{193941},$$

$$= \$653.55.$$

Hence the cash surrender value is

$$653.55 - 8 = \$645.55.$$

Example 2. Mr. Smith has a 30-payment whole life policy of $2500 which he bought when he was 32. After 20 years he decides that he can no longer keep up the payments and asks his insurance company for extended insurance of the same face value. If the insurance company charges $8 per $1000 of face value for a change of policy, find the length of time that Mr. Smith's policy will be extended.

Solution. We find that the 20th terminal reserve on this policy is $1099.41 (see Example 7, Article 177). Hence the cash surrender value is 1099.41 − 8(2.5) = $1079.41. This money is to be used to buy Mr. Smith an n-year term insurance of $2500. Since he is now 52, we have

$$2500 \frac{M_{52} - M_{52+n}}{D_{52}} = 1079.41,$$

$$M_{52+n} = M_{52} - 0.431764 D_{52},$$
$$= 136256.3 - 0.431764(218847),$$
$$= 41766.1.$$

We may now interpolate from the M_x table as follows:

x	M_x
74	46088.2 ⎫ 4322.1 ⎫
	41766.1 ⎭ ⎬ 4418.2
75	41670.0 ⎭

Using 365 days to a year, we have that $x = 74$ years and $\frac{4322.1}{4418.2}$ (365) days, or 74 years, 357 days. Hence the length of time the insurance is extended is 22 years, 357 days.

Example 3. Find the amount of paid-up, whole life insurance the person in Example 2 could receive in place of the cash surrender value.

Solution. Let X represent the amount or face of such a policy. Then

$$X \frac{M_{52}}{D_{52}} = 1079.41,$$

or
$$X = (1079.41) \frac{D_{52}}{M_{52}},$$
$$= (1079.41) \frac{218847}{136256},$$
$$= \$1733.68.$$

EXERCISE 5

Find the cash surrender value, the extended time, and the amount of a paid-up policy for each of the following if the policy is surrendered after t years. Assume a surrender charge of $10 per thousand of face value.

Prob. no.	Type of policy	Age of insured	Face of policy	t
1.	Whole life, payments for life	20	$2000	10
2.	30-payment, whole life	32	$5000	30
3.	30-payment, 30-year term	35	$2000	18
4.	20-payment, 20-year endowment	30	$4000	5
5.	20-payment, 20-year endowment	30	$4000	2

MISCELLANEOUS EXERCISE

1. Find the first five terminal reserves, by the method of Article 175, for a whole life policy of $1000, annual payments for life, for a person aged 55.

2. Using Fackler's formula, calculate the first three terminal reserves for a 10-payment, 10-year endowment insurance of $2000 for a person age 27.

3. Use the retrospective method of finding the terminal reserve to check the 4th terminal reserve in Problem 1.

4. Use the prospective method of finding the terminal reserve to check the 3rd terminal reserve in Problem 2.

5. Use Fackler's formula to calculate the 1st and 2nd terminal reserves for a single payment whole life policy of $5000 for a person aged 22.

6. Show that $_tV_{x:\overline{n}|} = \dfrac{A_{x+t:\overline{n-t}|} - A_{x:\overline{n}|}}{1 - A_{x:\overline{n}|}}$.

7. After making 15 payments on a whole life policy of $5000 (annual premiums for life), Mr. Jarvis, aged 30, decides to stop his payments. If the insurance company's surrender charge is $7 per $1000, how long can it extend Mr. Jarvis' insurance for the same face amount?

8. What cash surrender value would Mr. Jarvis (in Problem 7) receive if he elected the cash option?

9. What amount of fully paid, whole life insurance would Mr. Jarvis (Problem 7) receive if he elected this option?

10. Assuming no surrender charge, what is the cash surrender value of a 10-payment, 30-year endowment policy of $5000 for a person, aged 37, at the end of the 20th policy year?

Tables

		PAGE
I.	Six-Place Logarithms	452
II.	Seven-Place Logarithms of Numbers 10,000–11,000	478
III.	The Number of Each Day of the Year Counting from January 1	482
IV.	Ordinary and Exact Simple Interest on 1000 at 1%	483
V.	Amount of 1	484
VI.	Present Value of 1	494
VII.	Amount of 1 per Period	504
VIII.	Present Value of 1 per Period	514
IX.	Annuity Whose Present Value Is 1	524
X.	Amount of 1 for Certain Parts of a Period	534
XI.	Nominal Rate of Interest j Convertible p Times a Year Corresponding to Effective Rate of Interest i	535
XII.	1941 CSO Mortality Table	536
XIII.	Commutation Columns — 1941 CSO $2\frac{1}{2}$%	537

Table I — Six-Place Logarithms

N.	0	1	2	3	4	5	6	7	8	9	Diff.
1000	00 0000	0043	0087	0130	0174	0217	0260	0304	0347	0391	
01	0434	0477	0521	0564	0608	0651	0694	0738	0781	0824	
02	0868	0911	0954	0998	1041	1084	1128	1171	1214	1258	
03	1301	1344	1388	1431	1474	1517	1561	1604	1647	1690	
04	1734	1777	1820	1863	1907	1950	1993	2036	2080	2123	
05	00 2166	2209	2252	2296	2339	2382	2425	2468	2512	2555	
06	2598	2641	2684	2727	2771	2814	2857	2900	2943	2986	
07	3029	3073	3116	3159	3202	3245	3288	3331	3374	3417	
08	3461	3504	3547	3590	3633	3676	3719	3762	3805	3848	
09	3891	3934	3977	4020	4063	4106	4149	4192	4235	4278	44
1010	00 4321	4364	4407	4450	4493	4536	4579	4622	4665	4708	
11	4751	4794	4837	4880	4923	4966	5009	5052	5095	5138	
12	5181	5223	5266	5309	5352	5395	5438	5481	5524	5567	
13	5609	5652	5695	5738	5781	5824	5867	5909	5952	5995	
14	6038	6081	6124	6166	6209	6252	6295	6338	6380	6423	
1015	00 6466	6509	6552	6594	6637	6680	6723	6765	6808	6851	
16	6894	6936	6979	7022	7065	7107	7150	7193	7236	7278	
17	7321	7364	7406	7449	7492	7534	7577	7620	7662	7705	
18	7748	7790	7833	7876	7918	7961	8004	8046	8089	8132	
19	8174	8217	8259	8302	8345	8387	8430	8472	8515	8558	43
1020	00 8600	8643	8685	8728	8770	8813	8856	8898	8941	8983	
21	9026	9068	9111	9153	9196	9238	9281	9323	9366	9408	
22	9451	9493	9536	9578	9621	9663	9706	9748	9791	9833	
23	9876	9918	9961	*0003	*0045	*0088	*0130	*0173	*0215	*0258	
24	01 0300	0342	0385	0427	0470	0512	0554	0597	0639	0681	
1025	01 0724	0766	0809	0851	0893	0936	0978	1020	1063	1105	
26	1147	1190	1232	1274	1317	1359	1401	1444	1486	1528	
27	1570	1613	1655	1697	1740	1782	1824	1866	1909	1951	
28	1993	2035	2078	2120	2162	2204	2247	2289	2331	2373	
29	2415	2458	2500	2542	2584	2626	2669	2711	2753	2795	42
1030	01 2837	2879	2922	2964	3006	3048	3090	3132	3174	3217	
31	3259	3301	3343	3385	3427	3469	3511	3553	3596	3638	
32	3680	3722	3764	3806	3848	3890	3932	3974	4016	4058	
33	4100	4142	4184	4226	4268	4310	4353	4395	4437	4479	
34	4521	4563	4605	4647	4689	4730	4772	4814	4856	4898	
1035	01 4940	4982	5024	5066	5108	5150	5192	5234	5276	5318	
36	5360	5402	5444	5485	5527	5569	5611	5653	5695	5737	
37	5779	5821	5863	5904	5946	5988	6030	6072	6114	6156	
38	6197	6239	6281	6323	6365	6407	6448	6490	6532	6574	
39	6616	6657	6699	6741	6783	6824	6866	6908	6950	6992	41
1040	01 7033	7075	7117	7159	7200	7242	7284	7326	7367	7409	
41	7451	7492	7534	7576	7618	7659	7701	7743	7784	7826	
42	7868	7909	7951	7993	8034	8076	8118	8159	8201	8243	
43	8284	8326	8368	8409	8451	8492	8534	8576	8617	8659	
44	8700	8742	8784	8825	8867	8908	8950	8992	9033	9075	
1045	01 9116	9158	9199	9241	9282	9324	9366	9407	9449	9490	
46	9532	9573	9615	9656	9698	9739	9781	9822	9864	9905	
47	9947	9988	*0030	*0071	*0113	*0154	*0195	*0237	*0278	*0320	
48	02 0361	0403	0444	0486	0527	0568	0610	0651	0693	0734	
49	0775	0817	0858	0900	0941	0982	1024	1065	1107	1148	

PROPORTIONAL PARTS

Diff.	1	2	3	4	5	6	7	8	9
44	4.4	8.8	13.2	17.6	22.0	26.4	30.8	35.2	39.6
43	4.3	8.6	12.9	17.2	21.5	25.8	30.1	34.4	38.7
42	4.2	8.4	12.6	16.8	21.0	25.2	29.4	33.6	37.8
41	4.1	8.2	12.3	16.4	20.5	24.6	28.7	32.8	36.9

*From Kenneth P. Williams, *Mathematical Theory of Finance*, rev. ed. Copyright, 1947, by the Macmillan Company and used with their permission.

Table I — Six-Place Logarithms

N.	0	1	2	3	4	5	6	7	8	9	Diff.
1050	02 1189	1231	1272	1313	1355	1396	1437	1479	1520	1561	
51	1603	1644	1685	1727	1768	1809	1851	1892	1933	1974	
52	2016	2057	2098	2140	2182	2222	2263	2305	2346	2387	42
53	2428	2470	2511	2552	2593	2635	2676	2717	2758	2799	
54	2841	2882	2923	2964	3005	3047	3088	3129	3170	3211	
1055	02 3252	3294	3335	3376	3417	3458	3499	3541	3582	3623	
56	3664	3705	3746	3787	3828	3870	3911	3952	3993	4034	
57	4075	4116	4157	4198	4239	4280	4321	4363	4404	4445	
58	4486	4527	4568	4609	4650	4691	4732	4773	4814	4855	
59	4896	4937	4978	5019	5060	5101	5142	5183	5224	5265	
1060	02 5306	5347	5388	5429	5470	5511	5552	5593	5634	5674	
61	5715	5756	5797	5838	5879	5920	5961	6002	6043	6084	
62	6125	6165	6206	6247	6288	6329	6370	6411	6452	6492	41
63	6533	6574	6615	6656	6697	6737	6778	6819	6860	6901	
64	6942	6982	7023	7064	7105	7146	7186	7227	7268	7309	
1065	02 7350	7390	7431	7472	7513	7553	7594	7635	7676	7716	
66	7757	7798	7839	7879	7920	7961	8002	8042	8083	8124	
67	8164	8205	8246	8287	8327	8368	8409	8449	8490	8531	
68	8571	8612	8653	8693	8734	8775	8815	8856	8896	8937	
69	8978	9018	9059	9100	9140	9181	9221	9262	9303	9343	
1070	02 9384	9424	9465	9506	9546	9587	9627	9668	9708	9749	
71	9789	9830	9871	9911	9952	9992	*0033	*0073	*0114	*0154	
72	03 0195	0235	0276	0316	0357	0397	0438	0478	0519	0559	
73	0600	0640	0681	0721	0762	0802	0843	0883	0923	0964	
74	1004	1045	1085	1126	1166	1206	1247	1287	1328	1368	
1075	03 1408	1449	1489	1530	1570	1610	1651	1691	1732	1772	40
76	1812	1853	1893	1933	1974	2014	2054	2095	2135	2175	
77	2216	2256	2296	2337	2377	2417	2458	2498	2538	2578	
78	2619	2659	2699	2740	2780	2820	2860	2901	2941	2981	
79	3021	3062	3102	3142	3182	3223	3263	3303	3343	3384	
1080	03 3424	3464	3504	3544	3585	3625	3665	3705	3745	3786	
81	3826	3866	3906	3946	3986	4027	4067	4107	4147	4187	
82	4227	4267	4308	4348	4388	4428	4468	4508	4548	4588	
83	4628	4669	4709	4749	4789	4829	4869	4909	4949	4989	
84	5029	5069	5109	5149	5190	5230	5270	5310	5350	5390	
1085	03 5430	5470	5510	5550	5590	5630	5670	5710	5750	5790	
86	5830	5870	5910	5950	5990	6030	6070	6110	6150	6190	
87	6230	6269	6309	6349	6389	6429	6469	6509	6549	6589	
88	6629	6669	6709	6749	6789	6828	6868	6908	6948	6988	
89	7028	7068	7108	7148	7187	7227	7267	7307	7347	7387	
1090	03 7426	7466	7506	7546	7586	7626	7665	7705	7745	7785	39
91	7825	7865	7904	7944	7984	8024	8064	8103	8143	8183	
92	8223	8262	8302	8342	8382	8421	8461	8501	8541	8580	
93	8620	8660	8700	8739	8779	8819	8859	8898	8938	8978	
94	9017	9057	9097	9136	9176	9216	9255	9295	9335	9374	
1095	03 9414	9454	9493	9533	9573	9612	9652	9692	9731	9771	
96	9811	9850	9890	9929	9969	*0009	*0048	*0088	*0127	*0167	
97	04 0207	0246	0286	0325	0365	0405	0444	0484	0523	0563	
98	0602	0642	0681	0721	0761	0800	0840	0879	0919	0958	
99	0998	1037	1077	1116	1156	1195	1235	1274	1314	1353	

PROPORTIONAL PARTS

Diff.	1	2	3	4	5	6	7	8	9
42	4.2	8.4	12.6	16.8	21.0	25.2	29.4	33.6	37.8
41	4.1	8.2	12.3	16.4	20.5	24.6	28.7	32.8	36.9
40	4.0	8.0	12.0	16.0	20.0	24.0	28.0	32.0	36.0
39	3.9	7.8	11.7	15.6	19.5	23.4	27.3	31.2	35.1

Table I — Six-Place Logarithms

N.	0	1*	2	3	4	5	6	7	8	9	Diff.
110	04 1393	1787	2182	2576	2969	3362	3755	4148	4540	4932	393
1	5323	5714	6105	6495	6885	7275	7664	8053	8442	8830	390
2	9218	9606	9993	*0380	*0766	*1153	*1538	*1924	*2309	*2694	386
3	05 3078	3463	3846	4230	4613	4996	5378	5760	6142	6524	383
4	6905	7286	7666	8046	8426	8805	9185	9563	9942	*0320	379
115	06 0698	1075	1452	1829	2206	2582	2958	3333	3709	4083	376
6	4458	4832	5206	5580	5953	6326	6699	7071	7443	7815	373
7	8186	8557	8928	9298	9668	*0038	*0407	*0776	*1145	*1514	370
8	07 1882	2250	2617	2985	3352	3718	4085	4451	4816	5182	366
9	5547	5912	6276	6640	7004	7368	7731	8094	8457	8819	363

PROPORTIONAL PARTS

Diff.	1	2	3	4	5	6	7	8	9
395	39.5	79.0	118.5	158.0	197.5	237.0	276.5	316.0	355.5
394	39.4	78.8	118.2	157.6	197.0	236.4	275.8	315.2	354.6
393	39.3	78.6	117.9	157.2	196.5	235.8	275.1	314.4	353.7
392	39.2	78.4	117.6	156.8	196.0	235.2	274.4	313.6	352.8
391	39.1	78.2	117.3	156.4	195.5	234.6	273.7	312.8	351.9
390	39.0	78.0	117.0	156.0	195.0	234.0	273.0	312.0	351.0
389	38.9	77.8	116.7	155.6	194.5	233.4	272.3	311.2	350.1
388	38.8	77.6	116.4	155.2	194.0	232.8	271.6	310.4	349.2
387	38.7	77.4	116.1	154.8	193.5	232.2	270.9	309.6	348.3
386	38.6	77.2	115.8	154.4	193.0	231.6	270.2	308.8	347.4
385	38.5	77.0	115.5	154.0	192.5	231.0	269.5	308.0	346.5
384	38.4	76.8	115.2	153.6	192.0	230.4	268.8	307.2	345.6
383	38.3	76.6	114.9	153.2	191.5	229.8	268.1	306.4	344.7
382	38.2	76.4	114.6	152.8	191.0	229.2	267.4	305.6	343.8
381	38.1	76.2	114.3	152.4	190.5	228.6	266.7	304.8	342.9
380	38.0	76.0	114.0	152.0	190.0	228.0	266.0	304.0	342.0
379	37.9	75.8	113.7	151.6	189.5	227.4	265.3	303.2	341.1
378	37.8	75.6	113.4	151.2	189.0	226.8	264.6	302.4	340.2
377	37.7	75.4	113.1	150.8	188.5	226.2	263.9	301.6	339.3
376	37.6	75.2	112.8	150.4	188.0	225.6	263.2	300.8	338.4
375	37.5	75.0	112.5	150.0	187.5	225.0	262.5	300.0	337.5
374	37.4	74.8	112.2	149.6	187.0	224.4	261.8	299.2	336.6
373	37.3	74.6	111.9	149.2	186.5	223.8	261.1	298.4	335.7
372	37.2	74.4	111.6	148.8	186.0	223.2	260.4	297.6	334.8
371	37.1	74.2	111.3	148.4	185.5	222.6	259.7	296.8	333.9
370	37.0	74.0	111.0	148.0	185.0	222.0	259.0	296.0	333.0
369	36.9	73.8	110.7	147.6	184.5	221.4	258.3	295.2	332.1
368	36.8	73.6	110.4	147.2	184.0	220.8	257.6	294.4	331.2
367	36.7	73.4	110.1	146.8	183.5	220.2	256.9	293.6	330.3
366	36.6	73.2	109.8	146.4	183.0	219.6	256.2	292.8	329.4
365	36.5	73.0	109.5	146.0	182.5	219.0	255.5	292.0	328.5
364	36.4	72.8	109.2	145.6	182.0	218.4	254.8	291.2	327.6
363	36.3	72.6	108.9	145.2	181.5	217.8	254.1	290.4	326.7
362	36.2	72.4	108.6	144.8	181.0	217.2	253.4	289.6	325.8
361	36.1	72.2	108.3	144.4	180.5	216.6	252.7	288.8	324.9
360	36.0	72.0	108.0	144.0	180.0	216.0	252.0	288.0	324.0
359	35.9	71.8	107.7	143.6	179.5	215.4	251.3	287.2	323.1
358	35.8	71.6	107.4	143.2	179.0	214.8	250.6	286.4	322.2
357	35.7	71.4	107.1	142.8	178.5	214.2	249.9	285.6	321.3
356	35.6	71.2	106.8	142.4	178.0	213.6	249.2	284.8	320.4

Table I — Six-Place Logarithms

N.	0	1	2	3	4	5	6	7	8	9	Diff.
120	07 9181	9543	9904	*0266	*0626	*0987	*1347	*1707	*2067	*2426	360
1	08 2785	3144	3503	3861	4219	4576	4934	5291	5647	6004	357
2	6360	6716	7071	7426	7781	8136	8490	8845	9198	9552	355
3	9905	*0258	*0611	*0963	*1315	*1667	*2018	*2370	*2721	*3071	352
4	09 3422	3772	4122	4471	4820	5169	5518	5866	6215	6562	349
125	09 6910	7257	7604	7951	8298	8644	8990	9335	9681	*0026	346
6	10 0371	0715	1059	1403	1747	2091	2434	2777	3119	3462	343
7	3804	4146	4487	4828	5169	5510	5851	6191	6531	6871	341
8	7210	7549	7888	8227	8565	8903	9241	9579	9916	*0253	338
9	11 0590	0926	1263	1599	1934	2270	2605	2940	3275	3609	335
130	11 3943	4277	4611	4944	5278	5611	5943	6276	6608	6940	333
1	7271	7603	7934	8265	8595	8926	9256	9586	9915	*0245	330
2	12 0574	0903	1231	1560	1888	2216	2544	2871	3198	3525	328
3	3852	4178	4504	4830	5156	5481	5806	6131	6456	6781	325
4	7105	7429	7753	8076	8399	8722	9045	9368	9690	*0012	323

PROPORTIONAL PARTS

Diff.	1	2	3	4	5	6	7	8	9
355	35.5	71.0	106.5	142.0	177.5	213.0	248.5	284.0	319.5
354	35.4	70.8	106.2	141.6	177.0	212.4	247.8	283.2	318.6
353	35.3	70.6	105.9	141.2	176.5	211.8	247.1	282.4	317.7
352	35.2	70.4	105.6	140.8	176.0	211.2	246.4	281.6	316.8
351	35.1	70.2	105.3	140.4	175.5	210.6	245.7	280.8	315.9
350	35.0	70.0	105.0	140.0	175.0	210.0	245.0	280.0	315.0
349	34.9	69.8	104.7	139.6	174.5	209.4	244.3	279.2	314.1
348	34.8	69.6	104.4	139.2	174.0	208.8	243.6	278.4	313.2
347	34.7	69.4	104.1	138.8	173.5	208.2	242.9	277.6	312.3
346	34.6	69.2	103.8	138.4	173.0	207.6	242.2	276.8	311.4
345	34.5	69.0	103.5	138.0	172.5	207.0	241.5	276.0	310.5
344	34.4	68.8	103.2	137.6	172.0	206.4	240.8	275.2	309.6
343	34.3	68.6	102.9	137.2	171.5	205.8	240.1	274.4	308.7
342	34.2	68.4	102.6	136.8	171.0	205.2	239.4	273.6	307.8
341	34.1	68.2	102.3	136.4	170.5	204.6	238.7	272.8	306.9
340	34.0	68.0	102.0	136.0	170.0	204.0	238.0	272.0	306.0
339	33.9	67.8	101.7	135.6	169.5	203.4	237.3	271.2	305.1
338	33.8	67.6	101.4	135.2	169.0	202.8	236.6	270.4	304.2
337	33.7	67.4	101.1	134.8	168.5	202.2	235.9	269.6	303.3
336	33.6	67.2	100.8	134.4	168.0	201.6	235.2	268.8	302.4
335	33.5	67.0	100.5	134.0	167.5	201.0	234.5	268.0	301.5
334	33.4	66.8	100.2	133.6	167.0	200.4	233.8	267.2	300.6
333	33.3	66.6	99.9	133.2	166.5	199.8	233.1	266.4	299.7
332	33.2	66.4	99.6	132.8	166.0	199.2	232.4	265.6	298.8
331	33.1	66.2	99.3	132.4	165.5	198.6	231.7	264.8	297.9
330	33.0	66.0	99.0	132.0	165.0	198.0	231.0	264.0	297.0
329	32.9	65.8	98.7	131.6	164.5	197.4	230.3	263.2	296.1
328	32.8	65.6	98.4	131.2	164.0	196.8	229.6	262.4	295.2
327	32.7	65.4	98.1	130.8	163.5	196.2	228.9	261.6	294.3
326	32.6	65.2	97.8	130.4	163.0	195.6	228.2	260.8	293.4
325	32.5	65.0	97.5	130.0	162.5	195.0	227.5	260.0	292.5
324	32.4	64.8	97.2	129.6	162.0	194.4	226.8	259.2	291.6
323	32.3	64.6	96.9	129.2	161.5	193.8	226.1	258.4	290.7
322	32.2	64.4	96.6	128.8	161.0	193.2	225.4	257.6	289.8

Table I — Six-Place Logarithms

N.	0	1	2	3	4	5	6	7	8	9	Diff.
135	13 0334	0655	0977	1298	1619	1939	2260	2580	2900	3219	321
6	3539	3858	4177	4496	4814	5133	5451	5769	6086	6403	318
7	6721	7037	7354	7671	7987	8303	8618	8934	9249	9564	316
8	9879	*0194	*0508	*0822	*1136	*1450	*1763	*2076	*2389	*2702	314
9	14 3015	3327	3639	3951	4263	4574	4885	5196	5507	5818	311
140	14 6128	6438	6748	7058	7367	7676	7985	8294	8603	8911	309
1	9219	9527	9835	*0142	*0449	*0756	*1063	*1370	*1676	*1982	307
2	15 2288	2594	2900	3205	3510	3815	4120	4424	4728	5032	305
3	5336	5640	5943	6246	6549	6852	7154	7457	7759	8061	303
4	8362	8664	8965	9266	9567	9868	*0168	*0469	*0769	*1068	301
145	16 1368	1667	1967	2266	2564	2863	3161	3460	3758	4055	299
6	4353	4650	4947	5244	5541	5838	6134	6430	6726	7022	297
7	7317	7613	7908	8203	8497	8792	9086	9380	9674	9968	295
8	17 0262	0555	0848	1141	1434	1726	2019	2311	2603	2895	293
9	3186	3478	3769	4060	4351	4641	4932	5222	5512	5802	291

PROPORTIONAL PARTS

Diff.	1	2	3	4	5	6	7	8	9
322	32.2	64.4	96.6	128.8	161.0	193.2	225.4	257.6	289.8
321	32.1	64.2	96.3	128.4	160.5	192.6	224.7	256.8	288.9
320	32.0	64.0	96.0	128.0	160.0	192.0	224.0	256.0	288.0
319	31.9	63.8	95.7	127.6	159.5	191.4	223.3	255.2	287.1
318	31.8	63.6	95.4	127.2	159.0	190.8	222.6	254.4	286.2
317	31.7	63.4	95.1	126.8	158.5	190.2	221.9	253.6	285.3
316	31.6	63.2	94.8	126.4	158.0	189.6	221.2	252.8	284.4
315	31.5	63.0	94.5	126.0	157.5	189.0	220.5	252.0	283.5
314	31.4	62.8	94.2	125.6	157.0	188.4	219.8	251.2	282.6
313	31.3	62.6	93.9	125.2	156.5	187.8	219.1	250.4	281.7
312	31.2	62.4	93.6	124.8	156.0	187.2	218.4	249.6	280.8
311	31.1	62.2	93.3	124.4	155.5	186.6	217.7	248.8	279.9
310	31.0	62.0	93.0	124.0	155.0	186.0	217.0	248.0	279.0
309	30.9	61.8	92.7	123.6	154.5	185.4	216.3	247.2	278.1
308	30.8	61.6	92.4	123.2	154.0	184.8	215.6	246.4	277.2
307	30.7	61.4	92.1	122.8	153.5	184.2	214.9	245.6	276.3
306	30.6	61.2	91.8	122.4	153.0	183.6	214.2	244.8	275.4
305	30.5	61.0	91.5	122.0	152.5	183.0	213.5	244.0	274.5
304	30.4	60.8	91.2	121.6	152.0	182.4	212.8	243.2	273.6
303	30.3	60.6	90.9	121.2	151.5	181.8	212.1	242.4	272.7
302	30.2	60.4	90.6	120.8	151.0	181.2	211.4	241.6	271.8
301	30.1	60.2	90.3	120.4	150.5	180.6	210.7	240.8	270.9
300	30.0	60.0	90.0	120.0	150.0	180.0	210.0	240.0	270.0
299	29.9	59.8	89.7	119.6	149.5	179.4	209.3	239.2	269.1
298	29.8	59.6	89.4	119.2	149.0	178.8	208.6	238.4	268.2
297	29.7	59.4	89.1	118.8	148.5	178.2	207.9	237.6	267.3
296	29.6	59.2	88.8	118.4	148.0	177.6	207.2	236.8	266.4
295	29.5	59.0	88.5	118.0	147.5	177.0	206.5	236.0	265.5
294	29.4	58.8	88.2	117.6	147.0	176.4	205.8	235.2	264.6
293	29.3	58.6	87.9	117.2	146.5	175.8	205.1	234.4	263.7
292	29.2	58.4	87.6	116.8	146.0	175.2	204.4	233.6	262.8
291	29.1	58.2	87.3	116.4	145.5	174.6	203.7	232.8	261.9
290	29.0	58.0	87.0	116.0	145.0	174.0	203.0	232.0	261.0
289	28.9	57.8	86.7	115.6	144.5	173.4	202.3	231.2	260.1
288	28.8	57.6	86.4	115.2	144.0	172.8	201.6	230.4	259.2
287	28.7	57.4	86.1	114.8	143.5	172.2	200.9	229.6	258.3
286	28.6	57.2	85.8	114.4	143.0	171.6	200.2	228.8	257.4

Table I — Six-Place Logarithms

N.	0	1	2	3	4	5	6	7	8	9	Diff.
150	17 6091	6381	6670	6959	7248	7536	7825	8113	8401	8689	289
1	8977	9264	9552	9839	*0126	*0413	*0699	*0986	*1272	*1558	287
2	18 1844	2129	2415	2700	2985	3270	3555	3839	4123	4407	285
3	4691	4975	5259	5542	5825	6108	6391	6674	6956	7239	283
4	7521	7803	8084	8366	8647	8928	9209	9490	9771	*0051	281
155	19 0332	0612	0892	1171	1451	1730	2010	2289	2567	2846	279
6	3125	3403	3681	3959	4237	4514	4792	5069	5346	5623	278
7	5900	6176	6453	6729	7005	7281	7556	7832	8107	8382	276
8	8657	8932	9206	9481	9755	*0029	*0303	*0577	*0850	*1124	274
9	20 1397	1670	1943	2216	2488	2761	3033	3305	3577	3848	272
160	20 4120	4391	4663	4934	5204	5475	5746	6016	6286	6556	271
1	6826	7096	7365	7634	7904	8173	8441	8710	8979	9247	269
2	9515	9783	*0051	*0319	*0586	*0853	*1121	*1388	*1654	*1921	267
3	21 2188	2454	2720	2986	3252	3518	3783	4049	4314	4579	266
4	4844	5109	5373	5638	5902	6166	6430	6694	6957	7221	264
165	21 7484	7747	8010	8273	8536	8798	9060	9323	9585	9846	262
6	22 0108	0370	0631	0892	1153	1414	1675	1936	2196	2456	261
7	2716	2976	3236	3496	3755	4015	4274	4533	4792	5051	259
8	5309	5568	5826	6084	6342	6600	6858	7115	7372	7630	258
9	7887	8144	8400	8657	8913	9170	9426	9682	9938	*0193	256

PROPORTIONAL PARTS

Diff.	1	2	3	4	5	6	7	8	9
285	28.5	57.0	85.5	114.0	142.5	171.0	199.5	228.0	256.5
284	28.4	56.8	85.2	113.6	142.0	170.4	198.8	227.2	255.6
283	28.3	56.6	84.9	113.2	141.5	169.8	198.1	226.4	254.7
282	28.2	56.4	84.6	112.8	141.0	169.2	197.4	225.6	253.8
281	28.1	56.2	84.3	112.4	140.5	168.6	196.7	224.8	252.9
280	28.0	56.0	84.0	112.0	140.0	168.0	196.0	224.0	252.0
279	27.9	55.8	83.7	111.6	139.5	167.4	195.3	223.2	251.1
278	27.8	55.6	83.4	111.2	139.0	166.8	194.6	222.4	250.2
277	27.7	55.4	83.1	110.8	138.5	166.2	193.9	221.6	249.3
276	27.6	55.2	82.8	110.4	138.0	165.6	193.2	220.8	248.4
275	27.5	55.0	82.5	110.0	137.5	165.0	192.5	220.0	247.5
274	27.4	54.8	82.2	109.6	137.0	164.4	191.8	219.2	246.6
273	27.3	54.6	81.9	109.2	136.5	163.8	191.1	218.4	245.7
272	27.2	54.4	81.6	108.8	136.0	163.2	190.4	217.6	244.8
271	27.1	54.2	81.3	108.4	135.5	162.6	189.7	216.8	243.9
270	27.0	54.0	81.0	108.0	135.0	162.0	189.0	216.0	243.0
269	26.9	53.8	80.7	107.6	134.5	161.4	188.3	215.2	242.1
268	26.8	53.6	80.4	107.2	134.0	160.8	187.6	214.4	241.2
267	26.7	53.4	80.1	106.8	133.5	160.2	186.9	213.6	240.3
266	26.6	53.2	79.8	106.4	133.0	159.6	186.2	212.8	239.4
265	26.5	53.0	79.5	106.0	132.5	159.0	185.5	212.0	238.5
264	26.4	52.8	79.2	105.6	132.0	158.4	184.8	211.2	237.6
263	26.3	52.6	78.9	105.2	131.5	157.8	184.1	210.4	236.7
262	26.2	52.4	78.6	104.8	131.0	157.2	183.4	209.6	235.8
261	26.1	52.2	78.3	104.4	130.5	156.6	182.7	208.8	234.9
260	26.0	52.0	78.0	104.0	130.0	156.0	182.0	208.0	234.0
259	25.9	51.8	77.7	103.6	129.5	155.4	181.3	207.2	233.1
258	25.8	51.6	77.4	103.2	129.0	154.8	180.6	206.4	232.2
257	25.7	51.4	77.1	102.8	128.5	154.2	179.9	205.6	231.3
256	25.6	51.2	76.8	102.4	128.0	153.6	179.2	204.8	230.4
255	25.5	51.0	76.5	102.0	127.5	153.0	178.5	204.0	229.5

Table I — Six-Place Logarithms

N.	0	1	2	3	4	5	6	7	8	9	Diff.
170	23 0449	0704	0960	1215	1470	1724	1979	2234	2488	2742	255
1	2996	3250	3504	3757	4011	4264	4517	4770	5023	5276	253
2	5528	5781	6033	6285	6537	6789	7041	7292	7544	7795	252
3	8046	8297	8548	8799	9049	9299	9550	9800	*0050	*0300	250
4	24 0549	0799	1048	1297	1546	1795	2044	2293	2541	2790	249
175	24 3038	3286	3534	3782	4030	4277	4525	4772	5019	5266	248
6	5513	5759	6006	6252	6499	6745	6991	7237	7482	7728	246
7	7973	8219	8464	8709	8954	9198	9443	9687	9932	*0176	245
8	25 0420	0664	0908	1151	1395	1638	1881	2125	2368	2610	243
9	2853	3096	3338	3580	3822	4064	4306	4548	4790	5031	242
180	25 5273	5514	5755	5996	6237	6477	6718	6958	7198	7439	241
1	7679	7918	8158	8398	8637	8877	9116	9355	9594	9833	239
2	26 0071	0310	0548	0787	1025	1263	1501	1739	1976	2214	238
3	2451	2688	2925	3162	3399	3636	3873	4109	4346	4582	237
4	4818	5054	5290	5525	5761	5996	6232	6467	6702	6937	235
185	26 7172	7406	7641	7875	8110	8344	8578	8812	9046	9279	234
6	9513	9746	9980	*0213	*0446	*0679	*0912	*1144	*1377	*1609	233
7	27 1842	2074	2306	2538	2770	3001	3233	3464	3696	3927	232
8	4158	4389	4620	4850	5081	5311	5542	5772	6002	6232	230
9	6462	6692	6921	7151	7380	7609	7838	8067	8296	8525	229
190	27 8754	8982	9211	9439	9667	9895	*0123	*0351	*0578	*0806	228
1	28 1033	1261	1488	1715	1942	2169	2396	2622	2849	3075	227
2	3301	3527	3753	3979	4205	4431	4656	4882	5107	5332	226
3	5557	5782	6007	6232	6456	6681	6905	7130	7354	7578	225
4	7802	8026	8249	8473	8696	8920	9143	9366	9589	9812	223

PROPORTIONAL PARTS

Diff.	1	2	3	4	5	6	7	8	9
255	25.5	51.0	76.5	102.0	127.5	153.0	178.5	204.0	229.5
254	25.4	50.8	76.2	101.6	127.0	152.4	177.8	203.2	228.6
253	25.3	50.6	75.9	101.2	126.5	151.8	177.1	202.4	227.7
252	25.2	50.4	75.6	100.8	126.0	151.2	176.4	201.6	226.8
251	25.1	50.2	75.3	100.4	125.5	150.6	175.7	200.8	225.9
250	25.0	50.0	75.0	100.0	125.0	150.0	175.0	200.0	225.0
249	24.9	49.8	74.7	99.6	124.5	149.4	174.3	199.2	224.1
248	24.8	49.6	74.4	99.2	124.0	148.8	173.6	198.4	223.2
247	24.7	49.4	74.1	98.8	123.5	148.2	172.9	197.6	222.3
246	24.6	49.2	73.8	98.4	123.0	147.6	172.2	196.8	221.4
245	24.5	49.0	73.5	98.0	122.5	147.0	171.5	196.0	220.5
244	24.4	48.8	73.2	97.6	122.0	146.4	170.8	195.2	219.6
243	24.3	48.6	72.9	97.2	121.5	145.8	170.1	194.4	218.7
242	24.2	48.4	72.6	96.8	121.0	145.2	169.4	193.6	217.8
241	24.1	48.2	72.3	96.4	120.5	144.6	168.7	192.8	216.9
240	24.0	48.0	72.0	96.0	120.0	144.0	168.0	192.0	216.0
239	23.9	47.8	71.7	95.6	119.5	143.4	167.3	191.2	215.1
238	23.8	47.6	71.4	95.2	119.0	142.8	166.6	190.4	214.2
237	23.7	47.4	71.1	94.8	118.5	142.2	165.9	189.6	213.3
236	23.6	47.2	70.8	94.4	118.0	141.6	165.2	188.8	212.4
235	23.5	47.0	70.5	94.0	117.5	141.0	164.5	188.0	211.5
234	23.4	46.8	70.2	93.6	117.0	140.4	163.8	187.2	210.6
233	23.3	46.6	69.9	93.2	116.5	139.8	163.1	186.4	209.7
232	23.2	46.4	69.6	92.8	116.0	139.2	162.4	185.6	208.8
231	23.1	46.2	69.3	92.4	115.5	138.6	161.7	184.8	207.9
230	23.0	46.0	69.0	92.0	115.0	138.0	161.0	184.0	207.0
229	22.9	45.8	68.7	91.6	114.5	137.4	160.3	183.2	206.1
228	22.8	45.6	68.4	91.2	114.0	136.8	159.6	182.4	205.2
227	22.7	45.4	68.1	90.8	113.5	136.2	158.9	181.6	204.3

Table I — Six-Place Logarithms

N.	0	1	2	3	4	5	6	7	8	9	Diff.
195	29 0035	0257	0480	0702	0925	1147	1369	1591	1813	2034	222
6	2256	2478	2699	2920	3141	3363	3584	3804	4025	4246	221
7	4466	4687	4907	5127	5347	5567	5787	6007	6226	6446	220
8	6665	6884	7104	7323	7542	7761	7979	8198	8416	8635	219
9	8853	9071	9289	9507	9725	9943	*0161	*0378	*0595	*0813	218
200	30 1030	1247	1464	1681	1898	2114	2331	2547	2764	2980	217
1	3196	3412	3628	3844	4059	4275	4491	4706	4921	5136	216
2	5351	5566	5781	5996	6211	6425	6639	6854	7068	7282	215
3	7496	7710	7924	8137	8351	8564	8778	8991	9204	9417	213
4	9630	9843	*0056	*0268	*0481	*0693	*0906	*1118	*1330	*1542	212
205	31 1754	1966	2177	2389	2600	2812	3023	3234	3445	3656	211
6	3867	4078	4289	4499	4710	4920	5130	5340	5551	5760	210
7	5970	6180	6390	6599	6809	7018	7227	7436	7646	7854	209
8	8063	8272	8481	8689	8898	9106	9314	9522	9730	9938	208
9	32 0146	0354	0562	0769	0977	1184	1391	1598	1805	2012	207
210	32 2219	2426	2633	2839	3046	3252	3458	3665	3871	4077	206
1	4282	4488	4694	4899	5105	5310	5516	5721	5926	6131	205
2	6336	6541	6745	6950	7155	7359	7563	7767	7972	8176	204
3	8380	8583	8787	8991	9194	9398	9601	9805	*0008	*0211	203
4	33 0414	0617	0819	1022	1225	1427	1630	1832	2034	2236	202
215	33 2438	2640	2842	3044	3246	3447	3649	3850	4051	4253	202
6	4454	4655	4856	5057	5257	5458	5658	5859	6059	6260	201
7	6460	6660	6860	7060	7260	7459	7659	7858	8058	8257	200
8	8456	8656	8855	9054	9253	9451	9650	9849	*0047	*0246	199
9	34 0444	0642	0841	1039	1237	1435	1632	1830	2028	2225	198

PROPORTIONAL PARTS

Diff.	1	2	3	4	5	6	7	8	9
226	22.6	45.2	67.8	90.4	113.0	135.6	158.2	180.8	203.4
225	22.5	45.0	67.5	90.0	112.5	135.0	157.5	180.0	202.5
224	22.4	44.8	67.2	89.6	112.0	134.4	156.8	179.2	201.6
223	22.3	44.6	66.9	89.2	111.5	133.8	156.1	178.4	200.7
222	22.2	44.4	66.6	88.8	111.0	133.2	155.4	177.6	199.8
221	22.1	44.2	66.3	88.4	110.5	132.6	154.7	176.8	198.9
220	22.0	44.0	66.0	88.0	110.0	132.0	154.0	176.0	198.0
219	21.9	43.8	65.7	87.6	109.5	131.4	153.3	175.2	197.1
218	21.8	43.6	65.4	87.2	109.0	130.8	152.6	174.4	196.2
217	21.7	43.4	65.1	86.8	108.5	130.2	151.9	173.6	195.3
216	21.6	43.2	64.8	86.4	108.0	129.6	151.2	172.8	194.4
215	21.5	43.0	64.5	86.0	107.5	129.0	150.5	172.0	193.5
214	21.4	42.8	64.2	85.6	107.0	128.4	149.8	171.2	192.6
213	21.3	42.6	63.9	85.2	106.5	127.8	149.1	170.4	191.7
212	21.2	42.4	63.6	84.8	106.0	127.2	148.4	169.6	190.8
211	21.1	42.2	63.3	84.4	105.5	126.6	147.7	168.8	189.9
210	21.0	42.0	63.0	84.0	105.0	126.0	147.0	168.0	189.0
209	20.9	41.8	62.7	83.6	104.5	125.4	146.3	167.2	188.1
208	20.8	41.6	62.4	83.2	104.0	124.8	145.6	166.4	187.2
207	20.7	41.4	62.1	82.8	103.5	124.2	144.9	165.6	186.3
206	20.6	41.2	61.8	82.4	103.0	123.6	144.2	164.8	185.4
205	20.5	41.0	61.5	82.0	102.5	123.0	143.5	164.0	184.5
204	20.4	40.8	61.2	81.6	102.0	122.4	142.8	163.2	183.6
203	20.3	40.6	60.9	81.2	101.5	121.8	142.1	162.4	182.7
202	20.2	40.4	60.6	80.8	101.0	121.2	141.4	161.6	181.8
201	20.1	40.2	60.3	80.4	100.5	120.6	140.7	160.8	180.9
200	20.0	40.0	60.0	80.0	100.0	120.0	140.0	160.0	180.0
199	19.9	39.8	59.7	79.6	99.5	119.4	139.3	159.2	179.1
198	19.8	39.6	59.4	79.2	99.0	118.8	138.6	158.4	178.2

Table I — Six-Place Logarithms

N.	0	1	2	3	4	5	6	7	8	9	Diff.
220	34 2423	2620	2817	3014	3212	3409	3606	3802	3999	4196	197
1	4392	4589	4785	4981	5178	5374	5570	5766	5962	6157	196
2	6353	6549	6744	6939	7135	7330	7525	7720	7915	8110	195
3	8305	8500	8694	8889	9083	9278	9472	9666	9860	*0054	194
4	35 0248	0442	0636	0829	1023	1216	1410	1603	1796	1989	193
225	35 2183	2375	2568	2761	2954	3147	3339	3532	3724	3916	193
6	4108	4301	4493	4685	4876	5068	5260	5452	5643	5834	192
7	6026	6217	6408	6599	6790	6981	7172	7363	7554	7744	191
8	7935	8125	8316	8506	8696	8886	9076	9266	9456	9646	190
9	9835	*0025	*0215	*0404	*0593	*0783	*0972	*1161	*1350	*1539	189
230	36 1728	1917	2105	2294	2482	2671	2859	3048	3236	3424	188
1	3612	3800	3988	4176	4363	4551	4739	4926	5113	5301	188
2	5488	5675	5862	6049	6236	6423	6610	6796	6983	7169	187
3	7356	7542	7729	7915	8101	8287	8473	8659	8845	9030	186
4	9216	9401	9587	9772	9958	*0143	*0328	*0513	*0698	*0883	185
235	37 1068	1253	1437	1622	1806	1991	2175	2360	2544	2728	184
6	2912	3096	3280	3464	3647	3831	4015	4198	4382	4565	184
7	4748	4932	5115	5298	5481	5664	5846	6029	6212	6394	183
8	6577	6759	6942	7124	7306	7488	7670	7852	8034	8216	182
9	8398	8580	8761	8943	9124	9306	9487	9668	9849	*0030	181
240	38 0211	0392	0573	0754	0934	1115	1296	1476	1656	1837	181
1	2017	2197	2377	2557	2737	2917	3097	3277	3456	3636	180
2	3815	3995	4174	4353	4533	4712	4891	5070	5249	5428	179
3	5606	5785	5964	6142	6321	6499	6677	6856	7034	7212	178
4	7390	7568	7746	7923	8101	8279	8456	8634	8811	8989	178
245	38 9166	9343	9520	9698	9875	*0051	*0228	*0405	*0582	*0759	177
6	39 0935	1112	1288	1464	1641	1817	1993	2169	2345	2521	176
7	2697	2873	3048	3224	3400	3575	3751	3926	4101	4277	176
8	4452	4627	4802	4977	5152	5326	5501	5676	5850	6025	175
9	6199	6374	6548	6722	6896	7071	7245	7419	7592	7766	174

PROPORTIONAL PARTS

Diff.	1	2	3	4	5	6	7	8	9
198	19.8	39.6	59.4	79.2	99.0	118.8	138.6	158.6	178.2
197	19.7	39.4	59.1	78.8	98.5	118.2	137.9	157.6	177.3
196	19.6	39.2	58.8	78.4	98.0	117.6	137.2	156.8	176.4
195	19.5	39.0	58.5	78.0	97.5	117.0	136.5	156.0	175.5
194	19.4	38.8	58.2	77.6	97.0	116.4	135.8	155.2	174.6
193	19.3	38.6	57.9	77.2	96.5	115.8	135.1	154.4	173.7
192	19.2	38.4	57.6	76.8	96.0	115.2	134.4	153.6	172.8
191	19.1	38.2	57.3	76.4	95.5	114.6	133.7	152.8	171.9
190	19.0	38.0	57.0	76.0	95.0	114.0	133.0	152.0	171.0
189	18.9	37.8	56.7	75.6	94.5	113.4	132.3	151.2	170.1
188	18.8	37.6	56.4	75.2	94.0	112.8	131.6	150.4	169.2
187	18.7	37.4	56.1	74.8	93.5	112.2	130.9	149.6	168.3
186	18.6	37.2	55.8	74.4	93.0	111.6	130.2	148.8	167.4
185	18.5	37.0	55.5	74.0	92.5	111.0	129.5	148.0	166.5
184	18.4	36.8	55.2	73.6	92.0	110.4	128.8	147.2	165.6
183	18.3	36.6	54.9	73.2	91.5	109.8	128.1	146.4	164.7
182	18.2	36.4	54.6	72.8	91.0	109.2	127.4	145.6	163.8
181	18.1	36.2	54.3	72.4	90.5	108.6	126.7	144.8	162.9
180	18.0	36.0	54.0	72.0	90.0	108.0	126.0	144.0	162.0
179	17.9	35.8	53.7	71.6	89.5	107.4	125.3	143.2	161.1
178	17.8	35.6	53.4	71.2	89.0	106.8	124.6	142.4	160.2
177	17.7	35.4	53.1	70.8	88.5	106.2	123.9	141.6	159.3
176	17.6	35.2	52.8	70.4	88.0	105.6	123.2	140.8	158.4
175	17.5	35.0	52.5	70.0	87.5	105.0	122.5	140.0	157.5

Table I — Six-Place Logarithms

N.	0	1	2	3	4	5	6	7	8	9	Diff.
250	39 7940	8114	8287	8461	8634	8808	8981	9154	9328	9501	173
1	9674	9847	*0020	*0192	*0365	*0538	*0711	*0883	*1056	*1228	173
2	40 1401	1573	1745	1917	2089	2261	2433	2605	2777	2949	172
3	3121	3292	3464	3635	3807	3978	4149	4320	4492	4663	171
4	4834	5005	5176	5346	5517	5688	5858	6029	6199	6370	171
255	40 6540	6710	6881	7051	7221	7391	7561	7731	7901	8070	170
6	8240	8410	8579	8749	8918	9087	9257	9426	9595	9764	169
7	9933	*0102	*0271	*0440	*0609	*0777	*0946	*1114	*1283	*1451	169
8	41 1620	1788	1956	2124	2293	2461	2629	2796	2964	3132	168
9	3300	3467	3635	3803	3970	4137	4305	4472	4639	4806	167
260	41 4973	5140	5307	5474	5641	5808	5974	6141	6308	6474	167
1	6641	6807	6973	7139	7306	7472	7638	7804	7970	8135	166
2	8301	8467	8633	8798	8964	9129	9295	9460	9625	9791	165
3	9956	*0121	*0286	*0451	*0616	*0781	*0945	*1110	*1275	*1439	165
4	42 1604	1768	1933	2097	2261	2426	2590	2754	2918	3082	164
265	42 3246	3410	3574	3737	3901	4065	4228	4392	4555	4718	164
6	4882	5045	5208	5371	5534	5697	5860	6023	6186	6349	163
7	6511	6674	6836	6999	7161	7324	7486	7648	7811	7973	162
8	8135	8297	8459	8621	8783	8944	9106	9268	9429	9591	162
9	9752	9914	*0075	*0236	*0398	*0559	*0720	*0881	*1042	*1203	161
270	43 1364	1525	1685	1846	2007	2167	2328	2488	2649	2809	161
1	2969	3130	3290	3450	3610	3770	3930	4090	4249	4409	160
2	4569	4729	4888	5048	5207	5367	5526	5685	5844	6004	159
3	6163	6322	6481	6640	6799	6957	7116	7275	7433	7592	159
4	7751	7909	8067	8226	8384	8542	8701	8859	9017	9175	158
275	43 9333	9491	9648	9806	9964	*0122	*0279	*0437	*0594	*0752	158
6	44 0909	1066	1224	1381	1538	1695	1852	2009	2166	2323	157
7	2480	2637	2793	2950	3106	3263	3419	3576	3732	3889	157
8	4045	4201	4357	4513	4669	4825	4981	5137	5293	5449	156
9	5604	5760	5915	6071	6226	6382	6537	6692	6848	7003	155

PROPORTIONAL PARTS

Diff.	1	2	3	4	5	6	7	8	9
174	17.4	34.8	52.2	69.6	87.0	104.4	121.8	139.2	156.6
173	17.3	34.6	51.9	69.2	86.5	103.8	121.1	138.4	155.7
172	17.2	34.4	51.6	68.8	86.0	103.2	120.4	137.6	154.8
171	17.1	34.2	51.3	68.4	85.5	102.6	119.7	136.8	153.9
170	17.0	34.0	51.0	68.0	85.0	102.0	119.0	136.0	153.0
169	16.9	33.8	50.7	67.6	84.5	101.4	118.3	135.2	152.1
168	16.8	33.6	50.4	67.2	84.0	100.8	117.6	134.4	151.2
167	16.7	33.4	50.1	66.8	83.5	100.2	116.9	133.6	150.3
166	16.6	33.2	49.8	66.4	83.0	99.6	116.2	132.8	149.4
165	16.5	33.0	49.5	66.0	82.5	99.0	115.5	132.0	148.5
164	16.4	32.8	49.2	65.6	82.0	98.4	114.8	131.2	147.6
163	16.3	32.6	48.9	65.2	81.5	97.8	114.1	130.4	146.7
162	16.2	32.4	48.6	64.8	81.0	97.2	113.4	129.6	145.8
161	16.1	32.2	48.3	64.4	80.5	96.6	112.7	128.8	144.9
160	16.0	32.0	48.0	64.0	80.0	96.0	112.0	128.0	144.0
159	15.9	31.8	47.7	63.6	79.5	95.4	111.3	127.2	143.1
158	15.8	31.6	47.4	63.2	79.0	94.8	110.6	126.4	142.2
157	15.7	31.4	47.1	62.8	78.5	94.2	109.9	125.6	141.3
156	15.6	31.2	46.8	62.4	78.0	93.6	109.2	124.8	140.4
155	15.5	31.0	46.5	62.0	77.5	93.0	108.5	124.0	139.5

Table I — Six-Place Logarithms

N.	0	1	2	3	4	5	6	7	8	9	Diff.
280	44 7158	7313	7468	7623	7778	7933	8088	8242	8397	8552	155
1	8706	8861	9015	9170	9324	9478	9633	9787	9941	*0095	154
2	45 0249	0403	0557	0711	0865	1018	1172	1326	1479	1633	154
3	1786	1940	2093	2247	2400	2553	2706	2859	3012	3165	153
4	3318	3471	3624	3777	3930	4082	4235	4387	4540	4692	153
285	45 4845	4997	5150	5302	5454	5606	5758	5910	6062	6214	152
6	6366	6518	6670	6821	6973	7125	7276	7428	7579	7731	152
7	7882	8033	8184	8336	8487	8638	8789	8940	9091	9242	151
8	9392	9543	9694	9845	9995	*0146	*0296	*0447	*0597	*0748	151
9	46 0898	1048	1198	1348	1499	1649	1799	1948	2098	2248	150
290	46 2398	2548	2697	2847	2997	3146	3296	3445	3594	3744	150
1	3893	4042	4191	4340	4490	4639	4788	4936	5085	5234	149
2	5383	5532	5680	5829	5977	6126	6274	6423	6571	6719	149
3	6868	7016	7164	7312	7460	7608	7756	7904	8052	8200	148
4	8347	8495	8643	8790	8938	9085	9233	9380	9527	9675	148
295	46 9822	9969	*0116	*0263	*0410	*0557	*0704	*0851	*0998	*1145	147
6	47 1292	1438	1585	1732	1878	2025	2171	2318	2464	2610	146
7	2756	2903	3049	3195	3341	3487	3633	3779	3925	4071	146
8	4216	4362	4508	4653	4799	4944	5090	5235	5381	5526	146
9	5671	5816	5962	6107	6252	6397	6542	6687	6832	6976	145
300	47 7121	7266	7411	7555	7700	7844	7989	8133	8278	8422	145
1	8566	8711	8855	8999	9143	9287	9431	9575	9719	9863	144
2	48 0007	0151	0294	0438	0582	0725	0869	1012	1156	1299	144
3	1443	1586	1729	1872	2016	2159	2302	2445	2588	2731	143
4	2874	3016	3159	3302	3445	3587	3730	3872	4015	4157	143
305	48 4300	4442	4585	4727	4869	5011	5153	5295	5437	5579	142
6	5721	5863	6005	6147	6289	6430	6572	6714	6855	6997	142
7	7138	7280	7421	7563	7704	7845	7986	8127	8269	8410	141
8	8551	8692	8833	8974	9114	9255	9396	9537	9677	9818	141
9	9958	*0099	*0239	*0380	*0520	*0661	*0801	*0941	*1081	*1222	140
310	49 1362	1502	1642	1782	1922	2062	2201	2341	2481	2621	140
1	2760	2900	3040	3179	3319	3458	3597	3737	3876	4015	139
2	4155	4294	4433	4572	4711	4850	4989	5128	5267	5406	139
3	5544	5683	5822	5960	6099	6238	6376	6515	6653	6791	139
4	6930	7068	7206	7344	7483	7621	7759	7897	8035	8173	138

PROPORTIONAL PARTS

Diff.	1	2	3	4	5	6	7	8	9
155	15.5	31.0	46.5	62.0	77.5	93.0	108.5	124.0	139.5
154	15.4	30.8	46.2	61.6	77.0	92.4	107.8	123.2	138.6
153	15.3	30.6	45.9	61.2	76.5	91.8	107.1	122.4	137.7
152	15.2	30.4	45.6	60.8	76.0	91.2	106.4	121.6	136.8
151	15.1	30.2	45.3	60.4	75.5	90.6	105.7	120.8	135.9
150	15.0	30.0	45.0	60.0	75.0	90.0	105.0	120.0	135.0
149	14.9	29.8	44.7	59.6	74.5	89.4	104.3	119.2	134.1
148	14.8	29.6	44.4	59.2	74.0	88.8	103.6	118.4	133.2
147	14.7	29.4	44.1	58.8	73.5	88.2	102.9	117.6	132.3
146	14.6	29.2	43.8	58.4	73.0	87.6	102.2	116.8	131.4
145	14.5	29.0	43.5	58.0	72.5	87.0	101.5	116.0	130.5
144	14.4	28.8	43.2	57.6	72.0	86.4	100.8	115.2	129.6
143	14.3	28.6	42.9	57.2	71.5	85.8	100.1	114.4	128.7
142	14.2	28.4	42.6	56.8	71.0	85.2	99.4	113.6	127.8
141	14.1	28.2	42.3	56.4	70.5	84.6	98.7	112.8	126.9
140	14.0	28.0	42.0	56.0	70.0	84.0	98.0	112.0	126.0
139	13.9	27.8	41.7	55.6	69.5	83.4	97.3	111.2	125.1

Table I — Six-Place Logarithms

N.	0	1	2	3	4	5	6	7	8	9	Diff.
315	49 8311	8448	8586	8724	8862	8999	9137	9275	9412	9550	138
6	9687	9824	9962	*0099	*0236	*0374	*0511	*0648	*0785	*0922	137
7	50 1059	1196	1333	1470	1607	1744	1880	2017	2154	2291	137
8	2427	2564	2700	2837	2973	3109	3246	3382	3518	3655	136
9	3791	3927	4063	4199	4335	4471	4607	4743	4878	5014	136
320	50 5150	5286	5421	5557	5693	5828	5964	6099	6234	6370	136
1	6505	6640	6776	6911	7046	7181	7316	7451	7586	7721	135
2	7856	7991	8126	8260	8395	8530	8664	8799	8934	9068	135
3	9203	9337	9471	9606	9740	9874	*0009	*0143	*0277	*0411	134
4	51 0545	0679	0813	0947	1081	1215	1349	1482	1616	1750	134
325	51 1883	2017	2151	2284	2418	2551	2684	2818	2951	3084	133
6	3218	3351	3484	3617	3750	3883	4016	4149	4282	4415	133
7	4548	4681	4813	4946	5079	5211	5344	5476	5609	5741	133
8	5874	6006	6139	6271	6403	6535	6668	6800	6932	7064	132
9	7196	7328	7460	7592	7724	7855	7987	8119	8251	8382	132
330	51 8514	8646	8777	8909	9040	9171	9303	9434	9566	9697	131
1	9828	9959	*0090	*0221	*0353	*0484	*0615	*0745	*0876	*1007	131
2	52 1138	1269	1400	1530	1661	1792	1922	2053	2183	2314	131
3	2444	2575	2705	2835	2966	3096	3226	3356	3486	3616	130
4	3746	3876	4006	4136	4266	4396	4526	4656	4785	4915	130
335	52 5045	5174	5304	5434	5563	5693	5822	5951	6081	6210	129
6	6339	6469	6598	6727	6856	6985	7114	7243	7372	7501	129
7	7630	7759	7888	8016	8145	8274	8402	8531	8660	8788	129
8	8917	9045	9174	9302	9430	9559	9687	9815	9943	*0072	128
9	53 0200	0328	0456	0584	0712	0840	0968	1096	1223	1351	128
340	53 1479	1607	1734	1862	1990	2117	2245	2372	2500	2627	128
1	2754	2882	3009	3136	3264	3391	3518	3645	3772	3899	127
2	4026	4153	4280	4407	4534	4661	4787	4914	5041	5167	127
3	5294	5421	5547	5674	5800	5927	6053	6180	6306	6432	126
4	6558	6685	6811	6937	7063	7189	7315	7441	7567	7693	126
345	53 7819	7945	8071	8197	8322	8448	8574	8699	8825	8951	126
6	9076	9202	9327	9452	9578	9703	9829	9954	*0079	*0204	125
7	54 0329	0455	0580	0705	0830	0955	1080	1205	1330	1454	125
8	1579	1704	1829	1953	2078	2203	2327	2452	2576	2701	125
9	2825	2950	3074	3199	3323	3447	3571	3696	3820	3944	124

PROPORTIONAL PARTS

Diff.	1	2	3	4	5	6	7	8	9
138	13.8	27.6	41.4	55.2	69.0	82.8	96.6	110.4	124.2
137	13.7	27.4	41.1	54.8	68.5	82.2	95.9	109.6	123.3
136	13.6	27.2	40.8	54.4	68.0	81.6	95.2	108.8	122.4
135	13.5	27.0	40.5	54.0	67.5	81.0	94.5	108.0	121.5
134	13.4	26.8	40.2	53.6	67.0	80.4	93.8	107.2	120.6
133	13.3	26.6	39.9	53.2	66.5	79.8	93.1	106.4	119.7
132	13.2	26.4	39.6	52.8	66.0	79.2	92.4	105.6	118.8
131	13.1	26.2	39.3	52.4	65.5	78.6	91.7	104.8	117.9
130	13.0	26.0	39.0	52.0	65.0	78.0	91.0	104.0	117.0
129	12.9	25.8	38.7	51.6	64.5	77.4	90.3	103.2	116.1
128	12.8	25.6	38.4	51.2	64.0	76.8	89.6	102.4	115.2
127	12.7	25.4	38.1	50.8	63.5	76.2	88.9	101.6	114.3
126	12.6	25.2	37.8	50.4	63.0	75.6	88.2	100.8	113.4
125	12.5	25.0	37.5	50.0	62.5	75.0	87.5	100.0	112.5
124	12.4	24.8	37.2	49.6	62.0	74.4	86.8	99.2	111.6

Table I — Six-Place Logarithms

N.	0	1	2	3	4	5	6	7	8	9	Diff.
350	54 4068	4192	4316	4440	4564	4688	4812	4936	5060	5183	124
1	5307	5431	5555	5678	5802	5925	6049	6172	6296	6419	124
2	6543	6666	6789	6913	7036	7159	7282	7405	7529	7652	123
3	7775	7898	8021	8144	8267	8389	8512	8635	8758	8881	123
4	9003	9126	9249	9371	9494	9616	9739	9861	9984	*0106	123
355	55 0228	0351	0473	0595	0717	0840	0962	1084	1206	1328	122
6	1450	1572	1694	1816	1938	2060	2181	2303	2425	2547	122
7	2668	2790	2911	3033	3155	3276	3398	3519	3640	3762	121
8	3883	4004	4126	4247	4368	4489	4610	4731	4852	4973	121
9	5094	5215	5336	5457	5578	5699	5820	5940	6061	6182	121
360	55 6303	6423	6544	6664	6785	6905	7026	7146	7267	7387	120
1	7507	7627	7748	7868	7988	8108	8228	8349	8469	8589	120
2	8709	8829	8948	9068	9188	9308	9428	9548	9667	9787	120
3	9907	*0026	*0146	*0265	*0385	*0504	*0624	*0743	*0863	*0982	119
4	56 1101	1221	1340	1459	1578	1698	1817	1936	2055	2174	119
365	56 2293	2412	2531	2650	2769	2887	3006	3125	3244	3362	119
6	3481	3600	3718	3837	3955	4074	4192	4311	4429	4548	119
7	4666	4784	4903	5021	5139	5257	5376	5494	5612	5730	118
8	5848	5966	6084	6202	6320	6437	6555	6673	6791	6909	118
9	7026	7144	7262	7379	7497	7614	7732	7849	7967	8084	118
370	56 8202	8319	8436	8554	8671	8788	8905	9023	9140	9257	117
1	9374	9491	9608	9725	9842	9959	*0076	*0193	*0309	*0426	117
2	57 0543	0660	0776	0893	1010	1126	1243	1359	1476	1592	117
3	1709	1825	1942	2058	2174	2291	2407	2523	2639	2755	116
4	2872	2988	3104	3220	3336	3452	3568	3684	3800	3915	116
375	57 4031	4147	4263	4379	4494	4610	4726	4841	4957	5072	116
6	5188	5303	5419	5534	5650	5765	5880	5996	6111	6226	115
7	6341	6457	6572	6687	6802	6917	7032	7147	7262	7377	
8	7492	7607	7722	7836	7951	8066	8181	8295	8410	8525	
9	8639	8754	8868	8983	9097	9212	9326	9441	9555	9669	
380	57 9784	9898	*0012	*0126	*0241	*0355	*0469	*0583	*0697	*0811	114
1	58 0925	1039	1153	1267	1381	1495	1608	1722	1836	1950	
2	2063	2177	2291	2404	2518	2631	2745	2858	2972	3085	
3	3199	3312	3426	3539	3652	3765	3879	3992	4105	4218	113
4	4331	4444	4557	4670	4783	4896	5009	5122	5235	5348	
385	58 5461	5574	5686	5799	5912	6024	6137	6250	6362	6475	112
6	6587	6700	6812	6925	7037	7149	7262	7374	7486	7599	
7	7711	7823	7935	8047	8160	8272	8384	8496	8608	8720	
8	8832	8944	9056	9167	9279	9391	9503	9615	9726	9838	
9	9950	*0061	*0173	*0284	*0396	*0507	*0619	*0730	*0842	*0953	

PROPORTIONAL PARTS

Diff.	1	2	3	4	5	6	7	8	9
124	12.4	24.8	37.2	49.6	62.0	74.4	86.8	99.2	111.6
123	12.3	24.6	36.9	49.2	61.5	73.8	86.1	98.4	110.7
122	12.2	24.4	36.6	48.8	61.0	73.2	85.4	97.6	109.8
121	12.1	24.2	36.3	48.4	60.5	72.6	84.7	96.8	108.9
120	12.0	24.0	36.0	48.0	60.0	72.0	84.0	96.0	108.0
119	11.9	23.8	35.7	47.6	59.5	71.4	83.3	95.2	107.1
118	11.8	23.6	35.4	47.2	59.0	70.8	82.6	94.4	106.2
117	11.7	23.4	35.1	46.8	58.5	70.2	81.9	93.6	105.3
116	11.6	23.2	34.8	46.4	58.0	69.6	81.2	92.8	104.4
115	11.5	23.0	34.5	46.0	57.5	69.0	80.5	92.0	103.5
114	11.4	22.8	34.2	45.6	57.0	68.4	79.8	91.2	102.6
113	11.3	22.6	33.9	45.2	56.5	67.8	79.1	90.4	101.7
112	11.2	22.4	33.6	44.8	56.0	67.2	78.4	89.6	100.8

Table I — Six-Place Logarithms

N.	0	1	2	3	4	5	6	7	8	9	Diff.
390	59 1065	1176	1287	1399	1510	1621	1732	1843	1955	2066	111
1	2177	2288	2399	2510	2621	2732	2843	2954	3064	3175	
2	3286	3397	3508	3618	3729	3840	3950	4061	4171	4282	
3	4393	4503	4614	4724	4834	4945	5055	5165	5276	5386	110
4	5496	5606	5717	5827	5937	6047	6157	6267	6377	6487	
395	59 6597	6707	6817	6927	7037	7146	7256	7366	7476	7586	
6	7695	7805	7914	8024	8134	8243	8353	8462	8572	8681	
7	8791	8900	9009	9119	9228	9337	9446	9556	9665	9774	109
8	9883	9992	*0101	*0210	*0319	*0428	*0537	*0646	*0755	*0864	
9	60 0973	1082	1191	1299	1408	1517	1625	1734	1843	1951	
400	60 2060	2169	2277	2386	2494	2603	2711	2819	2928	3036	108
1	3144	3253	3361	3469	3577	3686	3794	3902	4010	4118	
2	4226	4334	4442	4550	4658	4766	4874	4982	5089	5197	
3	5305	5413	5521	5628	5736	5844	5951	6059	6166	6274	
4	6381	6489	6596	6704	6811	6919	7026	7133	7241	7348	107
405	60 7455	7562	7669	7777	7884	7991	8098	8205	8312	8419	
6	8526	8633	8740	8847	8954	9061	9167	9274	9381	9488	
7	9594	9701	9808	9914	*0021	*0128	*0234	*0341	*0447	*0554	
8	61 0660	0767	0873	0979	1086	1192	1298	1405	1511	1617	106
9	1723	1829	1936	2042	2148	2254	2360	2466	2572	2678	
410	61 2784	2890	2996	3102	3207	3313	3419	3525	3630	3736	
1	3842	3947	4053	4159	4264	4370	4475	4581	4686	4792	
2	4897	5003	5108	5213	5319	5424	5529	5634	5740	5845	105
3	5950	6055	6160	6265	6370	6476	6581	6686	6790	6895	
4	7000	7105	7210	7315	7420	7525	7629	7734	7839	7943	
415	61 8048	8153	8257	8362	8466	8571	8676	8780	8884	8989	
6	9093	9198	9302	9406	9511	9615	9719	9824	9928	*0032	104
7	62 0136	0240	0344	0448	0552	0656	0760	0864	0968	1072	
8	1176	1280	1384	1488	1592	1695	1799	1903	2007	2110	
9	2214	2318	2421	2525	2628	2732	2835	2939	3042	3146	
420	62 3249	3353	3456	3559	3663	3766	3869	3973	4076	4179	103
1	4282	4385	4488	4591	4695	4798	4901	5004	5107	5210	
2	5312	5415	5518	5621	5724	5827	5929	6032	6135	6238	
3	6340	6443	6546	6648	6751	6853	6956	7058	7161	7263	
4	7366	7468	7571	7673	7775	7878	7980	8082	8185	8287	102
425	62 8389	8491	8593	8695	8797	8900	9002	9104	9206	9308	
6	9410	9512	9613	9715	9817	9919	*0021	*0123	*0224	*0326	
7	63 0428	0530	0631	0733	0835	0936	1038	1139	1241	1342	
8	1444	1545	1647	1748	1849	1951	2052	2153	2255	2356	101
9	2457	2559	2660	2761	2862	2963	3064	3165	3266	3367	

PROPORTIONAL PARTS

Diff.	1	2	3	4	5	6	7	8	9
111	11.1	22.2	33.3	44.4	55.5	66.6	77.7	88.8	99.9
110	11.0	22.0	33.0	44.0	55.0	66.0	77.0	88.0	99.0
109	10.9	21.8	32.7	43.6	54.5	65.4	76.3	87.2	98.1
108	10.8	21.6	32.4	43.2	54.0	64.8	75.6	86.4	97.2
107	10.7	21.4	32.1	42.8	53.5	64.2	74.9	85.6	96.3
106	10.6	21.2	31.8	42.4	53.0	63.6	74.2	84.8	95.4
105	10.5	21.0	31.5	42.0	52.5	63.0	73.5	84.0	94.5
104	10.4	20.8	31.2	41.6	52.0	62.4	72.8	83.2	93.6
103	10.3	20.6	30.9	41.2	51.5	61.8	72.1	82.4	92.7
102	10.2	20.4	30.6	40.8	51.0	61.2	71.4	81.6	91.8
101	10.1	20.2	30.3	40.4	50.5	60.6	70.7	80.8	90.9

Table I — Six-Place Logarithms

N.	0	1	2	3	4	5	6	7	8	9	Diff.
430	63 3468	3569	3670	3771	3872	3973	4074	4175	4276	4376	
1	4477	4578	4679	4779	4880	4981	5081	5182	5283	5383	
2	5484	5584	5685	5785	5886	5986	6087	6187	6287	6388	100
3	6488	6588	6688	6789	6889	6989	7089	7189	7290	7390	
4	7490	7590	7690	7790	7890	7990	8090	8190	8290	8389	
435	63 8489	8589	8689	8789	8888	8988	9088	9188	9287	9387	
6	9486	9586	9686	9785	9885	9984	*0084	*0183	*0283	*0382	
7	64 0481	0581	0680	0779	0879	0978	1077	1177	1276	1375	99
8	1474	1573	1672	1771	1871	1970	2069	2168	2267	2366	
9	2465	2563	2662	2761	2860	2959	3058	3156	3255	3354	
440	64 3453	3551	3650	3749	3847	3946	4044	4143	4242	4340	
1	4439	4537	4636	4734	4832	4931	5029	5127	5226	5324	98
2	5422	5521	5619	5717	5815	5913	6011	6110	6208	6306	
3	6404	6502	6600	6698	6796	6894	6992	7089	7187	7285	
4	7383	7481	7579	7676	7774	7872	7969	8067	8165	8262	
445	64 8360	8458	8555	8653	8750	8848	8945	9043	9140	9237	
6	9335	9432	9530	9627	9724	9821	9919	*0016	*0113	*0210	97
7	65 0308	0405	0502	0599	0696	0793	0890	0987	1084	1181	
8	1278	1375	1472	1569	1666	1762	1859	1956	2053	2150	
9	2246	2343	2440	2536	2633	2730	2826	2923	3019	3116	
450	65 3213	3309	3405	3502	3598	3695	3791	3888	3984	4080	
1	4177	4273	4369	4465	4562	4658	4754	4850	4946	5042	96
2	5138	5235	5331	5427	5523	5619	5715	5810	5906	6002	
3	6098	6194	6290	6386	6482	6577	6673	6769	6864	6960	
4	7056	7152	7247	7343	7438	7534	7629	7725	7820	7916	
455	65 8011	8107	8202	8298	8393	8488	8584	8679	8774	8870	
6	8965	9060	9155	9250	9346	9441	9536	9631	9726	9821	95
7	9916	*0011	*0106	*0201	*0296	*0391	*0486	*0581	*0676	*0771	
8	66 0865	0960	1055	1150	1245	1339	1434	1529	1623	1718	
9	1813	1907	2002	2096	2191	2286	2380	2475	2569	2663	
460	66 2758	2852	2947	3041	3135	3230	3324	3418	3512	3607	
1	3701	3795	3889	3983	4078	4172	4266	4360	4454	4548	94
2	4642	4736	4830	4924	5018	5112	5206	5299	5393	5487	
3	5581	5675	5769	5862	5956	6050	6143	6237	6331	6424	
4	6518	6612	6705	6799	6892	6986	7079	7173	7266	7360	
465	66 7453	7546	7640	7733	7826	7920	8013	8106	8199	8293	
6	8386	8479	8572	8665	8759	8852	8945	9038	9131	9224	93
7	9317	9410	9503	9596	9689	9782	9875	9967	*0060	*0153	
8	67 0246	0339	0431	0524	0617	0710	0802	0895	0988	1080	
9	1173	1265	1358	1451	1543	1636	1728	1821	1913	2005	

PROPORTIONAL PARTS

Diff.	1	2	3	4	5	6	7	8	9
100	10.0	20.0	30.0	40.0	50.0	60.0	70.0	80.0	90.0
99	9.9	19.8	29.7	39.6	49.5	59.4	69.3	79.2	89.1
98	9.8	19.6	29.4	39.2	49.0	58.8	68.6	78.4	88.2
97	9.7	19.4	29.1	38.8	48.5	58.2	67.9	77.6	87.3
96	9.6	19.2	28.8	38.4	48.0	57.6	67.2	76.8	86.4
95	9.5	19.0	28.5	38.0	47.5	57.0	66.5	76.0	85.5
94	9.4	18.8	28.2	37.6	47.0	56.4	65.8	75.2	84.6
93	9.3	18.6	27.9	37.2	46.5	55.8	65.1	74.4	83.7
92	9.2	18.4	27.6	36.8	46.0	55.2	64.4	73.6	82.8

Table I — Six-Place Logarithms

N.	0	1	2	3	4	5	6	7	8	9	Diff.
470	67 2098	2190	2283	2375	2467	2560	2652	2744	2836	2929	92
1	3021	3113	3205	3297	3390	3482	3574	3666	3758	3850	
2	3942	4034	4126	4218	4310	4402	4494	4586	4677	4769	
3	4861	4953	5045	5137	5228	5320	5412	5503	5595	5687	
4	5778	5870	5962	6053	6145	6236	6328	6419	6511	6602	
475	67 6694	6785	6876	6968	7059	7151	7242	7333	7424	7516	91
6	7607	7698	7789	7881	7972	8063	8154	8245	8336	8427	
7	8518	8609	8700	8791	8882	8973	9064	9155	9246	9337	
8	9428	9519	9610	9700	9791	9882	9973	*0063	*0154	*0245	
9	68 0336	0426	0517	0607	0698	0789	0879	0970	1060	1151	
480	68 1241	1332	1422	1513	1603	1693	1784	1874	1964	2055	90
1	2145	2235	2326	2416	2506	2596	2686	2777	2867	2957	
2	3047	3137	3227	3317	3407	3497	3587	3677	3767	3857	
3	3947	4037	4127	4217	4307	4396	4486	4576	4666	4756	
4	4845	4935	5025	5114	5204	5294	5383	5473	5563	5652	
485	68 5742	5831	5921	6010	6100	6189	6279	6368	6458	6547	89
6	6636	6726	6815	6904	6994	7083	7172	7261	7351	7440	
7	7529	7618	7707	7796	7886	7975	8064	8153	8242	8331	
8	8420	8509	8598	8687	8776	8865	8953	9042	9131	9220	
9	9309	9398	9486	9575	9664	9753	9841	9930	*0019	*0107	
490	69 0196	0285	0373	0462	0550	0639	0728	0816	0905	0993	
1	1081	1170	1258	1347	1435	1524	1612	1700	1789	1877	88
2	1965	2053	2142	2230	2318	2406	2494	2583	2671	2759	
3	2847	2935	3023	3111	3199	3287	3375	3463	3551	3639	
4	3727	3815	3903	3991	4078	4166	4254	4342	4430	4517	
495	69 4605	4693	4781	4868	4956	5044	5131	5219	5307	5394	
6	5482	5569	5657	5744	5832	5919	6007	6094	6182	6269	87
7	6356	6444	6531	6618	6706	6793	6880	6968	7055	7142	
8	7229	7317	7404	7491	7578	7665	7752	7839	7926	8014	
9	8101	8188	8275	8362	8449	8535	8622	8709	8796	8883	
500	69 8970	9057	9144	9231	9317	9404	9491	9578	9664	9751	
1	9838	9924	*0011	*0098	*0184	*0271	*0358	*0444	*0531	*0617	
2	70 0704	0790	0877	0963	1050	1136	1222	1309	1395	1482	86
3	1568	1654	1741	1827	1913	1999	2086	2172	2258	2344	
4	2431	2517	2603	2689	2775	2861	2947	3033	3119	3205	
505	70 3291	3377	3463	3549	3635	3721	3807	3893	3979	4065	
6	4151	4236	4322	4408	4494	4579	4665	4751	4837	4922	
7	5008	5094	5179	5265	5350	5436	5522	5607	5693	5778	
8	5864	5949	6035	6120	6206	6291	6376	6462	6547	6632	85
9	6718	6803	6888	6974	7059	7144	7229	7315	7400	7485	
510	70 7570	7655	7740	7826	7911	7996	8081	8166	8251	8336	
1	8421	8506	8591	8676	8761	8846	8931	9015	9100	9185	
2	9270	9355	9440	9524	9609	9694	9779	9863	9948	*0033	
3	71 0117	0202	0287	0371	0456	0540	0625	0710	0794	0879	
4	0963	1048	1132	1217	1301	1385	1470	1554	1639	1723	

PROPORTIONAL PARTS

Diff.	1	2	3	4	5	6	7	8	9
91	9.1	18.2	27.3	36.4	45.5	54.6	63.7	72.8	81.9
90	9.0	18.0	27.0	36.0	45.0	54.0	63.0	72.0	81.0
89	8.9	17.8	26.7	35.6	44.5	53.4	62.3	71.2	80.1
88	8.8	17.6	26.4	35.2	44.0	52.8	61.6	70.4	79.2
87	8.7	17.4	26.1	34.8	43.5	52.2	60.9	69.6	78.3
86	8.6	17.2	25.8	34.4	43.0	51.6	60.2	68.8	77.4
85	8.5	17.0	25.5	34.0	42.5	51.0	59.5	68.0	76.5
84	8.4	16.8	25.2	33.6	42.0	50.4	58.8	67.2	75.6

Table I — Six-Place Logarithms

N.	0	1	2	3	4	5	6	7	8	9	Diff.
515	71 1807	1892	1976	2060	2144	2229	2313	2397	2481	2566	
6	2650	2734	2818	2902	2986	3070	3154	3238	3323	3407	84
7	3491	3575	3659	3742	3826	3910	3994	4078	4162	4246	
8	4330	4414	4497	4581	4665	4749	4833	4916	5000	5084	
9	5167	5251	5335	5418	5502	5586	5669	5753	5836	5920	
520	71 6003	6087	6170	6254	6337	6421	6504	6588	6671	6754	
1	6838	6921	7004	7088	7171	7254	7338	7421	7504	7587	83
2	7671	7754	7837	7920	8003	8086	8169	8253	8336	8419	
3	8502	8585	8668	8751	8834	8917	9000	9083	9165	9248	
4	9331	9414	9497	9580	9663	9745	9828	9911	9994	*0077	
525	72 0159	0242	0325	0407	0490	0573	0655	0738	0821	0903	
6	0986	1068	1151	1233	1316	1398	1481	1563	1646	1728	
7	1811	1893	1975	2058	2140	2222	2305	2387	2469	2552	82
8	2634	2716	2798	2881	2963	3045	3127	3209	3291	3374	
9	3456	3538	3620	3702	3784	3866	3948	4030	4112	4194	
530	72 4276	4358	4440	4522	4604	4685	4767	4849	4931	5013	
1	5095	5176	5258	5340	5422	5503	5585	5667	5748	5830	
2	5912	5993	6075	6156	6238	6320	6401	6483	6564	6646	
3	6727	6809	6890	6972	7053	7134	7216	7297	7379	7460	81
4	7541	7623	7704	7785	7866	7948	8029	8110	8191	8273	
535	72 8354	8435	8516	8597	8678	8759	8841	8922	9003	9084	
6	9165	9246	9327	9408	9489	9570	9651	9732	9813	9893	
7	9974	*0055	*0136	*0217	*0298	*0378	*0459	*0540	*0621	*0702	
8	73 0782	0863	0944	1024	1105	1186	1266	1347	1428	1508	
9	1589	1669	1750	1830	1911	1991	2072	2152	2233	2313	
540	73 2394	2474	2555	2635	2715	2796	2876	2956	3037	3117	80
1	3197	3278	3358	3438	3518	3598	3679	3759	3839	3919	
2	3999	4079	4160	4240	4320	4400	4480	4560	4640	4720	
3	4800	4880	4960	5040	5120	5200	5279	5359	5439	5519	
4	5599	5679	5759	5838	5918	5998	6078	6157	6237	6317	
545	73 6397	6476	6556	6635	6715	6795	6874	6954	7034	7113	
6	7193	7272	7352	7431	7511	7590	7670	7749	7829	7908	79
7	7987	8067	8146	8225	8305	8384	8463	8543	8622	8701	
8	8781	8860	8939	9018	9097	9177	9256	9335	9414	9493	
9	9572	9651	9731	9810	9889	9968	*0047	*0126	*0205	*0284	
550	74 0363	0442	0521	0600	0678	0757	0836	0915	0994	1073	
1	1152	1230	1309	1388	1467	1546	1624	1703	1782	1860	
2	1939	2018	2096	2175	2254	2332	2411	2489	2568	2647	78
3	2725	2804	2882	2961	3039	3118	3196	3275	3353	3431	
4	3510	3588	3667	3745	3823	3902	3980	4058	4136	4215	

PROPORTIONAL PARTS

Diff.	1	2	3	4	5	6	7	8	9
85	8.5	17.0	25.5	34.0	42.5	51.0	59.5	68.0	76.5
84	8.4	16.8	25.2	33.6	42.0	50.4	58.8	67.2	75.6
83	8.3	16.6	24.9	33.2	41.5	49.8	58.1	66.4	74.7
82	8.2	16.4	24.6	32.8	41.0	49.2	57.4	65.6	73.8
81	8.1	16.2	24.3	32.4	40.5	48.6	56.7	64.8	72.9
80	8.0	16.0	24.0	32.0	40.0	48.0	56.0	64.0	72.0
79	7.9	15.8	23.7	31.6	39.5	47.4	55.3	63.2	71.1
78	7.8	15.6	23.4	31.2	39.0	46.8	54.6	62.4	70.2

Table I — Six-Place Logarithms

N.	0	1	2	3	4	5	6	7	8	9	Diff.
555	74 4293	4371	4449	4528	4606	4684	4762	4840	4919	4997	
6	5075	5153	5231	5309	5387	5465	5543	5621	5699	5777	
7	5855	5933	6011	6089	6167	6245	6323	6401	6479	6556	
8	6634	6712	6790	6868	6945	7023	7101	7179	7256	7334	
9	7412	7489	7567	7645	7722	7800	7878	7955	8033	8110	
560	74 8188	8266	8343	8421	8498	8576	8653	8731	8808	8885	
1	8963	9040	9118	9195	9272	9350	9427	9504	9582	9659	77
2	9736	9814	9891	9968	*0045	*0123	*0200	*0277	*0354	*0431	
3	75 0508	0586	0663	0740	0817	0894	0971	1048	1125	1202	
4	1279	1356	1433	1510	1587	1664	1741	1818	1895	1972	
565	75 2048	2125	2202	2279	2356	2433	2509	2586	2663	2740	
6	2816	2893	2970	3047	3123	3200	3277	3353	3430	3506	
7	3583	3660	3736	3813	3889	3966	4042	4119	4195	4272	
8	4348	4425	4501	4578	4654	4730	4807	4883	4960	5036	76
9	5112	5189	5265	5341	5417	5494	5570	5646	5722	5799	
570	75 5875	5951	6027	6103	6180	6256	6332	6408	6484	6560	
1	6636	6712	6788	6864	6940	7016	7092	7168	7244	7320	
2	7396	7472	7548	7624	7700	7775	7851	7927	8003	8079	
3	8155	8230	8306	8382	8458	8533	8609	8685	8761	8836	
4	8912	8988	9063	9139	9214	9290	9366	9441	9517	9592	
575	75 9668	9743	9819	9894	9970	*0045	*0121	*0196	*0272	*0347	75
6	76 0422	0498	0573	0649	0724	0799	0875	0950	1025	1101	
7	1176	1251	1326	1402	1477	1552	1627	1702	1778	1853	
8	1928	2003	2078	2153	2228	2303	2378	2453	2529	2604	
9	2679	2754	2829	2904	2978	3053	3128	3203	3278	3353	
580	76 3428	3503	3578	3653	3727	3802	3877	3952	4027	4101	
1	4176	4251	4326	4400	4475	4550	4624	4699	4774	4848	
2	4923	4998	5072	5147	5221	5296	5370	5445	5520	5594	
3	5669	5743	5818	5892	5966	6041	6115	6190	6264	6338	74
4	6413	6487	6562	6636	6710	6785	6859	6933	7007	7082	
585	76 7156	7230	7304	7379	7453	7527	7601	7675	7749	7823	
6	7898	7972	8046	8120	8194	8268	8342	8416	8490	8564	
7	8638	8712	8786	8860	8934	9008	9082	9156	9230	9303	
8	9377	9451	9525	9599	9673	9746	9820	9894	9968	*0042	
9	77 0115	0189	0263	0336	0410	0484	0557	0631	0705	0778	
590	77 0852	0926	0999	1073	1146	1220	1293	1367	1440	1514	
1	1587	1661	1734	1808	1881	1955	2028	2102	2175	2248	
2	2322	2395	2468	2542	2615	2688	2762	2835	2908	2981	73
3	3055	3128	3201	3274	3348	3421	3494	3567	3640	3713	
4	3786	3860	3933	4006	4079	4152	4225	4298	4371	4444	
595	77 4517	4590	4663	4736	4809	4882	4955	5028	5100	5173	
6	5246	5319	5392	5465	5538	5610	5683	5756	5829	5902	
7	5974	6047	6120	6193	6265	6338	6411	6483	6556	6629	
8	6701	6774	6846	6919	6992	7064	7137	7209	7282	7354	
9	7427	7499	7572	7644	7717	7789	7862	7934	8006	8079	

PROPORTIONAL PARTS

Diff.	1	2	3	4	5	6	7	8	9
77	7.7	15.4	23.1	30.8	38.5	46.2	53.9	61.6	69.3
76	7.6	15.2	22.8	30.4	38.0	45.6	53.2	60.8	68.4
75	7.5	15.0	22.5	30.0	37.5	45.0	52.5	60.0	67.5
74	7.4	14.8	22.2	29.6	37.0	44.4	51.8	59.2	66.6
73	7.3	14.6	21.9	29.2	36.5	43.8	51.1	58.4	65.7
72	7.2	14.4	21.6	28.8	36.0	43.2	50.4	57.6	64.8
71	7.1	14.2	21.3	28.4	35.5	42.6	49.7	56.8	63.9

Table I — Six-Place Logarithms

N.	0	1	2	3	4	5	6	7	8	9	Diff.
600	77 8151	8224	8296	8368	8441	8513	8585	8658	8730	8802	72
1	8874	8947	9019	9091	9163	9236	9308	9380	9452	9524	
2	9596	9669	9741	9813	9885	9957	*0029	*0101	*0173	*0245	
3	78 0317	0389	0461	0533	0605	0677	0749	0821	0893	0965	
4	1037	1109	1181	1253	1324	1396	1468	1540	1612	1684	
605	78 1755	1827	1899	1971	2042	2114	2186	2258	2329	2401	
6	2473	2544	2616	2688	2759	2831	2902	2974	3046	3117	
7	3189	3260	3332	3403	3475	3546	3618	3689	3761	3832	
8	3904	3975	4046	4118	4189	4261	4332	4403	4475	4546	71
9	4617	4689	4760	4831	4902	4974	5045	5116	5187	5259	
610	78 5330	5401	5472	5543	5615	5686	5757	5828	5899	5970	
1	6041	6112	6183	6254	6325	6396	6467	6538	6609	6680	
2	6751	6822	6893	6964	7035	7106	7177	7248	7319	7390	
3	7460	7531	7602	7673	7744	7815	7885	7956	8027	8098	
4	8168	8239	8310	8381	8451	8522	8593	8663	8734	8804	
615	78 8875	8946	9016	9087	9157	9228	9299	9369	9440	9510	
6	9581	9651	9722	9792	9863	9933	*0004	*0074	*0144	*0215	70
7	79 0285	0356	0426	0496	0567	0637	0707	0778	0848	0918	
8	0988	1059	1129	1199	1269	1340	1410	1480	1550	1620	
9	1691	1761	1831	1901	1971	2041	2111	2181	2252	2322	
620	79 2392	2462	2532	2602	2672	2742	2812	2882	2952	3022	
1	3092	3162	3231	3301	3371	3441	3511	3581	3651	3721	
2	3790	3860	3930	4000	4070	4139	4209	4279	4349	4418	
3	4488	4558	4627	4697	4767	4836	4906	4976	5045	5115	
4	5185	5254	5324	5393	5463	5532	5602	5672	5741	5811	
625	79 5880	5949	6019	6088	6158	6227	6297	6366	6436	6505	
6	6574	6644	6713	6782	6852	6921	6990	7060	7129	7198	69
7	7268	7337	7406	7475	7545	7614	7683	7752	7821	7890	
8	7960	8029	8098	8167	8236	8305	8374	8443	8513	8582	
9	8651	8720	8789	8858	8927	8996	9065	9134	9203	9272	
630	79 9341	9409	9478	9547	9616	9685	9754	9823	9892	9961	
1	80 0029	0098	0167	0236	0305	0373	0442	0511	0580	0648	
2	0717	0786	0854	0923	0992	1061	1129	1198	1266	1335	
3	1404	1472	1541	1609	1678	1747	1815	1884	1952	2021	
4	2089	2158	2226	2295	2363	2432	2500	2568	2637	2705	
635	80 2774	2842	2910	2979	3047	3116	3184	3252	3321	3389	68
6	3457	3525	3594	3662	3730	3798	3867	3935	4003	4071	
7	4139	4208	4276	4344	4412	4480	4548	4616	4685	4753	
8	4821	4889	4957	5025	5093	5161	5229	5297	5365	5433	
9	5501	5569	5637	5705	5773	5841	5908	5976	6044	6112	
640	80 6180	6248	6316	6384	6451	6519	6587	6655	6723	6790	
1	6858	6926	6994	7061	7129	7197	7264	7332	7400	7467	
2	7535	7603	7670	7738	7806	7873	7941	8008	8076	8143	
3	8211	8279	8346	8414	8481	8549	8616	8684	8751	8818	
4	8886	8953	9021	9088	9156	9223	9290	9358	9425	9492	67
645	80 9560	9627	9694	9762	9829	9896	9964	*0031	*0098	*0165	
6	81 0233	0300	0367	0434	0501	0569	0636	0703	0770	0837	
7	0904	0971	1039	1106	1173	1240	1307	1374	1441	1508	
8	1575	1642	1709	1776	1843	1910	1977	2044	2111	2178	
9	2245	2312	2379	2445	2512	2579	2646	2713	2780	2847	

PROPORTIONAL PARTS

Diff.	1	2	3	4	5	6	7	8	9
70	7.0	14.0	21.0	28.0	35.0	42.0	49.0	56.0	63.0
69	6.9	13.8	20.7	27.6	34.5	41.4	48.3	55.2	62.1
68	6.8	13.6	20.4	27.2	34.0	40.8	47.6	54.4	61.2
67	6.7	13.4	20.1	26.8	33.5	40.2	46.9	53.6	60.3

Table I — Six-Place Logarithms

N.	0	1	2	3	4	5	6	7	8	9	Diff.
650	81 2913	2980	3047	3114	3181	3247	3314	3381	3448	3514	
1	3581	3648	3714	3781	3848	3914	3981	4048	4114	4181	
2	4248	4314	4381	4447	4514	4581	4647	4714	4780	4847	
3	4913	4980	5046	5113	5179	5246	5312	5378	5445	5511	
4	5578	5644	5711	5777	5843	5910	5976	6042	6109	6175	66
655	81 6241	6308	6374	6440	6506	6573	6639	6705	6771	6838	
6	6904	6970	7036	7102	7169	7235	7301	7367	7433	7499	
7	7565	7631	7698	7764	7830	7896	7962	8028	8094	8160	
8	8226	8292	8358	8424	8490	8556	8622	8688	8754	8820	
9	8885	8951	9017	9083	9149	9215	9281	9346	9412	9478	
660	81 9544	9610	9676	9741	9807	9873	9939	*0004	*0070	*0136	
1	82 0201	0267	0333	0399	0464	0530	0595	0661	0727	0792	
2	0858	0924	0989	1055	1120	1186	1251	1317	1382	1448	
3	1514	1579	1645	1710	1775	1841	1906	1972	2037	2103	65
4	2168	2233	2299	2364	2430	2495	2560	2626	2691	2756	
665	82 2822	2887	2952	3018	3083	3148	3213	3279	3344	3409	
6	3474	3539	3605	3670	3735	3800	3865	3930	3996	4061	
7	4126	4191	4256	4321	4386	4451	4516	4581	4646	4711	
8	4776	4841	4906	4971	5036	5101	5166	5231	5296	5361	
9	5426	5491	5556	5621	5686	5751	5815	5880	5945	6010	
670	82 6075	6140	6204	6269	6334	6399	6464	6528	6593	6658	
1	6723	6787	6852	6917	6981	7046	7111	7175	7240	7305	
2	7369	7434	7499	7563	7628	7692	7757	7821	7886	7951	
3	8015	8080	8144	8209	8273	8338	8402	8467	8531	8595	
4	8660	8724	8789	8853	8918	8982	9046	9111	9175	9239	64
675	82 9304	9368	9432	9497	9561	9625	9690	9754	9818	9882	
6	9947	*0011	*0075	*0139	*0204	*0268	*0332	*0396	*0460	*0525	
7	83 0589	0653	0717	0781	0845	0909	0973	1037	1102	1166	
8	1230	1294	1358	1422	1486	1550	1614	1678	1742	1806	
9	1870	1934	1998	2062	2126	2189	2253	2317	2381	2445	
680	83 2509	2573	2637	2700	2764	2828	2892	2956	3020	3083	
1	3147	3211	3275	3338	3402	3466	3530	3593	3657	3721	
2	3784	3848	3912	3975	4039	4103	4166	4230	4294	4357	
3	4421	4484	4548	4611	4675	4739	4802	4866	4929	4993	
4	5056	5120	5183	5247	5310	5373	5437	5500	5564	5627	
685	83 5691	5754	5817	5881	5944	6007	6071	6134	6197	6261	63
6	6324	6387	6451	6514	6577	6641	6704	6767	6830	6894	
7	6957	7020	7083	7146	7210	7273	7336	7399	7462	7525	
8	7588	7652	7715	7778	7841	7904	7967	8030	8093	8156	
9	8219	8282	8345	8408	8471	8534	8597	8660	8723	8786	
690	83 8849	8912	8975	9038	9101	9164	9227	9289	9352	9415	
1	9478	9541	9604	9667	9729	9792	9855	9918	9981	*0043	
2	84 0106	0169	0232	0294	0357	0420	0482	0545	0608	0671	
3	0733	0796	0859	0921	0984	1046	1109	1172	1234	1297	
4	1359	1422	1485	1547	1610	1672	1735	1797	1860	1922	
695	84 1985	2047	2110	2172	2235	2297	2360	2422	2484	2547	62
6	2609	2672	2734	2796	2859	2921	2983	3046	3108	3170	
7	3233	3295	3357	3420	3482	3544	3606	3669	3731	3793	
8	3855	3918	3980	4042	4104	4166	4229	4291	4353	4415	
9	4477	4539	4601	4664	4726	4788	4850	4912	4974	5036	

PROPORTIONAL PARTS

Diff.	1	2	3	4	5	6	7	8	9
66	6.6	13.2	19.8	26.4	33.0	39.6	46.2	52.8	59.4
65	6.5	13.0	19.5	26.0	32.5	39.0	45.5	52.0	58.5
64	6.4	12.8	19.2	25.6	32.0	38.4	44.8	51.2	57.6
63	6.3	12.6	18.9	25.2	31.5	37.8	44.1	50.4	56.7

[471]

Table I — Six-Place Logarithms

N.	0	1	2	3	4	5	6	7	8	9	Diff.
700	84 5098	5160	5222	5284	5346	5408	5470	5532	5594	5656	62
1	5718	5780	5842	5904	5966	6028	6090	6151	6213	6275	
2	6337	6399	6461	6523	6585	6646	6708	6770	6832	6894	
3	6955	7017	7079	7141	7202	7264	7326	7388	7449	7511	
4	7573	7634	7696	7758	7819	7881	7943	8004	8066	8128	
705	84 8189	8251	8312	8374	8435	8497	8559	8620	8682	8743	
6	8805	8866	8928	8989	9051	9112	9174	9235	9297	9358	61
7	9419	9481	9542	9604	9665	9726	9788	9849	9911	9972	
8	85 0033	0095	0156	0217	0279	0340	0401	0462	0524	0585	
9	0646	0707	0769	0830	0891	0952	1014	1075	1136	1197	
710	85 1258	1320	1381	1442	1503	1564	1625	1686	1747	1809	
1	1870	1931	1992	2053	2114	2175	2236	2297	2358	2419	
2	2480	2541	2602	2663	2724	2785	2846	2907	2968	3029	
3	3090	3150	3211	3272	3333	3394	3455	3516	3577	3637	
4	3698	3759	3820	3881	3941	4002	4063	4124	4185	4245	
715	85 4306	4367	4428	4488	4549	4610	4670	4731	4792	4852	
6	4913	4974	5034	5095	5156	5216	5277	5337	5398	5459	
7	5519	5580	5640	5701	5761	5822	5882	5943	6003	6064	
8	6124	6185	6245	6306	6366	6427	6487	6548	6608	6668	
9	6729	6789	6850	6910	6970	7031	7091	7152	7212	7272	60
720	85 7332	7393	7453	7513	7574	7634	7694	7755	7815	7875	
1	7935	7995	8056	8116	8176	8236	8297	8357	8417	8477	
2	8537	8597	8657	8718	8778	8838	8898	8958	9018	9078	
3	9138	9198	9258	9318	9379	9439	9499	9559	9619	9679	
4	9739	9799	9859	9918	9978	*0038	*0098	*0158	*0218	*0278	
725	86 0338	0398	0458	0518	0578	0637	0697	0757	0817	0877	
6	0937	0996	1056	1116	1176	1236	1295	1355	1415	1475	
7	1534	1594	1654	1714	1773	1833	1893	1952	2012	2072	
8	2131	2191	2251	2310	2370	2430	2489	2549	2608	2668	
9	2728	2787	2847	2906	2966	3025	3085	3144	3204	3263	
730	86 3323	3382	3442	3501	3561	3620	3680	3739	3799	3858	59
1	3917	3977	4036	4096	4155	4214	4274	4333	4392	4452	
2	4511	4570	4630	4689	4748	4808	4867	4926	4985	5045	
3	5104	5163	5222	5282	5341	5400	5459	5519	5578	5637	
4	5696	5755	5814	5874	5933	5992	6051	6110	6169	6228	
735	86 6287	6346	6405	6465	6524	6583	6642	6701	6760	6819	
6	6878	6937	6996	7055	7114	7173	7232	7291	7350	7409	
7	7467	7526	7585	7644	7703	7762	7821	7880	7939	7998	
8	8056	8115	8174	8233	8292	8350	8409	8468	8527	8586	
9	8644	8703	8762	8821	8879	8938	8997	9056	9114	9173	
740	86 9232	9290	9349	9408	9466	9525	9584	9642	9701	9760	
1	9818	9877	9935	9994	*0053	*0111	*0170	*0228	*0287	*0345	
2	87 0404	0462	0521	0579	0638	0696	0755	0813	0872	0930	
3	0989	1047	1106	1164	1223	1281	1339	1398	1456	1515	58
4	1573	1631	1690	1748	1806	1865	1923	1981	2040	2098	
745	87 2156	2215	2273	2331	2389	2448	2506	2564	2622	2681	
6	2739	2797	2855	2913	2972	3030	3088	3146	3204	3262	
7	3321	3379	3437	3495	3553	3611	3669	3727	3785	3844	
8	3902	3960	4018	4076	4134	4192	4250	4308	4366	4424	
9	4482	4540	4598	4656	4714	4772	4830	4888	4945	5003	

PROPORTIONAL PARTS

Diff.	1	2	3	4	5	6	7	8	9
62	6.2	12.4	18.6	24.8	31.0	37.2	43.4	49.6	55.8
61	6.1	12.2	18.3	24.4	30.5	36.6	42.7	48.8	54.9
60	6.0	12.0	18.0	24.0	30.0	36.0	42.0	48.0	54.0
59	5.9	11.8	17.7	23.6	29.5	35.4	41.3	47.2	53.1

Table I — Six-Place Logarithms

N.	0	1	2	3	4	5	6	7	8	9	Diff.
750	87 5061	5119	5177	5235	5293	5351	5409	5466	5524	5582	
1	5640	5698	5756	5813	5871	5929	5987	6045	6102	6160	
2	6218	6276	6333	6391	6449	6507	6564	6622	6680	6737	
3	6795	6853	6910	6968	7026	7083	7141	7199	7256	7314	
4	7371	7429	7487	7544	7602	7659	7717	7774	7832	7889	
755	87 7947	8004	8062	8119	8177	8234	8292	8349	8407	8464	
6	8522	8579	8637	8694	8752	8809	8866	8924	8981	9039	57
7	9096	9153	9211	9268	9325	9383	9440	9497	9555	9612	
8	9669	9726	9784	9841	9898	9956	*0013	*0070	*0127	*0185	
9	88 0242	0299	0356	0413	0471	0528	0585	0642	0699	0756	
760	88 0814	0871	0928	0985	1042	1099	1156	1213	1271	1328	
1	1385	1442	1499	1556	1613	1670	1727	1784	1841	1898	
2	1955	2012	2069	2126	2183	2240	2297	2354	2411	2468	
3	2525	2581	2638	2695	2752	2809	2866	2923	2980	3037	
4	3093	3150	3207	3264	3321	3377	3434	3491	3548	3605	
765	88 3661	3718	3775	3832	3888	3945	4002	4059	4115	4172	
6	4229	4285	4342	4399	4455	4512	4569	4625	4682	4739	
7	4795	4852	4909	4965	5022	5078	5135	5192	5248	5305	
8	5361	5418	5474	5531	5587	5644	5700	5757	5813	5870	
9	5926	5983	6039	6096	6152	6209	6265	6321	6378	6434	
770	88 6491	6547	6604	6660	6716	6773	6829	6885	6942	6998	56
1	7054	7111	7167	7223	7280	7336	7392	7449	7505	7561	
2	7617	7674	7730	7786	7842	7898	7955	8011	8067	8123	
3	8179	8236	8292	8348	8404	8460	8516	8573	8629	8685	
4	8741	8797	8853	8909	8965	9021	9077	9134	9190	9246	
775	88 9302	9358	9414	9470	9526	9582	9638	9694	9750	9806	
6	9862	9918	9974	*0030	*0086	*0141	*0197	*0253	*0309	*0365	
7	89 0421	0477	0533	0589	0645	0700	0756	0812	0868	0924	
8	0980	1035	1091	1147	1203	1259	1314	1370	1426	1482	
9	1537	1593	1649	1705	1760	1816	1872	1928	1983	2039	
780	89 2095	2150	2206	2262	2317	2373	2429	2484	2540	2595	
1	2651	2707	2762	2818	2873	2929	2985	3040	3096	3151	
2	3207	3262	3318	3373	3429	3484	3540	3595	3651	3706	
3	3762	3817	3873	3928	3984	4039	4094	4150	4205	4261	55
4	4316	4371	4427	4482	4538	4593	4648	4704	4759	4814	
785	89 4870	4925	4980	5036	5091	5146	5201	5257	5312	5367	
6	5423	5478	5533	5588	5644	5699	5754	5809	5864	5920	
7	5975	6030	6085	6140	6195	6251	6306	6361	6416	6471	
8	6526	6581	6636	6692	6747	6802	6857	6912	6967	7022	
9	7077	7132	7187	7242	7297	7352	7407	7462	7517	7572	
790	89 7627	7682	7737	7792	7847	7902	7957	8012	8067	8122	
1	8176	8231	8286	8341	8396	8451	8506	8561	8615	8670	
2	8725	8780	8835	8890	8944	8999	9054	9109	9164	9218	
3	9273	9328	9383	9437	9492	9547	9602	9656	9711	9766	
4	9821	9875	9930	9985	*0039	*0094	*0149	*0203	*0258	*0312	
795	90 0367	0422	0476	0531	0586	0640	0695	0749	0804	0859	
6	0913	0968	0122	1077	1131	1186	1240	1295	1349	1404	
7	1458	1513	1567	1622	1676	1731	1785	1840	1894	1948	
8	2003	2057	2112	2166	2221	2275	2329	2384	2438	2492	54
9	2547	2601	2655	2710	2764	2818	2873	2927	2981	3036	

PROPORTIONAL PARTS

Diff.	1	2	3	4	5	6	7	8	9
58	5.8	11.6	17.4	23.2	29.0	34.8	40.6	46.4	52.2
57	5.7	11.4	17.1	22.8	28.5	34.2	39.9	45.6	51.3
56	5.6	11.2	16.8	22.4	28.0	33.6	39.2	44.8	50.4
55	5.5	11.0	16.5	22.0	27.5	33.0	38.5	44.0	49.5

[473]

Table I — Six-Place Logarithms

N.	0	1	2	3	4	5	6	7	8	9	Diff.
800	90 3090	3144	3199	3253	3307	3361	3416	3470	3524	3578	54
1	3633	3687	3741	3795	3849	3904	3958	4012	4066	4120	
2	4174	4229	4283	4337	4391	4445	4499	4553	4607	4661	
3	4716	4770	4824	4878	4932	4986	5040	5094	5148	5202	
4	5256	5310	5364	5418	5472	5526	5580	5634	5688	5742	
805	90 5796	5850	5904	5958	6012	6066	6119	6173	6227	6281	
6	6335	6389	6443	6497	6551	6604	6658	6712	6766	6820	
7	6874	6927	6981	7035	7089	7143	7196	7250	7304	7358	
8	7411	7465	7519	7573	7626	7680	7734	7787	7841	7895	
9	7949	8002	8056	8110	8163	8217	8270	8324	8378	8431	
810	90 8485	8539	8592	8646	8699	8753	8807	8860	8914	8967	
1	9021	9074	9128	9181	9235	9289	9342	9396	9449	9503	
2	9556	9610	9663	9716	9770	9823	9877	9930	9984	*0037	
3	91 0091	0144	0197	0251	0304	0358	0411	0464	0518	0571	53
4	0624	0678	0731	0784	0838	0891	0944	0998	1051	1104	
815	91 1158	1211	1264	1317	1371	1424	1477	1530	1584	1637	
6	1690	1743	1797	1850	1903	1956	2009	2063	2116	2169	
7	2222	2275	2328	2381	2435	2488	2541	2594	2647	2700	
8	2753	2806	2859	2913	2966	3019	3072	3125	3178	3231	
9	3284	3337	3390	3443	3496	3549	3602	3655	3708	3761	
820	91 3814	3867	3920	3973	4026	4079	4132	4184	4237	4290	
1	4343	4396	4449	4502	4555	4608	4660	4713	4766	4819	
2	4872	4925	4977	5030	5083	5136	5189	5241	5294	5347	
3	5400	5453	5505	5558	5611	5664	5716	5769	5822	5875	
4	5927	5980	6033	6085	6138	6191	6243	6296	6349	6401	
825	91 6454	6507	6559	6612	6664	6717	6770	6822	6875	6927	
6	6980	7033	7085	7138	7190	7243	7295	7348	7400	7453	
7	7506	7558	7611	7663	7716	7768	7820	7873	7925	7978	
8	8030	8083	8135	8188	8240	8293	8345	8397	8450	8502	
9	8555	8607	8659	8712	8764	8816	8869	8921	8973	9026	52
830	91 9078	9130	9183	9235	9287	9340	9392	9444	9496	9549	
1	9601	9653	9706	9758	9810	9862	9914	9967	*0019	*0071	
2	92 0123	0176	0228	0280	0332	0384	0436	0489	0541	0593	
3	0645	0697	0749	0801	0853	0906	0958	1010	1062	1114	
4	1166	1218	1270	1322	1374	1426	1478	1530	1582	1634	
835	92 1686	1738	1790	1842	1894	1946	1998	2050	2102	2154	
6	2206	2258	2310	2362	2414	2466	2518	2570	2622	2674	
7	2725	2777	2829	2881	2933	2985	3037	3089	3140	3192	
8	3244	3296	3348	3399	3451	3503	3555	3607	3658	3710	
9	3762	3814	3865	3917	3969	4021	4072	4124	4176	4228	
840	92 4279	4331	4383	4434	4486	4538	4589	4641	4693	4744	
1	4796	4848	4899	4951	5003	5054	5106	5157	5209	5261	
2	5312	5364	5415	5467	5518	5570	5621	5673	5725	5776	
3	5828	5879	5931	5982	6034	6085	6137	6188	6240	6291	51
4	6342	6394	6445	6497	6548	6600	6651	6702	6754	6805	
845	92 6857	6908	6959	7011	7062	7114	7165	7216	7268	7319	
6	7370	7422	7473	7524	7576	7627	7678	7730	7781	7832	
7	7883	7935	7986	8037	8088	8140	8191	8242	8293	8345	
8	8396	8447	8498	8549	8601	8652	8703	8754	8805	8857	
9	8908	8959	9010	9061	9112	9163	9215	9266	9317	9368	

PROPORTIONAL PARTS

Diff.	1	2	3	4	5	6	7	8	9
55	5.5	11.0	16.5	22.0	27.5	33.0	38.5	44.0	49.5
54	5.4	10.8	16.2	21.6	27.0	32.4	37.8	43.2	48.6
53	5.3	10.6	15.9	21.2	26.5	31.8	37.1	42.4	47.7
52	5.2	10.4	15.6	20.8	26.0	31.2	36.4	41.6	46.8

Table I — Six-Place Logarithms

N.	0	1	2	3	4	5	6	7	8	9	Diff.
850	92 9419	9470	9521	9572	9623	9674	9725	9776	9827	9879	
1	9930	9981	*0032	*0083	*0134	*0185	*0236	*0287	*0338	*0389	51
2	93 0440	0491	0542	0592	0643	0694	0745	0796	0847	0898	
3	0949	1000	1051	1102	1153	1204	1254	1305	1356	1407	
4	1458	1509	1560	1610	1661	1712	1763	1814	1865	1915	
855	93 1966	2017	2068	2118	2169	2220	2271	2322	2372	2423	
6	2474	2524	2575	2626	2677	2727	2778	2829	2879	2930	
7	2981	3031	3082	3133	3183	3234	3285	3335	3386	3437	
8	3487	3538	3589	3639	3690	3740	3791	3841	3892	3943	
9	3993	4044	4094	4145	4195	4246	4296	4347	4397	4448	
860	93 4498	4549	4599	4650	4700	4751	4801	4852	4902	4953	
1	5003	5054	5104	5154	5205	5255	5306	5356	5406	5457	50
2	5507	5558	5608	5658	5709	5759	5809	5860	5910	5960	
3	6011	6061	6111	6162	6212	6262	6313	6363	6413	6463	
4	6514	6564	6614	6665	6715	6765	6815	6865	6916	6966	
865	93 7016	7066	7117	7167	7217	7267	7317	7367	7418	7468	
6	7518	7568	7618	7668	7718	7769	7819	7869	7919	7969	
7	8019	8069	8119	8169	8219	8269	8320	8370	8420	8470	
8	8520	8570	8620	8670	8720	8770	8820	8870	8920	8970	
9	9020	9070	9120	9170	9220	9270	9320	9369	9419	9469	
870	93 9519	9569	9619	9669	9719	9769	9819	9869	9918	9968	
1	94 0018	0068	0118	0168	0218	0267	0317	0367	0417	0467	
2	0516	0566	0616	0666	0716	0765	0815	0865	0915	0964	
3	1014	1064	1114	1163	1213	1263	1313	1362	1412	1462	
4	1511	1561	1611	1660	1710	1760	1809	1859	1909	1958	
875	94 2008	2058	2107	2157	2207	2256	2306	2355	2405	2455	
6	2504	2554	2603	2653	2702	2752	2801	2851	2901	2950	
7	3000	3049	3099	3148	3198	3247	3297	3346	3396	3445	
8	3495	3544	3593	3643	3692	3742	3791	3841	3890	3939	49
9	3989	4038	4088	4137	4186	4236	4285	4335	4384	4433	
880	94 4483	4532	4581	4631	4680	4729	4779	4828	4877	4927	
1	4976	5025	5074	5124	5173	5222	5272	5321	5370	5419	
2	5469	5518	5567	5616	5665	5715	5764	5813	5862	5912	
3	5961	6010	6059	6108	6157	6207	6256	6305	6354	6403	
4	6452	6501	6551	6600	6649	6698	6747	6796	6845	6894	
885	94 6943	6992	7041	7090	7140	7189	7238	7287	7336	7385	
6	7434	7483	7532	7581	7630	7679	7728	7777	7826	7875	
7	7924	7973	8022	8070	8119	8168	8217	8266	8315	8364	
8	8413	8462	8511	8560	8609	8657	8706	8755	8804	8853	
9	8902	8951	8999	9048	9097	9146	9195	9244	9292	9341	
890	94 9390	9439	9488	9536	9585	9634	9683	9731	9780	9829	
1	9878	9926	9975	*0024	*0073	*0121	*0170	*0219	*0267	*0316	
2	95 0365	0414	0462	0511	0560	0608	0657	0706	0754	0803	
3	0851	0900	0949	0997	1046	1095	1143	1192	1240	1289	
4	1338	1386	1435	1483	1532	1580	1629	1677	1726	1775	
895	95 1823	1872	1920	1969	2017	2066	2114	2163	2211	2260	
6	2308	2356	2405	2453	2502	2550	2599	2647	2696	2744	48
7	2792	2841	2889	2938	2986	3034	3083	3131	3180	3228	
8	3276	3325	3373	3421	3470	3518	3566	3615	3663	3711	
9	3760	3808	3856	3905	3953	4001	4049	4098	4146	4194	

PROPORTIONAL PARTS

Diff.	1	2	3	4	5	6	7	8	9
51	5.1	10.2	15.3	20.4	25.5	30.6	35.7	40.8	45.9
50	5.0	10.0	15.0	20.0	25.0	30.0	35.0	40.0	45.0
49	4.9	9.8	14.7	19.6	24.5	29.4	34.3	39.2	44.1
48	4.8	9.6	14.4	19.2	24.0	28.8	33.6	38.4	43.2

Table I — Six-Place Logarithms

N.	0	1	2	3	4	5	6	7	8	9	Diff.
900	95 4243	4291	4339	4387	4435	4484	4532	4580	4628	4677	48
1	4725	4773	4821	4869	4918	4966	5014	5062	5110	5158	
2	5207	5255	5303	5351	5399	5447	5495	5543	5592	5640	
3	5688	5736	5784	5832	5880	5928	5976	6024	6072	6120	
4	6168	6216	6265	6313	6361	6409	6457	6505	6553	6601	
905	95 6649	6697	6745	6793	6840	6888	6936	6984	7032	7080	
6	7128	7176	7224	7272	7320	7368	7416	7464	7512	7559	
7	7607	7655	7703	7751	7799	7847	7894	7942	7990	8038	
8	8086	8134	8181	8229	8277	8325	8373	8421	8468	8516	
9	8564	8612	8659	8707	8755	8803	8850	8898	8946	8994	
910	95 9041	9089	9137	9185	9232	9280	9328	9375	9423	9471	
1	9518	9566	9614	9661	9709	9757	9804	9852	9900	9947	
2	9995	*0042	*0090	*0138	*0185	*0233	*0280	*0328	*0376	*0423	
3	96 0471	0518	0566	0613	0661	0709	0756	0804	0851	0899	
4	0946	0994	1041	1089	1136	1184	1231	1279	1326	1374	
915	96 1421	1469	1516	1563	1611	1658	1706	1753	1801	1848	47
6	1895	1943	1990	2038	2085	2132	2180	2227	2275	2322	
7	2369	2417	2464	2511	2559	2606	2653	2701	2748	2795	
8	2843	2890	2937	2985	3032	3079	3126	3174	3221	3268	
9	3316	3363	3410	3457	3504	3552	3599	3646	3693	3741	
920	96 3788	3835	3882	3929	3977	4024	4071	4118	4165	4212	
1	4260	4307	4354	4401	4448	4495	4542	4590	4637	4684	
2	4731	4778	4825	4872	4919	4966	5013	5061	5108	5155	
3	5202	5249	5296	5343	5390	5437	5484	5531	5578	5625	
4	5672	5719	5766	5813	5860	5907	5954	6001	6048	6095	
925	96 6142	6189	6236	6283	6329	6376	6423	6470	6517	6564	
6	6611	6658	6705	6752	6799	6845	6892	6939	6986	7033	
7	7080	7127	7173	7220	7267	7314	7361	7408	7454	7501	
8	7548	7595	7642	7688	7735	7782	7829	7875	7922	7969	
9	8016	8062	8109	8156	8203	8249	8296	8343	8390	8436	
930	96 8483	8530	8576	8623	8670	8716	8763	8810	8856	8903	
1	8950	8996	9043	9090	9136	9183	9229	9276	9323	9369	
2	9416	9463	9509	9556	9602	9649	9695	9742	9789	9835	
3	9882	9928	9975	*0021	*0068	*0114	*0161	*0207	*0254	*0300	
4	97 0347	0393	0440	0486	0533	0579	0626	0672	0719	0765	
935	97 0812	0858	0904	0951	0997	1044	1090	1137	1183	1229	46
6	1276	1322	1369	1415	1461	1508	1554	1601	1647	1693	
7	1740	1786	1832	1879	1925	1971	2018	2064	2110	2157	
8	2203	2249	2295	2342	2388	2434	2481	2527	2573	2619	
9	2666	2712	2758	2804	2851	2897	2943	2989	3035	3082	
940	97 3128	3174	3220	3266	3313	3359	3405	3451	3497	3543	
1	3590	3636	3682	3728	3774	3820	3866	3913	3959	4005	
2	4051	4097	4143	4189	4235	4281	4327	4374	4420	4466	
3	4512	4558	4604	4650	4696	4742	4788	4834	4880	4926	
4	4972	5018	5064	5110	5156	5202	5248	5294	5340	5386	
945	97 5432	5478	5524	5570	5616	5662	5707	5753	5799	5845	
6	5891	5937	5983	6029	6075	6121	6167	6212	6258	6304	
7	6350	6396	6442	6488	6533	6579	6625	6671	6717	6763	
8	6808	6854	6900	6946	6992	7037	7083	7129	7175	7220	
9	7266	7312	7358	7403	7449	7495	7541	7586	7632	7678	

PROPORTIONAL PARTS

Diff.	1	2	3	4	5	6	7	8	9
48	4.8	9.6	14.4	19.2	24.0	28.8	33.6	38.4	43.2
47	4.7	9.4	14.1	18.8	23.5	28.2	32.9	37.6	42.3
46	4.6	9.2	13.8	18.4	23.0	27.6	32.2	36.8	41.4

Table I — Six-Place Logarithms

N.	0	1	2	3	4	5	6	7	8	9	Diff.
950	97 7724	7769	7815	7861	7906	7952	7998	8043	8089	8135	
1	8181	8226	8272	8317	8363	8409	8454	8500	8546	8591	
2	8637	8683	8728	8774	8819	8865	8911	8956	9002	9047	
3	9093	9138	9184	9230	9275	9321	9366	9412	9457	9503	
4	9548	9594	9639	9685	9730	9776	9821	9867	9912	9958	
955	98 0003	0049	0094	0140	0185	0231	0276	0322	0367	0412	
6	0458	0503	0549	0594	0640	0685	0730	0776	0821	0867	45
7	0912	0957	1003	1048	1093	1139	1184	1229	1275	1320	
8	1366	1411	1456	1501	1547	1592	1637	1683	1728	1773	
9	1819	1864	1909	1954	2000	2045	2090	2135	2181	2226	
960	98 2271	2316	2362	2407	2452	2497	2543	2588	2633	2678	
1	2723	2769	2814	2859	2904	2949	2994	3040	3085	3130	
2	3175	3220	3265	3310	3356	3401	3446	3491	3536	3581	
3	3626	3671	3716	3762	3807	3852	3897	3942	3987	4032	
4	4077	4122	4167	4212	4257	4302	4347	4392	4437	4482	
965	98 4527	4572	4617	4662	4707	4752	4797	4842	4887	4932	
6	4977	5022	5067	5112	5157	5202	5247	5292	5337	5382	
7	5426	5471	5516	5561	5606	5651	5696	5741	5786	5830	
8	5875	5920	5965	6010	6055	6100	6144	6189	6234	6279	
9	6324	6369	6413	6458	6503	6548	6593	6637	6682	6727	
970	98 6772	6817	6861	6906	6951	6996	7040	7085	7130	7175	
1	7219	7264	7309	7353	7398	7443	7488	7532	7577	7622	
2	7666	7711	7756	7800	7845	7890	7934	7979	8024	8068	
3	8113	8157	8202	8247	8291	8336	8381	8425	8470	8514	
4	8559	8604	8648	8693	8737	8782	8826	8871	8916	8960	
975	98 9005	9049	9094	9138	9183	9227	9272	9316	9361	9405	
6	9450	9494	9539	9583	9628	9672	9717	9761	9806	9850	
7	9895	9939	9983	*0028	*0072	*0117	*0161	*0206	*0250	*0294	44
8	99 0339	0383	0428	0472	0516	0561	0605	0650	0694	0738	
9	0783	0827	0871	0916	0960	1004	1049	1093	1137	1182	
980	99 1226	1270	1315	1359	1403	1448	1492	1536	1580	1625	
1	1669	1713	1758	1802	1846	1890	1935	1979	2023	2067	
2	2111	2156	2200	2244	2288	2333	2377	2421	2465	2509	
3	2554	2598	2642	2686	2730	2774	2819	2863	2907	2951	
4	2995	3039	3083	3127	3172	3216	3260	3304	3348	3392	
985	99 3436	3480	3524	3568	3613	3657	3701	3745	3789	3833	
6	3877	3921	3965	4009	4053	4097	4141	4185	4229	4273	
7	4317	4361	4405	4449	4493	4537	4581	4625	4669	4713	
8	4757	4801	4845	4889	4933	4977	5021	5065	5108	5152	
9	5196	5240	5284	5328	5372	5416	5460	5504	5547	5591	
990	99 5635	5679	5723	5767	5811	5854	5898	5942	5986	6030	
1	6074	6117	6161	6205	6249	6293	6337	6380	6424	6468	
2	6512	6555	6599	6643	6687	6731	6774	6818	6862	6906	
3	6949	6993	7037	7080	7124	7168	7212	7255	7299	7343	
4	7386	7430	7474	7517	7561	7605	7648	7692	7736	7779	
995	99 7823	7867	7910	7954	7998	8041	8085	8129	8172	8216	
6	8259	8303	8347	8390	8434	8477	8521	8564	8608	8652	
7	8695	8739	8782	8826	8869	8913	8956	9000	9043	9087	
8	9131	9174	9218	9261	9305	9348	9392	9435	9479	9522	
9	9565	9609	9652	9696	9739	9783	9826	9870	9913	9957	

PROPORTIONAL PARTS

Diff.	1	2	3	4	5	6	7	8	9
45	4.5	9.0	13.5	18.0	22.5	27.0	31.5	36.0	40.5
44	4.4	8.8	13.2	17.6	22.0	26.4	30.8	35.2	39.6
43	4.3	8.6	12.9	17.2	21.5	25.8	30.1	34.4	38.7

Table II — Seven-Place Logarithms of Numbers, 10,000–11,000

N	0	1	2	3	4	5	6	7	8	9	Diff.
1000	000 0000	0434	0869	1303	1737	2171	2605	3039	3473	3907	434
1001	4341	4775	5208	5642	6076	6510	6943	7377	7810	8244	
1002	8677	9111	9544	9977	*0411	*0844	*1277	*1710	*2143	*2576	433
1003	001 3009	3442	3875	4308	4741	5174	5607	6039	6472	6905	
1004	7337	7770	8202	8635	9067	9499	9932	*0364	*0796	*1228	432
1005	002 1661	2093	2525	2957	3389	3821	4253	4685	5116	5548	
1006	5980	6411	6843	7275	7706	8138	8569	9001	9432	9863	431
1007	003 0295	0726	1157	1588	2019	2451	2882	3313	3744	4174	
1008	4605	5036	5467	5898	6328	6759	7190	7620	8051	8481	
1009	8912	9342	9772	*0203	*0633	*1063	*1493	*1924	*2354	*2784	430
1010	004 3214	3644	4074	4504	4933	5363	5793	6223	6652	7082	
1011	7512	7941	8371	8800	9229	9659	*0088	*0517	*0947	*1376	429
1012	005 1805	2234	2663	3092	3521	3950	4379	4808	5237	5666	
1013	6094	6523	6952	7380	7809	8238	8666	9094	9523	9951	
1014	006 0380	0808	1236	1664	2092	2521	2949	3377	3805	4233	428
1015	4660	5088	5516	5944	6372	6799	7227	7655	8082	8510	
1016	8937	9365	9792	*0219	*0647	*1074	*1501	*1928	*2355	*2782	427
1017	007 3210	3637	4064	4490	4917	5344	5771	6198	6624	7051	
1018	7478	7904	8331	8757	9184	9610	*0037	*0463	*0889	*1316	426
1019	008 1742	2168	2594	3020	3446	3872	4298	4724	5150	5576	
1020	6002	6427	6853	7279	7704	8130	8556	8981	9407	9832	
1021	009 0257	0683	1108	1533	1959	2384	2809	3234	3659	4084	425
1022	4509	4934	5359	5784	6208	6633	7058	7483	7907	8332	
1023	8756	9181	9605	*0030	*0454	*0878	*1303	*1727	*2151	*2575	424
1024	010 3000	3424	3848	4272	4696	5120	5544	5967	6391	6815	
1025	7239	7662	8086	8510	8933	9357	9780	*0204	*0627	*1050	
1026	011 1474	1897	2320	2743	3166	3590	4013	4436	4859	5282	423
1027	5704	6127	6550	6973	7396	7818	8241	8664	9086	9509	
1028	9931	*0354	*0776	*1198	*1621	*2043	*2465	*2887	*3310	*3732	422
1029	012 4154	4576	4998	5420	5842	6264	6685	7107	7529	7951	
1030	8372	8794	9215	9637	*0059	*0480	*0901	*1323	*1744	*2165	421
1031	013 2587	3008	3429	3850	4271	4692	5113	5534	5955	6376	
1032	6797	7218	7639	8059	8480	8901	9321	9742	*0162	*0583	
1033	014 1003	1424	1844	2264	2685	3105	3525	3945	4365	4785	420
1034	5205	5625	6045	6465	6885	7305	7725	8144	8564	8984	
1035	9403	9823	*0243	*0662	*1082	*1501	*1920	*2340	*2759	*3178	419
1036	015 3598	4017	4436	4855	5274	5693	6112	6531	6950	7369	
1037	7788	8206	8625	9044	9462	9881	*0300	*0718	*1137	*1555	
1038	016 1974	2392	2810	3229	3647	4065	4483	4910	5319	5737	418
1039	6155	6573	6991	7409	7827	8245	8663	9080	9498	9916	
1040	017 0333	0751	1168	1586	2003	2421	2838	3256	3673	4090	417
1041	4507	4924	5342	5759	6176	6593	7010	7427	7844	8260	
1042	8677	9094	9511	9927	*0344	*0761	*1177	*1594	*2010	*2427	
1043	018 2843	3259	3676	4092	4508	4925	5341	5757	6173	6589	416
1044	7005	7421	7837	8253	8669	9084	9500	9916	*0332	*0747	
1045	019 1163	1578	1994	2410	2825	3240	3656	4071	4486	4902	
1046	5317	5732	6147	6562	6977	7392	7807	8222	8637	9052	415
1047	9467	9882	*0296	*0711	*1126	*1540	*1955	*2369	*2784	*3198	
1048	020 3613	4027	4442	4856	5270	5684	6099	6513	6927	7341	414
1049	7755	8169	8583	8997	9411	9824	*0238	*0652	*1066	*1479	
1050	021 1893	2307	2720	3134	3547	3961	4374	4787	5201	5614	
N	0	1	2	3	4	5	6	7	8	9	

Table II — Seven-Place Logarithms of Numbers

PROPORTIONAL PARTS FOR INTERPOLATION IN THE TABLE ON OPPOSITE PAGE

	435		434		433		432		431
1	43.5	1	43.4	1	43.3	1	43.2	1	43.1
2	87.0	2	86.8	2	86.6	2	86.4	2	86.2
3	130.5	3	130.2	3	129.9	3	129.6	3	129.3
4	174.0	4	173.6	4	173.2	4	172.8	4	172.4
5	217.5	5	217.0	5	216.5	5	216.0	5	215.5
6	261.0	6	260.4	6	259.8	6	259.2	6	258.6
7	304.5	7	303.8	7	303.1	7	302.4	7	301.7
8	348.0	8	347.2	8	346.4	8	345.6	8	344.8
9	391.5	9	390.6	9	389.7	9	388.8	9	387.9

	430		429		428		427		426
1	43.0	1	42.9	1	42.8	1	42.7	1	42.6
2	86.0	2	85.8	2	85.6	2	85.4	2	85.2
3	129.0	3	128.7	3	128.4	3	128.1	3	127.8
4	172.0	4	171.6	4	171.2	4	170.8	4	170.4
5	215.0	5	214.5	5	214.0	5	213.5	5	213.0
6	258.0	6	257.4	6	256.8	6	256.2	6	255.6
7	301.0	7	300.3	7	299.6	7	298.9	7	298.2
8	344.0	8	343.2	8	342.4	8	341.6	8	340.8
9	387.0	9	386.1	9	385.2	9	384.3	9	383.4

	425		424		423		422		421
1	42.5	1	42.4	1	42.3	1	42.2	1	42.1
2	85.0	2	84.8	2	84.6	2	84.4	2	84.2
3	127.5	3	127.2	3	126.9	3	126.6	3	126.3
4	170.0	4	169.6	4	169.2	4	168.8	4	168.4
5	212.5	5	212.0	5	211.5	5	211.0	5	210.5
6	255.0	6	254.4	6	253.8	6	253.2	6	252.6
7	297.5	7	296.8	7	296.1	7	295.4	7	294.7
8	340.0	8	339.2	8	338.4	8	337.6	8	336.8
9	382.5	9	381.6	9	380.7	9	379.8	9	378.9

	420		419		418		417		416
1	42.0	1	41.9	1	41.8	1	41.7	1	41.6
2	84.0	2	83.8	2	83.6	2	83.4	2	83.2
3	126.0	3	125.7	3	125.4	3	125.1	3	124.8
4	168.0	4	167.6	4	167.2	4	166.8	4	166.4
5	210.0	5	209.5	5	209.0	5	208.5	5	208.0
6	252.0	6	251.4	6	250.8	6	250.2	6	249.6
7	294.0	7	293.3	7	292.6	7	291.9	7	291.2
8	336.0	8	335.2	8	334.4	8	333.6	8	332.8
9	378.0	9	377.1	9	376.2	9	375.3	9	374.4

	415		414
1	41.5	1	41.4
2	83.0	2	82.8
3	124.5	3	124.2
4	166.0	4	165.6
5	207.5	5	207.0
6	249.0	6	248.4
7	290.5	7	289.8
8	332.0	8	331.2
9	373.5	9	372.6

Table II — Seven-Place Logarithms of Numbers

N	0	1	2	3	4	5	6	7	8	9	Diff.
1050	021 1893	2307	2720	3134	3547	3961	4374	4787	5201	5614	414
1051	6027	6440	6854	7267	7680	8093	8506	8919	9332	9745	413
1052	022 0157	0570	0983	1396	1808	2221	2634	3046	3459	3871	
1053	4284	4696	5109	5521	5933	6345	6758	7170	7582	7994	412
1054	8406	8818	9230	9642	*0054	*0466	*0878	*1289	*1701	*2113	
1055	023 2525	2936	3348	3759	4171	4582	4994	5405	5817	6228	
1056	6639	7050	7462	7873	8284	8695	9106	9517	9928	*0339	411
1057	024 0750	1161	1572	1982	2393	2804	3214	3625	4036	4446	
1058	4857	5267	5678	6088	6498	6909	7319	7729	8139	8549	410
1059	8960	9370	9780	*0190	*0600	*1010	*1419	*1829	*2239	*2649	
1060	025 3059	3468	3878	4288	4697	5107	5516	5926	6335	6744	
1061	7154	7563	7972	8382	8791	9200	9609	*0018	*0427	*0836	409
1062	026 1245	1654	2063	2472	2881	3289	3698	4107	4515	4924	
1063	5333	5741	6150	6558	6967	7375	7783	8192	8600	9008	408
1064	9416	9824	*0233	*0641	*1049	*1457	*1865	*2273	*2680	*3088	
1065	027 3496	3904	4312	4719	5127	5535	5942	6350	6757	7165	
1066	7572	7979	8387	8794	9201	9609	*0016	*0423	*0830	*1237	407
1067	028 1644	2051	2458	2865	3272	3679	4086	4492	4899	5306	
1068	5713	6119	6526	6932	7339	7745	8152	8558	8964	9371	
1069	9777	*0183	*0590	*0996	*1402	*1808	*2214	*2620	*3026	*3432	406
1070	029 3838	4244	4649	5055	5461	5867	6272	6678	7084	7489	
1071	7895	8300	8706	9111	9516	9922	*0327	*0732	*1138	*1543	405
1072	030 1948	2353	2758	3163	3568	3973	4378	4783	5188	5592	
1073	5997	6402	6807	7211	7616	8020	8425	8830	9234	9638	
1074	031 0043	0447	0851	1256	1660	2064	2468	2872	3277	3681	404
1075	4085	4489	4893	5296	5700	6104	6508	6912	7315	7719	
1076	8123	8526	8930	9333	9737	*0140	*0544	*0947	*1350	*1754	403
1077	032 2157	2560	2963	3367	3770	4173	4576	4979	5382	5785	
1078	6188	6590	6993	7396	7799	8201	8604	9007	9409	9812	
1079	033 0214	0617	1019	1422	1824	2226	2629	3031	3433	3835	402
1080	4238	4640	5042	5444	5846	6248	6650	7052	7453	7855	
1081	8257	8659	9060	9462	9864	*0265	*0667	*1068	*1470	*1871	
1082	034 2273	2674	3075	3477	3878	4279	4680	5081	5482	5884	401
1083	6285	6686	7087	7487	7888	8289	8690	9091	9491	9892	
1084	035 0293	0693	1094	1495	1895	2296	2696	3096	3497	3897	
1085	4297	4698	5098	5498	5898	6298	6698	7098	7498	7898	400
1086	8298	8698	9098	9498	9898	*0297	*0697	*1097	*1496	*1896	
1087	036 2295	2695	3094	3494	3893	4293	4692	5091	5491	5890	399
1088	6289	6688	7087	7486	7885	8284	8683	9082	9481	9880	
1089	037 0279	0678	1076	1475	1874	2272	2671	3070	3468	3867	
1090	4265	4663	5062	5460	5858	6257	6655	7053	7451	7849	398
1091	8248	8646	9044	9442	9839	*0237	*0635	*1033	*1431	*1829	
1092	038 2226	2624	3022	3419	3817	4214	4612	5009	5407	5804	
1093	6202	6599	6996	7393	7791	8188	8585	8982	9379	9776	397
1094	039 0173	0570	0967	1364	1761	2158	2554	2951	3348	3745	
1095	4141	4538	4934	5331	5727	6124	6520	6917	7313	7709	396
1096	8106	8502	8898	9294	9690	*0086	*0482	*0878	*1274	*1670	
1097	040 2066	2462	2858	3254	3650	4045	4441	4837	5232	5628	
1098	6023	6419	6814	7210	7605	8001	8396	8791	9187	9582	395
1099	9977	*0372	*0767	*1162	*1557	*1952	*2347	*2742	*3137	*3532	
1100	041 3927	4322	4716	5111	5506	5900	6295	6690	7084	7479	394
N	0	1	2	3	4	5	6	7	8	9	

Table II — Seven-Place Logarithms of Numbers

PROPORTIONAL PARTS FOR INTERPOLATION IN THE TABLE ON OPPOSITE PAGE

	414		413		412		411		410
1	41.4	1	41.3	1	41.2	1	41.1	1	41.0
2	82.8	2	82.6	2	82.4	2	82.2	2	82.0
3	124.2	3	123.9	3	123.6	3	123.3	3	123.0
4	165.6	4	165.2	4	164.8	4	164.4	4	164.0
5	207.0	5	206.5	5	206.0	5	205.5	5	205.0
6	248.4	6	247.8	6	247.2	6	246.6	6	246.0
7	289.8	7	289.1	7	288.4	7	287.7	7	287.0
8	331.2	8	330.4	8	329.6	8	328.8	8	328.0
9	372.6	9	371.7	9	370.8	9	369.9	9	369.0

	409		408		407		406		405
1	40.9	1	40.8	1	40.7	1	40.6	1	40.5
2	81.8	2	81.6	2	81.4	2	81.2	2	81.0
3	122.7	3	122.4	3	122.1	3	121.8	3	121.5
4	163.6	4	163.2	4	162.8	4	162.4	4	162.0
5	204.5	5	204.0	5	203.5	5	203.0	5	202.5
6	245.4	6	244.8	6	244.2	6	243.6	6	243.0
7	286.3	7	285.6	7	284.9	7	284.2	7	283.5
8	327.2	8	326.4	8	325.6	8	324.8	8	324.0
9	368.1	9	367.2	9	366.3	9	365.4	9	364.5

	404		403		402		401		400
1	40.4	1	40.3	1	40.2	1	40.1	1	40.0
2	80.8	2	80.6	2	80.4	2	80.2	2	80.0
3	121.2	3	120.9	3	120.6	3	120.3	3	120.0
4	161.6	4	161.2	4	160.8	4	160.4	4	160.0
5	202.0	5	201.5	5	201.0	5	200.5	5	200.0
6	242.4	6	241.8	6	241.2	6	240.6	6	240.0
7	282.8	7	282.1	7	281.4	7	280.7	7	280.0
8	323.2	8	322.4	8	321.6	8	320.8	8	320.0
9	363.6	9	362.7	9	361.8	9	360.9	9	360.0

	399		398		397		396
1	39.9	1	39.8	1	39.7	1	39.6
2	79.8	2	79.6	2	79.4	2	79.2
3	119.7	3	119.4	3	119.1	3	118.8
4	159.6	4	159.2	4	158.8	4	158.4
5	199.5	5	199.0	5	198.5	5	198.0
6	239.4	6	238.8	6	238.2	6	237.6
7	279.3	7	278.6	7	277.9	7	277.2
8	319.2	8	318.4	8	317.6	8	316.8
9	359.1	9	358.2	9	357.3	9	356.4

	395		394
1	39.5	1	39.4
2	79.0	2	78.8
3	118.5	3	118.2
4	158.0	4	157.6
5	197.5	5	197.0
6	237.0	6	236.4
7	276.5	7	275.8
8	316.0	8	315.2
9	355.5	9	354.6

Table III — The Number of Each Day of the Year Counting from January 1

Day of month	Jan.	Feb.	Mar.	Apr.	May	June	July	Aug.	Sept.	Oct.	Nov.	Dec.	Day of month
1	1	32	60	91	121	152	182	213	244	274	305	335	1
2	2	33	61	92	122	153	183	214	245	275	306	336	2
3	3	34	62	93	123	154	184	215	246	276	307	337	3
4	4	35	63	94	124	155	185	216	247	277	308	338	4
5	5	36	64	95	125	156	186	217	248	278	309	339	5
6	6	37	65	96	126	157	187	218	249	279	310	340	6
7	7	38	66	97	127	158	188	219	250	280	311	341	7
8	8	39	67	98	128	159	189	220	251	281	312	342	8
9	9	40	68	99	129	160	190	221	252	282	313	343	9
10	10	41	69	100	130	161	191	222	253	283	314	344	10
11	11	42	70	101	131	162	192	223	254	284	315	345	11
12	12	43	71	102	132	163	193	224	255	285	316	346	12
13	13	44	72	103	133	164	194	225	256	286	317	347	13
14	14	45	73	104	134	165	195	226	257	287	318	348	14
15	15	46	74	105	135	166	196	227	258	288	319	349	15
16	16	47	75	106	136	167	197	228	259	289	320	350	16
17	17	48	76	107	137	168	198	229	260	290	321	351	17
18	18	49	77	108	138	169	199	230	261	291	322	352	18
19	19	50	78	109	139	170	200	231	262	292	323	353	19
20	20	51	79	110	140	171	201	232	263	293	324	354	20
21	21	52	80	111	141	172	202	233	264	294	325	355	21
22	22	53	81	112	142	173	203	234	265	295	326	356	22
23	23	54	82	113	143	174	204	235	266	296	327	357	23
24	24	55	83	114	144	175	205	236	267	297	328	358	24
25	25	56	84	115	145	176	206	237	268	298	329	359	25
26	26	57	85	116	146	177	207	238	269	299	330	360	26
27	27	58	86	117	147	178	208	239	270	300	331	361	27
28	28	59	87	118	148	179	209	240	271	301	332	362	28
29	29	..	88	119	149	180	210	241	272	302	333	363	29
30	30	..	89	120	150	181	211	242	273	303	334	364	30
31	31	..	90	...	151	...	212	243	...	304	...	365	31

NOTE: For leap years, after February 28, the number of the day is one greater than that given in the table.

Table IV — Ordinary and Exact Simple Interest on 1000 at 1%

Days	Ordinary Interest	Exact Interest	Days	Ordinary Interest	Exact Interest
1	0.027 7778	0.027 3973	150	4.166 6667	4.109 5890
2	0.055 5556	0.054 7945	160	4.444 4444	4.383 5616
3	0.083 3333	0.082 1918	170	4.722 2222	4.657 5342
4	0.111 1111	0.109 5890	180	5.000 0000	4.931 5068
5	0.138 8889	0.136 9863	190	5.277 7778	5.205 4795
6	0.166 6667	0.164 3836	200	5.555 5556	5.479 4521
7	0.194 4444	0.191 7808	210	5.833 3333	5.753 4247
8	0.222 2222	0.219 1781	220	6.111 1111	6.027 3973
9	0.250 0000	0.246 5753	230	6.388 8889	6.301 3699
10	0.277 7778	0.273 9726	240	6.666 6667	6.575 3425
20	0.555 5556	9.547 9452	250	6.944 4444	6.849 3151
30	0.833 3333	0.821 9178	260	7.222 2222	7.123 2877
40	1.111 1111	1.095 8904	270	7.500 0000	7.397 2603
50	1.388 8889	1.369 8630	280	7.777 7778	7.671 2329
60	1.666 6667	1.643 8356	290	8.055 5556	7.945 2055
70	1.944 4444	1.917 8082	300	8.333 3333	8.219 1781
80	2.222 2222	2.191 7808	310	8.611 1111	8.493 1507
90	2.500 0000	2.465 7534	320	8.888 8889	8.767 1233
100	2.777 7778	2.739 7260	330	9.166 6667	9.041 0959
110	3.055 5556	3.013 6986	340	9.444 4444	9.315 0685
120	3.333 3333	3.287 6712	350	9.722 2222	9.589 0411
130	3.611 1111	3.561 6438	360	10.000 0000	9.863 0137
140	3.888 8889	3.835 6164	...	....	....

Table V — Amount of 1

$$s = (1+i)^n$$

n	$\frac{1}{4}$ per cent	$\frac{1}{3}$ per cent	$\frac{5}{12}$ per cent	$\frac{1}{2}$ per cent	$\frac{7}{12}$ per cent	n
1	1.0025 000	1.0033 333	1.0041 667	1.0050 000	1.0058 333	1
2	1.0050 062	1.0066 778	1.0083 507	1.0100 250	1.0117 007	2
3	1.0075 188	1.0100 334	1.0125 522	1.0150 751	1.0176 023	3
4	1.0100 376	1.0134 001	1.0167 711	1.0201 505	1.0235 383	4
5	1.0125 627	1.0167 781	1.0210 077	1.0252 513	1.0295 089	5
6	1.0150 941	1.0201 674	1.0252 619	1.0303 775	1.0355 144	6
7	1.0176 319	1.0235 680	1.0295 338	1.0355 294	1.0415 549	7
8	1.0201 759	1.0269 799	1.0338 235	1.0407 070	1.0476 306	8
9	1.0227 263	1.0304 031	1.0381 311	1.0459 106	1.0537 418	9
10	1.0252 831	1.0338 378	1.0424 567	1.0511 401	1.0598 886	10
11	1.0278 463	1.0372 839	1.0468 002	1.0563 958	1.0660 713	11
12	1.0304 160	1.0407 415	1.0511 619	1.0616 778	1.0722 901	12
13	1.0329 920	1.0442 107	1.0555 417	1.0669 862	1.0785 451	13
14	1.0355 745	1.0476 914	1.0599 398	1.0723 211	1.0848 366	14
15	1.0381 634	1.0511 837	1.0643 562	1.0776 827	1.0911 648	15
16	1.0407 588	1.0546 876	1.0687 911	1.0830 712	1.0975 300	16
17	1.0433 607	1.0582 033	1.0732 444	1.0884 865	1.1039 322	17
18	1.0459 691	1.0617 306	1.0777 162	1.0939 289	1.1103 718	18
19	1.0485 840	1.0652 697	1.0822 067	1.0993 986	1.1168 490	19
20	1.0512 055	1.0688 206	1.0867 159	1.1048 956	1.1233 639	20
21	1.0538 335	1.0723 833	1.0912 439	1.1104 201	1.1299 169	21
22	1.0564 681	1.0759 580	1.0957 907	1.1159 722	1.1365 081	22
23	1.0591 093	1.0795 445	1.1003 565	1.1215 520	1.1431 377	23
24	1.0617 570	1.0831 430	1.1049 413	1.1271 598	1.1498 060	24
25	1.0644 114	1.0867 534	1.1095 453	1.1327 956	1.1565 132	25
26	1.0670 725	1.0903 759	1.1141 684	1.1384 595	1.1632 595	26
27	1.0697 401	1.0940 105	1.1188 107	1.1441 519	1.1700 452	27
28	1.0724 145	1.0976 572	1.1234 724	1.1498 726	1.1768 705	28
29	1.0750 955	1.1013 161	1.1281 536	1.1556 220	1.1837 356	29
30	1.0777 833	1.1049 871	1.1328 542	1.1614 001	1.1906 407	30
31	1.0804 777	1.1086 704	1.1375 744	1.1672 071	1.1975 861	31
32	1.0831 789	1.1123 660	1.1423 143	1.1730 431	1.2045 720	32
33	1.0858 869	1.1160 739	1.1470 740	1.1789 083	1.2115 987	33
34	1.0886 016	1.1197 941	1.1518 535	1.1848 029	1.2186 663	34
35	1.0913 231	1.1235 268	1.1566 528	1.1907 269	1.2257 752	35
36	1.0940 514	1.1272 719	1.1614 722	1.1966 805	1.2329 256	36
37	1.0967 865	1.1310 294	1.1663 117	1.2026 639	1.2401 177	37
38	1.0995 285	1.1347 995	1.1711 713	1.2086 772	1.2473 517	38
39	1.1022 773	1.1385 822	1.1760 512	1.2147 206	1.2546 279	39
40	1.1050 330	1.1423 775	1.1809 514	1.2207 942	1.2619 466	40
41	1.1077 956	1.1461 854	1.1858 721	1.2268 982	1.2693 079	41
42	1.1105 651	1.1500 060	1.1908 132	1.2330 327	1.2767 122	42
43	1.1133 415	1.1538 394	1.1957 749	1.2391 979	1.2841 597	43
44	1.1161 248	1.1576 855	1.2007 573	1.2453 939	1.2916 506	44
45	1.1189 152	1.1615 445	1.2057 605	1.2516 208	1.2991 853	45
46	1.1217 124	1.1654 163	1.2107 845	1.2578 789	1.3067 638	46
47	1.1245 167	1.1693 010	1.2158 294	1.2641 683	1.3143 866	47
48	1.1273 280	1.1731 987	1.2208 954	1.2704 892	1.3220 539	48
49	1.1301 463	1.1771 093	1.2259 824	1.2768 416	1.3297 659	49
50	1.1329 717	1.1810 330	1.2310 907	1.2832 258	1.3375 228	50

Table V — Amount of 1

$$s = (1+i)^n$$

n	$\frac{1}{4}$ per cent	$\frac{1}{3}$ per cent	$\frac{5}{12}$ per cent	$\frac{1}{2}$ per cent	$\frac{7}{12}$ per cent	n
51	1.1358 041	1.1849 698	1.2362 200	1.2896 419	1.3453 250	51
52	1.1386 436	1.1889 197	1.2413 711	1.2960 902	1.3531 728	52
53	1.1414 903	1.1928 828	1.2465 435	1.3025 706	1.3610 663	53
54	1.1443 440	1.1968 590	1.2517 375	1.3090 835	1.3690 058	54
55	1.1472 048	1.2008 486	1.2569 530	1.3156 289	1.3769 917	55
56	1.1500 729	1.2048 514	1.2621 903	1.3222 070	1.3850 242	56
57	1.1529 480	1.2088 676	1.2674 495	1.3288 181	1.3931 035	57
58	1.1558 304	1.2128 971	1.2727 305	1.3354 621	1.4012 299	58
59	1.1587 200	1.2169 401	1.2780 335	1.3421 395	1.4094 037	59
60	1.1616 168	1.2209 966	1.2833 587	1.3488 502	1.4176 253	60
61	1.1645 208	1.2250 666	1.2887 060	1.3555 944	1.4258 947	61
62	1.1674 321	1.2291 501	1.2940 756	1.3623 724	1.4342 125	62
63	1.1703 507	1.2332 473	1.2994 676	1.3691 842	1.4425 787	63
64	1.1732 766	1.2373 581	1.3048 820	1.3760 302	1.4509 937	64
65	1.1762 098	1.2414 827	1.3103 191	1.3829 103	1.4594 579	65
66	1.1791 503	1.2456 209	1.3157 787	1.3898 249	1.4679 714	66
67	1.1820 982	1.2497 730	1.3212 611	1.3967 740	1.4765 345	67
68	1.1850 534	1.2539 389	1.3267 664	1.4037 579	1.4851 477	68
69	1.1880 161	1.2581 187	1.3322 946	1.4107 767	1.4938 110	69
70	1.1909 861	1.2623 124	1.3378 458	1.4178 305	1.5025 249	70
71	1.1939 636	1.2665 201	1.3434 202	1.4249 197	1.5112 896	71
72	1.1969 485	1.2707 419	1.3490 177	1.4320 443	1.5201 055	72
73	1.1999 408	1.2749 777	1.3546 387	1.4392 045	1.5289 728	73
74	1.2029 407	1.2792 276	1.3302 830	1.4464 005	1.5378 918	74
75	1.2059 480	1.2834 917	1.3659 508	1.4536 325	1.5468 628	75
76	1.2089 629	1.2877 700	1.3716 423	1.4609 007	1.5558 862	76
77	1.2119 853	1.2920 626	1.3773 575	1.4682 052	1.5649 622	77
78	1.2150 153	1.2963 695	1.3830 965	1.4755 462	1.5740 911	78
79	1.2180 528	1.3006 907	1.3888 594	1.4829 239	1.5832 733	79
80	1.2210 980	1.3050 263	1.3946 463	1.4903 386	1.5925 091	80
81	1.2241 507	1.3093 764	1.4004 573	1.4977 903	1.6017 987	81
82	1.2272 111	1.3137 410	1.4062 925	1.5052 792	1.6111 426	82
83	1.2302 791	1.3181 201	1.4121 521	1.5128 056	1.6205 409	83
84	1.2333 548	1.3225 139	1.4180 361	1.5203 696	1.6299 941	84
85	1.2364 382	1.3269 222	1.4239 445	1.5279 715	1.6395 024	85
86	1.2395 293	1.3313 453	1.4298 776	1.5356 113	1.6490 661	86
87	1.2426 281	1.3357 831	1.4358 355	1.5432 894	1.6586 857	87
88	1.2457 347	1.3402 357	1.4418 181	1.5510 058	1.6683 613	88
89	1.2488 490	1.3447 032	1.4478 257	1.5587 609	1.6780 934	89
90	1.2519 711	1.3491 855	1.4538 583	1.5665 547	1.6878 823	90
91	1.2551 011	1.3536 828	1.4599 160	1.5743 875	1.6977 283	91
92	1.2582 388	1.3581 951	1.4659 990	1.5822 594	1.7076 317	92
93	1.2613 844	1.3627 224	1.4721 073	1.5901 707	1.7175 929	93
94	1.2645 379	1.3672 648	1.4782 411	1.5981 215	1.7276 122	94
95	1.2676 992	1.3718 224	1.4844 005	1.6061 121	1.7376 899	95
96	1.2708 685	1.3763 951	1.4905 855	1.6141 427	1.7478 265	96
97	1.2740 456	1.3809 831	1.4967 962	1.6222 134	1.7580 221	97
98	1.2772 308	1.3855 864	1.5030 329	1.6303 245	1.7682 772	98
99	1.2804 238	1.3902 050	1.5092 955	1.6384 761	1.7785 922	99
100	1.2836 249	1.3948 390	1.5155 843	1.6466 685	1.7889 673	100

Table V — Amount of 1

$$s = (1+i)^n$$

n	$\frac{2}{3}$ per cent	$\frac{3}{4}$ per cent	1 per cent	$1\frac{1}{4}$ per cent	$1\frac{1}{2}$ per cent	n
1	1.0066 667	1.0075 000	1.0100 000	1.0125 000	1.0150 000	1
2	1.0133 778	1.0150 562	1.0201 000	1.0251 562	1.0302 250	2
3	1.0201 336	1.0226 692	1.0303 010	1.0379 707	1.0456 784	3
4	1.0269 345	1.0303 392	1.0406 040	1.0509 453	1.0613 636	4
5	1.0337 808	1.0380 667	1.0510 100	1.0640 822	1.0772 840	5
6	1.0406 726	1.0458 522	1.0615 202	1.0773 832	1.0934 433	6
7	1.0476 104	1.0536 961	1.0721 354	1.0908 505	1.1098 449	7
8	1.0545 945	1.0615 988	1.0828 567	1.1044 861	1.1264 926	8
9	1.0616 251	1.0695 608	1.0936 853	1.1182 922	1.1433 900	9
10	1.0687 026	1.0775 825	1.1046 221	1.1322 708	1.1605 408	10
11	1.0758 273	1.0856 644	1.1156 684	1.1464 242	1.1779 489	11
12	1.0829 995	1.0938 069	1.1268 250	1.1607 545	1.1956 182	12
13	1.0902 195	1.1020 104	1.1380 933	1.1752 640	1.2135 524	13
14	1.0974 876	1.1102 755	1.1494 742	1.1899 548	1.2317 557	14
15	1.1048 042	1.1186 026	1.1609 690	1.2048 292	1.2502 321	15
16	1.1121 696	1.1269 921	1.1725 786	1.2198 896	1.2689 856	16
17	1.1195 840	1.1354 446	1.1843 044	1.2351 382	1.2880 203	17
18	1.1270 479	1.1439 604	1.1961 475	1.2505 774	1.3073 406	18
19	1.1345 616	1.1525 401	1.2081 090	1.2662 096	1.3269 508	19
20	1.1421 253	1.1611 841	1.2201 900	1.2820 372	1.3468 550	20
21	1.1497 395	1.1698 930	1.2323 919	1.2980 627	1.3670 578	21
22	1.1574 044	1.1786 672	1.2447 159	1.3142 885	1.3875 637	22
23	1.1651 205	1.1875 072	1.2571 630	1.3307 171	1.4083 772	23
24	1.1728 879	1.1964 135	1.2697 346	1.3473 510	1.4295 028	24
25	1.1807 072	1.2053 866	1.2824 320	1.3641 929	1.4509 454	25
26	1.1885 786	1.2144 270	1.2952 563	1.3812 454	1.4727 095	26
27	1.1965 024	1.2235 352	1.3082 089	1.3985 109	1.4948 002	27
28	1.2044 791	1.2327 117	1.3212 910	1.4159 923	1.5172 222	28
29	1.2125 090	1.2419 571	1.3345 039	1.4336 922	1.5399 805	29
30	1.2205 924	1.2512 718	1.3478 489	1.4516 134	1.5630 802	30
31	1.2287 296	1.2606 563	1.3613 274	1.4697 585	1.5865 264	31
32	1.2369 212	1.2701 112	1.3749 407	1.4881 305	1.6103 243	32
33	1.2451 673	1.2796 371	1.3886 901	1.5067 321	1.6344 792	33
34	1.2534 684	1.2892 343	1.4025 770	1.5255 663	1.6589 964	34
35	1.2618 249	1.2989 036	1.4166 028	1.5446 359	1.6838 813	35
36	1.2702 371	1.3086 454	1.4307 688	1.5639 438	1.7091 395	36
37	1.2787 053	1.3184 602	1.4450 765	1.5834 931	1.7347 766	37
38	1.2872 300	1.3283 487	1.4595 272	1.6032 868	1.7607 983	38
39	1.2958 115	1.3383 113	1.4741 225	1.6233 279	1.7872 102	39
40	1.3044 503	1.3483 486	1.4888 637	1.6436 195	1.8140 184	40
41	1.3131 466	1.3584 612	1.5037 524	1.6641 647	1.8412 287	41
42	1.3219 009	1.3686 497	1.5187 899	1.6849 668	1.8688 471	42
43	1.3307 136	1.3789 146	1.5339 778	1.7060 288	1.8968 798	43
44	1.3395 850	1.3892 564	1.5493 176	1.7273 542	1.9253 330	44
45	1.3485 156	1.3996 758	1.5648 108	1.7489 461	1.9542 130	45
46	1.3575 057	1.4101 734	1.5804 588	1.7708 080	1.9835 262	46
47	1.3665 557	1.4207 497	1.5962 634	1.7929 431	2.0132 791	47
48	1.3756 661	1.4314 053	1.6122 261	1.8153 548	2.0434 783	48
49	1.3848 372	1.4421 409	1.6283 483	1.8380 468	2.0741 305	49
50	1.3940 695	1.4529 569	1.6446 318	1.8610 224	2.1052 424	50

Table V — Amount of 1

$$s = (1+i)^n$$

n	$\tfrac{2}{3}$ per cent	$\tfrac{3}{4}$ per cent	1 per cent	$1\tfrac{1}{4}$ per cent	$1\tfrac{1}{2}$ per cent	n
51	1.4033 633	1.4638 541	1.6610 781	1.8842 852	2.1368 211	51
52	1.4127 190	1.4748 330	1.6776 889	1.9078 387	2.1688 734	52
53	1.4221 371	1.4858 943	1.6944 658	1.9316 867	2.2014 065	53
54	1.4316 180	1.4970 385	1.7114 105	1.9558 328	2.2344 276	54
55	1.4411 622	1.5082 663	1.7285 246	1.9802 807	2.2679 440	55
56	1.4507 699	1.5195 783	1.7458 098	2.0050 342	2.3019 631	56
57	1.4604 417	1.5309 751	1.7632 679	2.0300 971	2.3364 926	57
58	1.4701 780	1.5424 574	1.7809 006	2.0554 733	2.3715 400	58
59	1.4799 792	1.5540 258	1.7987 096	2.0811 668	2.4071 131	59
60	1.4898 457	1.5656 810	1.8166 967	2.1071 813	2.4432 198	60
61	1.4997 780	1.5774 236	1.8348 637	2.1335 211	2.4798 681	61
62	1.5097 765	1.5892 543	1.8532 123	2.1601 901	2.5170 661	62
63	1.5198 417	1.6011 737	1.8717 444	2.1871 925	2.5548 221	63
64	1.5299 740	1.6131 825	1.8904 619	2.2145 324	2.5931 444	64
65	1.5401 738	1.6252 814	1.9093 665	2.2422 141	2.6320 416	65
66	1.5504 416	1.6374 710	1.9284 602	2.2702 417	2.6715 222	66
67	1.5607 779	1.6497 520	1.9477 448	2.2986 198	2.7115 950	67
68	1.5711 831	1.6621 252	1.9672 222	2.3273 525	2.7522 690	68
69	1.5816 577	1.6745 911	1.9868 944	2.3564 444	2.7935 530	69
70	1.5922 020	1.6871 505	2.0067 634	2.3859 000	2.8354 563	70
71	1.6028 167	1.6998 042	2.0268 310	2.4157 237	2.8779 881	71
72	1.6135 022	1.7125 527	2.0470 993	2.4459 203	2.9211 580	72
73	1.6242 588	1.7253 968	2.0675 703	2.4764 943	2.9649 753	73
74	1.6350 872	1.7383 373	2.0882 460	2.5074 504	3.0094 500	74
75	1.6459 878	1.7513 749	2.1091 285	2.5387 936	3.0545 917	75
76	1.6569 611	1.7645 102	2.1302 198	2.5705 285	3.1004 106	76
77	1.6680 075	1.7777 440	2.1515 220	2.6026 601	3.1469 167	77
78	1.6791 275	1.7910 771	2.1730 372	2.6351 934	3.1941 205	78
79	1.6903 217	1.8045 102	2.1947 675	2.6681 333	3.2420 323	79
80	1.7015 905	1.8180 440	2.2167 152	2.7014 849	3.2906 628	80
81	1.7129 345	1.8316 793	2.2388 824	2.7352 535	3.3400 227	81
82	1.7243 540	1.8454 169	2.2612 712	2.7694 442	3.3901 231	82
83	1.7358 497	1.8592 575	2.2838 839	2.8040 622	3.4409 749	83
84	1.7474 221	1.8732 020	2.3067 227	2.8391 130	3.4925 895	84
85	1.7590 715	1.8872 510	2.3297 900	2.8746 019	3.5449 784	85
86	1.7707 987	1.9014 054	2.3530 879	2.9105 344	3.5981 531	86
87	1.7826 040	1.9156 659	2.3766 187	2.9469 161	3.6521 254	87
88	1.7944 880	1.9300 334	2.4003 849	2.9837 526	3.7069 072	88
89	1.8064 513	1.9445 086	2.4243 888	3.0210 495	3.7625 108	89
90	1.8184 943	1.9590 925	2.4486 327	3.0588 126	3.8189 485	90
91	1.8306 176	1.9737 857	2.4731 190	3.0970 478	3.8762 327	91
92	1.8428 217	1.9885 890	2.4978 502	3.1357 608	3.9343 762	92
93	1.8551 072	2.0035 035	2.5228 287	3.1749 579	3.9933 919	93
94	1.8674 746	2.0185 297	2.5480 570	3.2146 448	4.0532 927	94
95	1.8799 244	2.0336 687	2.5735 376	3.2548 279	4.1140 921	95
96	1.8924 572	2.0489 212	2.5992 729	3.2955 132	4.1758 035	96
97	1.9050 736	2.0642 881	2.6252 657	3.3367 072	4.2384 406	97
98	1.9177 741	2.0797 703	2.6515 183	3.3784 160	4.3020 172	98
99	1.9305 593	2.0953 686	2.6780 335	3.4206 462	4.3665 474	99
100	1.9434 296	2.1110 838	2.7048 138	3.4634 043	4.4320 456	100

Table V — Amount of 1

$$s = (1+i)^n$$

n	$1\frac{3}{4}$ per cent	2 per cent	$2\frac{1}{4}$ per cent	$2\frac{1}{2}$ per cent	3 per cent	n
1	1.0175 000	1.0200 000	1.0225 000	1.0250 000	1.0300 000	1
2	1.0353 062	1.0404 000	1.0455 062	1.0506 250	1.0609 000	2
3	1.0534 241	1.0612 080	1.0690 301	1.0768 906	1.0927 270	3
4	1.0718 590	1.0824 322	1.0930 833	1.1038 129	1.1255 088	4
5	1.0906 166	1.1040 808	1.1176 777	1.1314 082	1.1592 741	5
6	1.1097 024	1.1261 624	1.1428 254	1.1596 934	1.1940 523	6
7	1.1291 221	1.1486 857	1.1685 390	1.1886 857	1.2298 739	7
8	1.1488 818	1.1716 594	1.1948 311	1.2184 029	1.2667 701	8
9	1.1689 872	1.1950 926	1.2217 148	1.2488 630	1.3047 732	9
10	1.1894 445	1.2189 944	1.2492 034	1.2800 845	1.3439 164	10
11	1.2102 598	1.2433 743	1.2773 105	1.3120 867	1.3842 339	11
12	1.2314 393	1.2682 418	1.3060 500	1.3448 888	1.4257 608	12
13	1.2529 895	1.2936 066	1.3354 361	1.3785 110	1.4685 337	13
14	1.2749 168	1.3194 788	1.3654 834	1.4129 738	1.5125 897	14
15	1.2972 279	1.3458 683	1.3962 068	1.4482 982	1.5579 674	15
16	1.3199 294	1.3727 857	1.4276 215	1.4845 056	1.6047 064	16
17	1.3430 281	1.4002 414	1.4597 429	1.5216 183	1.6528 476	17
18	1.3665 311	1.4282 462	1.4925 872	1.5596 587	1.7024 331	18
19	1.3904 454	1.4568 112	1.5261 704	1.5986 502	1.7535 061	19
20	1.4147 782	1.4859 474	1.5605 092	1.6386 164	1.8061 112	20
21	1.4395 368	1.5156 663	1.5956 207	1.6795 819	1.8602 946	21
22	1.4647 287	1.5459 797	1.6315 221	1.7215 714	1.9161 034	22
23	1.4903 615	1.5768 993	1.6682 314	1.7646 107	1.9735 865	23
24	1.5164 428	1.6084 372	1.7057 666	1.8087 259	2.0327 941	24
25	1.5429 805	1.6406 060	1.7441 463	1.8539 441	2.0937 779	25
26	1.5699 827	1.6734 181	1.7833 896	1.9002 927	2.1565 913	26
27	1.5974 574	1.7068 865	1.8235 159	1.9478 000	2.2212 890	27
28	1.6254 129	1.7410 242	1.8645 450	1.9964 950	2.2879 277	28
29	1.6538 576	1.7758 447	1.9064 973	2.0464 074	2.3565 655	29
30	1.6828 001	1.8113 616	1.9493 934	2.0975 676	2.4272 625	30
31	1.7122 491	1.8475 888	1.9932 548	2.1500 068	2.5000 803	31
32	1.7422 135	1.8845 406	2.0381 030	2.2037 569	2.5750 828	32
33	1.7727 022	1.9222 314	2.0839 603	2.2588 509	2.6523 352	33
34	1.8037 245	1.9606 760	2.1308 494	2.3153 221	2.7319 053	34
35	1.8352 897	1.9998 896	2.1787 936	2.3732 052	2.8138 625	35
36	1.8674 073	2.0398 873	2.2278 164	2.4325 353	2.8982 783	36
37	1.9000 869	2.0806 851	2.2779 423	2.4933 487	2.9852 267	37
38	1.9333 384	2.1222 988	2.3291 960	2.5556 824	3.0747 835	38
39	1.9671 718	2.1647 448	2.3816 030	2.6195 745	3.1670 270	39
40	2.0015 973	2.2080 397	2.4351 890	2.6850 638	3.2620 378	40
41	2.0366 253	2.2522 005	2.4899 807	2.7521 904	3.3598 989	41
42	2.0722 662	2.2972 445	2.5460 053	2.8209 952	3.4606 959	42
43	2.1085 309	2.3431 894	2.6032 904	2.8915 201	3.5645 168	43
44	2.1454 302	2.3900 531	2.6618 644	2.9638 081	3.6714 523	44
45	2.1829 752	2.4378 542	2.7217 564	3.0379 033	3.7815 958	45
46	2.2211 773	2.4866 113	2.7829 959	3.1138 509	3.8950 437	46
47	2.2600 479	2.5363 435	2.8456 133	3.1916 971	4.0118 950	47
48	2.2995 987	2.5870 704	2.9096 396	3.2714 896	4.1322 519	48
49	2.3398 417	2.6388 118	2.9751 065	3.3532 768	4.2562 194	49
50	2.3807 889	2.6915 880	3.0420 464	3.4371 087	4.3839 060	50

Table V — Amount of 1

$$s = (1+i)^n$$

n	$1\frac{3}{4}$ per cent	2 per cent	$2\frac{1}{4}$ per cent	$2\frac{1}{2}$ per cent	3 per cent	n
51	2.4224 527	2.7454 198	3.1104 924	3.5230 364	4.5154 232	51
52	2.4648 457	2.8003 282	3.1804 785	3.6111 123	4.6508 859	52
53	2.5079 805	2.8563 347	3.2520 393	3.7013 902	4.7904 125	53
54	2.5518 701	2.9134 614	3.3252 102	3.7939 249	4.9341 248	54
55	2.5965 278	2.9717 307	3.4000 274	3.8887 730	5.0821 486	55
56	2.6419 671	3.0311 653	3.4765 280	3.9859 924	5.2346 130	56
57	2.6882 015	3.0917 886	3.5547 499	4.0856 422	5.3916 514	57
58	2.7352 450	3.1536 244	3.6347 318	4.1877 832	5.5534 010	58
59	2.7831 118	3.2166 969	3.7165 132	4.2924 778	5.7200 030	59
60	2.8318 163	3.2810 308	3.8001 348	4.3997 897	5.8916 031	60
61	2.8813 731	3.3466 514	3.8856 378	4.5097 845	6.0683 512	61
62	2.9317 971	3.4135 844	3.9731 647	4.6225 291	6.2504 017	62
63	2.9831 035	3.4818 561	4.0624 586	4.7380 923	6.4379 138	63
64	3.0353 079	3.5514 932	4.1538 639	4.8565 446	6.6310 512	64
65	3.0884 257	3.6225 231	4.2473 259	4.9779 583	6.8299 827	65
66	3.1424 732	3.6949 736	4.3428 907	5.1024 072	7.0348 822	66
67	3.1974 665	3.7688 730	4.4406 058	5.2299 674	7.2459 287	67
68	3.2534 221	3.8442 505	4.5405 194	5.3607 166	7.4633 065	68
69	3.3103 570	3.9211 355	4.6426 811	5.4947 345	7.6872 057	69
70	3.3682 883	3.9995 582	4.7471 414	5.6321 029	7.9178 219	70
71	3.4272 333	4.0795 494	4.8539 521	5.7729 054	8.1553 566	71
72	3.4872 099	4.1611 404	4.9631 660	5.9172 281	8.4000 173	72
73	3.5482 361	4.2443 632	5.0748 372	6.0651 588	8.6520 178	73
74	3.6103 302	4.3292 504	5.1890 211	6.2167 877	8.9115 783	74
75	3.6735 110	4.4158 355	5.3057 740	6.3722 074	9.1789 257	75
76	3.7377 974	4.5041 522	5.4251 540	6.5315 126	9.4542 934	76
77	3.8032 089	4.5942 352	5.5472 199	6.6948 004	9.7379 222	77
78	3.8697 650	4.6861 199	5.6720 324	6.8621 704	10.0300 599	78
79	3.9374 859	4.7798 423	5.7996 531	7.0337 247	10.3309 617	79
80	4.0063 919	4.8754 392	5.9301 453	7.2095 678	10.6408 906	80
81	4.0765 038	4.9729 479	6.0635 736	7.3898 070	10.9601 173	81
82	4.1478 426	5.0724 069	6.2000 040	7.5745 522	11.2889 208	82
83	4.2204 298	5.1738 550	6.3395 041	7.7639 160	11.6275 884	83
84	4.2942 874	5.2773 321	6.4821 429	7.9580 139	11.9764 161	84
85	4.3694 374	5.3828 788	6.6279 911	8.1569 642	12.3357 085	85
86	4.4459 026	5.4905 364	6.7771 209	8.3608 883	12.7057 798	86
87	4.5237 058	5.6003 471	6.9296 061	8.5699 106	13.0869 532	87
88	4.6028 707	5.7123 540	7.0855 223	8.7841 583	13.4795 618	88
89	4.6834 209	5.8266 011	7.2449 465	9.0037 623	13.8839 487	89
90	4.7653 808	5.9431 331	7.4079 578	9.2288 563	14.3004 671	90
91	4.8487 750	6.0619 958	7.5746 369	9.4595 777	14.7294 811	91
92	4.9336 285	6.1832 357	7.7450 662	9.6960 672	15.1713 656	92
93	5.0199 670	6.3069 004	7.9193 302	9.9384 689	15.6265 065	93
94	5.1078 164	6.4330 384	8.0975 151	10.1869 306	16.0953 017	94
95	5.1972 032	6.5616 992	8.2797 092	10.4416 038	16.5781 608	95
96	5.2881 543	6.6929 332	8.4660 027	10.7026 439	17.0755 056	96
97	5.3806 970	6.8267 918	8.6564 877	10.9702 100	17.5877 708	97
98	5.4748 592	6.9633 277	8.8512 587	11.2444 653	18.1154 039	98
99	5.5706 692	7.1025 942	9.0504 120	11.5255 769	18.6588 660	99
100	5.6681 559	7.2446 461	9.2540 463	11.8137 164	19.2186 320	100

[489]

Table V — Amount of 1

$$s = (1+i)^n$$

n	$3\frac{1}{2}$ per cent	4 per cent	$4\frac{1}{2}$ per cent	5 per cent	$5\frac{1}{2}$ per cent	n
1	1.0350 000	1.0400 000	1.0450 000	1.0500 000	1.0550 000	1
2	1.0712 250	1.0816 000	1.0920 250	1.1025 000	1.1130 250	2
3	1.1087 179	1.1248 640	1.1411 661	1.1576 250	1.1742 414	3
4	1.1475 230	1.1698 586	1.1925 186	1.2155 062	1.2388 247	4
5	1.1876 863	1.2166 529	1.2461 819	1.2762 816	1.3069 600	5
6	1.2292 553	1.2653 190	1.3022 601	1.3400 956	1.3788 428	6
7	1.2722 793	1.3159 318	1.3608 618	1.4071 004	1.4546 792	7
8	1.3168 090	1.3685 691	1.4221 006	1.4774 554	1.5346 865	8
9	1.3628 974	1.4233 118	1.4860 951	1.5513 282	1.6190 943	9
10	1.4105 988	1.4802 443	1.5529 694	1.6288 946	1.7081 445	10
11	1.4599 697	1.5394 541	1.6228 530	1.7103 394	1.8020 924	11
12	1.5110 687	1.6010 322	1.6958 814	1.7958 563	1.9012 075	12
13	1.5639 561	1.6650 735	1.7721 961	1.8856 491	2.0057 739	13
14	1.6186 945	1.7316 764	1.8519 449	1.9799 316	2.1160 915	14
15	1.6753 488	1.8009 435	1.9352 824	2.0789 282	2.2324 765	15
16	1.7339 860	1.8729 812	2.0223 702	2.1828 746	2.3552 627	16
17	1.7946 756	1.9479 005	2.1133 768	2.2920 183	2.4848 021	17
18	1.8574 892	2.0258 165	2.2084 788	2.4066 192	2.6214 663	18
19	1.9225 013	2.1068 492	2.3078 603	2.5269 502	2.7656 469	19
20	1.9897 889	2.1911 231	2.4117 140	2.6532 977	2.9177 575	20
21	2.0594 315	2.2787 681	2 5202 412	2.7859 626	3.0782 342	21
22	2.1315 116	2.3699 188	2 6336 520	2.9252 607	3.2475 370	22
23	2.2061 145	2.4647 155	2.7521 663	3.0715 238	3.4261 516	23
24	2.2833 285	2.5633 042	2.8760 138	3.2250 999	3.6145 899	24
25	2.3632 450	2.6658 363	3.0054 345	3.3863 549	3.8133 923	25
26	2.4459 586	2.7724 698	3.1406 790	3.5556 727	4.0231 289	26
27	2.5315 671	2.8833 686	3.2820 096	3.7334 563	4.2444 010	27
28	2.6201 720	2.9987 033	3.4297 000	3.9201 291	4.4778 431	28
29	2.7118 780	3.1186 515	3.5840 365	4.1161 356	4.7241 244	29
30	2.8067 937	3.2433 975	3.7453 181	4.3219 424	4.9839 513	30
31	2.9050 315	3.3731 334	3.9138 575	4.5380 395	5.2580 686	31
32	3.0067 076	3.5080 587	4.0899 810	4.7649 415	5.5472 624	32
33	3.1119 424	3.6483 811	4.2740 302	5.0031 885	5.8523 618	33
34	3.2208 603	3.7943 163	4.4663 615	5.2533 480	6.1742 417	34
35	3.3335 904	3.9460 890	4.6673 478	5.5160 154	6.5138 250	35
36	3.4502 661	4.1039 326	4.8773 785	5.7918 161	6.8720 854	36
37	3.5710 254	4.2680 899	5.0968 605	6.0814 069	7.2500 501	37
38	3.6960 113	4.4388 135	5.3262 192	6.3854 773	7.6488 028	38
39	3.8253 717	4.6163 660	5.5658 991	6.7047 512	8.0694 870	39
40	3.9592 597	4.8010 206	5.8163 645	7.0399 887	8.5133 088	40
41	4.0978 338	4.9930 615	6.0781 009	7.3919 881	8.9815 408	41
42	4.2412 580	5.1927 839	6.3516 155	7.7615 876	9.4755 255	42
43	4.3897 020	5.4004 953	6.6374 382	8.1496 669	9.9966 794	43
44	4.5433 416	5.6165 151	6.9361 229	8.5571 503	10.5464 968	44
45	4.7023 586	5.8411 757	7.2482 484	8.9850 078	11.1265 541	45
46	4.8669 411	6.0748 227	7.5744 196	9.4342 582	11.7385 146	46
47	5.0372 840	6.3178 156	7.9152 685	9.9059 711	12.3841 329	47
48	5.2135 890	6.5705 282	8.2714 556	10.4012 696	13.0652 602	48
49	5.3960 646	6.8333 494	8.6436 711	10.9213 331	13.7838 495	49
50	5.5849 269	7.1066 833	9.0326 363	11.4673 998	14.5419 612	50

[490]

Table V — Amount of 1

$$s = (1+i)^n$$

n	3½ per cent	4 per cent	4½ per cent	5 per cent	5½ per cent	n
51	5.7803 993	7.3909 507	9.4391 049	12.0407 698	15.3417 691	51
52	5.9827 133	7.6865 887	9.8638 646	12.6428 083	16.1855 664	52
53	6.1921 082	7.9940 523	10.3077 385	13.2749 487	17.0757 725	53
54	6.4088 320	8.3138 143	10.7715 868	13.9386 961	18.0149 400	54
55	6.6331 411	8.6463 669	11.2563 082	14.6356 309	19.0057 617	55
56	6.8653 011	8.9922 216	11.7628 420	15.3674 125	20.0510 786	56
57	7.1055 866	9.3519 105	12.2921 699	16.1357 831	21.1538 879	57
58	7.3542 822	9.7259 869	12.8453 176	16.9425 722	22.3173 518	58
59	7.6116 820	10.1150 264	13.4233 569	17.7897 009	23.5448 061	59
60	7.8780 909	10.5196 274	14.0274 079	18.6791 859	24.8397 704	60
61	8.1538 241	10.9404 125	14.6586 413	19.6131 452	26.2059 578	61
62	8.4392 079	11.3780 290	15.3182 801	20.5938 024	27.6472 855	62
63	8.7345 802	11.8331 502	16.0076 027	21.6234 926	29.1678 862	63
64	9.0402 905	12.3064 762	16.7279 449	22.7046 672	30.7721 199	64
65	9.3567 007	12.7987 352	17.4807 024	23.8399 006	32.4645 865	65
66	9.6841 852	13.3106 846	18.2673 340	25.0318 956	34.2501 388	66
67	10.0231 317	13.8431 120	19.0893 640	26.2834 904	36.1338 964	67
68	10.3739 413	14.3968 365	19.9483 854	27.5976 649	38.1212 607	68
69	10.7370 292	14.9727 100	20.8460 628	28.9775 481	40.2179 301	69
70	11.1128 253	15.5716 184	21.7841 356	30.4264 255	42.4299 162	70
71	11.5017 741	16.1944 831	22.7644 217	31.9477 468	44.7635 616	71
72	11.9043 362	16.8422 624	23.7888 207	33.5451 342	47.2255 575	72
73	12.3209 880	17.5159 529	24.8593 176	35.2223 909	49.8229 632	73
74	12.7522 226	18.2165 910	25.9779 869	36.9835 104	52.5632 262	74
75	13.1985 504	18.9452 547	27.1469 963	38.8326 859	55.4542 036	75
76	13.6604 996	19.7030 648	28.3686 111	40.7743 202	58.5041 848	76
77	14.1386 171	20.4911 874	29.6451 986	42.8130 362	61.7219 150	77
78	14.6334 687	21.3108 349	30.9792 326	44.9536 880	65.1166 203	78
79	15.1456 401	22.1632 683	32.3732 980	47.2013 724	68.6980 344	79
80	15.6757 375	23.0497 991	33.8300 964	49.5614 411	72.4764 263	80
81	16.2243 884	23.9717 910	35.3524 508	52.0395 131	76.4626 297	81
82	16.7922 419	24.9306 627	36.9433 111	54.6414 888	80.6680 744	82
83	17.3799 704	25.9278 892	38.6057 601	57.3735 632	85.1048 185	83
84	17.9882 694	26.9650 047	40.3430 193	60.2422 414	89.7855 835	84
85	18.6178 588	28.0436 049	42.1584 551	63.2543 534	94.7237 906	85
86	19.2694 839	29.1653 491	44.0555 856	66.4170 711	99.9335 990	86
87	19.9439 158	30.3319 631	46.0380 870	69.7379 247	105.4299 470	87
88	20.6419 529	31.5452 416	48.1098 009	73.2248 209	111.2285 941	88
89	21.3644 212	32.8070 512	50.2747 419	76.8860 620	117.3461 667	89
90	22.1121 760	34.1193 333	52.5371 053	80.7303 650	123.8002 059	90
91	22.8861 021	35.4841 067	54.9012 750	84.7668 833	130.6092 172	91
92	23.6871 157	36.9034 709	57.3718 324	89.0052 275	137.7927 242	92
93	24.5161 647	38.3796 098	59.9535 649	93.4554 888	145.3713 240	93
94	25.3742 305	39.9147 942	62.6514 753	98.1282 633	153.3667 468	94
95	26.2623 286	41.5113 859	65.4707 917	103.0346 764	161.8019 179	95
96	27.1815 101	43.1718 414	68.4169 773	108.1864 103	170.7010 234	96
97	28.1328 629	44.8987 150	71.4957 413	113.5957 308	180.0895 796	97
98	29.1175 131	46.6946 636	74.7130 496	119.2755 173	189.9945 066	98
99	30.1366 261	48.5624 502	78.0751 369	125.2392 932	200.4442 044	99
100	31.1914 080	50.5049 482	81.5885 180	131.5012 578	211.4686 357	100

[491]

Table V — Amount of 1

$$s = (1+i)^n$$

n	6 per cent	6½ per cent	7 per cent	7½ per cent	8 per cent	n
1	1.0600 000	1.0650 000	1.0700 000	1.0750 000	1.0800 000	1
2	1.1236 000	1.1342 250	1.1449 000	1.1556 250	1.1664 000	2
3	1.1910 160	1.2079 496	1.2250 430	1.2422 969	1.2597 120	3
4	1.2624 770	1.2864 664	1.3107 960	1.3354 691	1.3604 890	4
5	1.3382 256	1.3700 867	1.4025 517	1.4356 293	1.4693 281	5
6	1.4185 191	1.4591 423	1.5007 304	1.5433 015	1.5868 743	6
7	1.5036 303	1.5539 865	1.6057 815	1.6590 491	1.7138 243	7
8	1.5938 481	1.6549 957	1.7181 862	1.7834 778	1.8509 302	8
9	1.6894 790	1.7625 704	1.8384 592	1.9172 387	1.9990 046	9
10	1.7908 477	1.8771 375	1.9671 514	2.0610 316	2.1589 250	10
11	1.8982 986	1.9991 514	2.1048 520	2.2156 089	2.3316 390	11
12	2.0121 965	2.1290 962	2.2521 916	2.3817 796	2.5181 701	12
13	2.1329 283	2.2674 875	2.4098 450	2.5604 131	2.7196 237	13
14	2.2609 040	2.4148 742	2.5785 342	2.7524 440	2.9371 936	14
15	2.3965 582	2.5718 410	2.7590 315	2.9588 774	3.1721 691	15
16	2.5403 517	2.7390 107	2.9521 637	3.1807 932	3.4259 426	16
17	2.6927 728	2.9170 464	3.1588 152	3.4193 526	3.7000 181	17
18	2.8543 392	3.1066 544	3.3799 323	3.6758 041	3.9960 195	18
19	3.0255 995	3.3085 869	3.6165 275	3.9514 894	4.3157 011	19
20	3.2071 355	3.5236 451	3.8696 845	4.2478 511	4.6609 571	20
21	3.3995 636	3.7526 820	4.1405 624	4.5664 399	5.0338 337	21
22	3.6035 374	3.9966 063	4.4304 017	4.9089 229	5.4365 404	22
23	3.8197 497	4.2563 857	4.7405 299	5.2770 921	5.8714 636	23
24	4.0489 346	4.5330 508	5.0723 670	5.6728 741	6.3411 807	24
25	4.2918 707	4.8276 991	5.4274 326	6.0983 396	6.8484 752	25
26	4.5493 830	5.1414 996	5.8073 529	6.5557 151	7.3963 532	26
27	4.8223 459	5.4756 970	6.2138 676	7.0473 937	7.9880 615	27
28	5.1116 867	5.8316 173	6.6488 384	7.5759 482	8.6271 064	28
29	5.4183 879	6.2106 725	7.1142 570	8.1441 444	9.3172 749	29
30	5.7434 912	6.6143 662	7.6122 550	8.7549 552	10.0626 569	30
31	6.0881 006	7.0443 000	8.1451 129	9.4115 768	10.8676 694	31
32	6.4533 867	7.5021 795	8.7152 708	10.1174 451	11.7370 830	32
33	6.8405 899	7.9898 211	9.3253 398	10.8762 535	12.6760 496	33
34	7.2510 253	8.5091 595	9.9781 135	11.6919 725	13.6901 336	34
35	7.6860 868	9.0622 549	10.6765 815	12.5688 704	14.7853 443	35
36	8.1472 520	9.6513 014	11.4239 422	13.5115 357	15.9681 718	36
37	8.6360 871	10.2786 360	12.2236 181	14.5249 009	17.2456 256	37
38	9.1542 523	10.9467 474	13.0792 714	15.6142 684	18.6252 756	38
39	9.7035 075	11.6582 860	13.9948 204	16.7853 386	20.1152 977	39
40	10.2857 179	12.4160 745	14.9744 578	18.0442 390	21.7245 215	40
41	10.9028 610	13.2231 194	16.0226 699	19.3975 569	23.4624 832	41
42	11.5570 327	14.0826 221	17.1442 568	20.8523 737	25.3394 819	42
43	12.2504 546	14.9979 926	18.3443 548	22.4163 017	27.3666 404	43
44	12.9854 819	15.9728 621	19.6284 596	24.0975 243	29.5559 717	44
45	13.7646 108	17.0110 981	21.0024 518	25.9048 386	31.9204 494	45
46	14.5904 875	18.1168 195	22.4726 234	27.8477 015	34.4740 853	46
47	15.4659 167	19.2944 128	24.0457 070	29.9362 791	37.2320 122	47
48	16.3938 717	20.5485 496	25.7289 065	32.1815 001	40.2105 731	48
49	17.3775 040	21.8842 053	27.5299 300	34.5951 126	43.4274 190	49
50	18.4201 543	23.3066 787	29.4570 251	37.1897 460	46.9016 125	50

Table V — Amount of 1

$$s = (1+i)^n$$

n	6 per cent	6½ per cent	7 per cent	7½ per cent	8 per cent	n
51	19.5253 635	24.8216 128	31.5190 168	39.9789 770	50.6537 415	51
52	20.6968 853	26.4350 176	33.7253 480	42.9774 003	54.7060 408	52
53	21.9386 985	28.1532 938	36.0861 224	46.2007 053	59.0825 241	53
54	23.2550 204	29.9832 579	38.6121 509	49.6657 582	63.8091 260	54
55	24.6503 216	31.9321 696	41.3150 015	53.3906 900	68.9138 561	55
56	26.1293 409	34.0077 607	44.2070 516	57.3949 918	74.4269 646	56
57	27.6971 013	36.2182 651	47.3015 452	61.6996 162	80.3811 218	57
58	29.3589 274	38.5724 523	50.6126 534	66.3270 874	86.8116 115	58
59	31.1204 631	41.0796 617	54.1555 391	71.3016 189	93.7565 404	59
60	32.9876 909	43.7498 397	57.9464 268	76.6492 404	101.2570 637	60
61	34.9669 523	46.5935 793	62.0026 767	82.3979 334	109.3576 288	61
62	37.0649 694	49.6221 620	66.3428 641	88.5777 784	118.1062 391	62
63	39.2888 676	52.8476 025	70.9868 646	95.2211 118	127.5547 382	63
64	41.6461 997	56.2826 967	75.9559 451	102.3626 952	137.7591 172	64
65	44.1149 716	59.9410 720	81.2728 612	110.0398 973	148.7798 466	65
66	46.7936 699	63.8372 416	86.9619 615	118.2928 896	160.6822 344	66
67	49.6012 901	67.9866 623	93.0492 988	127.1648 563	173.5368 131	67
68	52.5773 675	72.4057 954	99.5627 498	136.7022 205	187.4197 581	68
69	55.7320 096	77.1121 721	106.5321 422	146.9548 871	202.4133 388	69
70	59.0759 302	82.1244 633	113.9893 922	157.9765 036	218.6064 059	70
71	62.6204 860	87.4625 534	121.9686 497	169.8247 414	236.0949 184	71
72	66.3777 151	93.1476 194	130.5064 551	182.5615 970	254.9825 118	72
73	70.3603 781	99.2022 146	139.6419 070	196.2537 167	275.3811 128	73
74	74.5820 007	105.6503 586	149.4168 405	210.9727 455	297.4116 018	74
75	79.0569 208	112.5176 319	159.8760 193	226.7957 014	321.2045 300	75
76	83.8003 360	119.8312 779	171.0673 407	243.8053 790	346.9008 924	76
77	88.8283 562	127.6203 110	183.0420 545	262.0907 824	374.6529 637	77
78	94.1580 576	135.9156 312	195.8549 983	281.7475 911	404.6252 008	78
79	99.8075 410	144.7501 473	209.5648 482	302.8786 605	436.9952 169	79
80	105.7959 935	154.1589 068	224.2343 876	325.5945 600	471.9548 343	80
81	112.1437 531	164.1792 358	239.9307 947	350.0141 520	509.7112 210	81
82	118.8723 783	174.8508 861	256.7259 503	376.2652 134	550.4881 187	82
83	126.0047 210	186.2161 937	274.6967 669	404.4851 044	594.5271 682	83
84	133.5650 042	198.3202 463	293.9255 405	434.8214 872	642.0893 416	84
85	141.5789 045	211.2110 623	314.5003 284	467.4330 988	693.4564 890	85
86	150.0736 388	224.9397 813	336.5153 514	502.4905 812	748.9330 081	86
87	159.0780 571	239.5608 671	360.0714 260	540.1773 748	808.8476 487	87
88	168.6227 405	255.1323 235	385.2764 258	580.6906 779	873.5554 606	88
89	178.7401 049	271.7159 245	412.2457 756	624.2424 787	943.4398 975	89
90	189.4645 112	289.3774 596	441.1029 799	671.0606 646	1018.9150 893	90
91	200.8323 819	308.1869 945	471.9801 885	721.3902 145	1100.4282 964	91
92	212.8823 248	328.2191 491	505.0188 017	775.4944 806	1188.4625 601	92
93	225.6552 643	349.5533 938	540.3701 178	833.6565 666	1283.5395 649	93
94	239.1945 802	372.2743 644	578.1960 260	896.1808 091	1386.2227 301	94
95	253.5462 550	396.4721 981	618.6697 478	963.3943 698	1497.1205 486	95
96	268.7590 303	422.2428 910	661.9766 302	1035.6489 475	1616.8901 924	96
97	284.8845 721	449.6886 789	708.3149 943	1113.3226 186	1746.2414 078	97
98	301.9776 464	478.9184 430	757.8970 439	1196.8218 150	1885.9407 205	98
99	320.0963 052	510.0481 418	810.9498 370	1286.5834 511	2036.8159 781	99
100	339.3020 835	543.2012 710	867.7163 256	1383.0772 099	2199.7612 563	100

[493]

Table VI — Present Value of 1

$$v^n = (1+i)^{-n}$$

n	$\frac{1}{4}$ per cent	$\frac{1}{3}$ per cent	$\frac{5}{12}$ per cent	$\frac{1}{2}$ per cent	$\frac{7}{12}$ per cent	n
1	0.9975 062	0.9966 777	0.9958 506	0.9950 249	0.9942 005	1
2	0.9950 187	0.9933 665	0.9917 185	0.9900 745	0.9884 346	2
3	0.9925 373	0.9900 663	0.9876 034	0.9851 488	0.9827 022	3
4	0.9900 622	0.9867 770	0.9835 055	0.9802 475	0.9770 030	4
5	0.9875 932	0.9834 987	0.9794 246	0.9753 707	0.9713 369	5
6	0.9851 304	0.9802 313	0.9753 606	0.9705 181	0.9657 036	6
7	0.9826 737	0.9769 747	0.9713 134	0.9656 896	0.9601 030	7
8	0.9802 231	0.9737 289	0.9672 831	0.9608 852	0.9545 349	8
9	0.9777 787	0.9704 939	0.9632 695	0.9561 047	0.9489 991	9
10	0.9753 403	0.9672 697	0.9592 725	0.9513 479	0.9434 953	10
11	0.9729 081	0.9640 562	0.9552 921	0.9466 149	0.9380 235	11
12	0.9704 819	0.9608 534	0.9513 282	0.9419 053	0.9325 835	12
13	0.9680 617	0.9576 611	0.9473 808	0.9372 192	0.9271 749	13
14	0.9656 476	0.9544 795	0.9434 498	0.9325 565	0.9217 978	14
15	0.9632 395	0.9513 085	0.9395 351	0.9279 169	0.9164 518	15
16	0.9608 374	0.9481 480	0.9356 366	0.9233 004	0.9111 369	16
17	0.9584 413	0.9449 980	0.9317 543	0.9187 068	0.9058 527	17
18	0.9560 512	0.9418 585	0.9278 881	0.9141 362	0.9005 992	18
19	0.9536 670	0.9387 294	0.9240 379	0.9095 882	0.8953 762	19
20	0.9512 888	0.9356 107	0.9202 037	0.9050 629	0.8901 835	20
21	0.9489 165	0.9325 024	0.9163 854	0.9005 601	0.8850 208	21
22	0.9465 501	0.9294 043	0.9125 830	0.8960 797	0.8798 882	22
23	0.9441 896	0.9263 166	0.9087 964	0.8916 216	0.8747 852	23
24	0.9418 351	0.9232 392	0.9050 254	0.8871 857	0.8697 119	24
25	0.9394 863	0.9201 719	0.9012 701	0.8827 718	0.8646 680	25
26	0.9371 435	0.9171 149	0.8975 304	0.8783 799	0.8596 534	26
27	0.9348 065	0.9140 680	0.8938 062	0.8740 099	0.8546 678	27
28	0.9324 753	0.9110 312	0.8900 975	0.8696 616	0.8497 111	28
29	0.9301 499	0.9080 045	0.8864 041	0.8653 349	0.8447 833	29
30	0.9278 303	0.9049 879	0.8827 261	0.8610 297	0.8398 839	30
31	0.9255 165	0.9019 813	0.8790 633	0.8567 460	0.8350 130	31
32	0.9232 085	0.8989 847	0.8754 158	0.8524 836	0.8301 704	32
33	0.9209 062	0.8959 980	0.8717 833	0.8482 424	0.8253 558	33
34	0.9186 097	0.8930 213	0.8681 660	0.8440 223	0.8205 691	34
35	0.9163 189	0.8900 544	0.8645 636	0.8398 231	0.8158 103	35
36	0.9140 338	0.8870 974	0.8609 762	0.8356 449	0.8110 790	36
37	0.9117 545	0.8841 503	0.8574 037	0.8314 875	0.8063 751	37
38	0.9094 807	0.8812 129	0.8538 460	0.8273 507	0.8016 985	38
39	0.9072 127	0.8782 853	0.8503 031	0.8232 346	0.7970 491	39
40	0.9049 503	0.8753 674	0.8467 749	0.8191 389	0.7924 266	40
41	0.9026 936	0.8724 592	0.8432 613	0.8150 635	0.7878 309	41
42	0.9004 425	0.8695 607	0.8397 623	0.8110 085	0.7832 619	42
43	0.8981 970	0.8666 718	0.8362 778	0.8069 736	0.7787 194	43
44	0.8959 571	0.8637 924	0.8328 078	0.8029 588	0.7742 032	44
45	0.8937 228	0.8609 227	0.8293 521	0.7989 640	0.7697 132	45
46	0.8914 941	0.8580 625	0.8259 108	0.7949 891	0.7652 492	46
47	0.8892 709	0.8552 118	0.8224 838	0.7910 339	0.7608 112	47
48	0.8870 533	0.8523 706	0.8190 710	0.7870 984	0.7563 988	48
49	0.8848 412	0.8495 388	0.8156 724	0.7831 825	0.7520 121	49
50	0.8826 346	0.8467 164	0.8122 878	0.7792 861	0.7476 508	50

Table VI — Present Value of 1

$$v^n = (1+i)^{-n}$$

n	$\frac{1}{4}$ per cent	$\frac{1}{3}$ per cent	$\frac{5}{12}$ per cent	$\frac{1}{2}$ per cent	$\frac{7}{12}$ per cent	n
51	0.8804 335	0.8439 034	0.8089 173	0.7754 090	0.7433 148	51
52	0.8782 379	0.8410 997	0.8055 608	0.7715 513	0.7390 039	52
53	0.8760 478	0.8383 053	0.8022 183	0.7677 127	0.7347 181	53
54	0.8738 631	0.8355 203	0.7988 896	0.7638 932	0.7304 571	54
55	0.8716 839	0.8327 445	0.7955 747	0.7600 928	0.7262 208	55
56	0.8695 101	0.8299 779	0.7922 735	0.7563 112	0.7220 091	56
57	0.8673 418	0.8272 205	0.7889 861	0.7525 485	0.7178 218	57
58	0.8651 788	0.8244 722	0.7857 123	0.7488 045	0.7136 588	58
59	0.8630 213	0.8217 331	0.7824 521	0.7450 791	0.7095 199	59
60	0.8608 691	0.8190 031	0.7792 054	0.7413 722	0.7054 050	60
61	0.8587 223	0.8162 822	0.7759 722	0.7376 838	0.7013 140	61
62	0.8565 808	0.8135 703	0.7727 524	0.7340 137	0.6972 468	62
63	0.8544 447	0.8108 674	0.7695 459	0.7303 619	0.6932 031	63
64	0.8523 140	0.8081 735	0.7663 528	0.7267 283	0.6891 829	64
65	0.8501 885	0.8054 885	0.7631 729	0.7231 127	0.6851 859	65
66	0.8480 683	0.8028 125	0.7600 062	0.7195 151	0.6812 122	66
67	0.8459 534	0.8001 453	0.7568 527	0.7159 354	0.6772 615	67
68	0.8438 438	0.7974 870	0.7537 122	0.7123 736	0.6733 337	68
69	0.8417 395	0.7948 376	0.7505 847	0.7088 294	0.6694 287	69
70	0.8396 404	0.7921 969	0.7474 703	0.7053 029	0.6655 464	70
71	0.8375 465	0.7895 650	0.7443 687	0.7017 939	0.6616 865	71
72	0.8354 579	0.7869 419	0.7412 801	0.6983 024	0.6578 491	72
73	0.8333 744	0.7843 275	0.7382 042	0.6948 283	0.6540 339	73
74	0.8312 962	0.7817 217	0.7351 411	0.6913 714	0.6502 408	74
75	0.8292 231	0.7791 246	0.7320 908	0.6879 318	0.6464 697	75
76	0.8271 552	0.7765 362	0.7290 530	0.6845 092	0.6427 205	76
77	0.8250 925	0.7739 563	0.7260 279	0.6811 037	0.6389 931	77
78	0.8230 349	0.7713 850	0.7230 154	0.6777 151	0.6352 872	78
79	0.8209 825	0.7688 223	0.7200 153	0.6743 434	0.6316 029	79
80	0.8189 351	0.7662 681	0.7170 277	0.6709 885	0.6279 399	80
81	0.8168 929	0.7637 223	0.7140 525	0.6676 502	0.6242 982	81
82	0.8148 557	0.7611 850	0.7110 896	0.6643 286	0.6206 775	82
83	0.8128 237	0.7586 562	0.7081 390	0.6610 235	0.6170 779	83
84	0.8107 967	0.7561 357	0.7052 007	0.6577 348	0.6134 992	84
85	0.8087 748	0.7536 237	0.7022 745	0.6544 625	0.6099 412	85
86	0.8067 579	0.7511 199	0.6993 605	0.6512 064	0.6064 038	86
87	0.8047 460	0.7486 245	0.6964 586	0.6479 666	0.6028 870	87
88	0.8027 392	0.7461 374	0.6935 687	0.6447 429	0.5993 906	88
89	0.8007 373	0.7436 585	0.6906 909	0.6415 352	0.5959 144	89
90	0.7987 405	0.7411 879	0.6878 249	0.6383 435	0.5924 584	90
91	0.7967 486	0.7387 255	0.6849 709	0.6351 677	0.5890 224	91
92	0.7947 617	0.7362 712	0.6821 287	0.6320 076	0.5856 064	92
93	0.7927 798	0.7338 252	0.6792 983	0.6288 633	0.5822 101	93
94	0.7908 028	0.7313 872	0.6764 796	0.6257 346	0.5788 336	94
95	0.7888 307	0.7289 573	0.6736 726	0.6226 215	0.5754 767	95
96	0.7868 635	0.7265 356	0.6708 773	0.6195 239	0.5721 392	96
97	0.7849 012	0.7241 218	0.6680 936	0.6164 417	0.5688 211	97
98	0.7829 439	0.7217 161	0.6653 214	0.6133 748	0.5655 222	98
99	0.7809 914	0.7193 184	0.6625 607	0.6103 232	0.5622 424	99
100	0.7790 438	0.7169 286	0.6598 115	0.6072 868	0.5589 817	100

Table VI — Present Value of 1

$$v^n = (1+i)^{-n}$$

n	$\frac{2}{3}$ per cent	$\frac{3}{4}$ per cent	1 per cent	$1\frac{1}{4}$ per cent	$1\frac{1}{2}$ per cent	n
1	0.9933 775	0.9925 558	0.9900 990	0.9876 543	0.9852 217	1
2	0.9867 988	0.9851 671	0.9802 960	0.9754 611	0.9706 617	2
3	0.9802 637	0.9778 333	0.9705 901	0.9634 183	0.9563 170	3
4	0.9737 719	0.9705 542	0.9609 803	0.9515 243	0.9421 842	4
5	0.9673 231	0.9633 292	0.9514 657	0.9397 771	0.9282 603	5
6	0.9609 170	0.9561 580	0.9420 452	0.9281 749	0.9145 422	6
7	0.9545 533	0.9490 402	0.9327 181	0.9167 159	0.9010 268	7
8	0.9482 318	0.9419 754	0.9234 832	0.9053 984	0.8877 111	8
9	0.9419 521	0.9349 632	0.9143 398	0.8942 207	0.8745 922	9
10	0.9357 140	0.9280 032	0.9052 870	0.8831 809	0.8616 672	10
11	0.9295 172	0.9210 949	0.8963 237	0.8722 775	0.8489 332	11
12	0.9233 615	0.9142 382	0.8874 492	0.8615 086	0.8363 874	12
13	0.9172 465	0.9074 324	0.8786 626	0.8508 727	0.8240 270	13
14	0.9111 720	0.9006 773	0.8699 630	0.8403 681	0.8118 493	14
15	0.9051 377	0.8939 725	0.8613 495	0.8299 932	0.7998 515	15
16	0.8991 435	0.8873 177	0.8528 213	0.8197 463	0.7880 310	16
17	0.8931 889	0.8807 123	0.8443 775	0.8096 260	0.7763 853	17
18	0.8872 737	0.8741 561	0.8360 173	0.7996 306	0.7649 116	18
19	0.8813 977	0.8676 488	0.8277 399	0.7897 587	0.7536 075	19
20	0.8755 607	0.8611 899	0.8195 445	0.7800 085	0.7424 704	20
21	0.8697 622	0.8547 790	0.8114 302	0.7703 788	0.7314 979	21
22	0.8640 022	0.8484 159	0.8033 962	0.7608 680	0.7206 876	22
23	0.8582 804	0.8421 001	0.7954 418	0.7514 745	0.7100 371	23
24	0.8525 964	0.8358 314	0.7875 661	0.7421 971	0.6995 439	24
25	0.8469 500	0.8296 093	0.7797 684	0.7330 341	0.6892 058	25
26	0.8413 411	0.8234 336	0.7720 480	0.7239 843	0.6790 205	26
27	0.8357 693	0.8173 038	0.7644 040	0.7150 463	0.6689 857	27
28	0.8302 344	0.8112 197	0.7568 356	0.7062 185	0.6590 992	28
29	0.8247 362	0.8051 808	0.7493 421	0.6974 998	0.6493 589	29
30	0.8192 743	0.7991 869	0.7419 229	0.6888 887	0.6397 624	30
31	0.8138 487	0.7932 376	0.7345 771	0.6803 839	0.6303 078	31
32	0.8084 590	0.7873 326	0.7273 041	0.6719 841	0.6209 929	32
33	0.8031 049	0.7814 716	0.7201 031	0.6636 880	0.6118 157	33
34	0.7977 863	0.7756 542	0.7129 733	0.6554 943	0.6027 741	34
35	0.7925 030	0.7698 801	0.7059 142	0.6474 018	0.5938 661	35
36	0.7872 546	0.7641 490	0.6989 249	0.6394 092	0.5850 897	36
37	0.7820 410	0.7584 605	0.6920 049	0.6315 152	0.5764 431	37
38	0.7768 619	0.7528 144	0.6851 534	0.6237 187	0.5679 242	38
39	0.7717 172	0.7472 103	0.6783 697	0.6160 185	0.5595 313	39
40	0.7666 065	0.7416 480	0.6716 531	0.6084 133	0.5512 623	40
41	0.7615 296	0.7361 270	0.6650 031	0.6009 021	0.5431 156	41
42	0.7564 863	0.7306 472	0.6584 189	0.5934 835	0.5350 892	42
43	0.7514 765	0.7252 081	0.6518 999	0.5861 566	0.5271 815	43
44	0.7464 998	0.7198 095	0.6454 455	0.5789 201	0.5193 907	44
45	0.7415 561	0.7144 511	0.6390 549	0.5717 729	0.5117 149	45
46	0.7366 452	0.7091 326	0.6327 276	0.5647 140	0.5041 527	46
47	0.7317 667	0.7038 537	0.6264 630	0.5577 422	0.4967 021	47
48	0.7269 206	0.6986 141	0.6202 604	0.5508 565	0.4893 617	48
49	0.7221 065	0.6934 135	0.6141 192	0.5440 558	0.4821 297	49
50	0.7173 244	0.6882 516	0.6080 388	0.5373 391	0.4750 047	50

Table VI — Present Value of 1

$$v^n = (1+i)^{-n}$$

n	$\frac{2}{3}$ per cent	$\frac{3}{4}$ per cent	1 per cent	$1\frac{1}{4}$ per cent	$1\frac{1}{2}$ per cent	n
51	0.7125 739	0.6831 282	0.6020 186	0.5307 052	0.4679 849	51
52	0.7078 548	0.6780 429	0.5960 581	0.5241 533	0.4610 689	52
53	0.7031 671	0.6729 954	0.5901 565	0.5176 823	0.4542 550	53
54	0.6985 103	0.6679 855	0.5843 134	0.5112 912	0.4475 419	54
55	0.6938 844	0.6630 129	0.5785 281	0.5049 789	0.4409 280	55
56	0.6892 892	0.6580 773	0.5728 001	0.4987 446	0.4344 118	56
57	0.6847 243	0.6531 785	0.5671 288	0.4925 873	0.4279 919	57
58	0.6801 897	0.6483 161	0.5615 137	0.4865 059	0.4216 669	58
59	0.6756 852	0.6434 899	0.5559 541	0.4804 997	0.4154 354	59
60	0.6712 104	0.6386 997	0.5504 496	0.4745 676	0.4092 960	60
61	0.6667 653	0.6339 451	0.5449 996	0.4687 087	0.4032 473	61
62	0.6623 497	0.6292 259	0.5396 035	0.4629 222	0.3972 879	62
63	0.6579 633	0.6245 419	0.5342 610	0.4572 071	0.3914 167	63
64	0.6536 059	0.6198 927	0.5289 713	0.4515 626	0.3856 322	64
65	0.6492 774	0.6152 781	0.5237 339	0.4459 877	0.3799 332	65
66	0.6449 775	0.6106 978	0.5185 484	0.4404 817	0.3743 184	66
67	0.6407 061	0.6061 517	0.5134 143	0.4350 437	0.3687 866	67
68	0.6364 631	0.6016 394	0.5083 310	0.4296 728	0.3633 366	68
69	0.6322 481	0.5971 607	0.5032 980	0.4243 682	0.3579 671	69
70	0.6280 610	0.5927 153	0.4983 149	0.4191 291	0.3526 769	70
71	0.6239 017	0.5883 031	0.4933 810	0.4139 546	0.3474 649	71
72	0.6197 699	0.5839 236	0.4884 961	0.4088 441	0.3423 300	72
73	0.6156 654	0.5795 768	0.4836 595	0.4037 966	0.3372 709	73
74	0.6115 882	0.5752 623	0.4788 708	0.3988 115	0.3322 866	74
75	0.6075 379	0.5709 800	0.4741 295	0.3938 879	0.3273 760	75
76	0.6035 145	0.5667 295	0.4694 351	0.3890 251	0.3225 379	76
77	0.5995 177	0.5625 107	0.4647 873	0.3842 223	0.3177 714	77
78	0.5955 474	0.5583 233	0.4601 854	0.3794 788	0.3130 752	78
79	0.5916 034	0.5541 670	0.4556 291	0.3747 939	0.3084 485	79
80	0.5876 855	0.5500 417	0.4511 179	0.3701 668	0.3038 901	80
81	0.5837 935	0.5459 471	0.4466 514	0.3655 968	0.2993 992	81
82	0.5799 273	0.5418 830	0.4422 291	0.3610 833	0.2949 745	82
83	0.5760 867	0.5378 491	0.4378 506	0.3566 255	0.2906 153	83
84	0.5722 716	0.5338 453	0.4335 155	0.3522 227	0.2863 205	84
85	0.5684 817	0.5298 712	0.4292 232	0.3478 743	0.2820 892	85
86	0.5647 169	0.5259 268	0.4249 735	0.3435 795	0.2779 204	86
87	0.5609 771	0.5220 117	0.4207 658	0.3393 378	0.2738 132	87
88	0.5572 620	0.5181 257	0.4165 998	0.3351 484	0.2697 667	88
89	0.5535 715	0.5142 687	0.4124 751	0.3310 108	0.2657 800	89
90	0.5499 055	0.5104 404	0.4083 912	0.3269 242	0.2618 522	90
91	0.5462 637	0.5066 406	0.4043 477	0.3228 881	0.2579 824	91
92	0.5426 461	0.5028 691	0.4003 443	0.3189 019	0.2541 699	92
93	0.5390 524	0.4991 257	0.3963 805	0.3149 648	0.2504 137	93
94	0.5354 825	0.4954 101	0.3924 559	0.3110 764	0.2467 130	94
95	0.5319 363	0.4917 222	0.3885 702	0.3072 359	0.2430 670	95
96	0.5284 135	0.4880 617	0.3847 230	0.3034 429	0.2394 749	96
97	0.5249 141	0.4844 285	0.3809 138	0.2996 967	0.2359 358	97
98	0.5214 379	0.4808 223	0.3771 424	0.2959 967	0.2324 491	98
99	0.5179 846	0.4772 430	0.3734 083	0.2923 424	0.2290 139	99
100	0.5145 543	0.4736 903	0.3697 112	0.2887 333	0.2256 294	100

Table VI — Present Value of 1

$$v^n = (1+i)^{-n}$$

n	$1\frac{3}{4}$ per cent	2 per cent	$2\frac{1}{4}$ per cent	$2\frac{1}{2}$ per cent	3 per cent	n
1	0.9828 010	0.9803 922	0.9779 951	0.9756 098	0.9708 738	1
2	0.9658 978	0.9611 688	0.9564 744	0.9518 144	0.9425 959	2
3	0.9492 853	0.9423 223	0.9354 273	0.9285 994	0.9151 417	3
4	0.9329 585	0.9238 454	0.9148 433	0.9059 506	0.8884 870	4
5	0.9169 125	0.9057 308	0.8947 123	0.8838 543	0.8626 088	5
6	0.9011 425	0.8879 714	0.8750 243	0.8622 969	0.8374 843	6
7	0.8856 438	0.8705 602	0.8557 695	0.8412 652	0.8130 915	7
8	0.8704 116	0.8534 904	0.8369 383	0.8207 466	0.7894 092	8
9	0.8554 413	0.8367 553	0.8185 216	0.8007 284	0.7664 167	9
10	0.8407 286	0.8203 483	0.8005 101	0.7811 984	0.7440 939	10
11	0.8262 689	0.8042 630	0.7828 950	0.7621 448	0.7224 213	11
12	0.8120 579	0.7884 932	0.7656 675	0.7435 559	0.7013 799	12
13	0.7980 913	0.7730 325	0.7488 190	0.7254 204	0.6809 513	13
14	0.7843 649	0.7578 750	0.7323 414	0.7077 272	0.6611 178	14
15	0.7708 746	0.7430 147	0.7162 263	0.6904 656	0.6418 619	15
16	0.7576 163	0.7284 458	0.7004 658	0.6736 249	0.6231 669	16
17	0.7445 861	0.7141 626	0.6850 521	0.6571 951	0.6050 164	17
18	0.7317 799	0.7001 594	0.6699 776	0.6411 659	0.5873 946	18
19	0.7191 940	0.6864 308	0.6552 348	0.6255 277	0.5702 860	19
20	0.7068 246	0.6729 713	0.6408 165	0.6102 709	0.5536 758	20
21	0.6946 679	0.6597 758	0.6267 154	0.5953 863	0.5375 493	21
22	0.6827 203	0.6468 390	0.6129 246	0.5808 647	0.5218 925	22
23	0.6709 782	0.6341 559	0.5994 372	0.5666 972	0.5066 917	23
24	0.6594 380	0.6217 215	0.5862 467	0.5528 754	0.4919 337	24
25	0.6480 963	0.6095 309	0.5733 464	0.5393 906	0.4776 056	25
26	0.6369 497	0.5975 793	0.5607 300	0.5262 347	0.4636 947	26
27	0.6259 948	0.5858 620	0.5483 912	0.5133 997	0.4501 891	27
28	0.6152 283	0.5743 746	0.5363 239	0.5008 778	0.4370 768	28
29	0.6046 470	0.5631 123	0.5245 221	0.4886 613	0.4243 464	29
30	0.5942 476	0.5520 709	0.5129 801	0.4767 427	0.4119 868	30
31	0.5840 272	0.5412 460	0.5016 920	0.4651 148	0.3999 871	31
32	0.5739 825	0.5306 333	0.4906 523	0.4537 706	0.3883 370	32
33	0.5641 105	0.5202 287	0.4798 556	0.4427 030	0.3770 262	33
34	0.5544 084	0.5100 282	0.4692 964	0.4319 053	0.3660 449	34
35	0.5448 731	0.5000 276	0.4589 696	0.4213 711	0.3553 834	35
36	0.5355 018	0.4902 232	0.4488 700	0.4110 937	0.3450 324	36
37	0.5262 917	0.4806 109	0.4389 927	0.4010 670	0.3349 829	37
38	0.5172 400	0.4711 872	0.4293 327	0.3912 849	0.3252 262	38
39	0.5083 440	0.4619 482	0.4198 853	0.3817 414	0.3157 535	39
40	0.4996 010	0.4528 904	0.4106 458	0.3724 306	0.3065 568	40
41	0.4910 083	0.4440 102	0.4016 095	0.3633 469	0.2976 280	41
42	0.4825 635	0.4353 041	0.3927 722	0.3544 848	0.2889 592	42
43	0.4742 639	0.4267 688	0.3841 293	0.3458 389	0.2805 429	43
44	0.4661 070	0.4184 007	0.3756 765	0.3374 038	0.2723 718	44
45	0.4580 904	0.4101 968	0.3674 098	0.3291 744	0.2644 386	45
46	0.4502 117	0.4021 537	0.3593 250	0.3211 458	0.2567 365	46
47	0.4424 685	0.3942 684	0.3514 181	0.3133 129	0.2492 588	47
48	0.4348 585	0.3865 376	0.3436 852	0.3056 712	0.2419 988	48
49	0.4273 793	0.3789 584	0.3361 224	0.2982 158	0.2349 503	49
50	0.4200 288	0.3715 279	0.3287 261	0.2909 422	0.2281 071	50

Table VI — Present Value of 1

$$v^n = (1+i)^{-n}$$

n	$1\frac{3}{4}$ per cent	2 per cent	$2\frac{1}{4}$ per cent	$2\frac{1}{2}$ per cent	3 per cent	n
51	0.4128 048	0.3642 430	0.3214 925	0.2838 461	0.2214 632	51
52	0.4057 049	0.3571 010	0.3144 181	0.2769 230	0.2150 128	52
53	0.3987 272	0.3500 990	0.3074 994	0.2701 688	0.2087 503	53
54	0.3918 695	0.3432 343	0.3007 329	0.2635 793	0.2026 702	54
55	0.3851 297	0.3365 042	0.2941 153	0.2571 505	0.1967 672	55
56	0.3785 059	0.3299 061	0.2876 433	0.2508 786	0.1910 361	56
57	0.3719 959	0.3234 374	0.2813 137	0.2447 596	0.1854 719	57
58	0.3655 980	0.3170 955	0.2751 235	0.2387 898	0.1800 698	58
59	0.3593 100	0.3108 779	0.2690 694	0.2329 657	0.1748 251	59
60	0.3531 303	0.3047 823	0.2631 486	0.2272 836	0.1697 331	60
61	0.3470 568	0.2988 061	0.2573 580	0.2217 401	0.1647 894	61
62	0.3410 877	0.2929 472	0.2516 949	0.2163 318	0.1599 897	62
63	0.3352 214	0.2872 031	0.2461 564	0.2110 554	0.1553 298	63
64	0.3294 559	0.2815 717	0.2407 397	0.2059 077	0.1508 057	64
65	0.3237 896	0.2760 507	0.2354 423	0.2008 856	0.1464 133	65
66	0.3182 207	0.2706 379	0.2302 614	0.1959 859	0.1421 488	66
67	0.3127 476	0.2653 313	0.2251 945	0.1912 058	0.1380 085	67
68	0.3073 687	0.2601 287	0.2202 391	0.1865 422	0.1339 889	68
69	0.3020 822	0.2550 282	0.2153 928	0.1819 924	0.1300 863	69
70	0.2968 867	0.2500 276	0.2106 531	0.1775 536	0.1262 974	70
71	0.2917 805	0.2451 251	0.2060 177	0.1732 230	0.1226 188	71
72	0.2867 622	0.2403 187	0.2014 843	0.1689 980	0.1190 474	72
73	0.2818 302	0.2356 066	0.1970 507	0.1648 761	0.1155 800	73
74	0.2769 830	0.2309 869	0.1927 146	0.1608 548	0.1122 136	74
75	0.2722 191	0.2264 577	0.1884 739	0.1569 315	0.1089 452	75
76	0.2675 372	0.2220 174	0.1843 266	0.1531 039	0.1057 721	76
77	0.2629 359	0.2176 641	0.1802 705	0.1493 697	0.1026 913	77
78	0.2584 136	0.2133 962	0.1763 036	0.1457 265	0.0997 003	78
79	0.2539 692	0.2092 119	0.1724 241	0.1421 722	0.0967 964	79
80	0.2496 011	0.2051 097	0.1686 299	0.1387 046	0.0939 771	80
81	0.2453 082	0.2010 880	0.1649 192	0.1353 215	0.0912 399	81
82	0.2410 892	0.1971 451	0.1612 902	0.1320 210	0.0885 824	82
83	0.2369 427	0.1932 795	0.1577 410	0.1288 010	0.0860 024	83
84	0.2328 675	0.1894 897	0.1542 700	0.1256 595	0.0834 974	84
85	0.2288 624	0.1857 742	0.1508 753	0.1225 946	0.0810 655	85
86	0.2249 262	0.1821 316	0.1475 553	0.1196 045	0.0787 043	86
87	0.2210 577	0.1785 604	0.1443 083	0.1166 873	0.0764 120	87
88	0.2172 557	0.1750 592	0.1411 329	0.1138 413	0.0741 864	88
89	0.2135 191	0.1716 266	0.1380 272	0.1110 647	0.0720 256	89
90	0.2098 468	0.1682 614	0.1349 900	0.1083 558	0.0699 278	90
91	0.2062 377	0.1649 622	0.1320 195	0.1057 130	0.0678 911	91
92	0.2026 906	0.1617 276	0.1291 145	0.1031 346	0.0659 136	92
93	0.1992 045	0.1585 565	0.1262 733	0.1006 191	0.0639 938	93
94	0.1957 784	0.1554 475	0.1234 947	0.0981 650	0.0621 299	94
95	0.1924 112	0.1523 995	0.1207 772	0.0957 707	0.0603 203	95
96	0.1891 019	0.1494 113	0.1181 195	0.0934 349	0.0585 634	96
97	0.1858 495	0.1464 817	0.1155 203	0.0911 560	0.0568 577	97
98	0.1826 531	0.1436 095	0.1129 783	0.0889 326	0.0552 016	98
99	0.1795 116	0.1407 936	0.1104 922	0.0867 636	0.0535 938	99
100	0.1764 242	0.1380 330	0.1080 608	0.0846 474	0.0520 328	100

Table VI — Present Value of 1

$$v^n = (1+i)^{-n}$$

n	$3\frac{1}{2}$ per cent	4 per cent	$4\frac{1}{2}$ per cent	5 per cent	$5\frac{1}{2}$ per cent	n
1	0.9661 836	0.9615 385	0.9569 378	0.9523 810	0.9478 673	1
2	0.9335 107	0.9245 562	0.9157 300	0.9070 295	0.8984 524	2
3	0.9019 427	0.8889 964	0.8762 966	0.8638 376	0.8516 137	3
4	0.8714 422	0.8548 042	0.8385 613	0.8227 025	0.8072 167	4
5	0.8419 732	0.8219 271	0.8024 510	0.7835 262	0.7651 344	5
6	0.8135 006	0.7903 145	0.7678 957	0.7462 154	0.7252 458	6
7	0.7859 910	0.7599 178	0.7348 285	0.7106 813	0.6874 368	7
8	0.7594 116	0.7306 902	0.7031 851	0.6768 394	0.6515 989	8
9	0.7337 310	0.7025 867	0.6729 044	0.6446 089	0.6176 293	9
10	0.7089 188	0.6755 642	0.6439 277	0.6139 133	0.5854 306	10
11	0.6849 457	0.6495 809	0.6161 987	0.5846 793	0.5549 105	11
12	0.6617 833	0.6245 970	0.5896 639	0.5568 374	0.5259 815	12
13	0.6394 042	0.6005 741	0.5642 716	0.5303 214	0.4985 607	13
14	0.6177 818	0.5774 752	0.5399 729	0.5050 680	0.4725 694	14
15	0.5968 906	0.5552 645	0.5167 204	0.4810 171	0.4479 330	15
16	0.5767 059	0.5339 082	0.4944 693	0.4581 115	0.4245 811	16
17	0.5572 038	0.5133 732	0.4731 764	0.4362 967	0.4024 465	17
18	0.5383 611	0.4936 281	0.4528 004	0.4155 207	0.3814 659	18
19	0.5201 557	0.4746 424	0.4333 018	0.3957 340	0.3615 791	19
20	0.5025 659	0.4563 869	0.4146 429	0.3768 895	0.3427 290	20
21	0.4855 709	0.4388 336	0.3967 874	0.3589 424	0.3248 616	21
22	0.4691 506	0.4219 554	0.3797 009	0.3418 499	0.3079 257	22
23	0.4532 856	0.4057 263	0.3633 501	0.3255 713	0.2918 727	23
24	0.4379 571	0.3901 215	0.3477 035	0.3100 679	0.2766 566	24
25	0.4231 470	0.3751 168	0.3327 306	0.2953 028	0.2622 337	25
26	0.4088 377	0.3606 892	0.3184 025	0.2812 407	0.2485 628	26
27	0.3950 122	0.3468 166	0.3046 914	0.2678 483	0.2356 045	27
28	0.3816 543	0.3334 775	0.2915 707	0.2550 936	0.2233 218	28
29	0.3687 482	0.3206 514	0.2790 150	0.2429 463	0.2116 794	29
30	0.3562 784	0.3083 187	0.2670 000	0.2313 774	0.2006 440	30
31	0.3442 303	0.2964 603	0.2555 024	0.2203 595	0.1901 839	31
32	0.3325 897	0.2850 579	0.2444 999	0.2098 662	0.1802 691	32
33	0.3213 427	0.2740 942	0.2339 712	0.1998 725	0.1708 712	33
34	0.3104 761	0.2635 521	0.2238 959	0.1903 548	0.1619 632	34
35	0.2999 769	0.2534 155	0.2142 544	0.1812 903	0.1535 196	35
36	0.2898 327	0.2436 687	0.2050 282	0.1726 574	0.1455 162	36
37	0.2800 316	0.2342 968	0.1961 992	0.1644 356	0.1379 301	37
38	0.2705 619	0.2252 854	0.1877 504	0.1566 054	0.1307 394	38
39	0.2614 125	0.2166 206	0.1796 655	0.1491 480	0.1239 236	39
40	0.2525 725	0.2082 890	0.1719 287	0.1420 457	0.1174 631	40
41	0.2440 314	0.2002 779	0.1645 251	0.1352 816	0.1113 395	41
42	0.2357 791	0.1925 749	0.1574 403	0.1288 396	0.1055 350	42
43	0.2278 059	0.1851 682	0.1506 605	0.1227 044	0.1000 332	43
44	0.2201 023	0.1780 463	0.1441 728	0.1168 613	0.0948 182	44
45	0.2126 592	0.1711 984	0.1379 644	0.1112 965	0.0898 751	45
46	0.2054 679	0.1646 139	0.1320 233	0.1059 967	0.0851 897	46
47	0.1985 197	0.1582 826	0.1263 381	0.1009 492	0.0807 485	47
48	0.1918 065	0.1521 948	0.1208 977	0.0961 421	0.0765 389	48
49	0.1853 202	0.1463 411	0.1156 916	0.0915 639	0.0725 487	49
50	0.1790 534	0.1407 126	0.1107 096	0.0872 037	0.0687 665	50

Table VI — Present Value of 1

$$v^n = (1+i)^{-n}$$

n	$3\frac{1}{2}$ per cent	4 per cent	$4\frac{1}{2}$ per cent	5 per cent	$5\frac{1}{2}$ per cent	n
51	0.1729 984	0.1353 006	0.1059 422	0.0830 512	0.0651 815	51
52	0.1671 482	0.1300 967	0.1013 801	0.0790 964	0.0617 834	52
53	0.1614 959	0.1250 930	0.0970 145	0.0753 299	0.0585 625	53
54	0.1560 347	0.1202 817	0.0928 368	0.0717 427	0.0555 095	54
55	0.1507 581	0.1156 555	0.0888 391	0.0683 264	0.0526 156	55
56	0.1456 600	0.1112 072	0.0850 135	0.0650 728	0.0498 726	56
57	0.1407 343	0.1069 300	0.0813 526	0.0619 741	0.0472 726	57
58	0.1359 752	0.1028 173	0.0778 494	0.0590 229	0.0448 082	58
59	0.1313 770	0.0988 628	0.0744 970	0.0562 123	0.0424 722	59
60	0.1269 343	0.0950 604	0.0712 890	0.0535 355	0.0402 580	60
61	0.1226 418	0.0914 042	0.0682 191	0.0509 862	0.0381 593	61
62	0.1184 945	0.0878 887	0.0652 815	0.0485 583	0.0361 699	62
63	0.1144 875	0.0845 084	0.0624 703	0.0462 460	0.0342 843	63
64	0.1106 159	0.0812 580	0.0597 802	0.0440 438	0.0324 969	64
65	0.1068 753	0.0781 327	0.0572 059	0.0419 465	0.0308 028	65
66	0.1032 611	0.0751 276	0.0547 425	0.0399 490	0.0291 970	66
67	0.0997 692	0.0722 381	0.0523 852	0.0380 467	0.0276 748	67
68	0.0963 954	0.0694 597	0.0501 294	0.0362 349	0.0262 321	68
69	0.0931 356	0.0667 882	0.0479 707	0.0345 095	0.0248 645	69
70	0.0899 861	0.0642 194	0.0459 050	0.0328 662	0.0235 683	70
71	0.0869 431	0.0617 494	0.0439 282	0.0313 011	0.0223 396	71
72	0.0840 030	0.0593 744	0.0420 366	0.0298 106	0.0211 750	72
73	0.0811 623	0.0570 908	0.0402 264	0.0283 910	0.0200 711	73
74	0.0784 177	0.0548 950	0.0384 941	0.0270 391	0.0190 247	74
75	0.0757 659	0.0527 837	0.0368 365	0.0257 515	0.0180 329	75
76	0.0732 038	0.0507 535	0.0352 502	0.0245 252	0.0170 928	76
77	0.0707 283	0.0488 015	0.0337 323	0.0233 574	0.0162 017	77
78	0.0683 365	0.0469 245	0.0322 797	0.0222 451	0.0153 571	78
79	0.0660 256	0.0451 197	0.0308 897	0.0211 858	0.0145 565	79
80	0.0637 929	0.0433 843	0.0295 595	0.0201 770	0.0137 976	80
81	0.0616 356	0.0417 157	0.0282 866	0.0192 162	0.0130 783	81
82	0.0595 513	0.0401 112	0.0270 685	0.0183 011	0.0123 965	82
83	0.0575 375	0.0385 685	0.0259 029	0.0174 296	0.0117 502	83
84	0.0555 918	0.0370 851	0.0247 874	0.0165 996	0.0111 376	84
85	0.0537 119	0.0356 588	0.0237 200	0.0158 092	0.0105 570	85
86	0.0518 955	0.0342 873	0.0226 986	0.0150 564	0.0100 066	86
87	0.0501 406	0.0329 685	0.0217 211	0.0143 394	0.0094 850	87
88	0.0484 450	0.0317 005	0.0207 858	0.0136 566	0.0089 905	88
89	0.0468 068	0.0304 813	0.0198 907	0.0130 063	0.0085 218	89
90	0.0452 240	0.0293 089	0.0190 342	0.0123 869	0.0080 775	90
91	0.0436 946	0.0281 816	0.0182 145	0.0117 971	0.0076 564	91
92	0.0422 170	0.0270 977	0.0174 302	0.0112 353	0.0072 573	92
93	0.0407 894	0.0260 555	0.0166 796	0.0107 003	0.0068 789	93
94	0.0394 101	0.0250 534	0.0159 613	0.0101 907	0.0065 203	94
95	0.0380 774	0.0240 898	0.0152 740	0.0097 055	0.0061 804	95
96	0.0367 897	0.0231 632	0.0146 163	0.0092 433	0.0058 582	96
97	0.0355 456	0.0222 724	0.0139 868	0.0088 031	0.0055 528	97
98	0.0343 436	0.0214 157	0.0133 845	0.0083 840	0.0052 633	98
99	0.0331 822	0.0205 920	0.0128 082	0.0079 847	0.0049 889	99
100	0.0320 601	0.0198 000	0.0122 566	0.0076 045	0.0047 288	100

Table VI — Present Value of 1

$$v^n = (1+i)^{-n}$$

n	6 per cent	6½ per cent	7 per cent	7½ per cent	8 per cent	n
1	0.9433 962	0.9389 671	0.9345 794	0.9302 326	0.9259 259	1
2	0.8899 964	0.8816 593	0.8734 387	0.8653 326	0.8573 388	2
3	0.8396 193	0.8278 491	0.8162 979	0.8049 606	0.7938 322	3
4	0.7920 937	0.7773 231	0.7628 952	0.7488 005	0.7350 299	4
5	0.7472 581	0.7298 808	0.7129 862	0.6965 586	0.6805 832	5
6	0.7049 605	0.6853 341	0.6663 422	0.6479 615	0.6301 696	6
7	0.6650 571	0.6435 062	0.6227 497	0.6027 549	0.5834 904	7
8	0.6274 124	0.6042 312	0.5820 091	0.5607 022	0.5402 689	8
9	0.5918 985	0.5673 532	0.5439 337	0.5215 835	0.5002 490	9
10	0.5583 948	0.5327 260	0.5083 493	0.4851 939	0.4631 935	10
11	0.5267 875	0.5002 122	0.4750 928	0.4513 432	0.4288 829	11
12	0.4969 694	0.4696 829	0.4440 120	0.4198 541	0.3971 138	12
13	0.4688 390	0.4410 168	0.4149 644	0.3905 620	0.3676 979	13
14	0.4423 010	0.4141 002	0.3878 172	0.3633 135	0.3404 610	14
15	0.4172 651	0.3888 265	0.3624 460	0.3379 660	0.3152 417	15
16	0.3936 463	0.3650 953	0.3387 346	0.3143 870	0.2918 905	16
17	0.3713 644	0.3428 125	0.3165 744	0.2924 530	0.2702 690	17
18	0.3503 438	0.3218 897	0.2958 639	0.2720 493	0.2502 490	18
19	0.3305 130	0.3022 438	0.2765 083	0.2530 691	0.2317 121	19
20	0.3118 047	0.2837 970	0.2584 190	0.2354 131	0.2145 482	20
21	0.2941 554	0.2664 761	0.2415 131	0.2190 890	0.1986 557	21
22	0.2775 051	0.2502 123	0.2257 132	0.2037 107	0.1839 405	22
23	0.2617 973	0.2349 411	0.2109 469	0.1894 983	0.1703 153	23
24	0.2469 785	0.2206 020	0.1971 466	0.1762 775	0.1576 993	24
25	0.2329 986	0.2071 380	0.1842 492	0.1639 791	0.1460 179	25
26	0.2198 100	0.1944 958	0.1721 955	0.1525 387	0.1352 018	26
27	0.2073 680	0.1826 252	0.1609 304	0.1418 964	0.1251 868	27
28	0.1956 301	0.1714 790	0.1504 022	0.1319 967	0.1159 137	28
29	0.1845 567	0.1610 132	0.1405 628	0.1227 876	0.1073 275	29
30	0.1741 101	0.1511 861	0.1313 671	0.1142 210	0.0993 773	30
31	0.1642 548	0.1419 587	0.1227 730	0.1062 521	0.0920 160	31
32	0.1549 574	0.1332 946	0.1147 411	0.0988 392	0.0852 000	32
33	0.1461 862	0.1251 592	0.1072 347	0.0919 434	0.0788 889	33
34	0.1379 115	0.1175 204	0.1002 193	0.0855 288	0.0730 453	34
35	0.1301 052	0.1103 478	0.0936 629	0.0795 616	0.0676 345	35
36	0.1227 408	0.1036 130	0.0875 355	0.0740 108	0.0626 246	36
37	0.1157 932	0.0972 892	0.0818 088	0.0688 473	0.0579 857	37
38	0.1092 389	0.0913 513	0.0764 569	0.0640 440	0.0536 905	38
39	0.1030 555	0.0857 759	0.0714 550	0.0595 758	0.0497 134	39
40	0.0972 222	0.0805 408	0.0667 804	0.0554 194	0.0460 309	40
41	0.0917 190	0.0756 251	0.0624 116	0.0515 529	0.0426 212	41
42	0.0865 274	0.0710 095	0.0583 286	0.0479 562	0.0394 641	42
43	0.0816 296	0.0666 756	0.0545 127	0.0446 104	0.0365 408	43
44	0.0770 091	0.0626 062	0.0509 464	0.0414 980	0.0338 341	44
45	0.0726 501	0.0587 852	0.0476 135	0.0386 028	0.0313 279	45
46	0.0685 378	0.0551 973	0.0444 986	0.0359 096	0.0290 073	46
47	0.0646 583	0.0518 285	0.0415 875	0.0334 043	0.0268 586	47
48	0.0609 984	0.0486 652	0.0388 668	0.0310 738	0.0248 691	48
49	0.0575 457	0.0456 951	0.0363 241	0.0289 058	0.0230 269	49
50	0.0542 884	0.0429 062	0.0339 478	0.0268 891	0.0213 212	50

Table VI — Present Value of 1

$$v^n = (1+i)^{-n}$$

n	6 per cent	$6\frac{1}{2}$ per cent	7 per cent	$7\frac{1}{2}$ per cent	8 per cent	n
51	0.0512 154	0.0402 875	0.0317 269	0.0250 131	0.0197 419	51
52	0.0483 164	0.0378 286	0.0296 513	0.0232 680	0.0182 795	52
53	0.0455 816	0.0355 198	0.0277 115	0.0216 447	0.0169 255	53
54	0.0430 015	0.0333 519	0.0258 986	0.0201 346	0.0156 717	54
55	0.0405 674	0.0313 164	0.0242 043	0.0187 299	0.0145 109	55
56	0.0382 712	0.0294 051	0.0226 208	0.0174 231	0.0134 360	56
57	0.0361 049	0.0276 104	0.0211 410	0.0162 076	0.0124 407	57
58	0.0340 612	0.0259 252	0.0197 579	0.0150 768	0.0115 192	58
59	0.0321 332	0.0243 429	0.0184 653	0.0140 249	0.0106 659	59
60	0.0303 143	0.0228 572	0.0172 573	0.0130 464	0.0098 759	60
61	0.0285 984	0.0214 622	0.0161 283	0.0121 362	0.0091 443	61
62	0.0269 797	0.0201 523	0.0150 732	0.0112 895	0.0084 670	62
63	0.0254 525	0.0189 223	0.0140 871	0.0105 019	0.0078 398	63
64	0.0240 118	0.0177 674	0.0131 655	0.0097 692	0.0072 590	64
65	0.0226 526	0.0166 831	0.0123 042	0.0090 876	0.0067 213	65
66	0.0213 704	0.0156 648	0.0114 993	0.0084 536	0.0062 235	66
67	0.0201 608	0.0147 088	0.0107 470	0.0078 638	0.0057 625	67
68	0.0190 196	0.0138 110	0.0100 439	0.0073 152	0.0053 356	68
69	0.0179 430	0.0129 681	0.0093 868	0.0068 048	0.0049 404	69
70	0.0169 274	0.0121 766	0.0087 727	0.0063 301	0.0045 744	70
71	0.0159 692	0.0114 335	0.0081 988	0.0058 884	0.0042 356	71
72	0.0150 653	0.0107 356	0.0076 625	0.0054 776	0.0039 218	72
73	0.0142 125	0.0100 804	0.0071 612	0.0050 954	0.0036 313	73
74	0.0134 081	0.0094 652	0.0066 927	0.0047 399	0.0033 623	74
75	0.0126 491	0.0088 875	0.0062 548	0.0044 093	0.0031 133	75
76	0.0119 331	0.0083 451	0.0058 457	0.0041 016	0.0028 827	76
77	0.0112 577	0.0078 357	0.0054 632	0.0038 155	0.0026 691	77
78	0.0106 204	0.0073 575	0.0051 058	0.0035 493	0.0024 714	78
79	0.0100 193	0.0069 085	0.0047 718	0.0033 017	0.0022 884	79
80	0.0094 522	0.0064 868	0.0044 596	0.0030 713	0.0021 188	80
81	0.0089 171	0.0060 909	0.0041 679	0.0028 570	0.0019 619	81
82	0.0084 124	0.0057 192	0.0038 952	0.0026 577	0.0018 166	82
83	0.0079 362	0.0053 701	0.0036 404	0.0024 723	0.0016 820	83
84	0.0074 870	0.0050 423	0.0034 022	0.0022 998	0.0015 574	84
85	0.0070 632	0.0047 346	0.0031 796	0.0021 393	0.0014 421	85
86	0.0066 634	0.0044 456	0.0029 716	0.0019 901	0.0013 352	86
87	0.0062 862	0.0041 743	0.0027 772	0.0018 512	0.0012 363	87
88	0.0059 304	0.0039 195	0.0025 955	0.0017 221	0.0011 447	88
89	0.0055 947	0.0036 803	0.0024 257	0.0016 019	0.0010 600	89
90	0.0052 780	0.0034 557	0.0022 670	0.0014 902	0.0009 814	90
91	0.0049 793	0.0032 448	0.0021 187	0.0013 862	0.0009 087	91
92	0.0046 974	0.0030 467	0.0019 801	0.0012 895	0.0008 414	92
93	0.0044 315	0.0028 608	0.0018 506	0.0011 995	0.0007 791	93
94	0.0041 807	0.0026 862	0.0017 295	0.0011 158	0.0007 214	94
95	0.0039 441	0.0025 222	0.0016 164	0.0010 380	0.0006 679	95
96	0.0037 208	0.0023 683	0.0015 106	0.0009 656	0.0006 185	96
97	0.0035 102	0.0022 238	0.0014 118	0.0008 982	0.0005 727	97
98	0.0033 115	0.0020 880	0.0013 194	0.0008 355	0.0005 302	98
99	0.0031 241	0.0019 606	0.0012 331	0.0007 773	0.0004 910	99
100	0.0029 472	0.0018 409	0.0011 525	0.0007 230	0.0004 546	100

Table VII — Amount of 1 per Period

$$s_{\overline{n}|}=[(1+i)^n-1]/i$$

n	$\frac{1}{4}$ per cent	$\frac{1}{3}$ per cent	$\frac{5}{12}$ per cent	$\frac{1}{2}$ per cent	$\frac{7}{12}$ per cent	n
1	1.0000 000	1.0000 000	1.0000 000	1.0000 000	1.0000 000	1
2	2.0025 000	2.0033 333	2.0041 667	2.0050 000	2.0058 333	2
3	3.0075 062	3.0100 111	3.0125 174	3.0150 250	3.0175 340	3
4	4.0150 250	4.0200 445	4.0250 695	4.0301 001	4.0351 363	4
5	5.0250 626	5.0334 446	5.0418 406	5.0502 506	5.0586 746	5
6	6.0376 252	6.0502 228	6.0628 483	6.0755 019	6.0881 835	6
7	7.0527 193	7.0703 902	7.0881 102	7.1058 794	7.1236 979	7
8	8.0703 511	8.0939 582	8.1176 440	8.1414 088	8.1652 528	8
9	9.0905 270	9.1209 380	9.1514 675	9.1821 158	9.2128 835	9
10	10.1132 533	10.1513 411	10.1895 986	10.2280 264	10.2666 253	10
11	11.1385 364	11.1851 789	11.2320 553	11.2791 665	11.3265 140	11
12	12.1663 828	12.2224 629	12.2788 559	12.3355 624	12.3925 853	12
13	13.1967 987	13.2632 044	13.3300 174	13.3972 402	13.4648 754	13
14	14.2297 907	14.3074 151	14.3855 591	14.4642 264	14.5434 205	14
15	15.2653 652	15.3551 065	15.4454 990	15.5365 475	15.6282 571	15
16	16.3035 286	16.4062 902	16.5098 552	16.6142 303	16.7194 219	16
17	17.3442 874	17.4609 778	17.5786 463	17.6973 014	17.8169 519	17
18	18.3876 481	18.5191 811	18.6518 906	18.7857 879	18.9208 841	18
19	19.4336 173	19.5809 117	19.7296 068	19.8797 169	20.0312 559	19
20	20.4822 013	20.6461 814	20.8118 135	20.9791 154	21.1481 049	20
21	21.5334 068	21.7150 020	21.8985 294	22.0840 110	22.2714 689	21
22	22.5872 403	22.7873 853	22.9897 733	23.1944 311	23.4013 858	22
23	23.6437 084	23.8633 433	24.0855 640	24.3104 032	24.5378 939	23
24	24.7028 177	24.9428 877	25.1859 205	25.4319 552	25.6810 316	24
25	25.7645 747	26.0260 307	26.2908 619	26.5591 150	26.8308 376	25
26	26.8289 862	27.1127 841	27.4004 071	27.6919 106	27.9873 508	26
27	27.8960 587	28.2031 601	28.5145 755	28.8303 701	29.1506 103	27
28	28.9657 988	29.2971 706	29.6333 862	29.9745 220	30.3206 556	28
29	30.0382 133	30.3948 279	30.7568 587	31.1243 946	31.4975 261	29
30	31.1133 088	31.4961 440	31.8850 122	32.2800 166	32.6812 616	30
31	32.1910 921	32.6011 311	33.0178 665	33.4414 167	33.8719 023	31
32	33.2715 698	33.7098 015	34.1554 409	34.6086 237	35.0694 884	32
33	34.3547 488	34.8221 675	35.2977 552	35.7816 669	36.2740 604	33
34	35.4406 356	35.9382 414	36.4448 292	36.9605 752	37.4856 591	34
35	36.5292 372	37.0580 356	37.5966 827	38.1453 781	38.7043 255	35
36	37.6205 603	38.1815 624	38.7533 355	39.3361 050	39.9301 007	36
37	38.7146 117	39.3088 342	39.9148 078	40.5327 855	41.1630 263	37
38	39.8113 982	40.4398 637	41.0811 195	41.7354 494	42.4031 440	38
39	40.9109 267	41.5746 632	42.2522 908	42.9441 267	43.6504 956	39
40	42.0132 041	42.7132 454	43.4283 420	44.1588 473	44.9051 235	40
41	43.1182 371	43.8556 229	44.6092 934	45.3796 415	46.1670 701	41
42	44.2260 327	45.0018 083	45.7951 655	46.6065 397	47.4363 780	42
43	45.3365 977	46.1518 144	46.9859 787	47.8395 724	48.7130 902	43
44	46.4499 392	47.3056 537	48.1817 536	49.0787 703	49.9972 499	44
45	47.5660 641	48.4633 392	49.3825 109	50.3241 642	51.2889 005	45
46	48.6849 792	49.6248 837	50.5882 713	51.5757 850	52.5880 858	46
47	49.8066 917	50.7903 000	51.7990 558	52.8336 639	53.8948 496	47
48	50.9312 084	51.9596 010	53.0148 852	54.0978 322	55.2092 362	48
49	52.0585 364	53.1327 997	54.2357 806	55.3683 214	56.5312 901	49
50	53.1886 828	54.3099 090	55.4617 630	56.6451 630	57.8610 560	50

[504]

Table VII — Amount of 1 per Period

$$s_{\overline{n}|} = [(1+i)^n - 1]/i$$

n	$\frac{1}{4}$ per cent	$\frac{1}{3}$ per cent	$\frac{5}{12}$ per cent	$\frac{1}{2}$ per cent	$\frac{7}{12}$ per cent	n
51	54.3216 545	55.4909 420	56.6928 537	57.9283 888	59.1985 788	51
52	55.4574 586	56.6759 118	57.9290 739	59.2180 307	60.5439 038	52
53	56.5961 023	57.8648 315	59.1704 450	60.5141 209	61.8970 766	53
54	57.7375 925	59.0577 143	60.4169 885	61.8166 915	63.2581 429	54
55	58.8819 365	60.2545 734	61.6687 260	63.1257 750	64.6271 487	55
56	60.0291 413	61.4554 219	62.9256 790	64.4414 038	66.0041 404	56
57	61.1792 142	62.6602 733	64.1878 694	65.7636 109	67.3891 646	57
58	62.3321 622	63.8691 409	65.4553 188	67.0924 289	68.7822 680	58
59	63.4879 926	65.0820 381	66.7280 493	68.4278 911	70.1834 979	59
60	64.6467 126	66.2989 782	68.0060 828	69.7700 305	71.5929 016	60
61	65.8083 294	67.5199 748	69.2894 415	71.1188 807	73.0105 269	61
62	66.9728 502	68.7450 414	70.5781 475	72.4744 751	74.4364 216	62
63	68.1402 824	69.9741 915	71.8722 231	73.8368 474	75.8706 341	63
64	69.3106 331	71.2074 388	73.1716 907	75.2060 317	77.3132 128	64
65	70.4839 096	72.4447 969	74.4765 728	76.5820 618	78.7642 065	65
66	71.6601 194	73.6862 796	75.7868 918	77.9649 721	80.2236 644	66
67	72.8392 697	74.9319 005	77.1026 706	79.3547 970	81.6916 358	67
68	74.0213 679	76.1816 735	78.4239 317	80.7515 710	83.1681 703	68
69	75.2064 213	77.4356 124	79.7506 981	82.1553 288	84.6533 180	69
70	76.3944 374	78.6937 311	81.0829 926	83.5661 055	86.1471 290	70
71	77.5854 235	79.9560 436	82.4208 384	84.9839 360	87.6496 539	71
72	78.7793 870	81.2225 637	83.7642 586	86.4088 557	89.1609 436	72
73	79.9763 355	82.4933 056	85.1132 763	87.8409 000	90.6810 491	73
74	81.1762 763	83.7682 833	86.4679 150	89.2801 045	92.2100 219	74
75	82.3792 170	85.0475 109	87.8281 980	90.7265 050	93.7479 137	75
76	83.5851 651	86.3310 026	89.1941 488	92.1801 375	95.2947 765	76
77	84.7941 280	87.6187 726	90.5657 911	93.6410 382	96.8506 627	77
78	86.0061 133	88.9108 352	91.9431 485	95.1092 434	98.4156 249	78
79	87.2211 286	90.2072 046	93.3262 450	96.5847 896	99.9897 160	79
80	88.4391 814	91.5078 953	94.7151 044	98.0677 136	101.5729 894	80
81	89.6602 793	92.8129 216	96.1097 506	99.5580 521	103.1654 985	81
82	90.8844 300	94.1222 980	97.5102 079	101.0558 424	104.7672 972	82
83	92.1116 411	95.4360 390	98.9165 004	102.5611 216	106.3784 398	83
84	93.3419 202	96.7541 592	100.3286 525	104.0739 272	107.9989 807	84
85	94.5752 750	98.0766 730	101.7466 886	105.5942 969	109.6259 748	85
86	95.8117 132	99.4035 953	103.1706 331	107.1222 683	111.2684 771	86
87	97.0512 425	100.7349 406	104.6005 108	108.6578 797	112.9175 432	87
88	98.2938 706	102.0707 237	106.0363 462	110.2011 691	114.5762 289	88
89	99.5396 053	103.4109 595	107.4781 643	111.7521 749	116.2445 902	89
90	100.7884 543	104.7556 627	108.9259 900	113.3109 358	117.9226 837	90
91	102.0404 254	106.1048 482	110.3798 483	114.8774 905	119.6105 660	91
92	103.2955 265	107.4585 310	111.8397 643	116.4518 779	121.3082 943	92
93	104.5537 653	108.8167 261	113.3057 634	118.0341 373	123.0159 260	93
94	105.8151 497	110.1794 486	114.7778 707	119.6243 080	124.7335 189	94
95	107.0796 876	111.5467 134	116.2561 118	121.2224 295	126.4611 311	95
96	108.3473 868	112.9185 358	117.7405 123	122.8285 417	128.1988 210	96
97	109.6182 553	114.2949 309	119.2310 978	124.4426 844	129.9466 475	97
98	110.8923 009	115.6759 140	120.7278 940	126.0648 978	131.7046 696	98
99	112.1695 317	117.0615 004	122.2309 269	127.6952 223	133.4729 468	99
100	113.4499 555	118.4517 054	123.7402 224	129.3336 984	135.2515 390	100

[505]

Table VII — Amount of 1 per Period

$$s_{\overline{n}|} = [(1+i)^n - 1]/i$$

n	$\frac{2}{3}$ per cent	$\frac{3}{4}$ per cent	1 per cent	$1\frac{1}{4}$ per cent	$1\frac{1}{2}$ per cent	n
1	1.0000 000	1.0000 000	1.0000 000	1.0000 000	1.0000 000	1
2	2.0066 667	2.0075 000	2.0100 000	2.0125 000	2.0150 000	2
3	3.0200 444	3.0225 562	3.0301 000	3.0376 562	3.0452 250	3
4	4.0401 781	4.0452 254	4.0604 010	4.0756 270	4.0909 034	4
5	5.0671 126	5.0755 646	5.1010 050	5.1265 723	5.1522 669	5
6	6.1008 933	6.1136 313	6.1520 151	6.1906 544	6.2295 509	6
7	7.1415 660	7.1594 836	7.2135 352	7.2680 376	7.3229 942	7
8	8.1891 764	8.2131 797	8.2856 706	8.3588 881	8.4328 391	8
9	9.2437 709	9.2747 786	9.3685 273	9.4633 742	9.5593 317	9
10	10.3053 961	10.3443 394	10.4622 125	10.5816 664	10.7027 217	10
11	11.3740 987	11.4219 219	11.5668 347	11.7139 372	11.8632 625	11
12	12.4499 260	12.5075 864	12.6825 030	12.8603 614	13.0412 114	12
13	13.5329 255	13.6013 933	13.8093 280	14.0211 159	14.2368 296	13
14	14.6231 450	14.7034 037	14.9474 213	15.1963 799	15.4503 820	14
15	15.7206 327	15.8136 792	16.0968 955	16.3863 346	16.6821 378	15
16	16.8254 369	16.9322 818	17.2578 645	17.5911 638	17.9323 698	16
17	17.9376 065	18.0592 739	18.4304 431	18.8110 534	19.2013 554	17
18	19.0571 905	19.1947 185	19.6147 476	20.0461 915	20.4893 757	18
19	20.1842 384	20.3386 789	20.8108 950	21.2967 689	21.7967 164	19
20	21.3188 000	21.4912 190	22.0190 040	22.5629 785	23.1236 671	20
21	22.4609 254	22.6524 031	23.2391 940	23.8450 158	24.4705 221	21
22	23.6106 649	23.8222 961	24.4715 860	25.1430 785	25.8375 799	22
23	24.7680 693	25.0009 634	25.7163 018	26.4573 670	27.2251 436	23
24	25.9931 897	26.1884 706	26.9734 648	27.7880 840	28.6335 208	24
25	27.1060 777	27.3848 841	28.2431 995	29.1354 351	30.0630 236	25
26	28.2867 849	28.5902 707	29.5256 315	30.4996 280	31.5139 690	26
27	29.4753 634	29.8046 978	30.8208 878	31.8808 734	32.9866 785	27
28	30.6718 659	31.0282 330	32.1290 967	33.2793 843	34.4814 787	28
29	31.8763 450	32.2609 448	33.4503 877	34.6953 766	35.9987 008	29
30	33.0888 540	33.5029 018	34.7848 915	36.1290 688	37.5386 814	30
31	34.3094 463	34.7541 736	36.1327 404	37.5806 822	39.1017 616	31
32	35.5381 759	36.0148 299	37.4940 678	39.0504 407	40.6882 880	32
33	36.7750 971	37.2849 411	38.8690 085	40.5385 712	42.2986 123	33
34	38.0202 644	38.5645 782	40.2576 986	42.0453 033	43.9330 915	34
35	39.2737 329	39.8538 125	41.6602 756	43.5708 696	45.5920 879	35
36	40.5355 577	41.1527 161	43.0768 784	45.1155 055	47.2759 692	36
37	41.8057 948	42.4613 615	44.5076 471	46.6794 493	48.9851 087	37
38	43.0845 001	43.7798 217	45.9527 236	48.2629 424	50.7198 854	38
39	44.3717 301	45.1081 704	47.4122 508	49.8662 292	52.4806 837	39
40	45.6675 416	46.4464 816	48.8863 734	51.4895 571	54.2678 939	40
41	46.9719 919	47.7948 303	50.3752 371	53.1331 765	56.0819 123	41
42	48.2851 385	49.1532 915	51.8789 895	54.7973 412	57.9231 410	42
43	49.6070 394	50.5219 412	53.3977 794	56.4823 080	59.7919 881	43
44	50.9377 530	51.9008 557	54.9317 572	58.1883 369	61.6888 679	44
45	52.2773 381	53.2901 121	56.4810 747	59.9156 911	63.6142 010	45
46	53.6258 536	54.6897 880	58.0458 855	61.6646 372	65.5684 140	46
47	54.9833 593	56.0999 614	59.6263 443	63.4354 452	67.5519 402	47
48	56.3499 151	57.5207 111	61.2226 078	65.2283 882	69.5652 193	48
49	57.7255 812	58.9521 164	62.8348 338	67.0437 431	71.6086 976	49
50	59.1104 184	60.3942 573	64.4631 822	68.8817 899	73.6828 280	50

Table VII — Amount of 1 per Period

$$s_{\overline{n}|}=[(1+i)^n-1]/i$$

n	$\frac{2}{3}$ per cent	$\frac{3}{4}$ per cent	1 per cent	$1\frac{1}{4}$ per cent	$1\frac{1}{2}$ per cent	n
51	60.5044 878	61.8472 142	66.1078 140	70.7428 123	75.7880 705	51
52	61.9078 511	63.3110 684	67.7688 921	72.6270 974	77.9248 915	52
53	63.3205 701	64.7859 014	69.4465 811	74.5349 361	80.0937 649	53
54	64.7427 072	66.2717 956	71.1410 469	76.4666 228	82.2951 714	54
55	66.1743 253	67.7688 341	72.8524 573	78.4224 556	84.5295 989	55
56	67.6154 874	69.2771 003	74.5809 819	80.4027 363	86.7975 429	56
57	69.0662 574	70.7966 786	76.3267 917	82.4077 705	89.0995 061	57
58	70.5266 991	72.3276 537	78.0900 597	84.4378 676	91.4359 987	58
59	71.9968 771	73.8701 111	79.8709 603	86.4933 410	93.8075 386	59
60	73.4768 562	75.4241 369	81.6696 699	88.5745 078	96.2146 517	60
61	74.9667 020	76.9898 180	83.4863 666	90.6816 891	98.6578 715	61
62	76.4664 800	78.5672 416	85.3212 302	92.8152 102	101.1377 396	62
63	77.9762 565	80.1564 959	87.1744 425	94.9754 003	103.6548 057	63
64	79.4960 982	81.7576 696	89.0461 869	97.1625 928	106.2096 277	64
65	81.0260 722	83.3708 521	90.9366 488	99.3771 253	108.8027 722	65
66	82.5662 460	84.9961 335	92.8460 153	101.6193 393	111.4348 137	66
67	84.1166 877	86.6336 045	94.7744 755	103.8895 811	114.1063 359	67
68	85.6774 656	88.2833 566	96.7222 202	106.1882 008	116.8179 310	68
69	87.2486 487	89.9454 817	98.6894 424	108.5155 533	119.5701 999	69
70	88.8303 063	91.6200 729	100.6763 368	110.8719 978	122.3637 529	70
71	90.4225 084	93.3072 234	102.6831 002	113.2578 977	125.1992 092	71
72	92.0253 251	95.0070 276	104.7099 312	115.6736 215	128.0771 974	72
73	93.6388 273	96.7195 803	106.7570 305	118.1195 417	130.9983 553	73
74	95.2630 861	98.4449 771	108.8246 008	120.5960 360	133.9633 307	74
75	96.8981-734	100.1833 145	110.9128 468	123.1034 864	136.9727 806	75
76	98.5441 612	101.9346 893	113.0219 753	125.6422 800	140.0273 723	76
77	100.2011 222	103.6991 995	115.1521 951	128.2128 085	143.1277 829	77
78	101.8691 297	105.4769 435	117.3037 170	130.8154 686	146.2746 997	78
79	103.5482 573	107.2680 206	119.4767 542	133.4506 620	149.4688 202	79
80	105.2385 790	109.0725 307	121.6715 217	136.1187 953	152.7108 525	80
81	106.9401 695	110.8905 747	123.8882 369	138.8202 802	156.0015 153	81
82	108.6531 040	112.7222 540	126.1271 193	141.5555 337	159.3415 380	82
83	110.3774 580	114.5676 709	128.3883 905	144.3249 779	162.7316 611	83
84	112.1133 077	116.4269 284	130.6722 744	147.1290 401	166.1726 360	84
85	113.8607 298	118.3001 304	132.9789 971	149.9681 531	169.6652 255	85
86	115.6198 013	120.1873 814	135.3087 871	152.8427 550	173.2102 039	86
87	117.3906 000	122.0887 867	137.6618 750	155.7532 895	176.8083 569	87
88	119.1732 040	124.0044 526	140.0384 937	158.7002 056	180.4604 823	88
89	120.9676 920	125.9344 860	142.4388 787	161.6839 581	184.1673 895	89
90	122.7741 433	127.8789 947	144.8632 675	164.7050 076	187.9299 004	90
91	124.5926 376	129.8380 871	147.3119 001	167.7638 202	191.7488 489	91
92	126.4232 552	131.8118 728	149.7850 191	170.8608 680	195.6250 816	92
93	128.2660 769	133.8004 618	152.2828 693	173.9966 288	199.5594 578	93
94	130.1211 840	135.8039 653	154.8056 980	177.1715 867	203.5528 497	94
95	131.9886 586	137.8224 951	157.3537 550	180.3862 315	207.6061 425	95
96	133.8685 830	139.8561 638	159.9272 926	183.6410 594	211.7202 346	96
97	135.7610 402	141.9050 850	162.5265 655	186.9365 726	215.8960 381	97
98	137.6661 138	143.9693 731	165.1518 311	190.2732 798	220.1344 787	98
99	139.5838 879	146.0491 434	167.8033 494	193.6516 958	224.4364 959	99
100	141.5144 471	148.1445 120	170.4813 829	197.0723 420	228.8030 433	100

Table VII — Amount of 1 per Period

$$s_{\overline{n}|} = [(1+i)^n - 1]/i$$

n	$1\frac{3}{4}$ per cent	2 per cent	$2\frac{1}{4}$ per cent	$2\frac{1}{2}$ per cent	3 per cent	n
1	1.0000 000	1.0000 000	1.0000 000	1.0000 000	1.0000 000	1
2	2.0175 000	2.0200 000	2.0225 000	2.0250 000	2.0300 000	2
3	3.0528 062	3.0604 000	3.0680 062	3.0756 250	3.0909 000	3
4	4.1062 304	4.1216 080	4.1370 364	4.1525 156	4.1836 270	4
5	5.1780 894	5.2040 402	5.2301 197	5.2563 285	5.3091 358	5
6	6.2687 060	6.3081 210	6.3477 974	6.3877 367	6.4684 099	6
7	7.3784 083	7.4342 834	7.4906 228	7.5474 302	7.6624 622	7
8	8.5075 304	8.5829 690	8.6591 619	8.7361 159	8.8923 360	8
9	9.6564 122	9.7546 284	9.8539 930	9.9545 188	10.1591 061	9
10	10.8253 994	10.9497 210	11.0757 078	11.2033 818	11.4638 793	10
11	12.0148 439	12.1687 154	12.3249 113	12.4834 663	12.8077 957	11
12	13.2251 037	13.4120 897	13.6022 218	13.7955 530	14.1920 296	12
13	14.4565 430	14.6803 315	14.9082 718	15.1404 418	15.6177 904	13
14	15.7095 325	15.9739 382	16.2437 079	16.5189 528	17.0863 242	14
15	16.9844 494	17.2934 169	17.6091 913	17.9319 267	18.5989 139	15
16	18.2816 772	18.6392 852	19.0053 981	19.3802 248	20.1568 813	16
17	19.6016 066	20.0120 710	20.4330 196	20.8647 304	21.7615 877	17
18	20.9446 347	21.4123 124	21.8927 625	22.3863 487	23.4144 354	18
19	22.3111 658	22.8405 586	23.3853 497	23.9460 074	25.1168 684	19
20	23.7016 112	24.2973 698	24.9115 200	25.5446 576	26.8703 745	20
21	25.1163 894	25.7833 172	26.4720 292	27.1832 740	28.6764 857	21
22	26.5559 262	27.2989 835	28.0076 499	28.8628 559	30.5367 803	22
23	28.0206 549	28.8449 632	29.6991 720	30.5844 273	32.4528 837	23
24	29.5110 164	30.4218 625	31.3674 034	32.3490 380	34.4264 702	24
25	31.0274 592	32.0302 997	33.0731 700	34.1577 639	36.4592 643	25
26	32.5704 397	33.6709 057	34.8173 163	36.0117 080	38.5530 422	26
27	34.1404 224	35.3443 238	36.6007 059	37.9120 007	40.7096 335	27
28	35.7378 798	37.0512 103	38.4242 218	39.8598 008	42.9309 225	28
29	37.3632 927	38.7922 345	40.2887 668	41.8562 958	45.2188 502	29
30	39.0171 503	40.5680 792	42.1952 640	43.9027 032	47.5754 157	30
31	40.6999 504	42.3794 408	44.1446 575	46.0002 707	50.0026 782	31
32	42.4121 996	44.2270 296	46.1379 123	48.1502 775	52.5027 585	32
33	44.1544 130	46.1115 702	48.1760 153	50.3540 344	55.0778 413	33
34	45.9271 153	48.0338 016	50.2599 756	52.6128 853	57.7301 765	34
35	47.7308 398	49.9944 776	52.3908 251	54.9282 074	60.4620 818	35
36	49.5661 295	51.9943 672	54.5696 186	57.3014 126	63.2759 443	36
37	51.4335 368	54.0342 545	56.7974 351	59.7339 479	66.1742 226	37
38	53.3336 236	56.1149 396	59.0753 774	62.2272 966	69.1594 493	38
39	55.2669 621	58.2372 384	61.4045 733	64.7829 791	72.2342 328	39
40	57.2341 339	60.4019 832	63.7861 762	67.4025 535	75.4012 597	40
41	59.2357 312	62.6100 228	66.2213 652	70.0876 174	78.6632 975	41
42	61.2723 565	64.8622 233	68.7113 459	72.8398 078	82.0231 964	42
43	63.3446 228	67.1594 678	71.2573 512	75.6608 030	85.4838 923	43
44	65.4531 537	69.5026 571	73.8606 416	78.5523 231	89.0484 091	44
45	67.5985 839	71.8927 103	76.5225 060	81.5161 312	92.7198 614	45
46	69.7815 591	74.3305 645	79.2442 624	84.5540 344	96.5014 572	46
47	72.0027 364	76.8171 758	82.0272 583	87.6678 853	100.3965 010	47
48	74.2627 842	79.3535 193	84.8728 716	90.8595 824	104.4083 960	48
49	76.5623 830	81.9405 897	87.7825 113	94.1310 720	108.5406 478	49
50	78.9022 247	84.5794 014	90.7576 178	97.4843 488	112.7968 673	50

[508]

Table VII — Amount of 1 per Period

$$s_{\overline{n}|}=[(1+i)^n-1]/i$$

n	$1\frac{3}{4}$ per cent	2 per cent	$2\frac{1}{4}$ per cent	$2\frac{1}{2}$ per cent	3 per cent	n
51	81.2830 136	87.2709 895	93.7996 642	100.9214 575	117.1807 733	51
52	83.7054 663	90.0164 093	96.9101 566	104.4444 939	121.6961 965	52
53	86.1703 120	92.8167 375	100.0906 351	108.0556 063	126.3470 824	53
54	88.6782 925	95.6730 722	103.3426 744	111.7569 965	131.1374 949	54
55	91.2301 626	98.5865 337	106.6678 846	115.5509 214	136.0716 197	55
56	93.8266 904	101.5582 643	110.0679 120	119.4396 944	141.1537 683	56
57	96.4686 575	104.5894 296	113.5444 400	123.4256 868	146.3883 814	57
58	99.1568 590	107.6812 182	117.0991 899	127.5113 289	151.7800 328	58
59	101.8921 041	110.8348 426	120.7339 217	131.6991 121	157.3334 338	59
60	104.6752 159	114.0515 394	124.4504 349	135.9915 900	163.0534 368	60
61	107.5070 322	117.3325 702	128.2505 697	140.3913 797	168.9450 399	61
62	110.3884 052	120.6792 216	132.1362 075	144.9011 642	175.0133 911	62
63	113.3202 023	124.0928 060	136.1092 722	149.5236 933	181.2637 928	63
64	116.3033 058	127.5746 622	140.1717 308	154.2617 856	187.7017 066	64
65	119.3386 137	131.1261 554	144.3255 948	159.1183 303	194.3327 578	65
66	122.4270 394	134.7486 785	148.5729 207	164.0962 885	201.1627 406	66
67	125.5695 126	138.4436 521	152.9158 114	169.1986 957	208.1976 228	67
68	128.7669 791	142.2125 251	157.3564 171	174.4286 631	215.4435 515	68
69	132.0204 012	146.0567 756	161.8969 365	179.7893 797	222.9068 580	69
70	135.3307 583	149.9779 111	166.5396 176	185.2841 142	230.5940 637	70
71	138.6990 465	153.9774 694	171.2867 590	190.9162 171	238.5118 856	71
72	142.1262 798	158.0570 188	176.1407 111	196.6891 225	246.6672 422	72
73	145.6134 897	162.2181 591	181.1038 771	202.6063 506	255.0672 595	73
74	149.1617 258	166.4625 223	186.1787 143	208.6715 093	263.7192 773	74
75	152.7720 560	170.7917 728	191.3677 354	214.8882 970	272.6308 556	75
76	156.4455 670	175.2076 082	196.6735 094	221.2605 045	281.8097 813	76
77	160.1833 644	179.7117 604	202.0986 634	227.7920 171	291.2640 747	77
78	163.9865 733	184.3059 956	207.6458 833	234.4868 175	301.0019 969	78
79	167.8563 383	188.9921 155	213.3179 157	241.3489 880	311.0320 568	79
80	171.7938 242	193.7719 578	219.1175 688	248.3827 126	321.3630 185	80
81	175.8002 162	198.6473 970	225.0477 141	255.5922 805	332.0039 091	81
82	179.8767 199	203.6203 449	231.1112 876	262.9820 875	342.9640 264	82
83	184.0245 625	208.6927 518	237.3112 916	270.5566 397	354.2529 472	83
84	188.2449 924	213.8666 068	243.6507 957	278.3205 557	365.8805 356	84
85	192.5392 798	219.1439 390	250.1329 386	286.2785 695	377.8569 517	85
86	196.9087 172	224.5268 178	256.7609 297	294.4355 338	390.1926 602	86
87	201.3546 197	230.0173 541	263.5380 506	302.7964 221	402.8984 400	87
88	205.8783 256	235.6177 012	270.4676 567	311.3663 327	415.9853 932	88
89	210.4811 962	241.3300 552	277.5531 790	320.1504 910	429.4649 550	89
90	215.1646 172	247.1566 563	284.7981 255	329.1542 533	443.3489 037	90
91	219.9299 980	253.0997 894	292.2060 834	338.3831 096	457.6493 708	91
92	224.7787 730	259.1617 852	299.7807 202	347.8426 873	472.3788 519	92
93	229.7124 015	265.3450 209	307.5257 865	357.5387 545	487.5502 174	93
94	234.7323 685	271.6519 214	315.4451 166	367.4772 234	503.1767 240	94
95	239.8401 849	278.0849 598	323.5426 318	377.6641 540	519.2720 257	95
96	245.0373 882	284.6466 590	331.8223 410	388.1057 578	535.8501 865	96
97	250.3255 425	291.3395 922	340.2883 437	398.8084 018	552.9256 920	97
98	255.7062 395	298.1663 840	348.9448 314	409.7786 118	570.5134 628	98
99	261.1810 987	305.1297 117	357.7960 901	421.0230 771	588.6288 667	99
100	266.7517 679	312.2323 059	366.8465 021	432.5486 540	607.2877 327	100

[509]

Table VII — Amount of 1 per Period

$$s_{\overline{n}|} = [(1+i)^n - 1]/i$$

n	3½ per cent	4 per cent	4½ per cent	5 per cent	5½ per cent	n
1	1.000 0000	1.000 0000	1.000 0000	1.000 0000	1.0000 000	1
2	2.035 0000	2.040 0000	2.045 0000	2.050 0000	2.0550 000	2
3	3.106 2250	3.121 6000	3.137 0250	3.152 5000	3.1680 250	3
4	4.214 9429	4.246 4640	4.278 1911	4.310 1250	4.3422 664	4
5	5.362 4659	5.416 3226	5.470 7097	5.525 6312	5.5810 910	5
6	6.550 1522	6.632 9755	6.716 8917	6.801 9128	6.8880 510	6
7	7.779 4075	7.898 2945	8.019 1518	8.142 0084	8.2668 938	7
8	9.051 6868	9.214 2263	9.380 0136	9.549 1089	9.7215 730	8
9	10.368 4958	10.582 7953	10.802 1142	11.026 5643	11.2562 595	9
10	11.731 3932	12.006 1071	12.288 2094	12.577 8925	12.8753 538	10
11	13.141 9919	13.486 3514	13.841 1788	14.206 7872	14.5834 982	11
12	14.601 9616	15.025 8055	15.464 0318	15.917 1265	16.3855 907	12
13	16.113 0303	16.626 8377	17.159 9133	17.712 9828	18.2867 981	13
14	17.676 9864	18.291 9112	18.932 1094	19.598 6320	20.2925 720	14
15	19.295 6809	20.023 5876	20.784 0543	21.578 5636	22.4086 635	15
16	20.971 0297	21.824 5311	22.719 3367	23.657 4918	24.6411 400	16
17	22.705 0158	23.697 5124	24.741 7069	25.840 3664	26.9964 027	17
18	24.499 6913	25.645 4129	26.855 0837	28.132 3847	29.4812 048	18
19	26.357 1805	27.671 2294	29.063 5625	30.539 0039	32.1026 711	19
20	28.279 6818	29.778 0786	31.371 4228	33.065 9541	34.8683 180	20
21	30.269 4707	31.969 2017	33.783 1368	35.719 2518	37.7860 755	21
22	32.328 9022	34.247 9698	36.303 3780	38.505 2144	40.8643 097	22
23	34.460 4137	36.617 8886	38.937 0300	41.430 4751	44.1118 467	23
24	36.666 5282	39.082 6041	41.689 1963	44.501 9989	47.5379 983	24
25	38.949 8567	41.645 9083	44.565 2102	47.727 0988	51.1525 882	25
26	41.313 1017	44.311 7446	47.570 6446	51.113 4538	54.9659 805	26
27	43.759 0602	47.084 2144	50.711 3236	54.669 1264	58.9891 094	27
28	46.290 6273	49.967 5830	53.993 3332	58.402 5828	63.2335 105	28
29	48.910 7993	52.966 2863	57.423 0332	62.322 7119	67.7113 535	29
30	51.622 6773	56.084 9378	61.007 0697	66.438 8475	72.4354 780	30
31	54.429 4710	59.328 3353	64.752 3878	70.760 7899	77.4194 293	31
32	57.334 5025	62.701 4687	68.666 2452	75.298 8294	82.6774 979	32
33	60.341 2100	66.209 5274	72.756 2263	80.063 7708	88.2247 603	33
34	63.453 1524	69.857 9085	77.030 2565	85.066 9594	94.0771 221	34
35	66.674 0127	73.652 2249	81.496 6180	90.320 3074	100.2513 638	35
36	70.007 6032	77.598 3138	86.163 9658	95.836 3227	106.7651 888	36
37	73.457 8693	81.702 2464	91.041 3443	101.628 1389	113.6372 742	37
38	77.028 8947	85.970 3363	96.138 2048	107.709 5458	120.8873 242	38
39	80.724 9060	90.409 1497	101.464 4240	114.095 0231	128.5361 271	39
40	84.550 2778	95.025 5157	107.030 3231	120.799 7742	136.6056 141	40
41	88.509 5375	99.826 5363	112.846 6876	127.839 7630	145.1189 228	41
42	92.607 3713	104.819 5978	118.924 7885	135.231 7511	154.1004 636	42
43	96.848 6293	110.012 3817	125.276 4040	142.993 3387	163.5759 891	43
44	101.238 3313	115.412 8770	131.913 8422	151.143 0056	173.5726 685	44
45	105.781 6729	121.029 3920	138.849 9651	159.700 1559	184.1191 653	45
46	110.484 0314	126.870 5677	146.098 2135	168.685 1637	195.2457 194	46
47	115.350 9726	132.945 3904	153.672 6331	178.119 4218	206.9842 339	47
48	120.388 2566	139.263 2060	161.587 9016	188.025 3929	219.3683 668	48
49	125.601 8456	145.833 7343	169.859 3572	198.426 6626	232.4336 270	49
50	130.997 9102	152.667 0837	178.503 0283	209.347 9957	246.2174 764	50

[510]

Table VII — Amount of 1 per Period

$$s_{\overline{n}|} = [(1+i)^n - 1]/i$$

n	$3\frac{1}{2}$ per cent	4 per cent	$4\frac{1}{2}$ per cent	5 per cent	$5\frac{1}{2}$ per cent	n
51	136.5828 370	159.7737 670	187.5356 646	220.8153 955	260.7594 377	51
52	142.3632 363	167.1647 177	196.9747 695	232.8561 653	276.1012 067	52
53	148.3459 496	174.8513 064	206.8386 341	245.4989 735	292.2867 731	53
54	154.5380 578	182.8453 586	217.1463 726	258.7739 222	309.3625 456	54
55	160.9468 898	191.1591 730	227.9179 594	272.7126 183	327.3774 856	55
56	167.5800 310	199.8055 399	239.1742 676	287.3482 492	346.3832 473	56
57	174.4453 321	208.7977 615	250.9371 096	302.7156 617	366.4343 259	57
58	181.5509 187	218.1496 720	263.2292 795	318.8514 448	387.5882 139	58
59	188.9052 008	227.8756 588	276.0745 971	335.7940 170	409.9055 656	59
60	196.5168 829	237.9906 852	289.4979 540	353.5837 179	433.4503 717	60
61	204.3949 738	248.5103 126	303.5253 619	372.2629 038	458.2901 422	61
62	212.5487 979	259.4507 251	318.1840 032	391.8760 490	484.4961 000	62
63	220.9880 058	270.8287 541	333.5022 833	412.4698 514	512.1433 855	63
64	229.7225 860	282.6619 043	349.5098 861	434.0933 440	541.3112 717	64
65	238.7628 765	294.9683 805	366.2378 310	456.7980 112	572.0833 916	65
66	248.1195 772	307.7671 157	383.7185 334	480.6379 117	604.5479 782	66
67	257.8037 624	321.0778 003	401.9858 674	505.6698 073	638.7981 170	67
68	267.8268 941	334.9209 123	421.0752 314	531.9532 977	674.9320 134	68
69	278.2008 354	349.3177 488	441.0236 168	559.5509 626	713.0532 741	69
70	288.9378 646	364.2904 588	461.8696 795	588.5285 107	753.2712 042	70
71	300.0506 899	379.8620 771	483.6538 151	618.9549 362	795.7011 205	71
72	311.5524 640	396.0565 602	506.4182 368	650.9026 831	840.4646 821	72
73	323.4568 002	412.8988 226	530.2070 575	684.4478 172	887.6902 396	73
74	335.7777 882	430.4147 755	555.0663 751	719.6702 081	937.5132 028	74
75	348.5300 108	448.6313 665	581.0443 620	756.6537 185	990.0764 289	75
76	361.7285 612	467.5766 212	608.1913 582	795.4864 044	1045.5306 325	76
77	375.3890 609	487.2796 860	636.5599 693	836.2607 246	1104.0348 173	77
78	389.5276 780	507.7708 735	666.2051 680	879.0737 608	1165.7567 323	78
79	404.1611 467	529.0817 084	697.1844 005	924.0274 489	1230.8733 525	79
80	419.3067 868	551.2449 767	729.5576 985	971.2288 213	1299.5713 869	80
81	434.9825 244	574.2947 758	763.3877 950	1020.7902 624	1372.0478 132	81
82	451.2069 127	598.2665 668	798.7402 457	1072.8297 755	1448.5104 429	82
83	467.9991 547	623.1972 295	835.6835 568	1127.4712 643	1529.1785 173	83
84	485.3791 251	649.1251 187	874.2893 169	1184.8448 275	1614.2833 357	84
85	503.3673 945	676.0901 235	914.6323 361	1245.0870 689	1704.0689 192	85
86	521.9852 533	704.1337 284	956.7907 912	1308.3414 223	1798.7927 098	86
87	541.2547 372	733.2990 775	1000.8463 769	1374.7584 935	1898.7263 088	87
88	561.1986 530	763.6310 406	1046.8844 638	1444.4964 181	2004.1562 558	88
89	581.8406 058	795.1762 823	1094.9942 647	1517.7212 390	2115.3848 499	89
90	603.2050 270	827.9833 335	1145.2690 066	1594.6073 010	2232.7310 166	90
91	625.3172 030	862.1026 669	1197.8061 119	1675.5376 660	2356.5312 225	91
92	648.2033 051	897.5867 736	1252.7073 869	1760.1045 493	2487.1404 398	92
93	671.8904 207	934.4902 445	1310.0792 193	1849.1097 768	2624.9331 639	93
94	696.4065 855	972.8698 543	1370.0327 842	1942.5652 656	2770.3044 880	94
95	721.7808 160	1012.7846 485	1432.6842 595	2040.6935 289	2923.6712 348	95
96	748.0431 445	1054.2960 344	1498.1550 512	2143.7282 054	3085.4731 527	96
97	775.2246 546	1097.4678 758	1566.5720 285	2251.9146 156	3256.1741 761	97
98	803.3575 175	1142.3665 908	1638.0677 698	2365.5103 464	3436.2637 558	98
99	832.4750 306	1189.0612 544	1712.7808 194	2484.7858 637	3626.2582 624	99
100	862.6116 567	1237.6237 046	1790.8559 563	2610.0251 569	3826.7024 668	100

Table VII — Amount of 1 per Period

$$s_{\overline{n}|} = [(1+i)^n - 1]/i$$

n	6 per cent	6½ per cent	7 per cent	7½ per cent	8 per cent	n
1	1.0000 000	1.0000 000	1.0000 000	1.0000 000	1.0000 000	1
2	2.0600 000	2.0650 000	2.0700 000	2.0750 000	2.0800 000	2
3	3.1836 000	3.1992 250	3.2149 000	3.2306 250	3.2464 000	3
4	4.3746 160	4.4071 746	4.4399 430	4.4729 219	4.5061 120	4
5	5.6370 930	5.6936 410	5.7507 390	5.8083 910	5.8666 010	5
6	6.9753 185	7.0637 276	7.1532 907	7.2440 203	7.3359 290	6
7	8.3938 376	8.5228 699	8.6540 211	8.7873 219	8.9228 034	7
8	9.8974 679	10.0768 565	10.2598 026	10.4463 710	10.6366 276	8
9	11.4913 160	11.7318 522	11.9779 888	12.2298 488	12.4875 578	9
10	13.1807 949	13.4944 225	13.8164 480	14.1470 875	14.4865 625	10
11	14.9716 426	15.3715 600	15.7835 993	16.2081 191	16.6454 875	11
12	16.8699 412	17.3707 114	17.8884 513	18.4237 280	18.9771 265	12
13	18.8821 377	19.4998 076	20.1406 429	20.8055 076	21.4952 966	13
14	21.0150 659	21.7672 951	22.5504 879	23.3659 207	24.2149 203	14
15	23.2759 699	24.1821 693	25.1290 220	26.1183 647	27.1521 139	15
16	25.6725 281	26.7540 103	27.8880 536	29.0772 421	30.3242 830	16
17	28.2128 798	29.4930 210	30.8402 173	32.2580 352	33.7502 257	17
18	30.9056 526	32.4100 674	33.9990 325	35.6773 879	37.4502 437	18
19	33.7599 917	35.5167 218	37.3789 648	39.3531 919	41.4462 632	19
20	36.7855 912	38.8253 087	40.9954 923	43.3046 813	45.7619 643	20
21	39.9927 267	42.3489 537	44.8651 768	47.5525 324	50.4229 214	21
22	43.3922 903	46.1016 357	49.0057 392	52.1189 724	55.4567 552	22
23	46.9958 277	50.0982 420	53.4361 409	57.0278 953	60.8932 956	23
24	50.8155 774	54.3546 278	58.1766 708	62.3049 874	66.7647 592	24
25	54.8645 120	58.8876 786	63.2490 377	67.9778 615	73.1059 400	25
26	59.1563 827	63.7153 777	68.6764 704	74.0762 011	79.9544 152	26
27	63.7057 657	68.8568 772	74.4838 233	80.6319 162	87.3507 684	27
28	68.5281 116	74.3325 743	80.6976 909	87.6793 099	95.3388 298	28
29	73.6397 983	80.1641 916	87.3465 293	95.2552 582	103.9659 362	29
30	79.0581 862	86.3748 640	94.4607 863	103.3994 025	113.2832 111	30
31	84.8016 774	92.9892 302	102.0730 414	112.1543 577	123.3458 680	31
32	90.8897 780	100.0335 302	110.2181 543	121.5659 345	134.2135 374	32
33	97.3431 647	107.5357 096	118.9334 251	131.6833 796	145.9506 204	33
34	104.1837 546	115.5255 308	128.2587 648	142.5596 331	158.6266 701	34
35	111.4347 799	124.0346 903	138.2368 784	154.2516 056	172.3168 037	35
36	119.1208 667	133.0969 451	148.9134 598	166.8204 760	187.1021 480	36
37	127.2681 187	142.7482 466	160.3374 020	180.3320 117	203.0703 198	37
38	135.9042 058	153.0268 826	172.5610 202	194.8569 126	220.3159 454	38
39	145.0584 581	163.9736 300	185.6402 916	210.4711 810	238.9412 210	39
40	154.7619 656	175.6319 159	199.6351 120	227.2565 196	259.0565 187	40
41	165.0476 836	188.0479 904	214.6095 698	245.3007 586	280.7810 402	41
42	175.9505 446	201.2711 098	230.6322 397	264.6983 155	304.2435 234	42
43	187.5075 772	215.3537 320	247.7764 965	285.5506 891	329.5830 053	43
44	199.7580 319	230.3517 245	266.1208 512	307.9669 908	356.9496 457	44
45	212.7435 138	246.3245 866	285.7493 108	332.0645 151	386.5056 174	45
46	226.5081 246	263.3356 848	306.7517 626	357.9693 537	418.4260 668	46
47	241.0986 121	281.4525 043	329.2243 860	385.8170 553	452.9001 521	47
48	256.5645 288	300.7469 170	353.2700 930	415.7533 344	490.1321 643	48
49	272.9584 006	321.2954 666	378.9989 995	447.9348 345	530.3427 374	49
50	290.3359 046	343.1796 720	406.5289 295	482.5299 471	573.7701 564	50

Table VII — Amount of 1 per Period

$$s_{\overline{n}|} = [(1+i)^n - 1]/i$$

n	6 per cent	$6\frac{1}{2}$ per cent	7 per cent	$7\frac{1}{2}$ per cent	8 per cent	n
51	308.7560 589	366.4863 507	435.9859 545	519.7196 931	620.6717 689	51
52	328.2814 224	391.3079 635	467.5049 714	559.6986 701	671.3255 104	52
53	348.9783 077	417.7429 811	501.2303 193	602.6760 704	726.0315 513	53
54	370.9170 062	445.8962 748	537.3164 417	648.8767 756	785.1140 754	54
55	394.1720 266	475.8795 327	575.9285 926	698.5425 338	848.9232 014	55
56	418.8223 482	507.8117 023	617.2435 941	751.9332 239	917.8370 575	56
57	444.9516 891	541.8194 630	661.4506 457	809.3282 156	992.2640 221	57
58	472.6487 904	578.0377 281	708.7521 909	871.0278 318	1072.6451 439	58
59	502.0077 178	616.6101 804	759.3648 443	937.3549 192	1159.4567 554	59
60	533.1281 809	657.6898 421	813.5203 833	1008.6565 381	1253.2132 958	60
61	566.1158 717	701.4396 819	871.4668 102	1085.3057 785	1354.4703 595	61
62	601.0828 240	748.0332 612	933.4694 869	1167.7037 119	1463.8279 883	62
63	638.1477 935	797.6554 232	999.8123 510	1256.2814 903	1581.9342 273	63
64	677.4366 611	850.5030 257	1070.7992 155	1351.5026 021	1709.4889 655	64
65	719.0828 608	906.7857 223	1146.7551 606	1453.8652 972	1847.2480 828	65
66	763.2278 324	966.7267 943	1228.0280 219	1563.9051 945	1996.0279 294	66
67	810.0215 024	1030.5640 359	1314.9899 834	1682.1980 841	2156.7101 637	67
68	859.6227 925	1098.5506 983	1408.0392 823	1809.3629 404	2330.2469 768	68
69	912.2001 600	1170.9564 937	1507.6020 320	1946.0651 609	2517.6667 350	69
70	967.9321 696	1248.0686 657	1614.1341 743	2093.0200 480	2720.0800 738	70
71	1027.0080 998	1330.1931 290	1728.1235 664	2250.9965 516	2938.6864 797	71
72	1089.6285 858	1417.6556 824	1850.0922 161	2420.8212 930	3174.7813 980	72
73	1156.0063 010	1510.8033 018	1980.5986 712	2603.3828 899	3429.7639 099	73
74	1226.3666 790	1610.0055 164	2120.2405 782	2799.6366 067	3705.1450 227	74
75	1300.9486 798	1715.6558 749	2269.6574 187	3010.6093 522	4002.5566 245	75
76	1380.0056 006	1828.1735 068	2429.5334 380	3237.4050 536	4323.7611 545	76
77	1463.8059 366	1948.0047 847	2600.6007 787	3481.2104 326	4670.6620 468	77
78	1552.6342 928	2075.6250 958	2783.6428 332	3743.3012 151	5045.3150 106	78
79	1646.7923 503	2211.5407 270	2979.4978 315	4025.0488 062	5449.9402 114	79
80	1746.5998 914	2356.2908 742	3189.0626 797	4327.9274 667	5886.9354 283	80
81	1852.3958 849	2510.4497 811	3413.2970 673	4653.5220 267	6358.8902 626	81
82	1964.5396 379	2674.6290 168	3653.2278 620	5003.5361 787	6868.6014 836	82
83	2083.4120 162	2849.4799 029	3909.9538 123	5379.8013 921	7419.0896 023	83
84	2209.4167 372	3035.6960 966	4184.6505 792	5784.2864 965	8013.6167 705	84
85	2342.9817 414	3234.0163 429	4478.5761 197	6219.1079 837	8655.7061 121	85
86	2484.5606 459	3445.2274 052	4793.0764 481	6686.5410 825	9349.1626 011	86
87	2634.6342 847	3670.1671 865	5129.5917 995	7189.0316 637	10098.0956 091	87
88	2793.7123 417	3909.7280 536	5489.6632 254	7729.2090 384	10906.9432 579	88
89	2962.3350 822	4164.8603 771	5874.9396 512	8309.8997 163	11780.4987 185	89
90	3141.0751 872	4436.5763 016	6287.1854 268	8934.1421 950	12723.9386 160	90
91	3330.5396 984	4725.9537 612	6728.2884 067	9605.2028 597	13742.8537 053	91
92	3531.3720 803	5034.1407 557	7200.2685 951	10326.5930 741	14843.2820 017	92
93	3744.2544 051	5362.3599 049	7705.2873 968	11102.0875 547	16031.7445 618	93
94	3969.9096 694	5711.9132 987	8245.6575 146	11935.7441 213	17315.2841 268	94
95	4209.1042 496	6084.1876 631	8823.8535 406	12831.9249 304	18701.5068 569	95
96	4462.6505 046	6480.6598 612	9442.5232 884	13795.3193 002	20198.6274 054	96
97	4731.4095 349	6902.9027 522	10104.4999 186	14830.9682 477	21815.5175 979	97
98	5016.2941 070	7352.5914 310	10812.8149 129	15944.2908 663	23561.7590 057	98
99	5318.2717 534	7831.5098 741	11570.7119 568	17141.1126 812	25447.6997 262	99
100	5638.3680 586	8341.5580 159	12381.6617 938	18427.6961 323	27484.5157 043	100

Table VIII — Present Value of 1 per Period

$$a_{\overline{n}|} = (1 - v^n)/i$$

n	$\frac{1}{4}$ per cent	$\frac{1}{3}$ per cent	$\frac{5}{12}$ per cent	$\frac{1}{2}$ per cent	$\frac{7}{12}$ per cent	n
1	0.9975 062	0.9966 777	0.9958 506	0.9950 249	0.9942 005	1
2	1.9925 249	1.9900 443	1.9875 691	1.9850 994	1.9826 351	2
3	2.9850 623	2.9801 106	2.9751 725	2.9702 481	2.9653 373	3
4	3.9751 245	3.9668 876	3.9586 780	3.9504 957	3.9423 403	4
5	4.9627 177	4.9503 863	4.9381 026	4.9258 663	4.9136 772	5
6	5.9478 480	5.9306 176	5.9134 632	5.8963 844	5.8793 808	6
7	6.9305 217	6.9075 923	6.8847 766	6.8620 740	6.8394 838	7
8	7.9107 449	7.8813 212	7.8520 597	7.8229 592	7.7940 187	8
9	8.8885 236	8.8518 152	8.8153 292	8.7790 639	8.7430 178	9
10	9.8638 639	9.8190 849	9.7746 016	9.7304 119	9.6865 131	10
11	10.8367 720	10.7831 411	10.7298 937	10.6770 267	10.6245 367	11
12	11.8072 538	11.7439 944	11.6812 220	11.6189 321	11.5571 202	12
13	12.7753 156	12.7016 556	12.6286 028	12.5561 513	12.4842 951	13
14	13.7409 631	13.6561 351	13.5720 526	13.4887 078	13.4060 929	14
15	14.7042 026	14.6074 436	14.5115 876	14.4166 246	14.3225 447	15
16	15.6650 400	15.5555 917	15.4472 242	15.3399 250	15.2336 816	16
17	16.6234 813	16.5005 897	16.3789 784	16.2586 319	16.1395 343	17
18	17.5795 325	17.4424 482	17.3068 665	17.1727 680	17.0401 335	18
19	18.5331 995	18.3811 776	18.2309 044	18.0823 562	17.9355 097	19
20	19.4844 883	19.3167 883	19.1511 081	18.9874 191	18.8256 932	20
21	20.4334 048	20.2492 907	20.0674 935	19.8879 793	19.7107 140	21
22	21.3799 549	21.1786 950	20.9800 765	20.7840 590	20.5906 022	22
23	22.3241 445	22.1050 117	21.8888 729	21.6756 806	21.4653 874	23
24	23.2659 796	23.0282 508	22.7938 983	22.5628 662	22.3350 994	24
25	24.2054 659	23.9484 228	23.6951 684	23.4456 380	23.1997 674	25
26	25.1426 094	24.8655 376	24.5926 988	24.3240 179	24.0594 208	26
27	26.0774 158	25.7796 056	25.4865 051	25.1980 278	24.9140 886	27
28	27.0098 911	26.6906 368	26.3766 025	26.0676 894	25.7637 998	28
29	27.9400 410	27.5986 413	27.2630 067	26.9330 242	26.6085 831	29
30	28.8678 713	28.5036 293	28.1457 328	27.7940 540	27.4484 670	30
31	29.7933 879	29.4056 105	29.0247 961	28.6508 000	28.2834 801	31
32	30.7165 964	30.3045 952	29.9002 119	29.5032 835	29.1136 504	32
33	31.6375 026	31.2005 933	30.7719 952	30.3515 259	29.9390 061	33
34	32.5561 123	32.0936 145	31.6401 612	31.1955 482	30.7595 754	34
35	33.4724 313	32.9836 690	32.5047 249	32.0353 713	31.5753 857	35
36	34.3864 651	33.8707 664	33.3657 011	32.8710 162	32.3864 646	36
37	35.2982 196	34.7549 167	34.2231 048	33.7025 037	33.1928 397	37
38	36.2077 003	35.6361 296	35.0769 508	34.5298 544	33.9945 383	38
39	37.1149 130	36.5144 149	35.9272 539	35.3530 890	34.7915 874	39
40	38.0198 634	37.3897 823	36.7740 288	36.1722 279	35.5840 140	40
41	38.9225 570	38.2622 415	37.6172 901	36.9872 914	36.3718 449	41
42	39.8229 995	39.1318 021	38.4570 524	37.7982 999	37.1551 068	42
43	40.7211 965	39.9984 739	39.2933 301	38.6052 735	37.9338 261	43
44	41.6171 536	40.8622 663	40.1261 379	39.4082 324	38.7080 293	44
45	42.5108 764	41.7231 890	40.9554 900	40.2071 964	39.4777 425	45
46	43.4023 705	42.5812 515	41.7814 008	41.0021 855	40.2429 917	46
47	44.2916 414	43.4364 633	42.6038 846	41.7932 194	41.0038 029	47
48	45.1786 946	44.2888 339	43.4229 556	42.5803 178	41.7602 017	48
49	46.0635 358	45.1383 726	44.2386 280	43.3635 003	42.5122 138	49
50	46.9461 704	45.9850 890	45.0509 158	44.1427 863	43.2598 646	50

[514]

Table VIII — Present Value of 1 per Period

$$a_{\overline{n}|} = (1 - v^n)/i$$

n	$\frac{1}{4}$ per cent	$\frac{1}{3}$ per cent	$\frac{5}{12}$ per cent	$\frac{1}{2}$ per cent	$\frac{7}{12}$ per cent	n
51	47.8266 039	46.8289 924	45.8598 332	44.9181 954	44.0031 794	51
52	48.7048 418	47.6700 921	46.6653 940	45.6897 466	44.7421 830	52
53	49.5808 895	48.5083 974	47.4676 123	46.4574 593	45.4769 014	53
54	50.4547 526	49.3439 177	48.2665 018	47.2213 526	46.2073 585	54
55	51.3264 366	50.1766 621	49.0620 765	47.9814 454	46.9335 793	55
56	52.1959 467	51.0066 400	49.8543 500	48.7377 566	47.6555 884	56
57	53.0632 885	51.8338 605	50.6433 361	49.4903 050	48.3734 102	57
58	53.9284 673	52.6583 327	51.4290 484	50.2391 095	49.0870 690	58
59	54.7914 886	53.4800 658	52.2115 005	50.9841 886	49.7965 889	59
60	55.6523 577	54.2990 689	52.9907 058	51.7255 608	50.5019 939	60
61	56.5110 800	55.1153 511	53.7666 780	52.4632 445	51.2033 080	61
62	57.3676 608	55.9289 213	54.5394 309	53.1972 582	51.9005 548	62
63	58.2221 056	56.7397 887	55.3089 763	53.9276 201	52.5937 579	63
64	59.0744 195	57.5479 622	56.0753 296	54.6543 484	53.2829 407	64
65	59.9246 080	58.3534 507	56.8385 019	55.3774 611	53.9681 267	65
66	60.7726 763	59.1562 631	57.5985 081	56.0969 762	54.6493 389	66
67	61.6186 297	59.9564 084	58.3553 608	56.8129 116	55.3266 004	67
68	62.4624 736	60.7538 954	59.1090 730	57.5252 852	55.9999 341	68
69	63.3042 130	61.5487 330	59.8596 577	58.2341 147	56.6693 629	69
70	64.1438 534	62.3409 299	60.6071 280	58.9394 176	57.3349 087	70
71	64.9813 999	63.1304 949	61.3514 967	59.6412 115	57.9965 958	71
72	65.8168 577	63.9174 368	62.0927 768	60.3395 139	58.6544 449	72
73	66.6502 322	64.7017 642	62.8309 810	61.0343 422	59.3084 788	73
74	67.4815 283	65.4834 859	63.5661 222	61.7257 137	59.9587 196	74
75	68.3107 515	66.2626 106	64.2982 129	62.4136 454	60.6051 893	75
76	69.1379 067	67.0391 468	65.0272 660	63.0981 547	61.2479 099	76
77	69.9629 992	67.8131 031	65.7532 939	63.7792 584	61.8869 030	77
78	70.7860 341	68.5844 881	66.4763 092	64.4569 735	62.5221 902	78
79	71.6070 166	69.3533 104	67.1963 245	65.1313 169	63.1537 931	79
80	72.4259 517	70.1195 785	67.9133 522	65.8023 054	63.7817 330	80
81	73.2428 446	70.8833 008	68.6274 047	66.4699 556	64.4060 312	81
82	74.0577 003	71.6444 859	69.3384 943	67.1342 842	65.0267 087	82
83	74.8705 240	72.4031 421	70.0466 333	67.7953 076	65.6437 867	83
84	75.6813 207	73.1592 778	70.7518 339	68.4530 424	66.2572 851	84
85	76.4900 955	73.9129 015	71.4541 085	69.1075 049	66.8672 262	85
86	77.2968 533	74.6640 214	72.1534 690	69.7587 114	67.4736 309	86
87	78.1015 993	75.4126 459	72.8499 276	70.4066 780	68.0765 179	87
88	78.9043 385	76.1587 833	73.5434 963	71.0514 209	68.6759 076	88
89	79.7050 758	76.9024 418	74.2341 872	71.6929 561	69.2718 228	89
90	80.5038 163	77.6436 297	74.9220 121	72.3312 996	69.8642 812	90
91	81.3005 649	78.3823 552	75.6069 830	72.9664 672	70.4533 036	91
92	82.0953 265	79.1186 265	76.2891 117	73.5984 749	71.0389 100	92
93	82.8881 063	79.8524 516	76.9684 110	74.2273 382	71.6211 202	93
94	83.6789 090	80.5838 388	77.6448 906	74.8530 728	72.1999 538	94
95	84.4677 397	81.3127 962	78.3185 622	75.4756 943	72.7754 305	95
96	85.2546 031	82.0393 317	78.9894 395	76.0952 183	73.3475 697	96
97	86.0395 044	82.7634 535	79.6575 331	76.7116 600	73.9163 897	97
98	86.8224 483	83.4851 696	80.3228 545	77.3250 348	74.4819 129	98
99	87.6034 397	84.2044 880	80.9854 152	77.9353 580	75.0441 554	99
100	88.3824 835	84.9214 166	81.6452 268	78.5426 448	75.6031 371	100
∞	400.0000 000	300.0000 000	240.0000 000	200.0000 000	171.4285 714	∞

Table VIII — Present Value of 1 per Period

$$a_{\overline{n}|} = (1-v^n)/i$$

n	$\frac{2}{3}$ per cent	$\frac{3}{4}$ per cent	1 per cent	$1\frac{1}{4}$ per cent	$1\frac{1}{2}$ per cent	n
1	0.9933 774	0.9925 558	0.9900 990	0.9876 543	0.9852 217	1
2	1.9801 763	1.9777 229	1.9703 951	1.9631 154	1.9558 834	2
3	2.9604 400	2.9555 562	2.9409 852	2.9265 337	2.9122 004	3
4	3.9342 120	3.9261 104	3.9019 656	3.8780 580	3.8543 846	4
5	4.9015 351	4.8894 396	4.8534 312	4.8178 350	4.7826 450	5
6	5.8624 520	5.8455 976	5.7954 765	5.7460 099	5.6971 872	6
7	6.8170 053	6.7946 378	6.7281 945	6.6627 258	6.5982 140	7
8	7.7652 371	7.7366 132	7.6516 778	7.5681 243	7.4859 251	8
9	8.7071 892	8.6715 764	8.5660 176	8.4623 450	8.3605 173	9
10	9.6429 031	9.5995 796	9.4713 045	9.3455 259	9.2221 846	10
11	10.5724 203	10.5206 745	10.3676 282	10.2178 034	10.0711 178	11
12	11.4957 818	11.4349 127	11.2550 775	11.0793 120	10.9075 052	12
13	12.4130 283	12.3423 451	12.1337 401	11.9301 847	11.7315 322	13
14	13.3242 003	13.2430 224	13.0037 030	12.7705 528	12.5433 815	14
15	14.2293 380	14.1369 950	13.8650 525	13.6005 459	13.3432 330	15
16	15.1284 815	15.0243 126	14.7178 738	14.4202 923	14.1312 640	16
17	16.0216 703	15.9050 249	15.5622 513	15.2299 183	14.9076 493	17
18	16.9089 441	16.7791 811	16.3982 686	16.0295 489	15.6725 609	18
19	17.7903 418	17.6468 298	17.2260 085	16.8193 076	16.4261 684	19
20	18.6659 024	18.5080 197	18.0455 530	17.5993 161	17.1686 388	20
21	19.5356 647	19.3627 987	18.8569 831	18.3696 950	17.9001 367	21
22	20.3996 669	20.2112 146	19.6603 793	19.1305 629	18.6208 244	22
23	21.2579 472	21.0533 147	20.4558 211	19.8820 374	19.3308 614	23
24	22.1105 436	21.8891 461	21.2433 873	20.6242 345	20.0304 054	24
25	22.9574 936	22.7187 555	22.0231 557	21.3572 686	20.7196 112	25
26	23.7988 348	23.5421 891	22.7952 037	22.0812 530	21.3986 317	26
27	24.6346 041	24.3594 929	23.5596 076	22.7962 992	22.0676 175	27
28	25.4648 385	25.1707 125	24.3164 432	23.5025 178	22.7267 167	28
29	26.2895 746	25.9758 933	25.0657 853	24.2000 176	23.3760 756	29
30	27.1088 490	26.7750 802	25.8077 082	24.8889 062	24.0158 380	30
31	27.9226 977	27.5683 178	26.5422 854	25.5692 901	24.6461 458	31
32	28.7311 566	28.3556 504	27.2695 895	26.2412 742	25.2671 387	32
33	29.5342 615	29.1371 220	27.9896 926	26.9049 622	25.8789 544	33
34	30.3320 479	29.9127 762	28.7026 659	27.5604 564	26.4817 285	34
35	31.1245 509	30.6826 563	29.4085 801	28.2078 582	27.0755 946	35
36	31.9118 055	31.4468 053	30.1075 050	28.8472 674	27.6606 843	36
37	32.6938 465	32.2052 658	30.7995 099	29.4787 826	28.2371 274	37
38	33.4707 085	32.9580 802	31.4846 633	30.1025 013	28.8050 516	38
39	34.2424 256	33.7052 905	32.1630 330	30.7185 198	29.3645 829	39
40	35.0090 321	34.4469 384	32.8346 861	31.3269 332	29.9158 452	40
41	35.7705 617	35.1830 654	33.4996 892	31.9278 352	30.4589 608	41
42	36.5270 480	35.9137 126	34.1581 081	32.5213 187	30.9940 500	42
43	37.2785 245	36.6389 207	34.8100 081	33.1074 753	31.5212 316	43
44	38.0250 244	37.3587 302	35.4554 535	33.6863 954	32.0406 222	44
45	38.7665 805	38.0731 814	36.0945 084	34.2581 682	32.5523 372	45
46	39.5032 257	38.7823 140	36.7272 361	34.8228 822	33.0564 898	46
47	40.2349 924	39.4861 677	37.3536 991	35.3806 244	33.5531 920	47
48	40.9619 130	40.1847 819	37.9739 595	35.9314 809	34.0425 536	48
49	41.6840 195	40.8781 954	38.5880 787	36.4755 367	34.5246 834	49
50	42.4013 439	41.5664 471	39.1961 175	37.0128 757	34.9996 881	50

Table VIII — Present Value of 1 per Period

$$a_{\overline{n}|} = (1-v^n)/i$$

n	$\tfrac{2}{3}$ per cent	$\tfrac{3}{4}$ per cent	1 per cent	$1\tfrac{1}{4}$ per cent	$1\tfrac{1}{2}$ per cent	n
51	43.1139 178	42.2495 753	39.7981 362	37.5435 810	35.4676 730	51
52	43.8217 726	42.9276 181	40.3941 942	38.0677 343	35.9287 419	52
53	44.5249 397	43.6006 135	40.9843 507	38.5854 166	36.3829 969	53
54	45.2234 500	44.2685 990	41.5686 641	39.0967 078	36.8305 388	54
55	45.9173 344	44.9316 119	42.1471 922	39.6016 867	37.2714 668	55
56	46.6066 236	45.5896 893	42.7199 922	40.1004 313	37.7058 786	56
57	47.2913 480	46.2428 678	43.2871 210	40.5930 186	38.1338 706	57
58	47.9715 377	46.8911 839	43.8486 347	41.0795 245	38.5555 375	58
59	48.6472 229	47.5346 738	44.4045 888	41.5600 242	38.9709 729	59
60	49.3184 333	48.1733 735	44.9550 384	42.0345 918	39.3802 689	60
61	49.9851 987	48.8073 186	45.5000 380	42.5033 005	39.7835 161	61
62	50.6475 484	49.4365 445	46.0396 416	42.9662 228	40.1808 041	62
63	51.3055 116	50.0610 864	46.5739 026	43.4234 299	40.5722 208	63
64	51.9591 175	50.6809 791	47.1028 738	43.8749 925	40.9578 530	64
65	52.6083 949	51.2962 571	47.6266 078	44.3209 802	41.3377 862	65
66	53.2533 724	51.9069 550	48.1451 562	44.7614 619	41.7121 046	66
67	53.8940 785	52.5131 067	48.6585 705	45.1965 056	42.0808 912	67
68	54.5305 416	53.1147 461	49.1669 015	45.6261 784	42.4442 278	68
69	55.1627 896	53.7119 068	49.6701 995	46.0505 466	42.8021 949	69
70	55.7908 506	54.3046 221	50.1685 143	46.4696 756	43.1548 718	70
71	56.4147 523	54.8929 252	50.6618 954	46.8836 302	43.5023 368	71
72	57.0345 221	55.4768 488	51.1503 915	47.2924 743	43.8446 668	72
73	57.6501 876	56.0564 256	51.6340 510	47.6962 709	44.1819 377	73
74	58.2617 757	56.6316 879	52.1129 218	48.0950 824	44.5142 243	74
75	58.8693 136	57.2026 679	52.5870 512	48.4889 703	44.8416 003	75
76	59.4728 281	57.7693 975	53.0564 864	48.8779 953	45.1641 383	76
77	60.0723 458	58.3319 081	53.5212 736	49.2622 176	45.4819 096	77
78	60.6678 932	58.8902 314	53.9814 590	49.6416 964	45.7949 848	78
79	61.2594 965	59.4443 984	54.4370 882	50.0164 903	46.1034 333	79
80	61.8471 820	59.9944 401	54.8882 061	50.3866 571	46.4073 235	80
81	62.4309 755	60.5403 872	55.3348 575	50.7522 539	46.7067 227	81
82	63.0109 028	61.0822 702	55.7770 867	51.1133 372	47.0016 972	82
83	63.5869 895	61.6201 193	56.2149 373	51.4699 626	47.2923 125	83
84	64.1592 611	62.1539 646	56.6484 528	51.8221 853	47.5786 330	84
85	64.7277 429	62.6838 358	57.0776 760	52.1700 596	47.8607 222	85
86	65.2924 598	63.2097 626	57.5026 495	52.5136 391	48.1386 425	86
87	65.8534 369	63.7317 743	57.9234 154	52.8529 769	48.4124 557	87
88	66.4106 989	64.2499 000	58.3400 152	53.1881 253	48.6822 224	88
89	66.9642 704	64.7641 688	58.7524 903	53.5191 361	48.9480 023	89
90	67.5141 759	65.2746 092	59.1608 815	53.8460 604	49.2098 545	90
91	68.0604 396	65.7812 498	59.5652 292	54.1689 485	49.4678 370	91
92	68.6030 857	66.2841 189	59.9655 735	54.4878 504	49.7220 069	92
93	69.1421 381	66.7832 446	60.3619 539	54.8028 152	49.9724 206	93
94	69.6776 207	67.2786 547	60.7544 098	55.1138 915	50.2191 335	94
95	70.2095 570	67.7703 768	61.1429 800	55.4211 274	50.4622 005	95
96	70.7379 705	68.2584 386	61.5277 030	55.7245 703	50.7016 754	96
97	71.2628 846	68.7428 671	61.9086 168	56.0242 670	50.9376 112	97
98	71.7843 224	69.2236 894	62.2857 592	56.3202 637	51.1700 603	98
99	72.3023 071	69.7009 324	62.6591 676	56.6126 061	51.3990 742	99
100	72.8168 613	70.1746 227	63.0288 788	56.9013 394	51.6247 037	100
∞	150.0000 000	133.3333 333	100.0000 000	80.0000 000	66.6666 667	∞

[517]

Table VIII — Present Value of 1 per Period

$$a_{\overline{n}|} = (1-v^n)/i$$

n	$1\frac{3}{4}$ per cent	2 per cent	$2\frac{1}{4}$ per cent	$2\frac{1}{2}$ per cent	3 per cent	n
1	0.9828 010	0.9803 922	0.9779 951	0.9756 098	0.9708 738	1
2	1.9486 988	1.9415 609	1.9344 696	1.9274 242	1.9134 697	2
3	2.8979 840	2.8838 833	2.8698 969	2.8560 236	2.8286 114	3
4	3.8309 425	3.8077 287	3.7847 402	3.7619 742	3.7170 984	4
5	4.7478 551	4.7134 595	4.6794 525	4.6458 285	4.5797 072	5
6	5.6489 976	5.6014 309	5.5544 768	5.5081 254	5.4171 914	6
7	6.5346 414	6.4719 911	6.4102 463	6.3493 906	6.2302 830	7
8	7.4050 530	7.3254 814	7.2471 846	7.1701 372	7.0196 922	8
9	8.2604 943	8.1622 367	8.0657 062	7.9708 655	7.7861 089	9
10	9.1012 229	8.9825 850	8.8662 164	8.7520 639	8.5302 028	10
11	9.9274 918	9.7868 480	9.6491 113	9.5142 087	9.2526 241	11
12	10.7395 497	10.5753 412	10.4147 788	10.2577 646	9.9540 040	12
13	11.5376 410	11.3483 738	11.1635 979	10.9831 850	10.6349 553	13
14	12.3220 059	12.1062 488	11.8959 392	11.6909 122	11.2960 731	14
15	13.0928 805	12.8492 635	12.6121 655	12.3813 777	11.9379 351	15
16	13.8504 968	13.5777 093	13.3126 313	13.0550 027	12.5611 020	16
17	14.5950 828	14.2918 719	13.9976 834	13.7121 977	13.1661 185	17
18	15.3268 627	14.9920 312	14.6676 611	14.3533 636	13.7535 131	18
19	16.0460 567	15.6784 620	15.3228 959	14.9788 913	14.3237 991	19
20	16.7528 813	16.3514 333	15.9637 124	15.5891 623	14.8774 749	20
21	17.4475 492	17.0112 092	16.5904 278	16.1845 486	15.4150 241	21
22	18.1302 695	17.6580 482	17.2033 523	16.7654 132	15.9369 166	22
23	18.8012 476	18.2922 041	17.8027 896	17.3321 105	16.4436 084	23
24	19.4606 856	18.9139 256	18.3890 362	17.8849 858	16.9355 421	24
25	20.1087 820	19.5234 565	18.9623 826	18.4243 764	17.4131 477	25
26	20.7457 317	20.1210 358	19.5231 126	18.9506 111	17.8768 424	26
27	21.3717 264	20.7068 978	20.0715 038	19.4640 109	18.3270 315	27
28	21.9869 547	21.2812 724	20.6078 276	19.9648 887	18.7641 082	28
29	22.5916 017	21.8443 847	21.1323 498	20.4535 499	19.1884 546	29
30	23.1858 493	22.3964 556	21.6453 298	20.9302 926	19.6004 414	30
31	23.7698 765	22.9377 015	22.1470 219	21.3954 074	20.0004 285	31
32	24.3438 590	23.4683 348	22.6376 742	21.8491 780	20.3887 655	32
33	24.9079 695	23.9885 636	23.1175 298	22.2918 809	20.7657 918	33
34	25.4623 779	24.4985 917	23.5868 262	22.7237 863	21.1318 367	34
35	26.0072 510	24.9986 193	24.0457 958	23.1451 573	21.4872 201	35
36	26.5427 528	25.4888 425	24.4946 658	23.5562 511	21.8322 525	36
37	27.0690 446	25.9694 534	24.9336 585	23.9573 181	22.1672 354	37
38	27.5862 846	26.4406 406	25.3629 912	24.3486 030	22.4924 616	38
39	28.0946 286	26.9025 888	25.7828 765	24.7303 444	22.8082 151	39
40	28.5942 296	27.3554 792	26.1935 222	25.1027 750	23.1147 720	40
41	29.0852 379	27.7994 894	26.5951 317	25.4661 220	23.4124 000	41
42	29.5678 014	28.2347 936	26.9879 039	25.8206 068	23.7013 592	42
43	30.0420 652	28.6615 623	27.3720 332	26.1664 457	23.9819 021	43
44	30.5081 722	29.0799 631	27.7477 097	26.5038 494	24.2542 739	44
45	30.9662 626	29.4901 599	28.1151 195	26.8330 239	24.5187 125	45
46	31.4164 743	29.8923 136	28.4744 445	27.1541 696	24.7754 491	46
47	31.8589 428	30.2865 820	28.8258 626	27.4674 826	25.0247 078	47
48	32.2938 013	30.6731 196	29.1695 478	27.7731 537	25.2667 066	48
49	32.7211 806	31.0520 780	29.5056 702	28.0713 695	25.5016 569	49
50	33.1412 095	31.4236 059	29.8343 963	28.3623 117	25.7297 640	50

[518]

Table VIII — Present Value of 1 per Period

$$a_{\overline{n}|} = (1 - v^n)/i$$

n	$1\frac{3}{4}$ per cent	2 per cent	$2\frac{1}{4}$ per cent	$2\frac{1}{2}$ per cent	3 per cent	n
51	33.5540 142	31.7878 489	30.1558 888	28.6461 577	25.9512 272	51
52	33.9597 191	32.1449 499	30.4703 069	28.9230 807	26.1662 400	52
53	34.3584 463	32.4950 489	30.7778 062	29.1932 495	26.3749 903	53
54	34.7503 158	32.8382 833	31.0785 391	29.4568 288	26.5776 605	54
55	35.1354 455	33.1747 875	31.3726 544	29.7139 793	26.7744 276	55
56	35.5139 513	33.5046 936	31.6602 977	29.9648 578	26.9654 637	56
57	35.8859 473	33.8281 310	31.9416 114	30.2096 174	27.1509 357	57
58	36.2515 452	34.1452 265	32.2167 349	30.4484 072	27.3310 055	58
59	36.6108 553	34.4561 044	32.4858 043	30.6813 729	27.5058 306	59
60	36.9639 855	34.7608 867	32.7489 529	30.9086 565	27.6755 637	60
61	37.3110 423	35.0596 928	33.0063 109	31.1303 966	27.8403 531	61
62	37.6521 300	35.3526 400	33.2580 057	31.3467 284	28.0003 428	62
63	37.9873 514	35.6398 432	33.5041 621	31.5577 838	28.1556 726	63
64	38.3168 072	35.9214 149	33.7449 018	31.7636 915	28.3064 783	64
65	38.6405 968	36.1974 655	33.9803 440	31.9645 771	28.4528 915	65
66	38.9588 175	36.4681 035	34.2106 054	32.1605 630	28.5950 403	66
67	39.2715 651	36.7334 348	34.4357 999	32.3517 688	28.7330 488	67
68	39.5789 337	36.9935 635	34.6560 391	32.5383 110	28.8670 377	68
69	39.8810 160	37.2485 917	34.8714 318	32.7203 034	28.9971 240	69
70	40.1779 027	37.4986 193	35.0820 849	32.8978 570	29.1234 214	70
71	40.4696 832	37.7437 444	35.2881 026	33.0710 800	29.2460 401	71
72	40.7564 454	37.9840 631	35.4895 869	33.2400 780	29.3650 875	72
73	41.0382 756	38.2196 697	35.6866 376	33.4049 542	29.4806 675	73
74	41.3152 586	38.4506 566	35.8793 521	33.5658 089	29.5928 811	74
75	41.5874 777	38.6771 143	36.0678 261	33.7227 404	29.7018 263	75
76	41.8550 149	38.8991 317	36.2521 526	33.8758 443	29.8075 983	76
77	42.1179 508	39.1167 958	36.4324 231	34.0252 140	29.9102 896	77
78	42.3763 644	39.3301 919	36.6087 267	34.1709 405	30.0099 899	78
79	42.6303 336	39.5394 039	36.7811 509	34.3131 127	30.1067 863	79
80	42.8799 347	39.7445 136	36.9497 808	34.4518 172	30.2007 634	80
81	43.1252 430	39.9456 016	37.1147 000	34.5871 388	30.2920 033	81
82	43.3663 322	40.1427 466	37.2759 903	34.7191 598	30.3805 858	82
83	43.6032 749	40.3360 261	37.4337 313	34.8479 607	30.4665 881	83
84	43.8361 424	40.5255 158	37.5880 013	34.9736 202	30.5500 856	84
85	44.0650 048	40.7112 900	37.7388 766	35.0962 149	30.6311 510	85
86	44.2899 310	40.8934 216	37.8864 318	35.2158 194	30.7098 554	86
87	44.5109 887	41.0719 819	38.0307 402	35.3325 067	30.7862 673	87
88	44.7282 444	41.2470 411	38.1718 730	35.4463 480	30.8604 537	88
89	44.9417 636	41.4186 677	38.3099 003	35.5574 127	30.9324 794	89
90	45.1516 104	41.5869 292	38.4448 902	35.6657 685	31.0024 071	90
91	45.3578 480	41.7518 913	38.5769 098	35.7714 814	31.0702 982	91
92	45.5605 386	41.9136 190	38.7060 242	35.8746 160	31.1362 118	92
93	45.7597 431	42.0721 754	38.8322 975	35.9752 352	31.2002 057	93
94	45.9555 215	42.2276 230	38.9557 922	36.0734 002	31.2623 356	94
95	46.1479 327	42.3800 225	39.0765 694	36.1691 709	31.3226 559	95
96	46.3370 345	42.5294 339	39.1946 889	36.2626 057	31.3812 193	96
97	46.5228 841	42.6759 155	39.3102 092	36.3537 617	31.4380 770	97
98	46.7055 372	42.8195 250	39.4231 875	36.4426 943	31.4932 787	98
99	46.8850 488	42.9603 187	39.5336 797	36.5294 579	31.5468 725	99
100	47.0614 730	43.0983 516	39.6417 405	36.6141 053	31.5989 053	100
∞	57.1428 571	50.0000 000	44.4444 444	40.0000 000	33.3333 333	∞

Table VIII — Present Value of 1 per Period

$$a_{\overline{n}|} = (1-v^n)/i$$

n	$3\frac{1}{2}$ per cent	4 per cent	$4\frac{1}{2}$ per cent	5 per cent	$5\frac{1}{2}$ per cent	n
1	0.9661 836	0.9615 385	0.9569 378	0.9523 810	0.9478 673	1
2	1.8996 943	1.8860 947	1.8726 678	1.8594 104	1.8463 197	2
3	2.8016 370	2.7750 910	2.7489 644	2.7232 480	2.6979 334	3
4	3.6730 792	3.6298 952	3.5875 257	3.5459 505	3.5051 501	4
5	4.5150 524	4.4518 223	4.3899 767	4.3294 767	4.2702 845	5
6	5.3285 530	5.2421 369	5.1578 725	5.0756 921	4.9955 303	6
7	6.1145 440	6.0020 547	5.8927 009	5.7863 734	5.6829 671	7
8	6.8739 555	6.7327 449	6.5958 861	6.4632 128	6.3345 660	8
9	7.6076 865	7.4353 316	7.2687 905	7.1078 217	6.9521 952	9
10	8.3166 053	8.1108 958	7.9127 182	7.7217 349	7.5376 258	10
11	9.0015 510	8.7604 767	8.5289 169	8.3064 142	8.0925 363	11
12	9.6633 343	9.3850 738	9.1185 808	8.8632 516	8.6185 178	12
13	10.3027 385	9.9856 478	9.6828 524	9.3935 730	9.1170 785	13
14	10.9205 203	10.5631 229	10.2228 253	9.8986 409	9.5896 479	14
15	11.5174 109	11.1183 874	10.7395 457	10.3796 580	10.0375 809	15
16	12.0941 168	11.6522 956	11.2340 150	10.8377 696	10.4621 620	16
17	12.6513 206	12.1656 688	11.7071 914	11.2740 662	10.8646 086	17
18	13.1896 817	12.6592 970	12.1599 918	11.6895 869	11.2460 745	18
19	13.7098 374	13.1339 394	12.5932 936	12.0853 209	11.6076 535	19
20	14.2124 033	13.5903 263	13.0079 364	12.4622 103	11.9503 825	20
21	14.6979 742	14.0291 600	13.4047 239	12.8211 527	12.2752 441	21
22	15.1671 248	14.4511 153	13.7844 248	13.1630 026	12.5831 697	22
23	15.6204 105	14.8568 417	14.1477 749	13.4885 739	12.8750 424	23
24	16.0583 676	15.2469 631	14.4954 784	13.7986 418	13.1516 990	24
25	16.4815 146	15.6220 799	14.8282 090	14.0939 446	13.4139 327	25
26	16.8903 523	15.9827 692	15.1466 114	14.3751 853	13.6624 954	26
27	17.2853 645	16.3295 858	15.4513 028	14.6430 336	13.8980 999	27
28	17.6670 188	16.6630 632	15.7428 735	14.8981 273	14.1214 217	28
29	18.0357 670	16.9837 146	16.0218 885	15.1410 736	14.3331 012	29
30	18.3920 454	17.2920 333	16.2888 885	15.3724 510	14.5337 452	30
31	18.7362 758	17.5884 936	16.5443 910	15.5928 105	14.7239 291	31
32	19.0688 655	17.8735 515	16.7888 909	15.8026 767	14.9041 982	32
33	19.3902 082	18.1476 457	17.0228 621	16.0025 492	15.0750 694	33
34	19.7006 842	18.4111 978	17.2467 580	16.1929 040	15.2370 326	34
35	20.0006 611	18.6646 132	17.4610 124	16.3741 943	15.3905 522	35
36	20.2904 938	18.9082 820	17.6660 406	16.5468 517	15.5360 684	36
37	20.5705 254	19.1425 788	17.8622 398	16.7112 873	15.6739 985	37
38	20.8410 874	19.3678 642	18.0499 902	16.8678 927	15.8047 379	38
39	21.1024 999	19.5844 848	18.2296 557	17.0170 407	15.9286 615	39
40	21.3550 723	19.7927 739	18.4015 844	17.1590 864	16.0461 247	40
41	21.5991 037	19.9930 518	18.5661 095	17.2943 680	16.1574 642	41
42	21.8348 828	20.1856 267	18.7235 498	17.4232 076	16.2629 992	42
43	22.0626 887	20.3707 949	18.8742 103	17.5459 120	16.3630 324	43
44	22.2827 910	20.5488 413	19.0183 830	17.6627 733	16.4578 506	44
45	22.4954 503	20.7200 397	19.1563 474	17.7740 698	16.5477 257	45
46	22.7009 181	20.8846 536	19.2883 707	17.8800 665	16.6329 154	46
47	22.8994 378	21.0429 361	19.4147 088	17.9810 157	16.7136 639	47
48	23.0912 442	21.1951 309	19.5356 065	18.0771 578	16.7902 027	48
49	23.2765 645	21.3414 720	19.6512 981	18.1687 217	16.8627 514	49
50	23.4556 179	21.4821 846	19.7620 078	18.2559 255	16.9315 179	50

Table VIII — Present Value of 1 per Period

$$a_{\overline{n}|} = (1-v^n)/i$$

n	$3\frac{1}{2}$ per cent	4 per cent	$4\frac{1}{2}$ per cent	5 per cent	$5\frac{1}{2}$ per cent	n
51	23.6286 163	21.6174 852	19.8679 500	18.3389 766	16.9966 994	51
52	23.7957 645	21.7475 819	19.9693 302	18.4180 730	17.0584 829	52
53	23.9572 604	21.8726 749	20.0663 447	18.4934 028	17.1170 454	53
54	24.1132 951	21.9929 567	20.1591 815	18.5651 456	17.1725 549	54
55	24.2640 532	22.1086 122	20.2480 206	18.6334 720	17.2251 705	55
56	24.4097 133	22.2198 194	20.3330 340	18.6985 447	17.2750 431	56
57	24.5504 476	22.3267 494	20.4143 866	18.7605 188	17.3223 157	57
58	24.6864 228	22.4295 668	20.4922 360	18.8195 417	17.3671 239	58
59	24.8177 998	22.5284 296	20.5667 330	18.8757 540	17.4095 961	59
60	24.9447 341	22.6234 900	20.6380 220	18.9292 895	17.4498 542	60
61	25.0673 760	22.7148 942	20.7062 412	18.9802 757	17.4880 134	61
62	25.1858 705	22.8027 829	20.7715 227	19.0288 340	17.5241 833	62
63	25.3003 580	22.8872 912	20.8339 930	19.0750 800	17.5584 676	63
64	25.4109 739	22.9685 493	20.8937 732	19.1191 238	17.5909 646	64
65	25.5178 492	23.0466 820	20.9509 791	19.1610 703	17.6217 674	65
66	25.6211 103	23.1218 096	21.0057 217	19.2010 194	17.6509 643	66
67	25.7208 795	23.1940 477	21.0581 068	19.2390 661	17.6786 392	67
68	25.8172 749	23.2635 074	21.1082 362	19.2753 010	17.7048 713	68
69	25.9104 105	23.3302 956	21.1562 069	19.3098 105	17.7297 358	69
70	26.0003 966	23.3945 150	21.2021 119	19.3426 766	17.7533 041	70
71	26.0873 398	23.4562 644	21.2460 401	19.3739 778	17.7756 437	71
72	26.1713 428	23.5156 388	21.2880 766	19.4037 883	17.7968 186	72
73	26.2525 051	23.5727 297	21.3283 030	19.4321 794	17.8168 897	73
74	26.3309 228	23.6276 247	21.3667 971	19.4592 185	17.8359 144	74
75	26.4066 887	23.6804 083	21.4036 336	19.4849 700	17.8539 473	75
76	26.4798 924	23.7311 619	21.4388 838	19.5094 952	17.8710 401	76
77	26.5506 207	23.7799 633	21.4726 161	19.5328 526	17.8872 418	77
78	26.6189 572	23.8268 878	21.5048 958	19.5550 977	17.9025 989	78
79	26.6849 828	23.8720 075	21.5357 854	19.5762 835	17.9171 553	79
80	26.7487 757	23.9153 918	21.5653 450	19.5964 605	17.9309 529	80
81	26.8104 113	23.9571 075	21.5936 315	19.6156 767	17.9440 312	81
82	26.8699 626	23.9972 188	21.6207 000	19.6339 778	17.9564 277	82
83	26.9275 001	24.0357 873	21.6466 029	19.6514 074	17.9681 779	83
84	26.9830 919	24.0728 724	21.6713 903	19.6680 070	17.9793 155	84
85	27.0368 037	24.1085 312	21.6951 103	19.6838 162	17.9898 725	85
86	27.0886 993	24.1428 184	21.7178 089	19.6988 726	17.9998 792	86
87	27.1388 399	24.1757 869	21.7395 301	19.7132 120	18.0093 642	87
88	27.1872 849	24.2074 874	21.7603 159	19.7268 686	18.0183 547	88
89	27.2340 917	24.2379 687	21.7802 066	19.7398 748	18.0268 765	89
90	27.2793 156	24.2672 776	21.7992 407	19.7522 617	18.0349 540	90
91	27.3230 103	24.2954 592	21.8174 553	19.7640 588	18.0426 104	91
92	27.3652 273	24.3225 569	21.8348 854	19.7752 941	18.0498 677	92
93	27.4060 167	24.3486 124	21.8515 650	19.7859 944	18.0567 466	93
94	27.4454 268	24.3736 658	21.8675 263	19.7961 851	18.0632 669	94
95	27.4835 042	24.3977 556	21.8828 003	19.8058 906	18.0694 473	95
96	27.5202 939	24.4209 188	21.8974 166	19.8151 339	18.0753 055	96
97	27.5558 395	24.4431 912	21.9114 034	19.8239 370	18.0808 583	97
98	27.5901 831	24.4646 069	21.9247 879	19.8323 210	18.0861 216	98
99	27.6233 653	24.4851 990	21.9375 961	19.8403 057	18.0911 106	99
100	27.6554 254	24.5049 990	21.9498 527	19.8479 102	18.0958 394	100
∞	28.5714 286	25.0000 000	22.2222 222	20.0000 000	18.1818 182	∞

Table VIII — Present Value of 1 per Period

$$a_{\overline{n}|} = (1-v^n)/i$$

n	6 per cent	6½ per cent	7 per cent	7½ per cent	8 per cent	n
1	0.9433 962	0.9389 671	0.9345 794	0.9302 326	0.9259 259	1
2	1.8333 927	1.8206 264	1.8080 182	1.7955 652	1.7832 648	2
3	2.6730 120	2.6484 755	2.6243 160	2.6005 257	2.5770 970	3
4	3.4651 056	3.4257 986	3.3872 113	3.3493 263	3.3121 268	4
5	4.2123 638	4.1556 794	4.1001 974	4.0458 849	3.9927 100	5
6	4.9173 243	4.8410 136	4.7665 397	4.6938 464	4.6228 797	6
7	5.5823 814	5.4845 198	5.3892 894	5.2966 013	5.2063 701	7
8	6.2097 938	6.0887 510	5.9712 985	5.8573 036	5.7466 389	8
9	6.8016 923	6.6561 042	6.5152 322	6.3788 870	6.2468 879	9
10	7.3600 870	7.1888 302	7.0235 816	6.8640 810	6.7100 814	10
11	7.8868 746	7.6890 425	7.4986 744	7.3154 241	7.1389 643	11
12	8.3838 439	8.1587 253	7.9426 863	7.7352 783	7.5360 780	12
13	8.8526 830	8.5997 421	8.3576 508	8.1258 403	7.9037 759	13
14	9.2949 839	9.0138 423	8.7454 680	8.4891 537	8.2442 370	14
15	9.7122 490	9.4026 689	9.1079 140	8.8271 197	8.5594 787	15
16	10.1058 953	9.7677 642	9.4466 486	9.1415 067	8.8513 692	16
17	10.4772 597	10.1105 767	9.7632 230	9.4339 598	9.1216 381	17
18	10.8276 035	10.4324 664	10.0590 869	9.7060 091	9.3718 871	18
19	11.1581 165	10.7347 102	10.3355 952	9.9590 782	9.6035 992	19
20	11.4699 212	11.0185 072	10.5940 143	10.1944 914	9.8181 474	20
21	11.7640 766	11.2849 833	10.8355 273	10.4134 803	10.0168 032	21
22	12.0415 817	11.5351 956	11.0612 405	10.6171 910	10.2007 437	22
23	12.3033 790	11.7701 367	11.2721 874	10.8066 893	10.3710 590	23
24	12.5503 575	11.9907 387	11.4693 340	10.9829 668	10.5287 583	24
25	12.7833 562	12.1978 767	11.6535 832	11.1469 459	10.6747 762	25
26	13.0031 662	12.3923 725	11.8257 787	11.2994 845	10.8099 780	26
27	13.2105 341	12.5749 977	11.9867 090	11.4413 810	10.9351 648	27
28	13.4061 643	12.7464 767	12.1371 113	11.5733 776	11.0510 785	28
29	13.5907 210	12.9074 898	12.2776 741	11.6961 652	11.1584 060	29
30	13.7648 312	13.0586 759	12.4090 412	11.8103 863	11.2577 833	30
31	13.9290 860	13.2006 347	12.5318 142	11.9166 384	11.3497 994	31
32	14.0840 434	13.3339 293	12.6465 553	12.0154 776	11.4349 994	32
33	14.2302 296	13.4590 885	12.7537 900	12.1074 210	11.5138 884	33
34	14.3681 411	13.5766 089	12.8540 094	12.1929 498	11.5869 337	34
35	14.4982 464	13.6869 567	12.9476 723	12.2725 114	11.6545 682	35
36	14.6209 871	13.7905 697	13.0352 078	12.3465 222	11.7171 928	36
37	14.7367 803	13.8878 589	13.1170 166	12.4153 695	11.7751 785	37
38	14.8460 192	13.9792 102	13.1934 735	12.4794 135	11.8288 690	38
39	14.9490 747	14.0649 861	13.2649 285	12.5389 893	11.8785 824	39
40	15.0462 969	14.1455 269	13.3317 088	12.5944 087	11.9246 133	40
41	15.1380 159	14.2211 520	13.3941 204	12.6459 615	11.9672 346	41
42	15.2245 433	14.2921 615	13.4524 490	12.6939 177	12.0066 987	42
43	15.3061 729	14.3588 371	13.5069 617	12.7385 281	12.0432 395	43
44	15.3831 820	14.4214 433	13.5579 081	12.7800 261	12.0770 736	44
45	15.4558 321	14.4802 284	13.6055 216	12.8186 290	12.1084 015	45
46	15.5243 699	14.5354 257	13.6500 202	12.8545 386	12.1374 088	46
47	15.5890 282	14.5872 542	13.6916 076	12.8879 429	12.1642 674	47
48	15.6500 266	14.6359 195	13.7304 744	12.9190 166	12.1891 365	48
49	15.7075 723	14.6816 145	13.7667 986	12.9479 224	12.2121 634	49
50	15.7618 606	14.7245 207	13.8007 463	12.9748 116	12.2334 846	50

Table VIII — Present Value of 1 per Period

$$a_{\overline{n}|}=(1-v^n)/i$$

n	6 per cent	6½ per cent	7 per cent	7½ per cent	8 per cent	n
51	15.8130 761	14.7648 081	13.8324 732	12.9998 247	12.2532 265	51
52	15.8613 925	14.8026 368	13.8621 245	13.0230 928	12.2715 060	52
53	15.9069 741	14.8381 566	13.8898 359	13.0447 375	12.2884 315	53
54	15.9499 755	14.8715 085	13.9157 345	13.0648 720	12.3041 033	54
55	15.9905 430	14.9028 249	13.9399 388	13.0836 019	12.3186 141	55
56	16.0288 141	14.9322 300	13.9625 596	13.1010 250	12.3320 501	56
57	16.0649 190	14.9598 403	13.9837 006	13.1172 326	12.3444 908	57
58	16.0989 802	14.9857 656	14.0034 585	13.1323 094	12.3560 100	58
59	16.1311 134	15.0101 085	14.0219 238	13.1463 343	12.3666 760	59
60	16.1614 277	15.0329 657	14.0391 812	13.1593 808	12.3765 518	60
61	16.1900 261	15.0544 279	14.0553 095	13.1715 170	12.3856 961	61
62	16.2170 058	15.0745 802	14.0703 827	13.1828 065	12.3941 631	62
63	16.2424 583	15.0935 025	14.0844 698	13.1933 084	12.4020 029	63
64	16.2664 701	15.1112 700	14.0976 353	13.2030 775	12.4092 619	64
65	16.2891 227	15.1279 531	14.1099 398	13.2121 652	12.4159 832	65
66	16.3104 931	15.1436 179	14.1214 388	13.2206 188	12.4222 067	66
67	16.3306 539	15.1583 267	14.1321 858	13.2284 826	12.4279 692	67
68	16.3496 735	15.1721 377	14.1422 298	13.2357 977	12.4333 048	68
69	16.3676 165	15.1851 058	14.1516 166	13.2426 025	12.4382 452	69
70	16.3845 439	15.1972 825	14.1603 893	13.2489 326	12.4428 196	70
71	16.4005 131	15.2087 159	14.1685 882	13.2548 210	12.4470 552	71
72	16.4155 784	15.2194 516	14.1762 506	13.2602 986	12.4509 770	72
73	16.4297 909	15.2295 320	14.1834 118	13.2653 941	12.4546 084	73
74	16.4431 990	15.2389 972	14.1901 045	13.2701 340	12.4579 707	74
75	16.4558 481	15.2478 847	14.1963 593	13.2745 433	12.4610 840	75
76	16.4677 812	15.2562 297	14.2022 050	13.2786 449	12.4639 667	76
77	16.4790 389	15.2640 655	14.2076 682	13.2824 604	12.4666 358	77
78	16.4896 593	15.2714 230	14.2127 740	13.2860 097	12.4691 072	78
79	16.4996 786	15.2783 314	14.2175 458	13.2893 113	12.4713 956	79
80	16.5091 308	15.2848 183	14.2220 054	13.2923 826	12.4735 144	80
81	16.5180 479	15.2909 092	14.2261 733	13.2952 396	12.4754 763	81
82	16.5264 603	15.2966 283	14.2300 685	13.2978 973	12.4772 929	82
83	16.5343 965	15.3019 984	14.2337 089	13.3003 696	12.4789 749	83
84	16.5418 835	15.3070 408	14.2371 111	13.3026 694	12.4805 323	84
85	16.5489 467	15.3117 754	14.2402 908	13.3048 088	12.4819 744	85
86	16.5556 101	15.3162 210	14.2432 624	13.3067 988	12.4833 096	86
87	16.5618 963	15.3203 953	14.2460 396	13.3086 501	12.4845 459	87
88	16.5678 267	15.3243 149	14.2486 352	13.3103 722	12.4856 907	88
89	16.5734 214	15.3279 952	14.2510 609	13.3119 741	12.4867 506	89
90	16.5786 994	15.3314 509	14.2533 279	13.3134 643	12.4877 320	90
91	16.5836 787	15.3346 956	14.2554 467	13.3148 505	12.4886 408	91
92	16.5883 762	15.3377 424	14.2574 268	13.3161 409	12.4894 822	92
93	16.5928 077	15.3406 032	14.2592 774	13.3173 395	12.4902 613	93
94	16.5969 884	15.3432 894	14.2610 069	13.3184 554	12.4909 827	94
95	16.6009 324	15.3458 116	14.2626 233	13.3194 934	12.4916 506	95
96	16.6046 532	15.3481 799	14.2641 339	13.3204 590	12.4922 691	96
97	16.6081 634	15.3504 037	14.2655 457	13.3213 572	12.4928 418	97
98	16.6114 749	15.3524 917	14.2668 651	13.3221 927	12.4933 720	98
99	16.6145 990	15.3544 523	14.2680 983	13.3229 700	12.4938 630	99
100	16.6175 462	15.3562 933	14.2692 507	13.3236 929	12.4943 176	100
∞	16.6666 667	15.3846 154	14.2857 143	13.3333 333	12.5000 000	∞

Table IX — Annuity Whose Present Value Is 1

$$a_{\overline{n}|}^{-1} = i/(1-v^n) = s_{\overline{n}|}^{-1} + i$$

n	$\frac{1}{4}$ per cent	$\frac{1}{3}$ per cent	$\frac{5}{12}$ per cent	$\frac{1}{2}$ per cent	$\frac{7}{12}$ per cent	n
1	1.0025 000	1.0033 333	1.0041 667	1.0050 000	1.0058 333	1
2	0.5018 758	0.5025 014	0.5031 272	0.5037 531	0.5043 792	2
3	0.3350 014	0.3355 580	0.3361 150	0.3366 722	0.3372 298	3
4	0.2515 645	0.2520 868	0.2526 096	0.2531 328	0.2536 564	4
5	0.2015 025	0.2020 044	0.2025 069	0.2030 100	0.2035 136	5
6	0.1681 280	0.1686 165	0.1691 056	0.1695 955	0.1700 859	6
7	0.1442 893	0.1447 682	0.1452 480	0.1457 285	0.1462 099	7
8	0.1264 103	0.1268 823	0.1273 551	0.1278 289	0.1283 035	8
9	0.1125 046	0.1129 712	0.1134 388	0.1139 074	0.1143 770	9
10	0.1013 801	0.1018 425	0.1023 060	0.1027 706	0.1032 363	10
11	0.0922 784	0.0927 374	0.0931 976	0.0936 590	0.0941 218	11
12	0.0846 937	0.0851 499	0.0856 075	0.0860 664	0.0865 267	12
13	0.0782 760	0.0787 299	0.0791 853	0.0796 422	0.0801 006	13
14	0.0727 751	0.0732 272	0.0736 808	0.0741 361	0.0745 929	14
15	0.0680 078	0.0684 582	0.0689 104	0.0693 644	0.0698 200	15
16	0.0638 364	0.0642 856	0.0647 365	0.0651 894	0.0656 440	16
17	0.0601 559	0.0606 039	0.0610 539	0.0615 058	0.0619 597	17
18	0.0568 843	0.0573 314	0.0577 805	0.0582 317	0.0586 850	18
19	0.0539 572	0.0544 035	0.0548 519	0.0553 025	0.0557 553	19
20	0.0513 229	0.0517 684	0.0522 163	0.0526 664	0.0531 189	20
21	0.0489 395	0.0493 844	0.0498 318	0.0502 816	0.0507 338	21
22	0.0467 728	0.0472 173	0.0476 643	0.0481 138	0.0485 658	22
23	0.0447 945	0.0452 386	0.0456 853	0.0461 346	0.0465 866	23
24	0.0429 812	0.0434 249	0.0438 714	0.0443 206	0.0447 726	24
25	0.0413 130	0.0417 564	0.0422 027	0.0426 519	0.0431 039	25
26	0.0397 731	0.0402 163	0.0406 625	0.0411 116	0.0415 638	26
27	0.0383 474	0.0387 904	0.0392 365	0.0396 856	0.0401 379	27
28	0.0370 235	0.0374 663	0.0379 124	0.0383 617	0.0388 142	28
29	0.0357 909	0.0362 337	0.0366 797	0.0371 291	0.0375 819	29
30	0.0346 406	0.0350 833	0.0355 294	0.0359 789	0.0364 319	30
31	0.0335 645	0.0340 071	0.0344 533	0.0349 030	0.0353 563	31
32	0.0325 557	0.0329 983	0.0334 446	0.0338 945	0.0343 481	32
33	0.0316 081	0.0320 507	0.0324 971	0.0329 473	0.0334 012	33
34	0.0307 162	0.0311 588	0.0316 054	0.0320 559	0.0325 103	34
35	0.0298 753	0.0303 180	0.0307 648	0.0312 155	0.0316 702	35
36	0.0290 812	0.0295 240	0.0299 709	0.0304 219	0.0308 771	36
37	0.0283 300	0.0287 729	0.0292 200	0.0296 714	0.0301 270	37
38	0.0276 184	0.0280 614	0.0285 087	0.0289 604	0.0294 165	38
39	0.0269 433	0.0273 864	0.0278 340	0.0282 861	0.0287 426	39
40	0.0263 020	0.0267 453	0.0271 931	0.0276 455	0.0281 025	40
41	0.0256 920	0.0261 354	0.0265 835	0.0270 363	0.0274 938	41
42	0.0251 111	0.0255 547	0.0260 030	0.0264 562	0.0269 142	42
43	0.0245 572	0.0250 010	0.0254 496	0.0259 032	0.0263 617	43
44	0.0240 286	0.0244 725	0.0249 214	0.0253 754	0.0258 344	44
45	0.0235 234	0.0239 675	0.0244 168	0.0248 712	0.0253 307	45
46	0.0230 402	0.0234 845	0.0239 341	0.0243 889	0.0248 490	46
47	0.0225 776	0.0230 221	0.0234 720	0.0239 273	0.0243 880	47
48	0.0221 343	0.0225 791	0.0230 293	0.0234 850	0.0239 462	48
49	0.0217 091	0.0221 541	0.0226 047	0.0230 609	0.0235 227	49
50	0.0213 010	0.0217 462	0.0221 971	0.0226 538	0.0231 161	50

Table IX — Annuity Whose Present Value Is 1

$$a_{\overline{n}|}^{-1} = i/(1-v^n) = s_{\overline{n}|}^{-1} + i$$

n	$\frac{1}{4}$ per cent	$\frac{1}{3}$ per cent	$\frac{5}{12}$ per cent	$\frac{1}{2}$ per cent	$\frac{7}{12}$ per cent	n
51	0.0209 089	0.0213 543	0.0218 056	0.0222 627	0.0227 256	51
52	0.0205 318	0.0209 775	0.0214 292	0.0218 867	0.0223 503	52
53	0.0201 691	0.0206 150	0.0210 670	0.0215 251	0.0219 892	53
54	0.0198 197	0.0202 659	0.0207 183	0.0211 769	0.0216 416	54
55	0.0194 831	0.0199 296	0.0203 823	0.0208 414	0.0213 067	55
56	0.0191 586	0.0196 053	0.0200 584	0.0205 180	0.0209 839	56
57	0.0188 454	0.0192 924	0.0197 459	0.0202 060	0.0206 725	57
58	0.0185 431	0.0189 903	0.0194 443	0.0199 048	0.0203 720	58
59	0.0182 510	0.0186 986	0.0191 529	0.0196 139	0.0200 817	59
60	0.0179 687	0.0184 165	0.0188 712	0.0193 328	0.0198 012	60
61	0.0176 956	0.0181 438	0.0185 989	0.0190 610	0.0195 300	61
62	0.0174 314	0.0178 798	0.0183 354	0.0187 980	0.0192 676	62
63	0.0171 756	0.0176 243	0.0180 802	0.0185 434	0.0190 137	63
64	0.0169 278	0.0173 768	0.0178 332	0.0182 968	0.0187 677	64
65	0.0166 876	0.0171 369	0.0175 937	0.0180 579	0.0185 295	65
66	0.0164 548	0.0169 044	0.0173 616	0.0178 263	0.0182 985	66
67	0.0162 289	0.0166 788	0.0171 364	0.0176 016	0.0180 745	67
68	0.0160 096	0.0164 598	0.0169 179	0.0173 837	0.0178 572	68
69	0.0157 967	0.0162 473	0.0167 057	0.0171 721	0.0176 462	69
70	0.0155 900	0.0160 408	0.0164 997	0.0169 666	0.0174 414	70
71	0.0153 890	0.0158 402	0.0162 995	0.0167 669	0.0172 424	71
72	0.0151 937	0.0156 452	0.0161 049	0.0165 729	0.0170 490	72
73	0.0150 037	0.0154 555	0.0159 157	0.0163 842	0.0168 610	73
74	0.0148 189	0.0152 710	0.0157 316	0.0162 007	0.0166 781	74
75	0.0146 390	0.0150 915	0.0155 525	0.0160 221	0.0165 002	75
76	0.0144 638	0.0149 167	0.0153 782	0.0158 483	0.0163 271	76
77	0.0142 933	0.0147 464	0.0152 084	0.0156 791	0.0161 585	77
78	0.0141 271	0.0145 806	0.0150 430	0.0155 142	0.0159 943	78
79	0.0139 651	0.0144 189	0.0148 818	0.0153 536	0.0158 344	79
80	0.0138 072	0.0142 614	0.0147 246	0.0151 970	0.0156 785	80
81	0.0136 532	0.0141 077	0.0145 714	0.0150 444	0.0155 265	81
82	0.0135 030	0.0139 578	0.0144 220	0.0148 955	0.0153 783	82
83	0.0133 564	0.0138 116	0.0142 762	0.0147 503	0.0152 337	83
84	0.0132 133	0.0136 688	0.0141 339	0.0146 086	0.0150 927	84
85	0.0130 736	0.0135 294	0.0139 950	0.0144 702	0.0149 550	85
86	0.0129 371	0.0133 933	0.0138 593	0.0143 351	0.0148 206	86
87	0.0128 038	0.0132 604	0.0137 268	0.0142 032	0.0146 894	87
88	0.0126 736	0.0131 305	0.0135 974	0.0140 743	0.0145 611	88
89	0.0125 463	0.0130 035	0.0134 709	0.0139 484	0.0144 359	89
90	0.0124 218	0.0128 794	0.0133 472	0.0138 253	0.0143 135	90
91	0.0123 000	0.0127 580	0.0132 263	0.0137 049	0.0141 938	91
92	0.0121 810	0.0126 392	0.0131 080	0.0135 872	0.0140 768	92
93	0.0120 645	0.0125 231	0.0129 923	0.0134 721	0.0139 624	93
94	0.0119 504	0.0124 094	0.0128 791	0.0133 595	0.0138 504	94
95	0.0118 388	0.0122 982	0.0127 684	0.0132 493	0.0137 409	95
96	0.0117 296	0.0121 893	0.0126 599	0.0131 414	0.0136 337	96
97	0.0116 226	0.0120 826	0.0125 537	0.0130 358	0.0135 288	97
98	0.0115 178	0.0119 782	0.0124 498	0.0129 324	0.0134 261	98
99	0.0114 151	0.0118 759	0.0123 479	0.0128 311	0.0133 255	99
100	0.0113 145	0.0117 756	0.0122 481	0.0127 319	0.0132 270	100
∞	0.0025 000	0.0033 333	0.0041 667	0.0050 000	0.0058 333	∞

Table IX — Annuity Whose Present Value Is 1

$$a_{\overline{n}|}^{-1} = i/(1-v^n) = s_{\overline{n}|}^{-1} + i$$

n	$\frac{2}{3}$ per cent	$\frac{3}{4}$ per cent	1 per cent	$1\frac{1}{4}$ per cent	$1\frac{1}{2}$ per cent	n
1	1.0066 667	1.0075 000	1.0100 000	1.0125 000	1.0150 000	1
2	0.5050 055	0.5056 320	0.5075 124	0.5093 944	0.5112 779	2
3	0.3377 876	0.3383 458	0.3400 221	0.3417 012	0.3433 830	3
4	0.2541 805	0.2547 050	0.2562 811	0.2578 610	0.2594 448	4
5	0.2040 177	0.2045 224	0.2060 398	0.2075 621	0.2090 893	5
6	0.1705 771	0.1710 689	0.1725 484	0.1740 338	0.1755 252	6
7	0.1466 920	0.1471 749	0.1486 283	0.1500 887	0.1515 562	7
8	0.1287 791	0.1292 555	0.1306 903	0.1321 331	0.1335 840	8
9	0.1148 476	0.1153 193	0.1167 404	0.1181 706	0.1196 098	9
10	0.1037 032	0.1041 712	0.1055 821	0.1070 031	0.1084 342	10
11	0.0945 857	0.0950 509	0.0964 541	0.0978 684	0.0992 938	11
12	0.0869 884	0.0874 515	0.0888 488	0.0902 583	0.0916 800	12
13	0.0805 605	0.0810 219	0.0824 148	0.0838 210	0.0852 404	13
14	0.0750 514	0.0755 115	0.0769 012	0.0783 052	0.0797 233	14
15	0.0702 773	0.0707 364	0.0721 238	0.0735 265	0.0749 444	15
16	0.0661 005	0.0665 588	0.0679 446	0.0693 467	0.0707 651	16
17	0.0624 155	0.0628 732	0.0642 581	0.0656 602	0.0670 796	17
18	0.0591 403	0.0595 977	0.0609 820	0.0623 848	0.0638 058	18
19	0.0562 103	0.0566 674	0.0580 518	0.0594 555	0.0608 785	19
20	0.0535 736	0.0540 306	0.0554 153	0.0568 204	0.0582 457	20
21	0.0511 884	0.0516 454	0.0530 308	0.0544 375	0.0558 655	21
22	0.0490 204	0.0494 775	0.0508 637	0.0522 724	0.0537 033	22
23	0.0470 412	0.0474 985	0.0488 858	0.0502 967	0.0517 308	23
24	0.0452 273	0.0456 847	0.0470 735	0.0484 866	0.0499 241	24
25	0.0435 588	0.0440 165	0.0454 068	0.0468 225	0.0482 634	25
26	0.0420 189	0.0424 769	0.0438 689	0.0452 873	0.0467 320	26
27	0.0405 933	0.0410 518	0.0424 455	0.0438 668	0.0453 153	27
28	0.0392 698	0.0397 287	0.0411 244	0.0425 486	0.0440 011	28
29	0.0380 379	0.0384 972	0.0398 950	0.0413 223	0.0427 788	29
30	0.0368 883	0.0373 482	0.0387 481	0.0401 785	0.0416 392	30
31	0.0358 132	0.0362 735	0.0376 757	0.0391 094	0.0405 743	31
32	0.0348 054	0.0352 663	0.0366 709	0.0381 079	0.0395 771	32
33	0.0338 590	0.0343 205	0.0357 274	0.0371 679	0.0386 414	33
34	0.0329 684	0.0334 305	0.0348 400	0.0362 839	0.0377 619	34
35	0.0321 290	0.0325 917	0.0340 037	0.0354 511	0.0369 336	35
36	0.0313 364	0.0317 997	0.0332 143	0.0346 653	0.0361 524	36
37	0.0305 868	0.0310 508	0.0324 680	0.0339 227	0.0354 144	37
38	0.0298 769	0.0303 416	0.0317 615	0.0332 198	0.0347 161	38
39	0.0292 035	0.0296 689	0.0310 916	0.0325 536	0.0340 546	39
40	0.0285 641	0.0290 302	0.0304 556	0.0319 214	0.0334 271	40
41	0.0279 559	0.0284 228	0.0298 510	0.0313 206	0.0328 311	41
42	0.0273 770	0.0278 445	0.0292 756	0.0307 491	0.0322 643	42
43	0.0268 251	0.0272 934	0.0287 274	0.0302 047	0.0317 246	43
44	0.0262 985	0.0267 675	0.0282 044	0.0296 856	0.0312 104	44
45	0.0257 954	0.0262 652	0.0277 050	0.0291 901	0.0307 198	45
46	0.0253 144	0.0257 849	0.0272 278	0.0287 168	0.0302 512	46
47	0.0248 540	0.0253 253	0.0267 711	0.0282 641	0.0298 034	47
48	0.0244 129	0.0248 850	0.0263 338	0.0278 307	0.0293 750	48
49	0.0239 900	0.0244 629	0.0259 147	0.0274 156	0.0289 648	49
50	0.0235 842	0.0240 579	0.0255 127	0.0270 176	0.0285 717	50

Table IX — Annuity Whose Present Value Is 1

$$a_{\overline{n}|}^{-1} = i/(1-v^n) = s_{\overline{n}|}^{-1} + i$$

n	$\frac{2}{3}$ per cent	$\frac{3}{4}$ per cent	1 per cent	$1\frac{1}{4}$ per cent	$1\frac{1}{2}$ per cent	n
51	0.0231 944	0.0236 689	0.0251 268	0.0266 357	0.0281 947	51
52	0.0228 197	0.0232 950	0.0247 560	0.0262 690	0.0278 329	52
53	0.0224 593	0.0229 355	0.0243 996	0.0259 165	0.0274 854	53
54	0.0221 124	0.0225 894	0.0240 566	0.0255 776	0.0271 514	54
55	0.0217 783	0.0222 560	0.0237 264	0.0252 514	0.0268 302	55
56	0.0214 562	0.0219 348	0.0234 082	0.0249 374	0.0265 211	56
57	0.0211 455	0.0216 250	0.0231 016	0.0246 348	0.0262 234	57
58	0.0208 457	0.0213 260	0.0228 057	0.0243 430	0.0259 366	58
59	0.0205 562	0.0210 373	0.0225 202	0.0240 616	0.0256 601	59
60	0.0202 764	0.0207 584	0.0222 444	0.0237 900	0.0253 934	60
61	0.0200 059	0.0204 887	0.0219 780	0.0235 276	0.0251 360	61
62	0.0197 443	0.0202 280	0.0217 204	0.0232 741	0.0248 875	62
63	0.0194 911	0.0199 756	0.0214 713	0.0230 290	0.0246 474	63
64	0.0192 459	0.0197 313	0.0212 301	0.0227 920	0.0244 153	64
65	0.0190 084	0.0194 946	0.0209 967	0.0225 627	0.0241 909	65
66	0.0187 782	0.0192 652	0.0207 705	0.0223 406	0.0239 739	66
67	0.0185 549	0.0190 429	0.0205 514	0.0221 256	0.0237 638	67
68	0.0183 383	0.0188 272	0.0203 389	0.0219 172	0.0235 603	68
69	0.0181 282	0.0186 178	0.0201 328	0.0217 153	0.0233 633	69
70	0.0179 241	0.0184 146	0.0199 328	0.0215 194	0.0231 724	70
71	0.0177 259	0.0182 173	0.0197 387	0.0213 294	0.0229 873	71
72	0.0175 332	0.0180 255	0.0195 502	0.0211 450	0.0228 078	72
73	0.0173 460	0.0178 392	0.0193 671	0.0209 660	0.0226 337	73
74	0.0171 639	0.0176 580	0.0191 891	0.0207 921	0.0224 647	74
75	0.0169 868	0.0174 817	0.0190 161	0.0206 232	0.0223 007	75
76	0.0168 144	0.0173 102	0.0188 478	0.0204 591	0.0221 415	76
77	0.0166 466	0.0171 433	0.0186 842	0.0202 995	0.0219 868	77
78	0.0164 832	0.0169 807	0.0185 249	0.0201 444	0.0218 365	78
79	0.0163 240	0.0168 224	0.0183 698	0.0199 934	0.0216 904	79
80	0.0161 689	0.0166 682	0.0182 189	0.0198 465	0.0215 483	80
81	0.0160 177	0.0165 179	0.0180 718	0.0197 036	0.0214 102	81
82	0.0158 703	0.0163 714	0.0179 285	0.0195 644	0.0212 758	82
83	0.0157 265	0.0162 285	0.0177 889	0.0194 288	0.0211 451	83
84	0.0155 862	0.0160 891	0.0176 527	0.0192 968	0.0210 178	84
85	0.0154 493	0.0159 531	0.0175 200	0.0191 681	0.0208 940	85
86	0.0153 157	0.0158 203	0.0173 905	0.0190 427	0.0207 733	86
87	0.0151 852	0.0156 908	0.0172 642	0.0189 204	0.0206 558	87
88	0.0150 578	0.0155 642	0.0171 409	0.0188 012	0.0205 414	88
89	0.0149 333	0.0154 406	0.0170 206	0.0186 849	0.0204 298	89
90	0.0148 117	0.0153 199	0.0169 031	0.0185 715	0.0203 211	90
91	0.0146 928	0.0152 019	0.0167 883	0.0184 608	0.0202 152	91
92	0.0145 766	0.0150 866	0.0166 762	0.0183 527	0.0201 118	92
93	0.0144 630	0.0149 738	0.0165 667	0.0182 472	0.0200 110	93
94	0.0143 518	0.0148 636	0.0164 597	0.0181 442	0.0199 127	94
95	0.0142 431	0.0147 557	0.0163 551	0.0180 437	0.0198 168	95
96	0.0141 367	0.0146 502	0.0162 528	0.0179 454	0.0197 232	96
97	0.0140 326	0.0145 470	0.0161 528	0.0178 494	0.0196 319	97
98	0.0139 306	0.0144 459	0.0160 550	0.0177 556	0.0195 427	98
99	0.0138 308	0.0143 470	0.0159 594	0.0176 639	0.0194 556	99
100	0.0137 331	0.0142 502	0.0158 657	0.0175 743	0.0193 706	100
∞	0.0066 667	0.0075 000	0.0100 000	0.0125 000	0.0150 000	∞

Table IX — Annuity Whose Present Value Is 1

$$a_{\overline{n}|}^{-1} = i/(1-v^n) = s_{\overline{n}|}^{-1} + i$$

n	$1\frac{3}{4}$ per cent	2 per cent	$2\frac{1}{4}$ per cent	$2\frac{1}{2}$ per cent	3 per cent	n
1	1.0175 000	1.0200 000	1.0225 000	1.0250 000	1.0300 000	1
2	0.5131 630	0.5150 495	0.5169 376	0.5188 272	0.5226 108	2
3	0.3450 675	0.3467 547	0.3484 446	0.3501 372	0.3535 304	3
4	0.2610 324	0.2626 238	0.2642 189	0.2658 179	0.2690 270	4
5	0.2106 214	0.2121 584	0.2137 002	0.2152 469	0.2183 546	5
6	0.1770 226	0.1785 258	0.1800 350	0.1815 500	0.1845 975	6
7	0.1530 306	0.1545 120	0.1560 002	0.1574 954	0.1605 064	7
8	0.1350 429	0.1365 098	0.1379 846	0.1394 674	0.1424 564	8
9	0.1210 581	0.1225 154	0.1239 817	0.1254 569	0.1284 339	9
10	0.1098 754	0.1113 265	0.1127 877	0.1142 588	0.1172 305	10
11	0.1007 304	0.1021 779	0.1036 365	0.1051 060	0.1080 774	11
12	0.0931 138	0.0945 596	0.0960 174	0.0974 871	0.1004 621	12
13	0.0866 728	0.0881 184	0.0895 769	0.0910 483	0.0940 295	13
14	0.0811 556	0.0826 020	0.0840 623	0.0855 365	0.0885 263	14
15	0.0763 774	0.0778 255	0.0792 885	0.0807 665	0.0837 666	15
16	0.0721 996	0.0736 501	0.0751 166	0.0765 990	0.0796 108	16
17	0.0685 162	0.0699 698	0.0714 404	0.0729 278	0.0759 525	17
18	0.0652 449	0.0667 021	0.0681 772	0.0696 701	0.0727 087	18
19	0.0623 206	0.0637 818	0.0652 618	0.0667 606	0.0698 139	19
20	0.0596 912	0.0611 567	0.0626 421	0.0641 471	0.0672 157	20
21	0.0573 146	0.0587 848	0.0602 757	0.0617 873	0.0648 718	21
22	0.0551 564	0.0566 314	0.0581 282	0.0596 466	0.0627 474	22
23	0.0531 880	0.0546 681	0.0561 710	0.0576 964	0.0608 139	23
24	0.0513 856	0.0528 711	0.0543 802	0.0559 128	0.0590 474	24
25	0.0497 295	0.0512 204	0.0527 360	0.0542 759	0.0574 279	25
26	0.0482 021	0.0496 992	0.0512 213	0.0527 688	0.0559 383	26
27	0.0467 908	0.0482 931	0.0498 219	0.0513 769	0.0545 642	27
28	0.0454 815	0.0469 897	0.0485 253	0.0500 879	0.0532 932	28
29	0.0442 642	0.0457 784	0.0473 208	0.0488 913	0.0521 147	29
30	0.0431 298	0.0446 499	0.0461 993	0.0477 776	0.0510 193	30
31	0.0420 700	0.0435 964	0.0451 528	0.0467 390	0.0499 989	31
32	0.0410 781	0.0426 106	0.0441 742	0.0457 683	0.0490 466	32
33	0.0401 478	0.0416 865	0.0432 572	0.0448 594	0.0481 561	33
34	0.0392 736	0.0408 187	0.0423 966	0.0440 068	0.0473 220	34
35	0.0384 508	0.0400 022	0.0415 873	0.0432 056	0.0465 393	35
36	0.0376 751	0.0392 329	0.0408 252	0.0424 516	0.0458 038	36
37	0.0369 426	0.0385 068	0.0401 064	0.0417 409	0.0451 116	37
38	0.0362 499	0.0378 206	0.0394 275	0.0410 701	0.0444 593	38
39	0.0355 940	0.0371 711	0.0387 854	0.0404 362	0.0438 438	39
40	0.0349 721	0.0365 557	0.0381 774	0.0398 362	0.0432 624	40
41	0.0343 817	0.0359 719	0.0376 009	0.0392 679	0.0427 124	41
42	0.0338 206	0.0354 173	0.0370 536	0.0387 288	0.0421 917	42
43	0.0332 867	0.0348 899	0.0365 336	0.0382 169	0.0416 981	43
44	0.0327 781	0.0343 879	0.0360 390	0.0377 304	0.0412 298	44
45	0.0322 932	0.0339 096	0.0355 680	0.0372 675	0.0407 852	45
46	0.0318 304	0.0334 534	0.0351 192	0.0368 268	0.0403 625	46
47	0.0313 884	0.0330 179	0.0346 911	0.0364 067	0.0399 605	47
48	0.0309 657	0.0326 018	0.0342 823	0.0360 060	0.0395 778	48
49	0.0305 612	0.0322 040	0.0338 918	0.0356 235	0.0392 131	49
50	0.0301 739	0.0318 232	0.0335 184	0.0352 581	0.0388 655	50

Table IX — Annuity Whose Present Value Is 1

$$a_{\overline{n}|}^{-1} = i/(1-v^n) = s_{\overline{n}|}^{-1} + i$$

n	$1\tfrac{3}{4}$ per cent	2 per cent	$2\tfrac{1}{4}$ per cent	$2\tfrac{1}{2}$ per cent	3 per cent	n
51	0.0298 027	0.0314 586	0.0331 610	0.0349 087	0.0385 338	51
52	0.0294 467	0.0311 091	0.0328 188	0.0345 745	0.0382 172	52
53	0.0291 049	0.0307 739	0.0324 909	0.0342 545	0.0379 147	53
54	0.0287 767	0.0304 523	0.0321 765	0.0339 480	0.0376 256	54
55	0.0284 613	0.0301 434	0.0318 749	0.0336 542	0.0373 491	55
56	0.0281 579	0.0298 466	0.0315 853	0.0333 724	0.0370 845	56
57	0.0278 661	0.0295 612	0.0313 071	0.0331 020	0.0368 311	57
58	0.0275 850	0.0292 867	0.0310 398	0.0328 424	0.0365 885	58
59	0.0273 143	0.0290 224	0.0307 827	0.0325 931	0.0363 559	59
60	0.0270 534	0.0287 680	0.0305 353	0.0323 534	0.0361 330	60
61	0.0268 017	0.0285 228	0.0302 972	0.0321 229	0.0359 191	61
62	0.0265 589	0.0282 864	0.0300 679	0.0319 013	0.0357 138	62
63	0.0263 246	0.0280 585	0.0298 470	0.0316 879	0.0355 168	63
64	0.0260 982	0.0278 385	0.0296 341	0.0314 825	0.0353 276	64
65	0.0258 795	0.0276 262	0.0294 288	0.0312 846	0.0351 458	65
66	0.0256 681	0.0274 212	0.0292 307	0.0310 940	0.0349 711	66
67	0.0254 637	0.0272 232	0.0290 395	0.0309 102	0.0348 031	67
68	0.0252 660	0.0270 317	0.0288 550	0.0307 330	0.0346 416	68
69	0.0250 746	0.0268 467	0.0286 768	0.0305 621	0.0344 862	69
70	0.0248 893	0.0266 676	0.0285 046	0.0303 971	0.0343 366	70
71	0.0247 099	0.0264 945	0.0283 382	0.0302 379	0.0341 927	71
72	0.0245 360	0.0263 268	0.0281 773	0.0300 842	0.0340 540	72
73	0.0243 675	0.0261 645	0.0280 217	0.0299 357	0.0339 205	73
74	0.0242 041	0.0260 074	0.0278 712	0.0297 922	0.0337 919	74
75	0.0240 457	0.0258 551	0.0277 255	0.0296 536	0.0336 680	75
76	0.0238 920	0.0257 075	0.0275 846	0.0295 196	0.0335 485	76
77	0.0237 428	0.0255 645	0.0274 481	0.0293 900	0.0334 333	77
78	0.0235 981	0.0254 258	0.0273 159	0.0292 646	0.0333 222	78
79	0.0234 575	0.0252 912	0.0271 878	0.0291 434	0.0332 151	79
80	0.0233 209	0.0251 607	0.0270 638	0.0290 260	0.0331 117	80
81	0.0231 883	0.0250 340	0.0269 435	0.0289 125	0.0330 120	81
82	0.0230 594	0.0249 111	0.0268 269	0.0288 025	0.0329 158	82
83	0.0229 341	0.0247 917	0.0267 139	0.0286 961	0.0328 228	83
84	0.0228 122	0.0246 758	0.0266 042	0.0285 930	0.0327 331	84
85	0.0226 937	0.0245 632	0.0264 979	0.0284 931	0.0326 465	85
86	0.0225 785	0.0244 538	0.0263 947	0.0283 963	0.0325 628	86
87	0.0224 664	0.0243 475	0.0262 945	0.0283 025	0.0324 820	87
88	0.0223 572	0.0242 442	0.0261 973	0.0282 117	0.0324 039	88
89	0.0222 510	0.0241 437	0.0261 029	0.0281 235	0.0323 285	89
90	0.0221 476	0.0240 460	0.0260 113	0.0280 381	0.0322 556	90
91	0.0220 469	0.0239 510	0.0259 222	0.0279 552	0.0321 851	91
92	0.0219 488	0.0238 586	0.0258 358	0.0278 749	0.0321 169	92
93	0.0218 533	0.0237 687	0.0257 518	0.0277 969	0.0320 511	93
94	0.0217 602	0.0236 812	0.0256 701	0.0277 213	0.0319 874	94
95	0.0216 694	0.0235 960	0.0255 908	0.0276 479	0.0319 258	95
96	0.0215 810	0.0235 131	0.0255 137	0.0275 766	0.0318 662	96
97	0.0214 948	0.0234 324	0.0254 387	0.0275 075	0.0318 086	97
98	0.0214 107	0.0233 538	0.0253 658	0.0274 403	0.0317 528	98
99	0.0213 288	0.0232 773	0.0252 949	0.0273 752	0.0316 989	99
100	0.0212 488	0.0232 027	0.0252 259	0.0273 119	0.0316 467	100
∞	0.0175 000	0.0200 000	0.0225 000	0.0250 000	0.0300 000	∞

Table IX — Annuity Whose Present Value Is 1

$$a_{\overline{n}|}^{-1} = i/(1-v^n) = s_{\overline{n}|}^{-1} + i$$

n	$3\frac{1}{2}$ per cent	4 per cent	$4\frac{1}{2}$ per cent	5 per cent	$5\frac{1}{2}$ per cent	n
1	1.0350 000	1.0400 000	1.0450 000	1.0500 000	1.0550 000	1
2	0.5264 005	0.5301 961	0.5339 976	0.5378 049	0.5416 180	2
3	0.3569 342	0.3603 485	0.3637 734	0.3672 086	0.3706 541	3
4	0.2722 511	0.2754 900	0.2787 436	0.2820 118	0.2852 945	4
5	0.2214 814	0.2246 271	0.2277 916	0.2309 748	0.2341 764	5
6	0.1876 682	0.1907 619	0.1938 784	0.1970 175	0.2001 789	6
7	0.1635 445	0.1666 096	0.1697 015	0.1728 198	0.1759 644	7
8	0.1454 766	0.1485 278	0.1516 096	0.1547 218	0.1578 640	8
9	0.1314 460	0.1344 930	0.1375 745	0.1406 901	0.1438 395	9
10	0.1202 414	0.1232 909	0.1263 788	0.1295 046	0.1326 678	10
11	0.1110 920	0.1141 490	0.1172 482	0.1203 889	0.1235 707	11
12	0.1034 840	0.1065 522	0.1096 662	0.1128 254	0.1160 292	12
13	0.0970 616	0.1001 437	0.1032 754	0.1064 558	0.1096 843	13
14	0.0915 707	0.0946 690	0.0978 203	0.1010 240	0.1042 791	14
15	0.0868 251	0.0899 411	0.0931 138	0.0963 423	0.0996 256	15
16	0.0826 848	0.0858 200	0.0890 154	0.0922 699	0.0955 825	16
17	0.0790 431	0.0821 985	0.0854 176	0.0886 991	0.0920 420	17
18	0.0758 168	0.0789 933	0.0822 369	0.0855 462	0.0889 199	18
19	0.0729 403	0.0761 386	0.0794 073	0.0827 450	0.0861 501	19
20	0.0703 611	0.0735 818	0.0768 761	0.0802 426	0.0836 793	20
21	0.0680 366	0.0712 801	0.0746 006	0.0779 961	0.0814 648	21
22	0.0659 321	0.0691 988	0.0725 456	0.0759 705	0.0794 712	22
23	0.0640 188	0.0673 091	0.0706 825	0.0741 368	0.0776 696	23
24	0.0622 728	0.0655 868	0.0689 870	0.0724 709	0.0760 358	24
25	0.0606 740	0.0640 120	0.0674 390	0.0709 525	0.0745 494	25
26	0.0592 054	0.0625 674	0.0660 214	0.0695 643	0.0731 931	26
27	0.0578 524	0.0612 385	0.0647 195	0.0682 919	0.0719 523	27
28	0.0566 026	0.0600 130	0.0635 208	0.0671 225	0.0708 144	28
29	0.0554 454	0.0588 799	0.0624 146	0.0660 455	0.0697 686	29
30	0.0543 713	0.0578 301	0.0613 915	0.0650 514	0.0688 054	30
31	0.0533 724	0.0568 554	0.0604 434	0.0641 321	0.0679 167	31
32	0.0524 415	0.0559 486	0.0595 632	0.0632 804	0.0670 952	32
33	0.0515 724	0.0551 036	0.0587 445	0.0624 900	0.0663 347	33
34	0.0507 597	0.0543 148	0.0579 819	0.0617 554	0.0656 296	34
35	0.0499 984	0.0535 773	0.0572 704	0.0610 717	0.0649 749	35
36	0.0492 842	0.0528 869	0.0566 058	0.0604 345	0.0643 663	36
37	0.0486 132	0.0522 396	0.0559 840	0.0598 398	0.0637 999	37
38	0.0479 821	0.0516 319	0.0554 017	0.0592 842	0.0632 722	38
39	0.0473 878	0.0510 608	0.0548 557	0.0587 646	0.0627 799	39
40	0.0468 273	0.0505 235	0.0543 432	0.0582 782	0.0623 203	40
41	0.0462 982	0.0500 174	0.0538 616	0.0578 223	0.0618 909	41
42	0.0457 983	0.0495 402	0.0534 087	0.0573 947	0.0614 893	42
43	0.0453 254	0.0490 899	0.0529 824	0.0569 933	0.0611 134	43
44	0.0448 777	0.0486 645	0.0525 807	0.0566 162	0.0607 613	44
45	0.0444 534	0.0482 625	0.0522 020	0.0562 617	0.0604 313	45
46	0.0440 511	0.0478 820	0.0518 447	0.0559 282	0.0601 218	46
47	0.0436 692	0.0475 219	0.0515 073	0.0556 142	0.0598 313	47
48	0.0433 065	0.0471 806	0.0511 886	0.0553 184	0.0595 585	48
49	0.0429 617	0.0468 571	0.0508 872	0.0550 396	0.0593 023	49
50	0.0426 337	0.0465 502	0.0506 022	0.0547 767	0.0590 615	50

Table IX — Annuity Whose Present Value Is 1

$$a_{\overline{n}|}^{-1} = i/(1-v^n) = s_{\overline{n}|}^{-1} + i$$

n	$3\frac{1}{2}$ per cent	4 per cent	$4\frac{1}{2}$ per cent	5 per cent	$5\frac{1}{2}$ per cent	n
51	0.0423 216	0.0462 588	0.0503 323	0.0545 287	0.0588 350	51
52	0.0420 243	0.0459 821	0.0500 768	0.0542 945	0.0586 219	52
53	0.0417 410	0.0457 191	0.0498 347	0.0540 733	0.0584 213	53
54	0.0414 709	0.0454 691	0.0496 052	0.0538 644	0.0582 325	54
55	0.0412 132	0.0452 312	0.0493 875	0.0536 669	0.0580 546	55
56	0.0409 673	0.0450 049	0.0491 811	0.0534 801	0.0578 870	56
57	0.0407 325	0.0447 893	0.0489 851	0.0533 034	0.0577 290	57
58	0.0405 081	0.0445 840	0.0487 990	0.0531 363	0.0575 801	58
59	0.0402 937	0.0443 884	0.0486 222	0.0529 780	0.0574 396	59
60	0.0400 886	0.0442 018	0.0484 543	0.0528 282	0.0573 071	60
61	0.0398 925	0.0440 240	0.0482 946	0.0526 863	0.0571 820	61
62	0.0397 048	0.0438 543	0.0481 428	0.0525 518	0.0570 640	62
63	0.0395 251	0.0436 924	0.0479 985	0.0524 244	0.0569 526	63
64	0.0393 531	0.0435 378	0.0478 611	0.0523 037	0.0568 474	64
65	0.0391 883	0.0433 902	0.0477 305	0.0521 892	0.0567 480	65
66	0.0390 303	0.0432 492	0.0476 061	0.0520 806	0.0566 541	66
67	0.0388 789	0.0431 145	0.0474 876	0.0519 776	0.0565 654	67
68	0.0387 338	0.0429 858	0.0473 749	0.0518 799	0.0564 816	68
69	0.0385 945	0.0428 627	0.0472 675	0.0517 871	0.0564 024	69
70	0.0384 610	0.0427 451	0.0471 651	0.0516 992	0.0563 275	70
71	0.0383 328	0.0426 325	0.0470 676	0.0516 156	0.0562 568	71
72	0.0382 097	0.0425 249	0.0469 747	0.0515 363	0.0561 898	72
73	0.0380 916	0.0424 219	0.0468 861	0.0514 610	0.0561 265	73
74	0.0379 782	0.0423 233	0.0468 016	0.0513 895	0.0560 667	74
75	0.0378 692	0.0422 290	0.0467 210	0.0513 216	0.0560 100	75
76	0.0377 645	0.0421 387	0.0466 442	0.0512 571	0.0559 565	76
77	0.0376 639	0.0420 522	0.0465 709	0.0511 958	0.0559 058	77
78	0.0375 672	0.0419 694	0.0465 010	0.0511 376	0.0558 578	78
79	0.0374 743	0.0418 901	0.0464 343	0.0510 822	0.0558 124	79
80	0.0373 849	0.0418 141	0.0463 707	0.0510 296	0.0557 695	80
81	0.0372 989	0.0417 413	0.0463 100	0.0509 796	0.0557 288	81
82	0.0372 163	0.0416 715	0.0462 520	0.0509 321	0.0556 904	82
83	0.0371 368	0.0416 046	0.0461 966	0.0508 869	0.0556 539	83
84	0.0370 602	0.0415 405	0.0461 438	0.0508 440	0.0556 195	84
85	0.0369 866	0.0414 791	0.0460 933	0.0508 032	0.0555 868	85
86	0.0369 158	0.0414 202	0.0460 452	0.0507 643	0.0555 559	86
87	0.0368 476	0.0413 637	0.0459 992	0.0507 274	0.0555 267	87
88	0.0367 819	0.0413 095	0.0459 552	0.0506 923	0.0554 990	88
89	0.0367 187	0.0412 576	0.0459 132	0.0506 589	0.0554 727	89
90	0.0366 578	0.0412 078	0.0458 732	0.0506 271	0.0554 479	90
91	0.0365 992	0.0411 600	0.0458 349	0.0505 969	0.0554 244	91
92	0.0365 427	0.0411 141	0.0457 983	0.0505 681	0.0554 021	92
93	0.0364 883	0.0410 701	0.0457 633	0.0505 408	0.0553 810	93
94	0.0364 359	0.0410 279	0.0457 299	0.0505 148	0.0553 610	94
95	0.0363 855	0.0409 874	0.0456 980	0.0504 900	0.0553 420	95
96	0.0363 368	0.0409 485	0.0456 675	0.0504 665	0.0553 241	96
97	0.0362 899	0.0409 112	0.0456 383	0.0504 441	0.0553 071	97
98	0.0362 448	0.0408 754	0.0456 105	0.0504 227	0.0552 910	98
99	0.0362 012	0.0408 410	0.0455 838	0.0504 024	0.0552 758	99
100	0.0361 593	0.0408 080	0.0455 584	0.0503 831	0.0552 613	100
∞	0.0350 000	0.0400 000	0.0450 000	0.0500 000	0.0550 000	∞

Table IX — Annuity Whose Present Value Is 1

$$a_{\overline{n}|}^{-1} = i/(1-v^n) = s_{\overline{n}|}^{-1} + i$$

n	6 per cent	$6\frac{1}{2}$ per cent	7 per cent	$7\frac{1}{2}$ per cent	8 per cent	n
1	1.0600 000	1.0650 000	1.0700 000	1.0750 000	1.0800 000	1
2	0.5454 369	0.5492 615	0.5530 918	0.5569 277	0.5607 692	2
3	0.3741 098	0.3775 757	0.3810 517	0.3845 376	0.3880 335	3
4	0.2885 915	0.2919 027	0.2952 281	0.2985 675	0.3019 208	4
5	0.2373 964	0.2406 345	0.2438 907	0.2471 647	0.2504 564	5
6	0.2033 626	0.2065 683	0.2097 958	0.2130 449	0.2163 154	6
7	0.1791 350	0.1823 314	0.1855 532	0.1888 003	0.1920 724	7
8	0.1610 359	0.1642 373	0.1674 678	0.1707 270	0.1740 148	8
9	0.1470 222	0.1502 380	0.1534 865	0.1567 672	0.1600 797	9
10	0.1358 680	0.1391 047	0.1423 775	0.1456 859	0.1490 295	10
11	0.1267 929	0.1300 552	0.1333 569	0.1366 975	0.1400 763	11
12	0.1192 770	0.1225 682	0.1259 020	0.1292 778	0.1326 950	12
13	0.1129 601	0.1162 826	0.1196 508	0.1230 642	0.1265 218	13
14	0.1075 849	0.1109 405	0.1143 449	0.1177 974	0.1212 968	14
15	0.1029 628	0.1063 528	0.1097 946	0.1132 872	0.1168 295	15
16	0.0989 521	0.1023 776	0.1058 576	0.1093 912	0.1129 769	16
17	0.0954 448	0.0989 063	0.1024 252	0.1060 000	0.1096 294	17
18	0.0923 565	0.0958 546	0.0994 126	0.1030 290	0.1067 021	18
19	0.0896 209	0.0931 558	0.0967 530	0.1004 109	0.1041 276	19
20	0.0871 846	0.0907 564	0.0943 929	0.0980 922	0.1018 522	20
21	0.0850 046	0.0886 133	0.0922 890	0.0960 294	0.0998 322	21
22	0.0830 456	0.0866 912	0.0904 058	0.0941 869	0.0980 321	22
23	0.0812 785	0.0849 608	0.0887 139	0.0925 353	0.0964 222	23
24	0.0796 790	0.0833 977	0.0871 890	0.0910 501	0.0949 780	24
25	0.0782 267	0.0819 815	0.0858 105	0.0897 107	0.0936 788	25
26	0.0769 044	0.0806 948	0.0845 610	0.0884 996	0.0925 071	26
27	0.0756 972	0.0795 229	0.0834 257	0.0874 020	0.0914 481	27
28	0.0745 926	0.0784 531	0.0823 919	0.0864 052	0.0904 889	28
29	0.0735 796	0.0774 744	0.0814 486	0.0854 981	0.0896 185	29
30	0.0726 489	0.0765 774	0.0805 864	0.0846 712	0.0888 274	30
31	0.0717 922	0.0757 539	0.0797 969	0.0839 163	0.0881 073	31
32	0.0710 023	0.0749 966	0.0790 729	0.0832 260	0.0874 508	32
33	0.0702 729	0.0742 993	0.0784 081	0.0825 940	0.0868 516	33
34	0.0695 984	0.0736 561	0.0777 967	0.0820 146	0.0863 041	34
35	0.0689 739	0.0730 623	0.0772 340	0.0814 829	0.0858 033	35
36	0.0683 948	0.0725 133	0.0767 153	0.0809 945	0.0853 447	36
37	0.0678 574	0.0720 053	0.0762 368	0.0805 453	0.0849 244	37
38	0.0673 581	0.0715 348	0.0757 950	0.0801 320	0.0845 389	38
39	0.0668 938	0.0710 985	0.0753 868	0.0797 512	0.0841 851	39
40	0.0664 615	0.0706 937	0.0750 091	0.0794 003	0.0838 602	40
41	0.0660 589	0.0703 178	0.0746 596	0.0790 766	0.0835 615	41
42	0.0656 834	0.0699 684	0.0743 359	0.0787 779	0.0832 868	42
43	0.0653 331	0.0696 435	0.0740 359	0.0785 020	0.0830 341	43
44	0.0650 061	0.0693 412	0.0737 577	0.0782 471	0.0828 015	44
45	0.0647 005	0.0690 597	0.0734 996	0.0780 115	0.0825 873	45
46	0.0644 148	0.0687 974	0.0732 600	0.0777 935	0.0823 899	46
47	0.0641 477	0.0685 530	0.0730 374	0.0775 919	0.0822 080	47
48	0.0638 977	0.0683 251	0.0728 307	0.0774 053	0.0820 403	48
49	0.0636 636	0.0681 124	0.0726 385	0.0772 325	0.0818 856	49
50	0.0634 443	0.0679 139	0.0724 598	0.0770 724	0.0817 429	50

Table IX — Annuity Whose Present Value Is 1

$$a_{\overline{n}|}^{-1} = i/(1-v^n) = s_{\overline{n}|}^{-1} + i$$

n	6 per cent	6½ per cent	7 per cent	7½ per cent	8 per cent	n
51	0.0632 388	0.0677 286	0.0722 937	0.0769 241	0.0816 112	51
52	0.0630 462	0.0675 555	0.0721 390	0.0767 867	0.0814 896	52
53	0.0628 655	0.0673 938	0.0719 951	0.0766 593	0.0813 774	53
54	0.0626 960	0.0672 427	0.0718 611	0.0765 411	0.0812 737	54
55	0.0625 370	0.0671 014	0.0717 363	0.0764 316	0.0811 780	55
56	0.0623 876	0.0669 692	0.0716 201	0.0763 299	0.0810 895	56
57	0.0622 474	0.0668 456	0.0715 118	0.0762 356	0.0810 078	57
58	0.0621 157	0.0667 300	0.0714 109	0.0761 481	0.0809 323	58
59	0.0619 920	0.0666 218	0.0713 169	0.0760 668	0.0808 625	59
60	0.0618 757	0.0665 205	0.0712 292	0.0759 914	0.0807 979	60
61	0.0617 664	0.0664 256	0.0711 475	0.0759 214	0.0807 383	61
62	0.0616 637	0.0663 368	0.0710 713	0.0758 564	0.0806 831	62
63	0.0615 670	0.0662 537	0.0710 002	0.0757 960	0.0806 321	63
64	0.0614 761	0.0661 758	0.0709 339	0.0757 399	0.0805 850	64
65	0.0613 907	0.0661 028	0.0708 720	0.0756 878	0.0805 413	65
66	0.0613 102	0.0660 344	0.0708 143	0.0756 394	0.0805 010	66
67	0.0612 345	0.0659 703	0.0707 605	0.0755 945	0.0804 637	67
68	0.0611 633	0.0659 103	0.0707 102	0.0755 527	0.0804 291	68
69	0.0610 963	0.0658 540	0.0706 633	0.0755 139	0.0803 972	69
70	0.0610 331	0.0658 012	0.0706 195	0.0754 778	0.0803 676	70
71	0.0609 737	0.0657 518	0.0705 787	0.0754 442	0.0803 403	71
72	0.0609 177	0.0657 054	0.0705 405	0.0754 131	0.0803 150	72
73	0.0608 650	0.0656 619	0.0705 049	0.0753 841	0.0802 916	73
74	0.0608 154	0.0656 211	0.0704 716	0.0753 572	0.0802 699	74
75	0.0607 687	0.0655 829	0.0704 406	0.0753 322	0.0802 498	75
76	0.0607 246	0.0655 470	0.0704 116	0.0753 089	0.0802 313	76
77	0.0606 832	0.0655 133	0.0703 845	0.0752 873	0.0802 141	77
78	0.0606 441	0.0654 818	0.0703 592	0.0752 671	0.0801 982	78
79	0.0606 072	0.0654 522	0.0703 356	0.0752 484	0.0801 835	79
80	0.0605 725	0.0654 244	0.0703 136	0.0752 311	0.0801 699	80
81	0.0605 398	0.0653 983	0.0702 930	0.0752 149	0.0801 573	81
82	0.0605 090	0.0653 739	0.0702 737	0.0751 999	0.0801 456	82
83	0.0604 800	0.0653 509	0.0702 558	0.0751 859	0.0801 348	83
84	0.0604 526	0.0653 294	0.0702 390	0.0751 729	0.0801 248	84
85	0.0604 268	0.0653 092	0.0702 233	0.0751 608	0.0801 155	85
86	0.0604 025	0.0652 903	0.0702 086	0.0751 496	0.0801 070	86
87	0.0603 796	0.0652 725	0.0701 949	0.0751 391	0.0800 990	87
88	0.0603 579	0.0652 558	0.0701 822	0.0751 294	0.0800 917	88
89	0.0603 376	0.0652 401	0.0701 702	0.0751 203	0.0800 849	89
90	0.0603 184	0.0652 254	0.0701 591	0.0751 119	0.0800 786	90
91	0.0603 003	0.0652 116	0.0701 486	0.0751 041	0.0800 728	91
92	0.0602 832	0.0651 986	0.0701 389	0.0750 968	0.0800 674	92
93	0.0602 671	0.0651 865	0.0701 298	0.0750 901	0.0800 624	93
94	0.0602 519	0.0651 751	0.0701 213	0.0750 838	0.0800 578	94
95	0.0602 376	0.0651 644	0.0701 133	0.0750 779	0.0800 535	95
96	0.0602 241	0.0651 543	0.0701 059	0.0750 725	0.0800 495	96
97	0.0602 114	0.0651 449	0.0700 990	0.0750 674	0.0800 458	97
98	0.0601 994	0.0651 360	0.0700 925	0.0750 627	0.0800 424	98
99	0.0601 880	0.0651 277	0.0700 864	0.0750 583	0.0800 393	99
100	0.0601 774	0.0651 199	0.0700 808	0.0750 543	0.0800 364	100
∞	0.0600 000	0.0650 000	0.0700 000	0.0750 000	0.0800 000	∞

Table X — Amount of 1 for Certain Parts of a Period

$$(1+i)^{\frac{1}{p}}$$

p	$\frac{1}{4}$ per cent	$\frac{1}{3}$ per cent	$\frac{5}{12}$ per cent	$\frac{1}{2}$ per cent	$\frac{7}{12}$ per cent	p
2	1.0012 492	1.0016 653	1.0020 812	1.0024 969	1.0029 124	2
4	1.0006 244	1.0008 323	1.0010 400	1.0012 477	1.0014 552	4
12	1.0002 089	1.0002 774	1.0003 466	1.0004 157	1.0004 848	12
13	1.0001 921	1.0002 560	1.0003 199	1.0003 837	1.0004 475	13
52	1.0000 480	1.0000 640	1.0000 800	1.0000 959	1.0001 119	52
365	1.0000 068	1.0000 091	1.0000 114	1.0000 137	1.0000 159	365
∞	1.0000 000	1.0000 000	1.0000 000	1.0000 000	1.0000 000	∞

p	$\frac{2}{3}$ per cent	$\frac{3}{4}$ per cent	1 per cent	$1\frac{1}{4}$ per cent	$1\frac{1}{2}$ per cent	p
2	1.0033 278	1.0037 430	1.0049 876	1.0062 306	1.0074 721	2
4	1.0016 625	1.0018 697	1.0024 907	1.0031 105	1.0037 291	4
12	1.0005 539	1.0006 229	1.0008 295	1.0010 357	1.0012 415	12
13	1.0005 112	1.0005 749	1.0007 657	1.0009 560	1.0011 459	13
52	1.0001 278	1.0001 437	1.0001 914	1.0002 389	1.0002 864	52
365	1.0000 182	1.0000 205	1.0000 273	1.0000 340	1.0000 408	365
∞	1.0000 000	1.0000 000	1.0000 000	1.0000 000	1.0000 000	∞

p	$1\frac{3}{4}$ per cent	2 per cent	$2\frac{1}{4}$ per cent	$2\frac{1}{2}$ per cent	3 per cent	p
2	1.0087 121	1.0099 505	1.0111 874	1.0124 228	1.0148 892	2
4	1.0043 466	1.0049 629	1.0055 782	1.0061 922	1.0074 171	4
12	1.0014 468	1.0016 516	1.0018 559	1.0020 598	1.0024 663	12
13	1.0013 354	1.0015 244	1.0017 130	1.0019 012	1.0022 763	13
52	1.0003 337	1.0003 809	1.0004 280	1.0004 750	1.0005 686	52
365	1.0000 475	1.0000 543	1.0000 610	1.0000 676	1.0000 810	365
∞	1.0000 000	1.0000 000	1.0000 000	1.0000 000	1.0000 000	∞

p	$3\frac{1}{2}$ per cent	4 per cent	$4\frac{1}{2}$ per cent	5 per cent	$5\frac{1}{2}$ per cent	p
2	1.0173 495	1.0198 039	1.0222 524	1.0246 951	1.0271 319	2
4	1.0086 374	1.0098 534	1.0110 650	1.0122 722	1.0134 752	4
12	1.0028 709	1.0032 737	1.0036 748	1.0040 741	1.0044 717	12
13	1.0026 498	1.0030 215	1.0033 916	1.0037 601	1.0041 270	13
52	1.0006 618	1.0007 545	1.0008 468	1.0009 387	1.0010 302	52
365	1.0000 942	1.0001 075	1.0001 206	1.0001 337	1.0001 467	365
∞	1.0000 000	1.0000 000	1.0000 000	1.0000 000	1.0000 000	∞

p	6 per cent	$6\frac{1}{2}$ per cent	7 per cent	$7\frac{1}{2}$ per cent	8 per cent	p
2	1.0295 630	1.0319 884	1.0344 080	1.0368 221	1.0392 305	2
4	1.0146 738	1.0158 683	1.0170 585	1.0182 446	1.0194 265	4
12	1.0048 676	1.0052 617	1.0056 541	1.0060 449	1.0064 340	12
13	1.0044 923	1.0048 560	1.0052 181	1.0055 786	1.0059 376	13
52	1.0011 212	1.0012 118	1.0013 020	1.0013 918	1.0014 811	52
365	1.0001 596	1.0001 726	1.0001 854	1.0001 982	1.0002 109	365
∞	1.0000 000	1.0000 000	1.0000 000	1.0000 000	1.0000 000	∞

Table XI — Nominal Rate of Interest j Convertible p Times a Year Corresponding to Effective Rate of Interest i

$$j_{(p)} = p[(1+i)^{1/p} - 1]$$

p	$\frac{1}{4}$ per cent	$\frac{1}{3}$ per cent	$\frac{5}{12}$ per cent	$\frac{1}{2}$ per cent	$\frac{7}{12}$ per cent	p
2	.0024 984	.0033 306	.0041 623	.0049 938	.0058 249	2
4	.0024 977	.0033 292	.0041 602	.0049 907	.0058 206	4
12	.0024 971	.0033 283	.0041 587	.0049 886	.0058 178	12
13	.0024 971	.0033 282	.0041 587	.0049 885	.0058 177	13
52	.0024 969	.0033 279	.0041 582	.0049 878	.0058 167	52
365	.0024 969	.0033 278	.0041 580	.0049 876	.0058 164	365
∞	.0024 969	.0033 278	.0041 580	.0049 875	.0058 164	∞

p	$\frac{2}{3}$ per cent	$\frac{3}{4}$ per cent	1 per cent	$1\frac{1}{4}$ per cent	$1\frac{1}{2}$ per cent	p
2	.0066 556	.0074 860	.0099 751	.0124 612	.0149 442	2
4	.0066 501	.0074 790	.0099 627	.0124 418	.0149 164	4
12	.0066 464	.0074 743	.0099 545	.0124 290	.0148 979	12
13	.0066 462	.0074 742	.0099 541	.0124 285	.0148 971	13
52	.0066 450	.0074 725	.0099 513	.0124 240	.0148 907	52
365	.0066 446	.0074 721	.0099 505	.0124 227	.0148 889	365
∞	.0066 445	.0074 720	.0099 503	.0124 225	.0148 886	∞

p	$1\frac{3}{4}$ per cent	2 per cent	$2\frac{1}{4}$ per cent	$2\frac{1}{2}$ per cent	3 per cent	p
2	.0174 241	.0199 010	.0223 748	.0248 457	.0297 783	2
4	.0173 863	.0198 517	.0223 126	.0247 690	.0296 683	4
12	.0173 612	.0198 190	.0222 713	.0247 180	.0295 952	12
13	.0173 602	.0198 177	.0222 697	.0247 161	.0295 924	13
52	.0173 515	.0198 064	.0222 554	.0246 985	.0295 672	52
365	.0173 490	.0198 032	.0222 513	.0246 934	.0295 600	365
∞	.0173 486	.0198 026	.0222 506	.0246 926	.0295 588	∞

p	$3\frac{1}{2}$ per cent	4 per cent	$4\frac{1}{2}$ per cent	5 per cent	$5\frac{1}{2}$ per cent	p
2	.0346 990	.0396 078	.0445 048	.0493 902	.0542 639	2
4	.0345 498	.0394 136	.0442 600	.0490 889	.0539 007	4
12	.0344 508	.0392 849	.0440 977	.0488 895	.0536 604	12
13	.0344 470	.0392 799	.0440 915	.0488 818	.0536 512	13
52	.0344 128	.0392 355	.0440 355	.0488 131	.0535 683	52
365	.0344 030	.0392 228	.0440 195	.0487 934	.0535 447	365
∞	.0344 014	.0392 207	.0440 169	.0487 902	.0535 408	∞

p	6 per cent	$6\frac{1}{2}$ per cent	7 per cent	$7\frac{1}{2}$ per cent	8 per cent	p
2	.0591 260	.0639 767	.0688 161	.0736 441	.0784 610	2
4	.0586 954	.0634 731	.0682 341	.0729 784	.0777 062	4
12	.0584 106	.0631 403	.0678 497	.0725 390	.0772 084	12
13	.0583 997	.0631 276	.0678 359	.9725 222	.0771 893	13
52	.0583 016	.0630 129	.0677 027	.0723 710	.0770 180	52
365	.0582 736	.0629 802	.0676 649	.0723 278	.0769 692	365
∞	.0582 689	.0629 748	.0676 586	.0723 207	.0769 619	∞

Table XII — 1941 Commissioners Standard Ordinary Mortality Table

Age x	Number living l_x	Deaths each yr. d_x	Deaths per 1000 $1000q_x$	Age x	Number living l_x	Deaths each yr. d_x	Deaths per 1000 $1000q_x$
0	1023102	23102	22.58	50	810900	9990	12.32
1	1000000	5770	5.77	51	800910	10628	13.27
2	994230	4116	4.14	52	790282	11301	14.30
3	990114	3347	3.38	53	778981	12020	15.43
4	986767	2950	2.99	54	766961	12770	16.65
5	983817	2715	2.76	55	754191	13560	17.98
6	981102	2561	2.61	56	740631	14390	19.43
7	978541	2417	2.47	57	726241	15251	21.00
8	976124	2255	2.31	58	710990	16147	22.71
9	973869	2065	2.12	59	694843	17072	24.57
10	971804	1914	1.97	60	677771	18022	26.59
11	969890	1852	1.91	61	659749	18988	28.78
12	968038	1859	1.92	62	640761	19979	31.18
13	966179	1913	1.98	63	620782	20958	33.76
14	964266	1996	2.07	64	599824	21942	36.58
15	962270	2069	2.15	65	577882	22907	39.64
16	960201	2103	2.19	66	554975	23842	42.96
17	958098	2156	2.25	67	531133	24730	46.56
18	955942	2199	2.30	68	506403	25553	50.46
19	953743	2260	2.37	69	480850	26302	54.70
20	951483	2312	2.43	70	454548	26955	59.30
21	949171	2382	2.51	71	427593	27481	64.27
22	946789	2452	2.59	72	400112	27872	69.66
23	944337	2531	2.68	73	372240	28104	75.50
24	941806	2609	2.77	74	344136	28154	81.81
25	939197	2705	2.88	75	315982	28009	88.64
26	936492	2800	2.99	76	287973	27651	96.02
27	933692	2904	3.11	77	260322	27071	103.99
28	930788	3025	3.25	78	233251	26262	112.59
29	927763	3154	3.40	79	206989	25224	121.86
30	924609	3292	3.56	80	181765	23966	131.85
31	921317	3437	3.73	81	157799	22502	142.60
32	917880	3598	3.92	82	135297	20857	154.16
33	914282	3767	4.12	83	114440	19062	166.57
34	910515	3961	4.35	84	95378	17157	179.88
35	906554	4161	4.59	85	78221	15185	194.13
36	902393	4386	4.86	86	63036	13198	209.37
37	898007	4625	5.15	87	49838	11245	225.63
38	893382	4878	5.46	88	38593	9378	243.00
39	888504	5162	5.81	89	29215	7638	261.44
40	883342	5459	6.18	90	21577	6063	280.99
41	877883	5785	6.59	91	15514	4681	301.73
42	872098	6131	7.03	92	10833	3506	323.64
43	865967	6503	7.51	93	7327	2540	346.66
44	859464	6910	8.04	94	4787	1776	371.00
45	852554	7340	8.61	95	3011	1193	396.21
46	845214	7801	9.23	96	1818	813	447.19
47	837413	8299	9.91	97	1005	551	548.26
48	829114	8822	10.64	98	454	329	724.67
49	820292	9392	11.45	99	125	125	1000.00

Table XIII — Commutation Columns — 1941 CSO $2\frac{1}{2}\%$

Age x	D_x	N_x	M_x
0	1023102.00	31374229.80	257876.8839
1	975609.76	30351127.80	235338.3473
2	946322.43	29375518.04	229846.3782
3	919419.28	28429195.61	226024.2630
4	893962.20	27509776.33	222992.0462
5	869550.88	26615814.13	220384.6760
6	846001.18	25746263.25	218043.5400
7	823212.53	24900262.07	215889.0597
8	801150.42	24077049.54	213905.3152
9	779804.53	23275899.12	212099.6727
10	759171.73	22496094.59	210486.4980
11	739196.60	21736922.86	209027.7529
12	719790.36	20997726.26	207650.6874
13	700885.94	20277935.90	206302.1309
14	682437.28	19577049.96	204948.2488
15	664414.29	18894612.68	203570.0795
16	646815.33	18230198.39	202176.3495
17	629657.27	17583383.06	200794.2683
18	612917.42	16953725.79	199411.9146
19	596592.68	16340808.37	198036.3791
20	580662.42	15744215.69	196657.1668
21	565123.40	15163553.27	195280.6337
22	549956.28	14598429.87	193897.0141
23	535153.17	14048473.59	192507.4725
24	520701.32	13513320.42	191108.1450
25	506594.02	12992619.10	189700.8750
26	492814.61	12486025.08	188277.4101
27	479357.22	11993210.47	186839.8909
28	466211.03	11513853.25	185385.3418
29	453361.83	11047642.22	183907.1415
30	440800.58	10594280.39	182403.4951
31	428518.18	10153479.81	180872.3371
32	416506.91	9724961.63	179312.7277
33	404755.37	9308454.72	177719.8824
34	393256.29	8903699.35	176092.8950
35	381995.63	8510443.06	174423.8442
36	370968.10	8128447.43	172713.2832
37	360161.02	7757479.33	170954.2031
38	349566.90	7397318.31	169144.5103
39	339178.75	7047751.41	167282.3758
40	328983.61	6708572.66	165359.8889
41	318976.11	6379589.05	163376.3779
42	309145.51	6060612.94	161325.6832
43	299485.04	5751467.43	159205.3451
44	289986.39	5451982.39	157011.2084
45	280638.95	5161996.00	154736.6133
46	271436.89	4881357.05	152379.4034
47	262372.33	4609920.16	149935.2492
48	253436.24	4347547.83	147398.4842
49	244624.00	4094111.59	144767.6248

Table XIII — Commutation Columns — 1941 CSO $2\frac{1}{2}\%$ (Cont.)

Age x	D_x	N_x	M_x
50	235925.04	3849487.59	142035.0956
51	227335.15	3613562.55	139199.4735
52	218847.25	3386227.40	136256.3361
53	210456.33	3167380.15	133203.1589
54	202155.03	2956923.82	130034.9360
55	193940.61	2754768.79	126751.1239
56	185808.43	2560828.18	123349.2108
57	177754.43	2375019.75	119827.1207
58	169777.17	2197265.32	116185.3372
59	161874.57	2027488.15	112423.6404
60	154046.23	1865613.58	108543.4550
61	146292.80	1711567.35	104547.2551
62	138616.97	1565274.55	100439.5471
63	131019.40	1426657.58	96222.8711
64	123508.39	1295638.18	91907.4573
65	116088.15	1172129.79	87499.6261
66	108767.29	1056041.64	83010.1764
67	101555.70	947274.35	78451.4482
68	94465.545	845718.651	73838.2589
69	87511.050	751253.106	69187.8068
70	80706.625	663742.056	64517.7925
71	74068.942	583035.431	59848.5665
72	67618.148	508966.489	55204.3311
73	61373.498	441348.341	50608.9030
74	55355.921	379974.843	46088.2403
75	49587.526	324618.922	41669.9911
76	44089.787	275031.396	37381.7042
77	38884.206	230941.609	33251.4840
78	33990.850	192057.403	29306.5222
79	29428.077	158066.553	25572.7964
80	25211.636	128638.476	22074.1123
81	21353.602	103426.840	18830.9965
82	17862.047	82073.238	15860.2597
83	14739.984	64211.191	13173.8577
84	11985.151	49471.207	10778.5365
85	9589.4746	37486.0561	8675.1804
86	7539.3905	27896.5815	6858.9858
87	5815.4632	20357.1910	5318.9464
88	4393.4773	14541.7278	4038.8010
89	3244.7546	10148.2505	2997.2364
90	2337.9929	6903.4959	2169.6149
91	1640.0309	4565.5030	1528.6772
92	1117.2571	2925.4721	1045.9042
93	737.2363	1808.2150	693.1335
94	469.9158	1070.9787	443.7944
95	288.3657	601.0629	273.7056
96	169.8646	312.6972	162.2378
97	91.6117	142.8326	88.1280
98	40.3755	51.2209	39.1261
99	10.8454	10.8454	10.5810

Answers to Odd-Numbered Problems

Page 1, Exercise 1, Chapter 1
1. $8c$ **3.** $3x + 5y$ **5.** $x - 5$ **7.** $\frac{365}{7}n$ or approximately $52n$
9. The area of a triangle is equal to one half of the product of the base by the height.
11. $5000 - x$

Page 3, Exercise 2, Chapter 1
1. 6 **3.** -6 **5.** -1 **7.** -11 **9.** -4
11. 2 **13.** -10 **15.** -4 **17.** 12 **19.** 11
21. -12 **23.** -40 **25.** 18 **27.** -48 **29.** 12
31. 2 **33.** -5 **35.** 7 **37.** -4 **39.** 6

Page 4, Exercise 3, Chapter 1
1. $5x$ **3.** $11x - 7y$ **5.** $4x^2 + 3y^2$ **7.** $-a^2b + 7a^2b^3$
9. $3m + 3n + p$ **11.** $11x$ **13.** $9a - 7b$ **15.** $4a + 4b + 2c$
17. $9x^3 - 12x^2 + 17x - 10$ **19.** $x - 4$ **21.** $2x$
23. $a + 9b$ **25.** $-x^2 + y^2$ **27.** $3a + 2b - 6c$
29. $4x^2 - 7xy - 3y^2$ **31.** $-a - 2b - c - 5d$
33. $-3ac + 14bc$ **35.** $a^3 + a^2b - 3ab^2 + 5b^3$
37. $7m^2 + 11$ **39.** $-2s^3 - 8s^2 + 12s + 2$

Page 7, Exercise 4, Chapter 1
1. x^9 **3.** 2^7 **5.** a^3b^2 **7.** $12a^3b^4$ **9.** $(1+i)^{125}$ **11.** $x^2 + xy - xz$
13. $a^2b - 2ab^2 + 3abc$ **15.** $ab + acd$ **17.** $x^2 + 5x + 6$ **19.** $x^2 - 9x + 20$
21. $x^2 - x - 6$ **23.** $9x^2 - 4y^2$ **25.** $a^3 + b^3$ **27.** $1 - x + x^2 - x^4$
29. $a^5 - 2a^4b + 3a^3b^2 - 3a^2b^3 + 2ab^4 - b^5$ **31.** $1 - a - b + ab$
33. $5x^4 - 26x^3 + 32x^2 - 34x + 8$
35. $2a^6 - 5a^5 + 7a^4 - 8a^3 + 6a^2 - 3a + 1$ **37.** $1 - 2x + 3x^2 - 2x^3 + x^4$
39. $a^4 - 4a^3b + 6a^2b^2 - 4ab^3 + b^4$

Page 8, Exercise 5, Chapter 1
1. x^4 **3.** $3ab^2$ **5.** 2^6 **7.** $a^2b^2 - ab^3 + b^4$ **9.** $x - 5$
11. $x + y$ **13.** $a^2 + 2ab + b^2$ **15.** $a^2 + ab + b^2$
17. $a + b$ **19.** $x^5 + x^4y + x^3y^2 + x^2y^3 + xy^4 + y^5$
21. $1 - x$ **23.** $1 + 2x + x^2$ **25.** $a^2 + 2ab + b^2$

ANSWERS

Page 9, Exercise 6, Chapter 1

1. $ax - bx$
3. $a^2 - 9$
5. $4x^2 - y^2$
7. $x^2 + 2xy + y^2$
9. $4x^2 + 12xy + 9y^2$
11. $x^2 + 5x + 6$
13. $r^2 - 9r + 20$
15. $x^2 + 7x - 8$
17. $8x^2 + 2x - 15$
19. $24m^2 - 18mn + 3n^2$
21. $x^3 - y^3$
23. $x^3 - 8$
25. $12ac - 15ad - 8bc + 10bd$
27. $P(1 + i)$
29. $(r - x)(r + x)$
31. $(3x + 4y)(3x - 4y)$
33. $(4x + 3)(4x - 3)$
35. $(m - n)^2$
37. $(2a - 3b)^2$
39. $(3m + n)^2$
41. $(m + 7)(m + 1)$
43. $(x + 4)(x - 3)$
45. $(a - 4)(a - 3)$
47. $(x + 10)(x - 9)$
49. $(x - m)(x^2 + mx + m^2)$
51. $(3x + 4y)(9x^2 - 12xy + 16y^2)$
53. $(x - 5y)(x^2 + 5xy + 25y^2)$
55. $(a - b)(x + y)$

Page 11, Exercise 7, Chapter 1

1. -23
3. 13
5. -12
7. 240
9. -26
11. 115
13. 20
15. 0.56
17. 56.2432
19. 120
21. 113
23. 1131.0
25. 33.5
27. $x^3 - xy^2 + xz^2 + x^2y - y^3 + yz^2 - x^2z + y^2z - z^3$
29. $y^3 + z^3$
31. $a^2 + 2ab + b^2$
33. $a^3 + a^2b + ab^2 + b^3$
35. $a^3 - 3a^2b + 3ab^2 - b^3$

Page 12, Exercise 8, Chapter 1

1. $-4x - 2$
3. $6a - 37$
5. $7a - 23b + 32$
7. $5x + 6$
9. $-57m - 80n$
11. $-23s$
13. 203
15. 230
17. 41
19. 1.0404
21. 42.864

Page 13, Miscellaneous Exercise, Chapter 1

1. $5x - 3y + 7z$
3. $-3x^3 - 3x^2 + 15x - 6$
5. $x^3 - 9x^2 + 26x - 24$
7. $8x - 2$
9. 9
11. 11
13. -23
15. $P(1 - x)(1 + y)$
17. $(3r - 7)(r + 8)$
19. $P(1 - a)$
21. 250
23. 1.0609
25. 49
27. 11
29. 3
31. 45.08
33. 1169.85856
35. 1.0816
37. $5a - b$
39. $2a + 19b$
41. 110.25
43. 54.63635
45. 2^{10}
47. $(1 + x)^{125}$
49. 1.04^{115}
51. $1 - x + x^2 - x^3 + x^4$

Page 17, Exercise 1, Chapter 2

1. 3
3. 11
5. 5
7. 24
9. 2
11. 3
13. 4
15. -2
17. 8
19. -10.5
21. -21.5
23. $-\dfrac{2a}{5}$
25. $762\tfrac{2}{29}$
27. $969\tfrac{2}{17}$
29. $d = 2$
31. $x = 2$
33. $x = -2$
35. $y = -5$
37. $l = 58$

Page 21, Exercise 2, Chapter 2

1. 21, 52
3. \$2.35, \$4.63
5. 359 miles, 436 miles
7. 2 gal.
9. Cost price \$40,000 and \$45,000; selling price \$44,800 and \$46,350
11. 5 pounds of 30¢ tea; 15 pounds of mixture
13. 7 dimes, 3 quarters
15. 3 nickels, 4 dimes, and 5 quarters
17. Oats, 35¢ per bushel; wheat, 83¢ per bushel
19. 6 miles; 4 miles per hour
21. $11\tfrac{1}{9}$ days
23. $1\tfrac{1}{2}$ hours

ANSWERS

Page 26, Exercise 3, Chapter 2

1. $x = 2, y = 3$ **3.** $x = 5, y = 4$ **5.** Inconsistent
7. $x = 3\frac{2}{7}, y = 2\frac{6}{7}$ **9.** $x = 22, y = 18$ **11.** $x = 2, y = 9$
13. $x = 2, y = 16$ **15.** $x = 40, y = 20$ **17.** $x = 3000, y = 2000$
19. $x = 0.5, y = 0.3$ **21.** $x = \dfrac{ce - bf}{ae - bd}$; $y = \dfrac{af - cd}{ae - bd}$; $(ae - bd \neq 0)$
23. $x = \frac{1}{5}, y = \frac{1}{2}$ **25.** $x = 2.5, y = \frac{1}{3}$

Page 29, Exercise 4, Chapter 2

1. $x = 6, y = 3$ **3.** $x = \frac{7}{13}, y = -\frac{22}{13}$ **5.** $x = 3, y = 5$
7. $x = 14, y = 9$ **9.** $x = \frac{2}{3}, y = -\frac{1}{5}$

Page 30, Exercise 5, Chapter 2

1. 235,152   **3.** $22\frac{8}{11}$ lb. of cream; $477\frac{3}{11}$ lb. of 3% milk
5. 3 miles per hour, 10 miles   **7.** $11\frac{1}{4}$ hours, father; 9 hours, son
9. Algebra, 90; geometry, 82   **11.** $m = 3, b = -5$
13. Wheat, 82 cents; oats, 38 cents   **15.** 17 nickels, 15 dimes

Page 32, Exercise 6, Chapter 2

1. $x = 2, y = 4, z = 5$ **3.** $x = -2, y = 3, z = -4$
5. $x = 5, y = 6, z = 2$ **7.** $x = 8, y = 19, z = -5$
9. $x = \frac{1}{6}, y = \frac{1}{5}, z = \frac{1}{3}$ **11.** $x = 1\frac{2}{7}, y = \frac{3}{8}, z = 4\frac{1}{2}$
13. $x = 4, y = -3, z = 5$

Page 33, Miscellaneous Exercise, Chapter 2

1. 4   **3.** $-\frac{1}{2}$ **5.** $-2\frac{3}{4}$ **7.** -2 **9.** 3   **11.** $13\frac{3}{4}, 28\frac{3}{4}$
13. 8, 8, 11   **15.** $x = 2, y = 3$ **17.** $x = -6, y = -3$
19. $x = \frac{1}{5}, y = -\frac{1}{3}$ **21.** $x = \frac{1}{3}, y = \frac{1}{4}$
23. $x = 1, y = 5, z = 2$ **25.** $x = \frac{1}{2}, y = -\frac{1}{3}, z = \frac{1}{5}$
27. 50 lb. of 35¢ coffee, 25 lb. of 50¢ coffee
29. 25 Holsteins, 15 Guernseys   **31.** 25 at $7.30, 5 at $9

Page 37, Exercise 1, Chapter 3

1. $\frac{4}{9}$ **3.** $\frac{6}{7}$ **5.** ab^2 **7.** $\dfrac{a + b}{a - b}$ **9.** $\dfrac{x}{x + 3y}$
11. $\dfrac{x}{x - y}$ **13.** $\dfrac{1}{1 - m}$ **15.** $\dfrac{x - 3}{x - 8}$ **17.** $a^2 + ab + b^2$

Page 38, Exercise 2, Chapter 3

1. $2x$ **3.** $\dfrac{7a}{c}$ **5.** $-\dfrac{11a}{42}$ **7.** $\dfrac{2x + 1}{2}$ **9.** $\dfrac{38x - 16y}{21}$
11. $\dfrac{-11m - 47n}{35}$ **13.** $\dfrac{41}{105}$ **15.** $\dfrac{4x - 7}{(x - 2)(x - 1)}$ **17.** $\dfrac{7}{a - b}$ **19.** $\dfrac{2x}{y^2 - 1}$
21. $\dfrac{-x^3 + 8x^2 - 4x^2y + 3xy}{x^2 - 1}$ **23.** $\dfrac{7x - 7}{x^2 + x - 6}$ **25.** $\dfrac{a - 7}{(a - 5)(a - 1)(a - 3)}$

Page 39, Exercise 3, Chapter 3

1. $\dfrac{am}{cn}$ 3. $\dfrac{12y}{x^2}$ 5. $\dfrac{56}{9}$ 7. $\dfrac{a}{c(a+b)}$ 5. $\dfrac{11}{15}$

11. $x+y$ 13. 1 15. $\dfrac{a^2+b^2}{a+b}$ 17. $\dfrac{3x^2}{6x-4}$

Page 40, Exercise 4, Chapter 3

1. $\tfrac{1}{4}$ 3. 4 5. 0.082 7. 0.05 9. 94.26

Page 42, Exercise 5, Chapter 3

1. 9 3. $\tfrac{2}{3}$ 5. $\dfrac{xz}{y}$ 7. 1

9. $-\dfrac{75}{28}$ 11. $\dfrac{x^2}{x^2-y^2}$ 13. $\dfrac{a}{x}$ 15. $\dfrac{a^2+abc}{b^2-abc}$

17. $1\tfrac{1}{3}$ 19. $\dfrac{Pd}{1-nd}$ 21. $\dfrac{x}{b+a-x}$ 23. $\dfrac{acf-bf}{cdf-ec}$

Page 44, Exercise 6, Chapter 3

1. 6 3. 8 5. $\tfrac{282}{85}$ 7. 35 9. 12

Page 45, Exercise 7, Chapter 3

1. $\dfrac{I}{ni}$ 3. $\dfrac{S-P}{Pi}$ 5. $\dfrac{d}{1-dn}$ 7. $\dfrac{S-a}{S}$ 9. $\dfrac{i}{1+i}$ 11. $\dfrac{l-a+d}{d}$

13. $\dfrac{360I}{Pt}$ 15. $\dfrac{1-r_2-F}{1-r_2}$ 17. $\dfrac{I-P}{I}$ 19. $\dfrac{I}{I+100p}$ 21. $\dfrac{r-r_2}{1-r_2}$

23. $\dfrac{Pj-g'C}{j-g'}$ 25. 3 27. 5 29. $\tfrac{21}{253}$ 31. $\tfrac{1}{2}$ 33. 0.01999 35. 4 37. 0.02

Page 48, Exercise 8, Chapter 3

1. 3 3. 5 5. $\tfrac{1}{2}$ 7. $\tfrac{8}{3}$ 9. $\tfrac{1}{6}$ 11. 32 13. 12 15. 20 17. 54
19. 18 21. $1\tfrac{1}{3}$ 23. $92\tfrac{6}{7}$ 25. $47\tfrac{1}{2}$ 27. 91.39 29. 54 feet 31. $\tfrac{1}{7}$
33. Yes 35. $4\tfrac{1}{2}$ 39. $3150 41. $14,000 43. 40 45. $150

Page 49, Miscellaneous Exercise, Chapter 3

1. $1+i$ 3. $\dfrac{1}{x}$ 5. $\dfrac{2+i}{1-i^2}$ 7. $\dfrac{2mn-n^2}{m^2-n^2}$ 9. $\tfrac{2}{11}$ 11. 1

13. $\dfrac{y(1+x)}{x}$ 15. $\dfrac{b-a}{b+a}$ 17. 94.34 19. 0.51 21. 1.20 23. 723.57

27. -1 29. 9 31. $a=\dfrac{2s}{n}-l$

33. $n=\dfrac{S-P}{Sd}$ 35. $k=\dfrac{xi-gc}{i-g}$ 39. $\tfrac{1}{4}$

ANSWERS

Page 51, Exercise 1, Chapter 4

1. 24%   **3.** 12%   **5.** $6\frac{1}{2}$%   **7.** $2\frac{1}{4}$%   **9.** $1\frac{1}{2}$%   **11.** $1\frac{1}{8}$%
13. $\frac{1}{8}$%   **15.** $\frac{5}{8}$%   **17.** 50%   **19.** $12\frac{1}{2}$%   **21.** $62\frac{1}{2}$%   **23.** $33\frac{1}{3}$%
25. $41\frac{2}{3}$%   **27.** $4\frac{1}{6}$%   **29.** $29\frac{1}{6}$%   **31.** $\frac{3}{100}$; 0.03   **33.** $\frac{13}{200}$; 0.065
35. $\frac{1}{80}$; 0.0125   **37.** $\frac{9}{800}$; 0.01125   **39.** $\frac{3}{400}$; 0.0075
41. $\frac{1}{160}$; 0.00625   **43.** $\frac{11}{400}$; 0.0275   **45.** $\frac{7}{1200}$; $0.0058\frac{1}{3}$

Page 53, Exercise 2, Chapter 4

1. 18   **3.** 120   **5.** 200   **7.** 10.4   **9.** 26   **11.** 400   **13.** 20,000
15. $742\frac{6}{7}$ **17.** $1\frac{9}{16}$ **19.** $17\frac{1}{6}$ **21.** 20%   **23.** 10%   **25.** $12\frac{1}{2}$%
27. $11\frac{1}{9}$%   **29.** $8\frac{1}{2}$%   **31.** $10,285.71   **33.** $11\frac{1}{9}$%   **35.** $30,434.78
37. $4444.44   **39.** $50   **41.** $202.83   **43.** Cost of lot, $2,135; 21.6% approx.
45. 20 gals.   **47.** $300,000   **49.** $14.76   **51.** $25   **53.** No   **55.** $9,000

Page 57, Exercise 3, Chapter 4

1. $N.C.$, 60%; E_1, 1%; $G.C.$, 61%; $M.$, 39%; E_2, 25%; $N.P.$, 14%
3. $2, $33\frac{1}{3}$%   **5.** $180, $16\frac{2}{3}$%   **7.** $0.12, approx.   **11.** $20

Page 59, Exercise 4, Chapter 4

1. $300.20   **3.** $36   **5.** $75.85   **7.** $33.06

Page 62, Exercise 5, Chapter 4

1. $213.75   **3.** $107.73   **5.** 20%, 20%, 10%
7. 0.76   **9.** $200   **11.** $10.68
13. 16%   **15.** 30% and 10%   **17.** $520.83
19. Factor, 0.684; hammer, $0.65; saw, $0.89; planer, $1.64

Page 63, Miscellaneous Exercise, Chapter 4

1. $r_2 = 1 - \dfrac{N}{L(1 - r_1)}$ **3.** $60   **5.** 41.86%   **7.** 20%   **9.** $96.90
11. 3%   **13.** $80   **15.** $9   **17.** 25%   **19.** 0.76   **21.** $205.71

Page 66, Exercise 1, Chapter 5

1. a^7 **3.** m^9 **5.** $(1 + i)^{106}$ **7.** 3^6 **9.** y^8 **11.** 5^6 **13.** m^3n^3
15. a^6b^9 **17.** $\dfrac{x^2}{y^2}$ **19.** $\dfrac{x^4y^6}{z^2}$ **21.** $\frac{4}{9}$ **23.** $\dfrac{a^{10}}{b^5}$ **25.** x^6 **27.** 4
29. $(1 + i)^{100}$ **31.** $(x + y)^2$ **33.** $\dfrac{1}{r^3}$ **35.** $\frac{1}{27}$ **37.** a^2bc^3 **39.** $\dfrac{1}{(1 + i)^8}$
41. x^{2n+4} **43.** a^{2m^2} **45.** x^{2n} **47.** x^{mn}
49. a^{2m+8} **51.** $\dfrac{r^{12n}}{s^{6n}}$ **53.** 1.0201   **55.** 1.04060401
57. 1.104   **59.** 1.1040808   **61.** 1.0816   **63.** 1.16985856

Page 69, Exercise 2, Chapter 5

1. $a^{\frac{5}{6}}$ **3.** $a^{\frac{5}{7}}$ **5.** $m^{3.7}$ **7.** $y^{\frac{10}{3}}$ **9.** $2^{\frac{2}{3}}$ **11.** mn **13.** $(1+i)^{\frac{11}{6}}$
15. $x^{\frac{1}{3}}y^{\frac{1}{3}}$ **17.** $a^{\frac{2}{3}}b^{\frac{2}{3}}c^{\frac{2}{3}}$ **19.** $\dfrac{a^{\frac{1}{2}}}{b^{\frac{1}{2}}}$ **21.** $\dfrac{1}{2^{\frac{1}{2}}}$ **23.** $a^{\frac{1}{6}}$ **25.** $y^{\frac{1}{6}}$ **27.** $\dfrac{1}{a^{\frac{1}{3}}}$
31. -2 **33.** 4   **35.** 3   **37.** 512   **39.** $\frac{5}{3}$ **41.** $\frac{2}{3}$ **43.** 4   **45.** $\frac{1}{2}$

Page 71, Exercise 3, Chapter 5

1. 1   **3.** a^6 **5.** $12x$ **7.** $\frac{1}{64}$ **9.** $\dfrac{b^4}{a^3}$ **11.** $\dfrac{n^7}{m^6}$ **13.** 1   **15.** $1\frac{1}{16}$ **17.** 1
19. x^5 **21.** $\dfrac{1}{a^8}$ **23.** $2\frac{1}{3}$ **25.** $\dfrac{1}{x^6}$
27. $\dfrac{b^2 - a^2}{b^2 + a^2}$ **29.** $\dfrac{x+y}{xy}$ **33.** 0.9426   **37.** 1.8861

Page 72, Exercise 4, Chapter 5

1. Radicand, 5; index, 2; order, second
3. Radicand, $a+b$; index, 2; order, second
5. Radicand, a^2b^2; index, 3; order, third
7. Radicand, $b^2 - 4ac$; index, 2; order, second
9. Radicand, $5+x$; index, 6; order, sixth
11. Radicand, S; index, m; order, mth

Page 73, Exercise 5, Chapter 5

1. There is a fraction under the radical sign.   **3.** Simplest form
5. There is a radical in the denominator.
7. There is a factor in the radicand raised to a power whose exponent equals the index of the root; also, the index of the radical is not as small as possible.
9. Since $8 = 2^3$, the radicand contains a factor raised to a power whose exponent equals the index of the root.
11. There is a fraction under the radical sign.
13. There is a radical in the denominator.

Page 74, Exercise 6, Chapter 5

1. $\sqrt{32}$ **3.** $\sqrt{5a^2}$ **5.** $\sqrt[3]{48}$ **7.** $\sqrt[3]{a^3b^3c}$ **9.** $\sqrt[4]{96}$
11. $5\sqrt{3}$ **13.** $4\sqrt{2}$ **15.** $3\sqrt[3]{2}$ **17.** $2\sqrt[3]{3}$ **19.** $x\sqrt{x}$
21. $xy^2\sqrt{x}$ **23.** $xy\sqrt[3]{x^2y}$ **25.** $rs\sqrt[3]{s}$ **27.** $c\sqrt{c}$ **29.** $a\sqrt[3]{a^2}$
31. $a^2\sqrt{b}$ **33.** $\frac{2}{7}\sqrt{7}$ **35.** $\frac{1}{3}\sqrt{3}$ **37.** $\frac{2}{3}\sqrt{6}$ **39.** $\frac{3}{2}\sqrt{2}$
41. $\frac{6}{5}\sqrt{5}$ **43.** $\frac{1}{5}\sqrt[3]{100}$ **45.** $\frac{1}{5}\sqrt[3]{50}$ **47.** $\dfrac{1}{a}\sqrt{3a}$ **49.** $11\sqrt{3}$
51. $6\sqrt{x}$ **53.** $-5\sqrt[3]{4}$ **55.** $-14\sqrt{6}$ **57.** $8\sqrt{5}$
59. $19\sqrt[3]{6}$ **61.** $\frac{7}{12}\sqrt{6}$ **63.** $\sqrt[6]{8}, \sqrt[6]{9}$ **65.** $\sqrt[6]{a^3}, \sqrt[6]{b^2}$
67. $\sqrt[12]{625}, \sqrt[12]{8}$ **69.** $\sqrt[12]{729}, \sqrt[12]{81}, \sqrt[12]{27}$ **71.** $\sqrt[6]{4}, \sqrt[6]{3}$ **73.** $\sqrt[12]{x^8}, \sqrt[12]{x^9}$

ANSWERS

Page 77, Exercise 7, Chapter 5

1. $\sqrt{21}$ **3.** $2\sqrt{6}$ **5.** $12\sqrt{10}$ **7.** $8a\sqrt{b}$ **9.** $\sqrt[4]{15}$ **11.** $\sqrt[6]{12{,}348}$
13. $\sqrt[15]{864}$ **15.** $x\sqrt[12]{x^5}$ **17.** 4 **19.** $5 + 2\sqrt{6}$ **21.** $m + 2\sqrt{mn} + n$
23. -1 **25.** $3\sqrt{6} - 3\sqrt{15} + 9$ **27.** 0 **29.** 0 **31.** 3 **33.** $\sqrt{6}$
35. $\sqrt[4]{8}$ **37.** $\frac{1}{7}\sqrt{70}$ **39.** $\frac{2}{3}\sqrt{3}$ **41.** $\sqrt[3]{2}$ **43.** $\sqrt[3]{x}$ **45.** $\frac{2}{3}\sqrt{3}$
47. $\dfrac{12 - 2\sqrt{3}}{33}$ **49.** $\dfrac{2 + \sqrt{2}}{2}$ **51.** $-2 - \sqrt{3}$ **53.** $\dfrac{a + 2\sqrt{ab} + b}{a - b}$

Page 79, Exercise 8, Chapter 5

1. 2 **3.** 2 **5.** 5 **7.** 2 **9.** $6\frac{1}{4}$ **11.** $\frac{8}{27}$ **13.** 28
15. 0.03 **17.** 2 **19.** $\frac{1}{8}$ **21.** $2\frac{1}{64}$ **23.** 512 **25.** 16 **27.** $\sqrt[3]{\dfrac{S}{P}} - 1$

Page 79, Miscellaneous Exercise, Chapter 5

1. $13\frac{1}{9}$ **3.** 30 **5.** $\frac{11}{64}$ **7.** 3.464 **9.** 2.249
11. 1.155 **13.** 5.196 **15.** 0.02 **17.** 0.0025 **19.** $\left(\dfrac{S}{P}\right)^{\frac{1}{5}} - 1$
21. 11.9 **23.** 86.0 **25.** 19.5 **27.** $\sqrt{7}$ **29.** $\sqrt[5]{x^3}$
31. $3\sqrt[3]{3}$ **33.** $\dfrac{1}{(a+b)^{\frac{1}{2}}}$ **35.** $\dfrac{1}{a^2} + \dfrac{1}{b^2}$ **37.** $\dfrac{4}{x^{\frac{1}{3}}}$ **39.** $\dfrac{3}{x^2} + \dfrac{4}{y}$
41. $\frac{3}{2}, \sqrt[3]{8}$ **43.** $3^{-2}, \sqrt[4]{16}, \sqrt[3]{27}$ **45.** $4\sqrt{2}$ **47.** $\sqrt{3} + 1$ **49.** $\dfrac{17 + 8\sqrt{2}}{23}$

Page 84, Exercise 1, Chapter 6

1. 4 **3.** 3 **5.** 7 **7.** 2 **9.** 5 **11.** 6 **13.** 4 **15.** 6 **17.** 2
19. 7   **21.** 3.98909   **23.** 1.04680
25. 0.874010   **27.** 0.0150564   **29.** 232.279
31. 8,206,200, where the terminal zeros are not significant
33. 455,560, where terminal zero is not significant
35. 455,540, where terminal zero is not significant
37. 916.02   **39.** 2.0186

Page 87, Exercise 2, Chapter 6

1. 3 **3.** 1 **5.** 5 **7.** 2 **9.** 1 **11.** 5 **13.** 0 **15.** 0
17. $9 - 10$ **19.** $8 - 10$ **21.** $6 - 10$ **23.** $9 - 10$ **25.** $8 - 10$
27. 0   **29.** 0   **31.** $7 - 10$
35. 4.301030   **37.** $5.301030 - 10$ **39.** $8.301030 - 10$
43. 0.954242   **45.** 2.477121   **47.** 1.431363
49. $9.823909 - 10$ **51.** 0.150515   **53.** 0.100343
55. 0.698970   **57.** 0.829303   **59.** 4.778151

Page 89, Exercise 3, Chapter 6

1. 3.097951   **3.** 1.273001   **5.** 0.966986
7. 5.025306   **9.** $8.992642 - 10$ **11.** $9.992377 - 10$

ANSWERS

13. 3.109849
15. 3.478927
17. 2.603826
19. 0.604086
21. 9.172574 − 10
23. 4.444638
25. 4.659231
27. 2.840407
29. 2.477469
31. 1.616088
33. 2.024410
35. 1.527662

Page 91, Exercise 4, Chapter 6

1. 3.109849
3. 3.517288
5. 3.991514
7. 3.699222
9. 2.929297
11. 1.818444
13. 0.845296
15. 9.907185 − 10
17. 8.788572 − 10
19. 6.129561 − 10
21. 0.025928
23. 0.613200
25. 2.462901
27. 1.958515
29. 3.798456

Page 93, Exercise 5, Chapter 6

1. 364.000
3. 0.235800
5. 1475.50
7. 27216.1
9. 8.48482
11. 0.0212079
13. 0.000882426
15. 3162.28
17. 16456900
19. 447.545

Page 94, Exercise 6, Chapter 6

1. 1.06184
3. 941.493
5. 1.02316
7. 5298.39
9. 71823.8
11. 0.0299593
13. 188811
15. 25.6406
17. 0.0503106
19. 316.228

Page 96, Exercise 7, Chapter 6

1. 18944.0
3. 1900.49
5. 0.465382
7. 116.426
9. 4672.23
11. 3.07358
13. 486.807
15. 265.316
17. 0.826892
19. 0.0904462
21. 15298.9
23. 9938730
25. 0.00302262
27. 9218.64
29. 2247.09

Page 99, Exercise 8, Chapter 6

1. 40002
3. 0.00000034868
5. 187229
7. 42878
9. 0.0047911
11. 1.3459
13. 1.40047
15. 1.5364
17. 0.590786
19. 0.52240
21. 22157
23. 705.66
25. 16116
27. 2264.9
29. 30374
31. 4.10366
33. 20.8015
35. 0.409024
37. 3.49741
39. 162437
41. 1.01316
43. 1.05205
45. 1.01990
47. 14.21
49. 8.1922

Page 102, Exercise 9, Chapter 6

1. 35.003
3. 8.31037
5. 75.8039
7. 7.81876
9. 9.40415
11. 1.020
13. 22.3170
15. 0.03715
17. 0.01449
19. 0.08600

Page 104, Miscellaneous Exercise, Chapter 6

1. 2
3. 0, 1, 2, − 1
5. 1.397940
7. 9.795880 − 10
9. 0.301030
11. 0.2553
13. 12
15. 0.0275584
17. 590.982
19. $x = 0.53503$

Page 107, Exercise 1, Chapter 7

1. $800, $5800
3. $87.50, $962.50
5. $4.20
7. $1385.44
9. $21.67
11. 0.04
13. 0.045
15. $2100.00
17. 0.06
19. $15,000.00

ANSWERS

Page 110, Exercise 2, Chapter 7
1. 48 days **3.** 188 days **5.** 331 days **7.** 299 days **9.** 180 days
11. 231 days **13.** 35 days **15.** 122 days **17.** 422 days **19.** 772 days

Page 113, Exercise 3, Chapter 7
1. $I_o = \$28.13$, $I_e = \$27.75$ **3.** $I_o = \$28.10$, $I_e = \$27.71$
5. $I_o = \$26.21$, $I_e = \$25.85$ **7.** $I_o = \$7.33$, $I_e = \$7.23$
9. $I_o = \$7.95$, $I_e = \$7.84$ **11.** $79.64
13. $I_o = \$270.83$ (exact time); $I_e = \$267.12$ (exact time); $I_o = \$266.67$ (approximate time); $I_e = \$263.01$ (approximate time)
15. $I_o = \$1.25$, $I_e = \$1.23$

Page 115, Exercise 4, Chapter 7
1. $6.90 **3.** $19.00 **5.** $6.67
7. $1.63 **9.** $4.00 **11.** $3.10
13. $20.80 **15.** $11.19 **17.** $I_o = 0.02P$
19. $\dfrac{0.25P}{24}$ **21.** $I_o = \$3.02$; $I_e = \$2.98$ **23.** $I_o = \$1.48$; $I_e = \$1.46$

Page 117, Exercise 5, Chapter 7
1. $1818.18 **3.** $865.38 **5.** $585.37 **7.** $3855.42, $3827.75
9. $943.40, $892.86, $847.46 **11.** $491.04 **13.** $2968.64 **15.** $794.72

Page 120, Exercise 6, Chapter 7
1. $1000, 95 days, $1013.19, $1002.61 **3.** $495.07
5. $913.18 **7.** $i = \dfrac{S - P}{Pn}$ **9.** $600

Page 122, Exercise 7, Chapter 7
1. $1477.50 **3.** $476.67 **5.** $1173.60 **7.** $694.90
9. $8280.96 **11.** $518.14 **13.** $486.25 **15.** $900

Page 124, Exercise 8, Chapter 7
1. $490.92 **3.** $495.43 **5.** 90 days, May 2, 1948, July 31, 1948
7. $1007.73 **9.** $1012.66

Page 126, Exercise 9, Chapter 7
1. $595.10 **3.** $995.42 **5.** $998.33

Page 129, Exercise 10, Chapter 7
1. 0.0606061, 0.0609137 **3.** 0.0725388 **5.** $i = \dfrac{d}{1 - d}$
7. 0.060315, 0.0606061, 0.0612245, 0.0609137, 0.0618556, 0.0638297
9. 0.0512820 **11.** 0.0526316
13. 0.0416667, 0.0526316, 0.0638297, 0.0752688, 0.0869564
15. $1041.67, 0.0833334 **17.** $504.20, 0.03 **19.** $2059.11, $2085.17

ANSWERS

Page 132, Exercise 11, Chapter 7

1. U.S. Rule, $76.01; Merchants Rule, $75.00
3. U.S. Rule, $674.98; Merchants Rule, $674.20
5. The regular payment plus $1383.43 by the U.S. Rule or $1360.00 by the Merchants Rule

Page 135, Exercise 12, Chapter 7

1. $977.20, $1010.00 3. $398.04 5. $3100, $2982.33
7. $1530.00, $1525.00 9. $598.76

Page 139, Exercise 13, Chapter 7

1. 70 days 3. 35 days (approx.) 5. 10 days before Mar. 10, $3.50
7. $2304.73 9. 7 mos. 1 day (approx.), $1537.50

Page 144, Exercise 14, Chapter 7

1. (a) 16.6% (b) 14.5% 3. 57.1%, 48.0%, 53.3% 5. $90.83, 12.4%

Page 144, Miscellaneous Exercise, Chapter 7

1. $2, $202 3. 8 mos. 5. 288 days
7. $20.56, $20.27 9. $4.50 11. $952.38, $950
13. 7%, 7.39% 15. Discount rate of $5\frac{1}{2}$% more profitable
17. $1518.75, $15.95 19. $607.52, $12.50 21. $1500.02
23. 10.4% 25. 400 days 27. 14.4% 29. $4\frac{4}{149}$%

Page 147, Exercise 1, Chapter 8

1. $3x^2 - 8x + 7 = 0; a = 3, b = -8, c = 7$
3. $8x^2 - 11x + 2 = 0; a = 8, b = -11, c = 2$
5. $x^2 + x + 4 = 0; a = 1, b = 1, c = 4$
7. $-x^2 + 6x + 4 = 0; a = -1, b = 6, c = 4$
9. $3x^2 + 7x + 0 = 0; a = 3, b = 7, c = 0$
11. $5x^2 + 0x - 2 = 0; a = 5, b = 0, c = -2$
13. $-x^2 - 3x + 6 = 0; a = -1, b = -3, c = 6$
15. $x^2 + px + q = 0; a = 1, b = p, c = q$
17. $nx^2 - mx + 0 = 0; a = n, b = -m, c = 0$
19. $5x^2 - 16x + 9 = 0; a = 5, b = -16, c = 9$

Page 149, Exercise 2, Chapter 8

1. $0, \frac{9}{7}$ 3. 0, 9 5. 0, -2 7. 0, 4 9. 0, 1

Page 150, Exercise 3, Chapter 8

1. Real 3. Real 5. Imaginary 7. $4i$
9. $10i$ 11. $\sqrt{3}\,i$ 13. 10 15. $-14 + 2i$
17. $-1 - 4i$ 19. -3 21. 17 23. 25
25. $x^2 + b^2$ 27. 40 29. $71 + 19i$

ANSWERS

Page 151, Exercise 4, Chapter 8

1. ± 5
3. $\pm 4i$
5. ± 10
7. $\pm 10i$
9. $\pm \sqrt{6}$
11. $\pm \frac{1}{2}\sqrt{15}\, i$
13. $\pm \sqrt{3}\, i$
15. $\pm 2\sqrt{3}$

Page 153, Exercise 5, Chapter 8

1. $-2, -4$
3. $2, 5$
5. $-2, -9$
7. $8, -2$
9. $3, -9$
11. $\frac{3}{-2}, -5$
13. $\frac{1}{-3}, -4$
15. $\frac{1}{2}, \frac{3}{2}$
17. $\frac{3}{2}, -\frac{1}{5}$
19. $8, -\frac{1}{2}$

Page 154, Exercise 6, Chapter 8

1. 25
3. 36
5. 64
7. 1
9. $\frac{81}{4}$
11. $\frac{25}{4}$
13. $\frac{361}{4}$
15. $\frac{1}{16}$
17. $\frac{1}{9}$
19. $\frac{1}{64}$
21. $-3, -5$
23. $-3, -7$
25. $3, 8$
27. $-4 \pm 2\sqrt{3}$
29. $\dfrac{5 \pm \sqrt{17}}{2}$
31. $\frac{1}{2}, -\frac{1}{3}$
33. $1, \frac{1}{5}$
35. $4 \pm \sqrt{10}$
37. $\dfrac{-3 \pm 3\sqrt{3}\, i}{2}$
39. $\dfrac{-1 \pm \sqrt{15}\, i}{2}$

Page 156, Exercise 7, Chapter 8

1. $-2, -7$
3. $-3, -3$
5. $-2, -10$
7. $\dfrac{8 \pm \sqrt{19}}{3}$
9. $1, \frac{1}{5}$
11. $-4 \pm 2\sqrt{3}$
13. $-5 \pm 2\sqrt{6}$
15. $\dfrac{-9 \pm \sqrt{129}}{8}$
17. $\dfrac{-7 \pm \sqrt{57}}{2}$
19. $-1 \pm 2\sqrt{2}\, i$
21. $\dfrac{-3 \pm \sqrt{31}\, i}{2}$
23. $\dfrac{-1 \pm \sqrt{14}\, i}{3}$
25. $\dfrac{-7 \pm \sqrt{17}}{8}$

Page 157, Exercise 8, Chapter 8

1. $0, -\frac{9}{5}$
3. $0, -17$
5. $-1 \pm \sqrt{11}\, i$
7. $\dfrac{-1 \pm \sqrt{17}}{2}$
9. $\pm \sqrt{5}$
11. $\dfrac{7 \pm \sqrt{41}}{2}$
13. $0, 2$
15. $2 \pm \sqrt{15}$
17. $\pm 2\sqrt{3}$
19. $\dfrac{9 \pm \sqrt{15}\, i}{4}$

Page 160, Exercise 9, Chapter 8

1. $x^2 - 11x + 24 = 0$
3. $x^2 - x - 6 = 0$
5. $x^2 + 15x + 54 = 0$
7. $3x^2 + 10x - 8 = 0$
9. $28x^2 - 5x - 12 = 0$
11. $x^2 - 8x + 11 = 0$
13. $9x^2 - 6x - 5 = 0$
15. $x^2 - 6x + 25 = 0$
17. $-5, 4$
19. $\frac{5}{3}, 2$
21. $\dfrac{7}{-2}, 4$
23. $\frac{15}{4}, \frac{7}{4}$
25. $1, \frac{13}{6}$
27. Real and unequal
29. Real and unequal
31. Real and equal
33. Real and unequal
35. Imaginary
37. Real and equal
39. Real and unequal

ANSWERS

Page 161, Exercise 10, Chapter 8

1. 6, 5   **3.** 16, 10; −10, −16   **5.** 40, $15   **7.** 13, 14   **9.** 100 shares

Page 162, Miscellaneous Exercise, Chapter 8

1. −3, −5   **3.** 0, $\frac{1}{10}$ **5.** $\frac{1 \pm \sqrt{47}\,i}{8}$ **7.** $\pm 7i$ **9.** ± 9

11. $1 \pm \sqrt{2}$ **15.** $-\frac{s}{r}; \frac{t}{r}$ **17.** $-5 + \sqrt{5}\,i$

19. 13   **21.** Real and equal   **23.** Real and unequal

25. Imaginary   **27.** $x^2 + 4x + 4 = 0$ **29.** $x^2 - 4x - 1 = 0$

31. 2, 3   **33.** $\frac{1}{3}, \frac{1}{5}$ **35.** $\frac{-7 \pm \sqrt{193}}{12}$

Page 164, Exercise 1, Chapter 9

1. −12, −9, −5   **3.** 4, 1, 0, 1, 4

5. 8, 1, 0, −1, −8   **7.** −3, 2, 5, 6, 5, 2

9. −24, −15, −8, −3, 0, 1, 0, −3   **11.** 0.301030, 0.477121, 0.602060

13. $\frac{1}{9}, \frac{1}{3}, 1, 3, 9$ **15.** 1.04040, 1.06090

17. 1.04000, 1.08160, 1.12486   **19.** 2, undefined, 0, $\frac{1}{2}, \frac{2}{3}$

Page 166, Exercise 2, Chapter 9

5. Yes

9. On a straight line parallel to the Y-axis and 4 units to the right of the Y-axis

Page 172, Exercise 4, Chapter 9

27. (4, 16), highest point   **29.** (4, 34), highest point

Page 182, Exercise 7, Chapter 9

1. $x = 8, y = 2$ **3.** $x = -9, y = 21$

5. Equivalent equations; any pair of values that satisfies one of the equations satisfies the other also.

7. Inconsistent equations; no solutions

9. Equivalent equations; any pair of values that satisfies one of the equations satisfies the other also.

Page 186, Exercise 8, Chapter 9

1. $y = 1.5x + 3.75; y = 1.6x + 3.3$ **3.** $y = x + 3; y = x + 3$

5. $y = \frac{3500}{3}x + 6500; 34{,}500$ **7.** $y = 24.8x + 2; 1118$

Page 190, Exercise 9, Chapter 9

1. Averages, $y = -\frac{5}{4}x^2 + \frac{9}{4}x + 1$; least squares, $y = -x^2 + \frac{8}{5}x + \frac{11}{10}$

3. Averages, $y = 3x^2 - 9x + 9$; least squares, $y = 3x^2 - 9x + 9$

Page 191, Miscellaneous Exercise, Chapter 9

9. (c) **15.** $k = 90$

Page 196, Exercise 1, Chapter 10

1. $l = 36, s = 234$ **3.** $l = 500, s = 25{,}250$
5. $l = -90, s = -2025$ **7.** $l = 6\frac{1}{4}, s = 81\frac{1}{4}$
9. $l = -\frac{4}{3}; s = \frac{-121}{12}$ **11.** $l = 1, s = 4.5$ **13.** $a = 3, s = 255$
15. $n = 7, l = 37$ **17.** $a = 15, l = 510$ **19.** $a = 23, n = 9$
21. $d = 3, l = 118$ **23.** \$9.30 **25.** $6\frac{1}{2}$

Page 197, Exercise 2, Chapter 10

1. 6, 9, 12, 15 **3.** $14\frac{1}{2}$ **5.** 6, 14, 22
7. $-\frac{1}{3}, -\frac{1}{6}, 0, \frac{1}{6}, \frac{1}{3}$ **9.** $\dfrac{2x+y}{3}, \dfrac{x+2y}{3}$

Page 200, Exercise 3, Chapter 10

1. $l = 486, s = 728$ **3.** $l = 2560, s = 3410$
5. $l = -896, s = -595$ **7.** $l = \frac{1}{512}, s = \frac{511}{512}$
9. $l = 1.1255, s = 4.4091$ **11.** 431.01 **15.** 1092 **17.** ± 1152

Page 202, Exercise 4, Chapter 10

1. 8, 16, 32 and $-8, 16, -32$ **3.** 15, 45, 135 and $-15, 45, -135$
5. $5, -2\frac{1}{2}, 1\frac{1}{4}$ and $-5, -2\frac{1}{2}, -1\frac{1}{4}$
7. $\frac{3}{2}, \frac{9}{4}, \frac{27}{8}, \frac{81}{16}, \frac{243}{32}$ and $-\frac{3}{2}, \frac{9}{4}, -\frac{27}{8}, \frac{81}{16}, -\frac{243}{32}$ **9.** $\pm\sqrt{2}$

Page 203, Exercise 5, Chapter 10

1. $\frac{3}{2}$ **3.** 4 **5.** 3 **7.** $-\frac{16}{3}$ **9.** $\frac{1}{3}$

Page 204, Exercise 6, Chapter 10

1. $a^{10} + 10a^9x + 45a^8x^2 + 120a^7x^3 + 210a^6x^4 + 252a^5x^5 + 210a^4x^6 + 120a^3x^7 + 45a^2x^8 + 10ax^9 + x^{10}$
3. $x^6 + 6x^5y + 15x^4y^2 + 20x^3y^3 + 15x^2y^4 + 6xy^5 + y^6$
5. $a^4 - 4a^3x + 6a^2x^2 - 4ax^3 + x^4$
7. $a^5 + 10a^4x + 40a^3x^2 + 80a^2x^3 + 80ax^4 + 32x^5$
9. $64c^6 + 576c^5d + 2160c^4d^2 + 4320c^3d^3 + 4860c^2d^4 + 2916cd^5 + 729d^6$
11. $x^6 - 6x^4y + 12x^2y^2 - 8y^3$
13. $a^{10}x^5 - 5a^8x^4by^2 + 10a^6x^3b^2y^4 - 10a^4x^2b^3y^6 + 5a^2xb^4y^8 - b^5y^{10}$
15. $x^5 + 15x^4 + 90x^3 + 270x^2 + 405x + 243$
17. $x^{16} + 16x^{15}y + 120x^{14}y^2 + 560x^{13}y^3$
19. $m^{25} - 25m^{24}n + 300m^{23}n^2 - 2300m^{22}n^3$

Page 205, Exercise 7, Chapter 10

1. $15{,}504a^{15}x^5$ **3.** $-2{,}035{,}800m^{23}(2)^7$ **5.** $61{,}236a^5$
7. $-57{,}671{,}680x^6y^9$ **9.** $658{,}008a^{35}x^{35}b^5$

Page 206, Exercise 8, Chapter 10

1. 68,921
3. 12,117,361
5. 96,059,601
7. 20,736
9. 1.040604
11. 1.171648
13. 1.216640
15. 1.220140
17. 0.960596
19. 0.783688

Page 207, Exercise 9, Chapter 10

1. 0.91
3. 0.85
5. 1.00
7. 0.75
9. 1.01
11. 10.15
13. 7.07
15. 5.04
17. 3.98
19. 9.99
21. $1 + \frac{3}{2}x + \frac{3}{8}x^2 - \frac{1}{16}x^3$
23. $1 - 8x + 36x^2 - 120x^3$
25. $1 + 3x + 6x^2 + 10x^3$
27. $1 - 2y^2 - 2y^4 - 4y^6$
29. $1 - 20i + 210i^2 - 1540i^3$

Page 208, Miscellaneous Exercise, Chapter 10

1. Arithmetical progression
3. Geometrical progression
5. $l = 345, s = 8675$
7. $l = 100i, s = 2550i$
9. $l = 16,807, s = 19,607$
11. $l = -\frac{1}{2}, s = -\frac{11}{2}$
13. $l = (1 + i)^9, s = \dfrac{(1 + i)^{11} - (1 + i)}{(1 + i)^2 - 1}$
15. $7, \pm 4\sqrt{3}$
17. $20, \pm 12$
19. $\frac{5}{18}, \pm \frac{1}{6}$
21. (a) and (b)
23. $5, 15, 45$
25. $4096
27. $s = \dfrac{n(n + 1)}{2}$
29. $s = n^2$
31. $a^4 - 20a^3b + 150a^2b^2 - 500ab^3 + 625b^4$
33. $\dfrac{x^4}{y^4} + 4\dfrac{x^3a}{y^3} + 6\dfrac{x^2a^2}{y^2} + 4\dfrac{xa^3}{y} + a^4$
35. $1 + \frac{1}{6}i - \frac{5}{72}i^2 + \frac{55}{1296}i^3$
37. $9 + \frac{1}{18} - \frac{1}{5,832} + \frac{1}{944,784}$
39. $495a^4x^8$
41. $12,870x^8y^8$

Page 211, Exercise 1, Chapter 11

1. 20
3. 24
5. 9000
7. 6
9. 24
11. 256

Page 213, Exercise 2, Chapter 11

1. 60; 120
3. 15; 120
5. 720
7. 12
9. abc, acb, bac, bca, cab, cba

Page 214, Exercise 3, Chapter 11

1. 90
3. 15
5. 34,650
7. 15,120
9. 10

Page 216, Exercise 4, Chapter 11

1. 35
3. 56
5. 6
7. 3360
9. 6; 28; 1326
11. 15

Page 217, Exercise 5, Chapter 11

1. $\frac{1}{2}$
3. $\frac{1}{6}; \frac{1}{3}$
5. $\frac{1}{4}; \frac{3}{4}$
7. $\frac{10}{17}$
9. $\frac{1}{2}$
11. (a) $\frac{1}{35}$ (b) $\frac{4}{35}$ (c) $\frac{12}{35}$

Page 219, Exercise 6, Chapter 11

1. $\frac{4}{9}$
3. $\frac{11}{16}$
5. $\frac{1}{32}$
7. $\frac{35}{48}; \frac{1}{48}$
9. $\frac{1}{32}$

ANSWERS

Page 223, Exercise 7, Chapter 11

1. 951,483; 924,609; 883,342
5. 0.1935
7. 0.9211
9. 0.002430
11. 0.6119
13. 0.5373
15. 0.7915
17. 0.3999; 0.6001; 1
19. 0.53317; 0.99591

Page 224, Exercise 8, Chapter 11

1. $0.10
3. $0.30
5. $6

Page 226, Exercise 9, Chapter 11

1. 0.78
3. 1.63
5. 3.66

Page 226, Miscellaneous Exercise, Chapter 11

1. 13,824
3. 4, 3, 2, 1
5. *abc, acb, bac, bca, cab, cba*
7. 15
9. $\frac{4}{11}$
11. 52
13. 0.104982

Page 229, Exercise 1, Chapter 12

1. 79
3. 342
5. $13,500
7. $28\frac{8}{9}$
9. 30
11. 88.2

Page 232, Exercise 2, Chapter 12

1. 11
3. 33
5. (*a*) $40\frac{5}{14}$, (*b*) 50, (*c*) 50
7. (*a*) 0.279, (*b*) 0.290
9. (*a*) 15, 15 (*b*) $211\frac{1}{4}$, $17\frac{1}{2}$
11. 24, 98, 123

Page 235, Exercise 3, Chapter 12

1. 1055.5
3. 999.4
5. $79\frac{10}{13}$
7. 28.64
9. 95.49

Page 238, Exercise 4, Chapter 12

1. (*a*) 38.4 (*b*) 38.4
3. 165 lb.

Page 243, Exercise 5, Chapter 12

1. (*a*) 1.41 (*b*) 14.1
3. 0.61
5. 0.295, 0.300; 0.011, 0.008

Page 244, Miscellaneous Exercise, Chapter 12

1. $40\frac{1}{3}$
3. $\frac{1}{2}[2a + (n-1)d]$
5. 1010.025
9. 8.07
11. 19, 19
13. 200, 192; 24.5, 17.2
17. $\dfrac{a-b}{2}$

Page 250, Exercise 1, Chapter 13

1. $1012.91; $512.91
3. $5612.48; $3862.48
5. $5858.30; $858.30
7. $9510.80; $8210.80
9. $7789.84
11. $6623.06
13. 1.02018
15. $638.14
19. 99,639

Page 254, Exercise 2, Chapter 13

1. $m = 2, i = 0.015$
3. $m = 12, i = 0.00\frac{2}{3}$
5. $m = 24, i = 0.005$
7. $i = 0.0302$
9. $j = 0.0489$
11. $j = 0.0596$
13. 5% converted annually yields less than 4.9% nominal, converted monthly.
15. $j = 0.0288$

Page 255, Exercise 3, Chapter 13

1. $13,265.50
3. $719.40

Page 256, Exercise 4, Chapter 13

1. $1408.43
3. $1375.39
5. $2247.22
7. $5789.48
9. 3% for 10 years is better by 16 cents.

Page 259, Exercise 5, Chapter 13

1. 17 yrs. 4 mos. 28 days
3. 2.88%
5. 10 yrs. 18 days

Page 261, Exercise 6, Chapter 13

1. $1640.70; $359.30
3. $3784.18; $1215.82
5. $361.47; $2903.53
7. $1015.26; $484.74
9. $2534.98
11. $898.57
13. Second offer better by $51.84
15. $509.24
17. $735.56

Page 265, Exercise 7, Chapter 13

1. $786.76
3. $619.64
5. $1175.23
7. $1763.11
9. Saves by borrowing from the bank, $12.64
11. 5 years, 2 months, 7 days; Nov. 22, 1952
13. 5 years, 10 months, 12 days

Page 267, Miscellaneous Exercise, Chapter 13

1. $36,005.10
3. No; $585.43
5. $i = 0.051642$
7. $6904.81; $888.78
9. $411.93
11. 43 years

Page 273, Exercise 1, Chapter 14

1. $R = \$250, n = 24, i = 0.02, A_n = \$4728.48, S_n = \$7605.47$
3. $R = \$100, n = 24, i = 0.00\frac{2}{3}, A_n = \$2211.05, S_n = \$2593.32$
5. $R = \$500, n = 80, i = 0.01\frac{1}{4}, A_n = \$25{,}193.33, S_n = \$68{,}059.40$
7. $R = \$232.50, n = 18, i = 0.04, A_n = \$2943.29, S_n = \$5962.56$
9. $R = \$71, n = 102, i = 0.00\frac{7}{12}, A_n = \$5446.51, S_n = \$9857.61$

ANSWERS

11. $8375.73   **13.** $4540.87   **15.** $3,816,677.09   **17.** $4390.48
19. (a) $1103.22   (b) $624.35

Page 277, Exercise 2, Chapter 14

1. $76.14   **3.** $624.59   **5.** $167.55
7. $343.55   **9.** $244.96   **11.** $238.00
13. $968.69 annual payment, $75.35 monthly payment

Page 280, Exercise 3, Chapter 14

1. 6   **3.** 61   **5.** 56   **7.** 69, $33.09
9. 71 full monthly payments; no partial payment needed since fund accumulates to $2000 in 5 days after last full payment
11. $88.48, 10 months

Page 283, Exercise 4, Chapter 14

1. 4.0%   **3.** 1.0%   **5.** 5.2%   **7.** 3.6%   **9.** 18%   **11.** Yes   **13.** 3.8%

Page 285, Miscellaneous Exercise, Chapter 14

1. $22,880.30   **3.** $44,747.80   **5.** $115.20   **7.** 18%   **9.** $2210.20
11. 8 payments; last payment $413.16
13. Second plan cheaper by $1.49 per month
15. $44.81   **17.** $249.87; $235.49   **19.** $28,511.90
21. Will take 12 years, 7 mos., 19 days; no partial payment needed

Page 290, Exercise 1, Chapter 15

1. (a) $2621.25 (b) $2569.85   **3.** (a) $69,760.79 (b) $66,438.85
5. (a) $50,885.07 (b) $79,714.24   **7.** $27,240.03   **9.** $0.82
11. Installment offer better by $2.54   **13.** Avoids long division

Page 294, Exercise 2, Chapter 15

1. $2471.33   **3.** $25,998.73   **5.** $637.44
7. $1632.98; $3859.14   **9.** $4331.95   **11.** $9999.44
13. $45,212.70   **15.** $84,353.32; $2571.20   **17.** $356.49

Page 298, Exercise 3, Chapter 15

1. $3785.47   **3.** $9567.20   **5.** $2595.89
7. $307.73   **9.** $4256.03   **11.** $143.17

Page 303, Exercise 4, Chapter 15

1. $1365.07   **3.** $3385.50   **5.** $56,165.10   **7.** $4835.10   **13.** $7716.90
15. First payment $9.08; last payment $181.60.

Page 307, Exercise 5, Chapter 15

1. $3750   **3.** $16,666.67   **5.** $4779.10   **7.** $3333.33
9. $2137.01   **11.** $365.85   **13.** $23,187.03

ANSWERS

Page 311, Exercise 6, Chapter 15

1. $2244.78   3. $3868.92   5. $6934.52   7. $734.93
9. $58,807.40   11. $11,704.00   15. $2819.81   17. $1352.35

Page 312, Miscellaneous Exercise, Chapter 15

1. (a) $652.57 (b) $749.60 (c) $764.59 (d) $878.28 (e) $1070.62
   (f) $1092.03 (g) $1205.69
3. $6541.08   5. $3683.08   7. $32,231.60
9. $16,200.50 11. $10,952.72   13. $50,000
15. $73.06   17. Approximately 85   19. $7466.42
21. $10.76   23. $147,538.40

Page 318, Exercise 1, Chapter 16

1. $449.71; $2002.03   3. $116.22; $447.96   5. $35.19; $551.25
7. $106.38; $5736.82   9. $29.10; $1669.40   11. $269.55
13. (a) $401.13 (b) $5352.36 (c) $80.28
15. $72.54   17. $1695.58   19. $631.00   21. $749.93   23. $234.03

Page 322, Exercise 2, Chapter 16

1. Make payments as nearly equal to $11,723.05 as possible.

Page 327, Exercise 3, Chapter 16

1. $20.67; $1891.47   3. $56.54; $2188.92   5. $85.98; $4751.86
7. $112.12; $985.23   9. $20.24; $1222.38   11. $282.53
13. (a) $1167.58 (b) $3880.66 (c) $2119.34
15. 3.3%   17. $24,730.92   19. $414.53   21. $4040.22

Page 331, Exercise 4, Chapter 16

3. $3156.54   5. 38 quarters; $78.81   7. 11 years; $42.39

Page 332, Miscellaneous Exercise, Chapter 16

1. $161.42   5. $803.80
7. Total annual payment under sinking fund method smaller by $112.11
9. $608.41   11. 5.3%   13. (a) 12 years (b) $257.61 (c) $1332.30
17. $1585.28

Page 339, Exercise 1, Chapter 17

1. $150, $250   3. $200, $2400
5. $275.00, $137.50   7. $70   9. (a) $8 (b) $120 (c) $200

Page 342, Exercise 2, Chapter 17

1. 0.318708, $146.78   3. 0.088277, $293.52   5. 0.319625, $70.47
7. 0.079813   9. $342.47

ANSWERS

Page 345, Exercise 3, Chapter 17

1. $46.16, $49.93 **3.** $55.65, $392.50 **5.** $124.70, $155.40
7. $167.04, $179.90 **9.** $135.59

Page 349, Exercise 4, Chapter 17

1. $5.41 **3.** $4.84 **5.** $3.04 **7.** $457.58
9. $315.51 **11.** $1941.15 **13.** 1042

Page 351, Exercise 5, Chapter 17

1. $246,736 **3.** $87,899.00 **5.** $342.823 **7.** $32,371.40 **9.** $7331.64

Page 353, Miscellaneous Exercise, Chapter 17

1. (a) $340 (b) $1180 **3.** (a) $13.43 (b) $17.67
5. (a) $87.23 (b) $775.68 **7.** 15 years **9.** (a) $3200 (b) $764.27
11. (a) 16.4040% (b) $51.19 **13.** (a) $233.83 (b) $425.01
15. $6.05, $60.93 **19.** $262.87 **21.** Yes **23.** $496,864 **25.** 5.73260%

Page 359, Exercise 1, Chapter 18

1. $F = \$500, r = 0.03, C = \$500, n = 45, i = 0.035$
$V_n = \$555.25, I = \$15.00, P_n = \$55.25$
3. $F = \$500, r = 0.02, C = \$500, n = 8, i = 0.015$
$V_n = \$539.18, I = \$10.00, P_n = \$39.18$
5. $F = \$500, r = 0.025, C = \$500, n = 40, i = 0.0225$
$V_n = \$516.05, I = \$12.50, P_n = \$16.05$

Page 361, Exercise 2, Chapter 18

1. $1153.37 **3.** $885.31 **5.** $77.32 **7.** $968.48
9. $1107.40 **11.** $939.20 **13.** $341.97 **15.** $90.84

Page 364, Exercise 3, Chapter 18

1. $13.89; $113.89 **3.** -66.34; $441.16
5. $124.25; $1124.25 **7.** Premium $50.75
9. (a) Discount $72.49 (b) Discount $64.99

Page 370, Exercise 5, Chapter 18

1. $853.44; $841.77 **3.** $594.97; $590.80 **5.** $1103.32; $1095.82
7. $91.06; $90.12 **9.** $1116.26; $1111.26 **11.** $103.33
13. $1002.50 **15.** $1057.75 **17.** $1039.04; $1052.79
19. $854.77; $854.90 **23.** $1083.94

Page 376, Exercise 6, Chapter 18

1. 3.05%; 3.09%; 3.10% **3.** 4.51%; 4.30%; 4.29%
5. 2.09%; 2.12%; 2.18% **7.** 4.05%; 4.05%; 4.07%
9. 1.95%; 1.92%; 1.93% **11.** Second bond gives better yield rate

ANSWERS

Page 379, Exercise 7, Chapter 18

1. 5.19% **3.** 4.97% **5.** Between 3.15% and 2.97%

Page 382, Exercise 8, Chapter 18

1. 2.92% **3.** $25,583.52 **5.** $111.11 **7.** 5%

Page 385, Exercise 9, Chapter 18

1. $15,335.40 **3.** First plan better by $641.63 **5.** $470.59
7. $807.64 **9.** 4.58% **11.** 3.99%
15. $\log(1 + i') = \dfrac{\log(C + Is_{\overline{n}|r}) - \log V'}{n}$ **19.** 3.92%

Page 388, Miscellaneous Exercise, Chapter 18

1. $59,612.65 **3.** $1103.85 **5.** $537.94
7. (a) $1126.28 (b) $1116.28 **9.** (a) $1018.22 (b) 3.95%
11. 2.96% **13.** 3.93% **15.** 2.76%
17. $9325.70 **19.** $1250 **21.** $16,966.97
23. 2.13% **25.** $1112.61 **27.** $1050.58

Page 392, Exercise 1, Chapter 19

1. Immediate whole life annuity due
3. Deferred ordinary whole life annuity
5. Immediate temporary life annuity due
7. Deferred temporary life annuity due
9. 20-year pure endowment of $2000

Page 395, Exercise 2, Chapter 19

1. $530.58 **3.** $2140.87 **5.** $2679.83
7. (a) $395.92 (b) $377.02 **9.** $2016.33; $2696.95
11. Second choice is better **13.** $3203.43

Page 398, Exercise 3, Chapter 19

1. $46,068.30 **3.** $14,448.30 **5.** $14,816.20 **7.** $45,484.50
9. $24,982.80 **11.** $103.60 **13.** $3460.62

Page 400, Exercise 4, Chapter 19

1. $1473.81 **3.** $2947.62 **5.** $782.03 **7.** $4308.72
9. $468.48 **11.** $10,157.60 **13.** $1331.02

Page 403, Exercise 5, Chapter 19

1. $14,949.80 **3.** $12,021.20 **5.** $24,415.80 **7.** $20,817.40
9. (a) $30,515.90 (b) $17,713.20 (c) $31,178.20
11. $1209.03 **13.** $140.60 **15.** $3118.10

ANSWERS

Page 407, Exercise 6, Chapter 19

1. $39,473.20
3. $6816.55
5. $32,218.20
7. $5306.13
9. $39,274.90
13. $31,342.19
15. $18,771.30
17. For 20 payments certain, cost is $4978.85
19. $810.41
21. With 14 payments certain, annual payment is $727.49

Page 411, Exercise 7, Chapter 19

1. $18,929.90
3. $2659.83
5. $10,132.20
7. $204.87
9. $27,765.80
11. $50.38
13. $305.47
15. $107.27
17. $632.33
19. $788.58

Page 412, Miscellaneous Exercise, Chapter 19

1. $12,998.00
3. $1484.51
5. $2016.92
7. $50,404.00
9. $297.48
11. $29,022.60
13. $39,612.50
15. $4990.42
17. $22,716.30

Page 415, Exercise 1, Chapter 20

1. Whole life policy of $5000 for a person aged 20. $5000 to the beneficiary.
3. 10-year endowment policy of $2000 for a person aged 30. $2000 to insured.
5. 20-year term policy of $1000 for a person aged 40. Nothing.
7. Whole life insurance for a person aged 20, deferred 30 years. $3000 to beneficiary.

Page 418, Exercise 2, Chapter 20

1. $502.64; $24.65; $57.84
3. $3386.77; $124.91; $165.33
5. $1241.40; $51.65; $140.83
7. $374.46; $14.60; $16.05
9. $456.61; $20.50; $21.31
11. $4566.12
13. $204.95
15. Best plan was that of Problem 13
17. $4775.49
19. $2594.16
21. $5.23
23. $2783.26

Page 421, Exercise 3, Chapter 20

1. $305.45
3. $41.30
5. $45.17
7. $32.61
9. $3593.85
11. $232.50
13. $2477.70

Page 425, Exercise 4, Chapter 20

1. $49.09
3. $188.14
5. $12.09
7. $33.36
9. $709.79
11. $5.45
13. $13.95
15. $151.27
17. (a) Nothing (b) $980.09

Page 427, Exercise 5, Chapter 20

1. $1747.40
3. $198.06
5. $448.58
7. $3162.51
9. $474.82
11. (a) $10,000 (b) $9101.61
13. Endowment $1509.45; whole life $1507.92
15. (a) $3661.76 (b) $3500 (c) $143.37

ANSWERS

Page 431, Exercise 6, Chapter 20
1. $391.36   **3.** $1105.56   **5.** $63.11; $94.66   **7.** $452.99

Page 433, Exercise 7, Chapter 20
1. $15.18; $7.74; $14.74; $7.41   **3.** $57.52; $29.32; $55.91; $28.11
5. $69.21; $35.27; $67.41; $33.92   **7.** $21.29

Page 435, Exercise 8, Chapter 20
1. Pays $1000 to beneficiary when insured dies.
Quantity given represents single premium at age 40.
3. Pays $5000 to beneficiary when insured dies.
Quantity given represents annual premium for 20 years beginning at age 40.
5. Pays $3000 to beneficiary if insured dies before he reaches 50; pays insured $3000 if he reaches 50; pays nothing thereafter.
Quantity given represents the annual premium for 20 years starting at age 30.
7. Pays $4000 to beneficiary if insured dies before he reaches 50; pays $10,000 to insured if he reaches 50; pays nothing thereafter.
Quantity given represents annual premium for 30 years starting at age 20.
9. Pays $5000 to beneficiary if insured dies before 70 and pays insured $2500 per year, starting at age 70, provided that he reaches age 70.
Quantity given represents single premium paid at age 25.

Page 435, Miscellaneous Exercise, Chapter 20
1. $1727.77   **3.** $111.16   **5.** $199.73   **7.** $1799.65   **9.** $66.41
11. 2.2%; no; because no insurance would have been provided

Page 440, Exercise 2, Chapter 21
1. $176.41; $362.48; $560.12; $771.65; $1000

Page 442, Exercise 3, Chapter 21
1. $44.71; $90.56   **3.** $47.75; $96.41

Page 446, Exercise 4, Chapter 21
1. $653.55   **3.** $653.55   **5.** $9.95
7. $90.51   **9.** $2324.06   **11.** $483.87

Page 448, Exercise 5, Chapter 21
1. $207.19; 21 years, 305 days; $500.70
3. $189.73; 5 years, 286 days; $873.66
5. $272.32; 14 years, 212 days; $415.16

Page 449, Miscellaneous Exercise, Chapter 21
1. $29.78; $59.35; $88.86; $118.22; $147.38   **5.** $1798.62; $1838.09
7. 19 years, 89 days   **9.** $2064.73

Index

Abscissa, 165
Absolute value, 2
Acceptance, trade, 125
Accrued interest, 369
Accumulated value of an annuity, 274
Accumulation of bond discount, 365
Addition, 2
  elimination by, 24
  of algebraic expressions, 4
  of fractions, 35, 37
After-date draft, 125
Algebraic language, 1
Amortization method, 316
Amortization of bonded debt, 320
Amortization of bond premium, 362, 365
Amortization schedule, 317
Amount, 105
  compound, 249
Annuitant, 391
Annuity, 269
  accumulated value of, 271
  amount of, 271
  contingent, 269
  decreasing, 299
  deferred, 292
  deferred life, 391, 399
  general case, 296
  immediate, 292
  immediate life, 391, 395
  increasing, 299
  life, 391
  ordinary, 269
  ordinary life, 391
  present value of, 271
  refund, 406
  temporary life, 391, 401
  whole life, 391, 395
Annuity due, 270, 288
  forborne temporary life, 404
  life, 391
Antilogarithm, 93
A posteriori probability, 217
Approximate numbers, 83
Approximate time, 108
Approximate yield rate, 374
A priori probability, 217
Arithmetical mean, 228
Arithmetical means, 197
Arithmetical progressions, 193
  last term of, 194
  sum of n terms, 195
Averages, method of, 184
Axes, 165

Bank discount, 120
Bank draft, 126
Banker's Rule, 113
Base, in percentage problems, 52
  of a power of a number, 6
  of common logarithms, 81, 102
  of natural logarithms, 103
Beneficiary, 414
Benefit, 414
Binomial, 6
Binomial coefficients, 216
Binomial formula, 204
  computations by, 205
  general term of, 204
Binomial theorem, 203, 204, 206
Braces, 12

INDEX

Brackets, 12
Buying and selling merchandize, 55
Buying, installment, 140
Bond, 320, 356
   accumulation of discount, 365
   amortization of premium, 362, 365
   annuity, 380
   book value of, 365
   callable, 377
   discount on, 363
   perpetual, 381
   premium on, 362
   purchase price of, 359
   quoted price of, 369
   registered, 357
   serial, 380
   United States Government, 379
   unregistered, 357
Bond interest, 357
Bond rate of interest, 356
Bonded debt, amortization of, 320
Book value of a bond, 365

Calculation of logarithms, 103
Callable bonds, 377
Capitalized cost, 308
Carrying charge, 143
Cash discount, 58
Cash surrender charge, 447
Central tendency, measure of, 243
Changing the subject of a formula, 44
Characteristic of a logarithm, 82, 85
Charge, carrying, 143
   depreciation, 337
   surrender, 447
Class interval, 237
Class mark, 237
Classes, 237
Coefficient, 4
Coefficient of variation, 245
Coefficients, binomial, 216
Cologarithm, 95
Combination, 215
Commissioners 1941 Standard Ordinary Table, 221
Common difference, 193
Common logarithm, 81
Common ratio, 198
Company, insurance, 414
Complement of mark-up per cent, 56

Complete expectation of life, 225
Completing the square, 153
Complex fractions, 41
Complex numbers, 150
Compound amount, 249
   at changing rates, 255
Compound discount, 259
Compound interest, 248
Compound interest formula, 249
Computations by binomial formula, 205
Conditional equation, 15
Consistent equations, 182
Constant, 163
Constant per cent method, 340
Contingent annuity, 269
Contribution, periodical, 336
Conversion period, 252
Coordinate system, rectangular, 164, 165
Coordinates, 165
Cost, capitalized, 308
   gross, 55
   net, 55
   original, 336
Coupon, 357
Current yield rate, 373
Curtate expectation of life, 225
Curve, normal frequency, 240
Curve-fitting, 183, 187
Curves, frequency, 240

Data, empirical, 183
Date, equated, 137, 265
   focal, 134, 263
   maturity, 123
Decimal, repeating, 202
Decreasing annuity, 299
Deferred annuity, 292
Deferred whole life annuity, 391, 399
Deferred whole life policy, 414, 420
Definition of common logarithm, 81
Denomination of a bond, 356
Denominator, rationalizing the, 74
Dependent equations, 23, 182
Dependent events, 219
Depletion, 350
Depreciation, 336

INDEX

Depreciation charge, 337
Depreciation fund, 336
Deviation, 229
  standard, 242
Difference, common, 193
  tabular, 88
Digits, significant, 82
Discount, 362
  accumulation of, 365
  bank, 120
  cash, 58
  compound, 259
  on a bond, 363
  on par value, 357
  on the redemption price, 356
  rate 120, 126
  simple, 116, 117, 126
  trade, 59, 60
Discriminant of quadratic equation, 159
Dispersion, measure of, 243
Distribution, frequency, 238
Division, 3
  by zero, 8
  of algebraic expressions, 7
  of fractions, 39
  of radicals, 75
  using logarithms, 94
Draft, 125
  after-date, 125
  bank, 126
  time, 125
Drawee, of note, 19, 123
  of trade acceptance, 21, 125
Drawer, of note, 123
  of trade acceptance, 125

Effective rate of interest, 252
Elements of progressions, 193
Elimination, by addition, 24
  by substitution, 27
  by subtraction, 24
Empirical data, 183
Empirical probability, 221
Endowment, n-year pure, 391
  policy, 415, 426
  present value of, 392
Equated date, 137, 265
Equated time, 137, 265
Equation, 15

  conditional, 15
  identical, 15
  linear, 167
Equation of time, 136
Equation of value, 133, 134, 234, 263
Equations, consistent, 182
  dependent, 23, 182
  equivalent, 16, 23, 182
  exponential, 78, 99, 176
  incompatible, 23
  inconsistent, 23, 182
  involving fractions, 43
  of the first degree, 16
  quadratic, 147
  solution of quadratic, 157
  special types of, 78
  systems of, 23
Equivalent rate of interest, 252
Events, dependent, 219
  independent, 218
  mutually exclusive, 219
Exact numbers, 83
Exact simple interest, 110
Exact time, 108
Expectation, complete, 225
  curtate, 225
  mathematical, 224
Exponent, 4
  negative, 70
  zero, 69
Exponential equation, 78, 99, 176
Exponential function, 173
Exponents, 65
  fractional, 66
  positive integral, 65
Extremes, 47
  of a geometrical progression, 201

Face of note, 120, 123
Face value, 356
Fackler's formula, 440
Factoring, 9
  solution of quadratic equation by, 152
Factors, 5
Fitting curves to data, 183, 187
Focal date, 134, 263
Forborne temporary life annuity due, 404

INDEX

Form, typical, 147
Formula, binomial, 204
  changing subject of, 44
  compound interest, 249
  Fackler's, 440
  general term of binomial, 204
  Makeham's, 364
  quadratic, 155
Formulas, substitution in, 10, 40
Fourth proportional, 47
Fractional exponents, 66
Fractions, 35
  addition of, 35, 37
  complex, 41
  division of, 39
  equations involving, 43
  multiplication of, 39
  operations with, 35
  subtraction of, 37
Frequency, 229
Frequency curves, 240
  normal, 240
Frequency distribution, 238
Function, 163
  exponential, 173
  linear, 166, 167
  logarithmic, 173
  quadratic, 168
Fund, depreciation, 336
Fundamental operations, 2
Fundamental principle, 210

General case annuity, 296
General term of the binomial formula, 204
Geometrical mean, 232
Geometrical means, 201
Geometrical progression, 198
  infinite, 202
  nth or last term of, 198
  sum of, 199
  "sum" of infinite, 202
Graphical representation, 163
Graphical solution of linear equation, 180
Gross cost, 55
Gross profit, 55
Grouping, symbols of, 12

Histogram, rectangular, 238

Identical equation, 15
Identity, 15
Imaginary number, 149
  pure, 150
Immediate annuity, 292
Immediate life annuity, 391, 395
Incompatible equations, 23
Incomplete quadratic, 148, 151
Inconsistent equations, 23, 182
Increasing annuity, 299
Independent events, 218
Index, 72
Infinite geometrical progression, 202
  "sum" of, 202
Installment buying, 140
Insurance, m-payment, 417
Insurance company, 414
Insurance policy, 414
Integral exponents, 65
Interest, accrued, 369
  bond, 357
  compound, 248
  effective rate of, 252
  equivalent rate of, 252
  exact, 110
  for a fractional part of a period, 254
  nominal rate of, 251
  ordinary, 110
  quoted rate, 251
  rate of, 105, 127, 136, 248
  simple, 105
Interpolation, 87, 88, 91, 174
Interval, class, 237
Investment rate of interest, 356
Irrational number, 72

Last term, arithmetical progression, 194
  geometrical progression, 198
Least common denominator, 38
Least squares, method of, 185
Level premium, 437
Life, expectation of, 225
Life annuity, 391
  deferred, 391
  due, 391
  forborne temporary, 404
  immediate, 391, 395
  whole, 391, 395

INDEX

Linear equation, 167
  graphical solution of, 180
Linear function, 166, 167
Linear interpolation, 174
List price, 59
Literal number, 4
Loading, 392, 414
Logarithm, base of, 81, 102
  characteristic of, 82, 85
  common, 81
  mantissa of, 82
  of a given number, 87, 90
Logarithmic function, 173
Logarithms, 81
  calculation of, 103
  division by, 94
  multiplication by, 94
  Napierian, 103
  natural, 103
  powers and roots of, 97
  properties of, 84

Makeham's formula, 364
Maker of note, 123
Mantissa of logarithm, 82
Margin, 55
Mark, class, 237
Mark-up, 56
Mathematical expectation, 224
Maturity date, 123
Maturity value, 121, 123
Maximum, 172
Mean, arithmetical, 228
  geometrical, 232
Mean proportional, 47
Means, 47
  arithmetical, 197
  geometrical, 201
Measure, of central tendency, 243
  of dispersion, 243
Median, 231
Merchandise, buying and selling, 55
Merchants' Rule, 130, 131
Method, amortization, 316
  constant per cent, 340
  mutual fund, 396
  of averages, 184
  of least squares, 185
  of selected points, 183
  prospective, 330, 442
  retrospective, 330, 442
  sinking fund, 323, 343
  straight line, 337
  unit cost, 345
Methods of counting time, 108
Minimum, 171
Mode, 231
Monomial, 6
Mortality table, 221
m-payment insurance, 417
Multinomial, 6
Multiplication, 3
  of algebraic expressions, 5
  of fractions, 39
  of radicals, 75
  using logarithms, 94
Mutual fund method, 396
Mutually exclusive events, 219

Napierian logarithms, 103
Natural logarithms, 103
Natural premium, 425, 438
Negative exponents, 70
Net annual premium, 415
Net cost, 55
Net premium, 392, 414
Net profit, 55
Net selling price, 55
Net single premium, 415
Nominal rate of interest, 251
Normal frequency curve, 240
Note, 120
  drawee of, 123
  drawer of, 123
  maker of, 123
  promissory, 123
nth term, arithmetical progression, 194
  geometrical progression, 198
Number, complex, 150
  corresponding to a given logarithm, 91, 93
  imaginary, 149
  irrational, 72
  pure imaginary, 150
  rational, 72
Numbers, approximate, 83
  exact, 83
Numerical coefficient, 4
n-year pure endowment, 391

INDEX

Office premium, 414
Operations, with fractions, 35
  with radicals, 73
Ordinary annuity, 269
  accumulated value, 271
  amount of, 271
  present value of, 271
Ordinary life annuity, 391
Ordinary perpetuity, 270
Ordinary simple interest, 110
Ordinate, 165
Origin, 165
Original cost, 336

Par value, 356
  discount on, 356
  premium on, 356
Parabola, 168, 187
Parentheses, 4, 12
Partial payments, 130
Parts, proportional, 90
Payee of trade acceptance, 125
Payment period, 269
Payments, partial, 130
Per cent, 51
Percentage, 52
Percentiles, 231
Period, conversion, 252
  payment, 269
Periodical contribution, 336
Permissible operations, 16
Permutations, 211, 214
Perpetual bond, 381
Perpetuity, 270, 304
  ordinary, 270
Plan, $r\%$, 143
Policy, 392, 414
  deferred life, 414, 420
  endowment, 415, 426
  insurance, 414
  term, 414, 422
  whole life, 414, 416
  year, 414
Polynomial, 6
Power of a number, 6
Premium, 356, 362
  amortization of, 362, 365
  gross, 392, 414
  level, 437
  natural, 425, 437, 438

net, 392, 414
net annual, 415
net single, 415
office, 414
on the par value, 356
on the redemption price, 356
single, 415
Present value, 116, 118, 259
  of an annuity, 271
  of pure endowment, 392
Price, list, 59
  redemption, 356
Principal, 105, 248
Principal root, 67
Principle, fundamental, 210
Probability, a priori, 221
  a posteriori, 217
  empirical, 221
Problem, reinvestment, 383
Proceeds, 120
Profit, gross, 55
  net, 55
Progression, arithmetical, 193
  elements of arithmetical, 193
  geometrical, 198
  infinite geometrical, 202
  nth term of arithmetical, 194
  nth term of geometrical, 198
  sum of arithmetical, 195
  sum of geometrical, 199
  "sum" of infinite geometrical, 202
  terms of arithmetical, 193
Promissory note, 123
Properties of logarithms, 84
Proportion, 46
Proportional, fourth, 47
  mean, 47
  third, 47
Proportional parts, 90
Prospective method, 330, 442, 444
Purchase price, 356
  of a bond, 359
Pure endowment, n-year, 391
  present value of, 392
Pure imaginary number, 150

Quadrant, 165
Quadratic equation, 147
  discriminant of, 159
  incomplete, 148, 151

solution by completing the square, 153
solution by factoring, 152
solution by quadratic formula, 155
solution of, 157
special, 148
stated problems, 160
theorems on, 158
Quadratic formula, 155
function, 168
Quartiles, 231
Quoted price of a bond, 369
Quoted rate of interest, 251

$r\%$ plan, 143
Radical, 72
Radical sign, 67
Radicals, division of, 75
multiplication of, 75
operations with, 73
similar, 74
Radicals in simplest form, 73
Radicand, 72
Rate, 52
discount, 120, 126, 127
interest, 105, 126, 127
trade discount, 60
Rate of interest, bond, 356
investment, 356
yield, 356
Ratio, 46
common, 198
Rational number, 72
Rationalizing the denominator, 74
Reciprocal, 36
Rectangular coordinate system, 164, 165
Rectangular histogram, 238
Redemption date, 356
Redemption price, 356
discount on, 356
Reduction to lowest terms, 36
Refund annuity, 406
Registered bond, 357
Reinvestment problem, 383
Removing parentheses, 12
Rent, 269
annual, 269
of an annuity, 275
Repeating decimal, 202

Replacement reserve, 336
Reserve, 437
replacement, 336
terminal, 437
Retrospective method, 330, 442, 444
Root, principal, 67
Roots of a quadratic equation, 158
Rule, Banker's, 113
Merchants', 130, 131
United States, 130

Salvage value, 308, 336
Schedule, amortization, 317
Selected points, method of, 183
Selling price, net, 55
Serial bond, 380
Sign, radical, 67
Significant digits, 82
Similar radicals, 74
Simple discount, 116, 117, 126
Simple interest, 105
sixty-day, 6% method, 114
table, 115
Simplest form of radicals, 73
Single premium, 415
Sinking fund, 316
method, 316, 323, 343
Solution of quadratic equations, 157
by completing the square, 153
by factoring, 152
by quadratic formula, 155
Solution of stated problems, using one unknown, 18
using two unknowns, 29
Special quadratics, 148
Special types of equations, 78
Standard deviation, 242
Stated problems, 18
quadratic equations, 160
Straight line, curve fitting, 183
Straight line method, 337
Subject of a formula, 44
Subscript notation, 10
Substitution in formulas, 10, 40
Subtraction, elimination by, 24
of algebraic expressions, 4
of fractions, 37
of signed numbers, 3
Sum, of arithmetical progression, **195**
of geometrical progression, 199

Sum of arithmetical progression, *continued*
  of infinite geometrical progression, 202
Surrender charge, 447
Surrender value, cash, 447
Symbols of grouping, 12
System of equations of first degree, 23, 31
System of linear equations, graphical solution, 180

Table, mortality, 221
  simple interest, 115
Tabular difference, 88
Temporary life annuity, 391, 401
Term, algebraic, 6
  of an annuity, 269
  of a note, 120
Term policy, 414, 422
Terminal reserve, 437
Terms of an arithmetical progression, 193
Theorem, binomial, 203, 204, 206
Theorems on the roots of a quadratic equation, 158
Third proportional, 47
Three equations in three unknowns, 31
Time, 105
  approximate, 108
  equated, 137, 265
  equation of, 136
  exact, 108
  methods of counting, 108
Time draft, 125
Trade acceptance, 125
  drawee, of 125
  drawer of, 125
  payee of, 125
Trade discount, 59, 60
  rate, 60
Transposition, 16

Trinomial, 6
Type products, 9
Typical form, 147

Unit cost, 345
  method, 345
United States Government Savings Bonds, 379
United States Rule, 130
Unregistered bond, 357
Use of logarithms for powers and roots, 97

Value, book, 336, 365
  discounted, 260
  equation of, 133, 134, 263
  face, 356
  maturity, 121, 123
  par, 356
  present, 116, 118, 259
  salvage, 308, 336
  wearing, 308, 336
Variable, 163
Variation, coefficient of, 245
Vinculum, 12

Wearing value, 308, 336
Weight, 229
Whole life annuity, 391
Whole life policy, 414, 416

X-axis, 165

Y-axis, 165
Year, policy, 414
Yield rate, approximate, 374
  by interpolation, 374
  current, 373
  of interest, 356

Zero, division by, 8
  exponent, 69

ST. MARY'S COLLEGE OF MARYLAND LIBRARY
ST. MARY'S CITY, MARYLAND

DATE
SE 29 '86
'87